The Physiology and B
of the Mout.

G. NEIL JENKINS

MSc(L'pool), PhD(Cantab), FDSRCS(Eng)
Professor of Oral Physiology, Dental School
University of Newcastle upon Tyne

Fourth Edition

BLACKWELL SCIENTIFIC PUBLICATIONS
OXFORD LONDON EDINBURGH MELBOURNE

© 1960, 1966, 1978 Blackwell Scientific Publications
Osney Mead, Oxford, OX2 0EL
8 John Street, London WC1N 2ES
9 Forrest Road, Edinburgh EH1 2QH
P.O. Box 9, North Balwyn, Victoria, Australia

First published 1954
Second edition 1960
Third edition 1966
Revised reprint 1970
Fourth edition 1978

British Library Cataloguing in Publication Data

Jenkins, George Neil
   The physiology and biochemistry of the mouth. — 4th ed.
   1. Mouth
   I. Title
   612'.31   QP146
   ISBN 0-632-00138-0

Distributed in the United States of America by
J.B. Lippincott Company, Philadelphia,
and in Canada by
J.B. Lippincott Company of Canada Ltd,
Toronto

Printed in Great Britain
at the Alden Press, Oxford
and bound at
Kemp Hall Bindery, Oxford

CONTENTS

PREFACE TO FOURTH EDITION

The results of dental research during the last decade show gratifying progress in clarifying much that was previously obscure and adding detail to what was previously known only in outline. This knowledge explosion has made the task of revision extremely difficult. An attempt has been made to cover the main physiological and biochemical concepts relevant to the mouth in the literature up to the end of about 1975. A few of the more important references in 1976 and 1977 which seem likely to influence future thinking have also been included. I have been generously allowed to quote some work still in the course of publication and I am most grateful to the friends and colleagues who have made this possible.

The enormous bulk of the literature has necessitated a selection of references. I have, in general, included the most recent of groups of references or those which include extensive bibliographies. The exclusion of any particular reference in no way implies that it was not used or valued but means that it may be readily traced from more recent sources. Although, as in former editions, emphasis has been given to broad concepts some detailed information has been included. It is realized that a certain amount of this information may not be of interest to all readers but it has been included for the possible benefit of those engaged in advanced studies. It is hoped by reading selectively the book will be helpful to several classes of reader.

In a field with such rapidly changing ideas it becomes difficult to decide how to deal with the older or obsolescent material; some readers may think I have devoted too much space to the exposition of older ideas. However, an account of older work is often necessary to put the newer ideas into perspective. Also in dental research, as in other human endeavours, old ideas have a habit of reasserting themselves!

Part of the revision was carried out while I was a Visiting Professor in the Dental School in Adelaide, South Australia, and I am most grateful for the facilities that were made available to me there and for the help given me by members of the staff, especially Professor Max Horsnall and Professor John Thonard. I am also grateful to Mrs Shirley Hastings for able secretarial assistance while in Adelaide.

It is a pleasure to acknowledge the help given to me by many other friends and colleagues who have read sections of the manuscript, made suggestions and discussed points with me or helped with references. I would particularly like to thank Dr Mike Edgar, Dr Andrew Rugg-Gunn of the Department of Oral Physiology in Newcastle and Dr Hans 's-Gravenmade of the University of Groningen. I owe a debt of gratitude to Miss M.Hodgson, Mrs Meg Hall and Mrs Wendy Wood who, at various stages of the revision of the book, have carried out the exacting secretarial work. I would also like to thank my publishers and especially Mrs J.Batten who have tolerated much rewriting and the insertion of new material even at the later stages of this book.

Newcastle upon Tyne   G.NEIL JENKINS
September 1977

PREFACE TO FIRST EDITION

The aim of this book is to provide an account of certain topics in physiology and biochemistry which are of importance in dental surgery but which tend to be neglected, or given a non-dental emphasis, in the standard textbooks. It has been assumed that the reader has already acquired a general knowledge of physiology and biochemistry.

Although the book has been written primarily for undergraduate students it is realized that with certain subjects on which general reviews are not readily available (for example calcification and saliva) the treatment has been somewhat fuller than they require. It is hoped by this means that the book may be of interest to post-graduate workers in dental surgery and to physiologists interested in this and allied fields.

No attempt has been made to give full references but those included are either reviews, papers with extensive bibliographies, or papers which are of outstanding interest in themselves. From these sources most of the statements in the book can be traced to their origin. The text has been written almost entirely from the original papers.

It is a pleasure to record my thanks to Professor R.V.Bradlaw, Dean of the Sutherland Dental School, for his most valuable criticisms and helpful suggestions, and to Professor A.A.Harper, Professor G.E.M.Hallett, Professor R.W.Lovel, Dr P.A.Armstrong, Miss M.E.Morley, Mr J.B. Masterton, Mr R.L.Speirs, Dr C.H.Tonge and Dr D.E.Wright who have discussed points with me and have read parts or the whole of the manuscript. Mrs A.P.Jobling and Mr J.Farrell have kindly allowed me to quote their unpublished results. I am also most grateful to Miss A.C.Heckels and my wife for their secretarial assistance, and to Mr R.L.Speirs who drew many of the diagrams.

Newcastle upon Tyne   G.N.J.
November 1953

ACKNOWLEDGMENTS

I would like to thank the following authors and publishers who have so readily allowed me to use illustrations from their works:

Dr C.A.L.Bassett and *Scientific American* for Figs I.6 and I.7; Dr R.S.Manly and *Journal of Dental Research* for Figs II.2 and II.3; Dr J.A.Weatherell and *Archives of Oral Biology* for Figs II.5 and II.6, and *Caries Research* for Figs II.7, II.27, II.28 and II.29, and *Nature* for Fig. IV.14; Dr J.Thewlis and H.M.S.O. for Figs II.8, II.10, II.17 and II.18; Dr A.J.Gwinnett and *Archives of Oral Biology* for Fig. II.11; Dr K.Selvig and *Calcified Tissue Research* for Fig. II.13; Dr J.Eastoe and *Archives of Oral Biology* for Figs II.19 and IV.11 and Butterworth & Co. Ltd. for Fig. II.20; Professor C.H.Tonge and Mr E.H.Boult for Figs II.21 and VIII.6c; Dr D.R.Cooper and *Clinical Orthopedics* for Fig. II.23; Dr R.W.Cox and *Clinical Orthopedics* for Fig. II.24; Dr A.Serafini-Fracassini and Churchill Livingstone for Fig. II.25; Dr M.E.Nimni and *Journal of Oral Pathology* for Fig. II.26; Dr F.Brudevold for Fig. II.30; Dr K.Little and the Royal Microscopical Society for Fig. II.31; Dr S.Fitton Jackson and the Royal Society for Figs III.1 and III.2; Dr E.Bonucci and *Journal of Ultrastructure Research* for Figs III.3 and III.4; Dr E.J.Reith and *Journal of Ultrastructure Research* for Figs IV.2 and IV.7, and *Journal of Cell Biology* for Figs IV.12(a) and (b), and *Archives of Oral Biology* for Fig. IV.16; Dr E.Rönnholm and *Journal of Ultrastructure Research* for Figs IV.3(a) and (b); Professor J.W.Osborn and Springer Verlag for Figs IV.4, IV.5 and IV.6; Dr G.W.Bernard and *Journal of Ultrastructure Research* for Fig. IV.8; Dr W.E.G.Cooper and *Archives of Oral Biology* for Fig. IV.10; Dr R.C.Greulich and *Archives of Oral Biology* for Fig. IV.13; Professor H.M.S.Crabb and *Caries Research* for Figs IV.15(a) and (b); Dr D.B.Scott and *International Dental Journal* for Fig. V.3; Professor Robert Frank and *Calcified Tissue Research* for Fig. V.4; the late Professor G.Bergman and *Archives of Oral Biology* for Fig. V.7; Professor R.B.Lucas and *Archives of Oral Biology* for Figs V.8(a) and (b); the late Sir Wilfred Fish and the Royal Society for Figs V.9, V.10 and V.11; Dr M.Brännström and Pergamon Press for Figs V.12 and XIV.6; Dr I.A. Mjör and *Archives of Oral Biology* for Figs V.13(a) and (b) and V.14(a) and (b); Professor A.E.W.Miles for Fig. V.15; Dr R.G.McMinn and *Archives of Oral Biology* for Figs VI.2 and VI.3; Dr B.K.B.Berkovitz and *Archives of Oral Biology* for Figs VI.4 and VI.5; Professor I.Schour and *American Journal of Pathology* for Figs VII.2, VII.4, VII.5, VII.6 and VII.7; Dr J.T.Irving and

Acknowledgments

Journal of Dental Research for Fig. VII.3, and *Journal of Physiology* for Figs VIII.4, and VIII.5; Professor B.J.Kruger and *Journal of Dental Research* for Fig. VIII.2; Dr J.Duckworth and *Journal of Physiology* for Fig. VIII.3; Dr S.W.Wolbach and *American Journal of Pathology* for Figs VIII.6(a), (b), and (c); Lady Mellanby and *Dental Record, British Dental Journal* and H.M.S.O. for Figs VIII.7, VIII.8, VIII.9 and VIII.10; the late Sir Wilfred Fish for Figs VIII.11 and VIII.12; Professor I.Glickman and *Journal of Dental Research* for Fig. VIII.15; Dr W.A.Curby and *Journal of Laboratory and Clinical Medicine* for Fig. IX.2; the late Dr L.H.Schneyer and Dr E.L.Truelove and *Journal of Dental Research* for Fig. IX.3; Dr S.A.Leach for Fig. IX.5; *Journal of Physiology* for Fig. IX.6; Dr C.Dawes and *Archives of Oral Biology* for Figs IX.7 and IX.8; Dr D.B.Ferguson and *Archives of Oral Biology* for Fig. IX.9; Dr N.Brill and *Acta Odontologica Scandanavica* for Fig. IX.12; Dr G.H.Meckel and *Archives of Oral Biology* for Fig. X.1; Dr R.Frank and *Archives of Oral Biology* for Fig. X.2, and the University of Dundee for Fig. X.6; Dr P.Turner and *Dental Practitioner* for Fig. X.3; Professor H.Mühlemann and *Helvetica Odontologica Acta* and *Journal of Periodontology* for Figs X.4, X.5, X.14, X.15, X.16 and X.22, and XIII.6; Dr C.A.Saxton and *Caries Research* and Courtesy of Unilever Limited for Figs X.7 and X.11; Dr R.J.Gibbons and the University of Dundee for Fig. X.8; Dr H.E.Schroeder and the University of Dundee for Figs X.9 and X.10; Dr I.Kleinberg and *Journal of Dental Research* for Fig. X.13, and Academic Press for Fig. X.19; Dr N.G.Clarke and *Australian Dental Journal* for Fig. X.17; Dr H.Löe and *Journal of Periodontology* for Fig. X.20; Dr M.Levine and *Archives of Oral Biology* for Fig. X.21; Dr L.Silverstone and Munksgaard for Figs XI.2, XI.3 and XI.6; Professor N.W.Johnson for Figs XI.7 and XI.8; Professor N.W.Johnson and *Archives of Oral Biology* for Fig. XI.4 and, *Scandanavian Journal of Dental Research* for Fig. XII.2; Professor T.Lehner and *Archives of Oral Biology* for Fig. XI.9; *British Dental Journal* for Figs XI.10, XI.11 and XI.12; Dr B.E.Gustaffson and *Acta Odontologica Scandanavica* for Fig. XI.13; Miss J.F.Forrest and *British Dental Journal* for Fig. XII.1; Professor J.J.Murray and *British Dental Journal* for Figs XII.4, XII.5 and XII.6; Dr J.A.Weatherell and *Archives of Oral Biology* for Fig. XII.7, and *Caries Research* for Fig. XII.8, and Blackwell Scientific Publications Ltd. for Fig. XII.10; Dr J.Ahlgren and *Acta Odontologica Scandanavica* for Figs XII.2 and XIII.3; Dr R.M.Watson and John Wright and Sons for Figs XIII.4 and XIII.5; Professor H.K.Worner and *Australian Journal of Dentistry* for Figs XIII.9 and XIII.10; Professor D.J.Anderson and *Journal of Dental Research* for Figs XIII.11 and XIII.12; Dr H.G.B.Robinson and C.V.Mosby and Co. for Fig. XIII.13; Dr W.T.Pommerenke and *American Journal of Physiology* for Fig. XIII.14; Dr R.I.Henkin courtesy of Charles C.Thomas, Publisher, Springfield, Illinois for Fig. XIV.1; Dr C.Pfaffmann and *Journal of Neurophysiology* for Fig. XIV.2; the late Dr G.von Békésy and *Journal of Applied Physiology* for Fig. XIV.3; Dr D.Guthrie and the Oxford University Press for Figs XV.1, XV.2 and XV.3.

CHAPTER I

CALCIUM AND PHOSPHORUS METABOLISM

A somewhat detailed account of the metabolism of calcium and phosphorus may seem a curious beginning to a book on the Physiology of the Mouth. However, for a full understanding of the formation and maintenance of the teeth and of the bone which supports them, it is necessary to consider the general metabolism of these minerals. Consequently, this first chapter has been included to give a more comprehensive picture of certain aspects of their metabolism than is readily obtainable from most textbooks on physiology and biochemistry. Two points require emphasis: (1) calcium metabolism is very complicated and controversial and there are many topics on which no conclusions have been reached which would be accepted by all workers; and (2) this chapter deals with the factors influencing calcium metabolism in the body as a whole, but it must not be assumed that all these factors necessarily affect the teeth.

The Absorption of Calcium and Phosphorus

Although the major foodstuffs are absorbed almost completely from the gut, the proportion of certain inorganic ions absorbed may be small. Calcium and phosphate are among the ions which are poorly absorbed and many factors influence the process, some favouring and others hindering it.

Some factors which modify calcium absorption influence the cells which are concerned in this process, while other factors increase or decrease the solubility of calcium and phosphate, thereby altering the amounts available for absorption. Because the formation of insoluble calcium phosphate is one factor in reducing absorption it is clear that the absorption of neither ion can be considered alone. If, for example, calcium absorption is increased the calcium concentration in the intestine is reduced and, by the law of mass action, the tendency for calcium to precipitate with phosphate is diminished, thereby indirectly favouring the absorption of phosphate also.

1

Methods of measuring calcium and phosphorus absorption

(1) METHODS APPLICABLE TO THE HUMAN SUBJECT AND INTACT
ANIMAL

In man, the absorption is measured by (*a*) estimating the amount of calcium
and phosphate (usually expressed as P) in the food by analysing an aliquot of
each article of food eaten, and (*b*) collecting the faeces and analysing them for
calcium and phosphorus. Ideally this procedure should be continued for at
least a week and many experiments have given uncertain results because they
were carried on for too short a period. The food calcium minus the faecal
calcium is taken to be the calcium absorbed. A typical result would be:
1·0 g of calcium in the food, 0·7 g in the faeces, absorption 0·3 g (30%). This
difference represents *net* absorption. Faecal calcium is not merely unabsorbed
food calcium, however, but part of it comes from the calcium of the digestive
juices which is presumably treated in the same way as calcium in the food and
may, or may not, be reabsorbed. Failure to consider this point could lead to
fallacious results. Suppose, for example, that some dietary influence decreased
the difference between food calcium and faecal calcium (say, food calcium,
1·0 g, faecal calcium 0·8 g) then net absorption (0·2 g or 20%) would appear
to have decreased from the 30% previously found. The same net result
would be found, however, if absorption remained at 0·3 g, but the calcium
secreted in the digestive juices had increased by 0·1 g. Nevertheless, it is *net*
absorption which is important as far as the amount of calcium being available
for the tissues is concerned, and whether it arises from the food or from
endogenous calcium is irrelevant.

Endogenous faecal calcium has been measured most simply by feeding
^{47}Ca and measuring the proportion of ^{47}Ca in the total calcium (the 'specific
activity') in the faeces (any ^{40}Ca must be endogenous). An error can arise
because some of the newly-absorbed ^{47}Ca may be rapidly secreted into the
gut and would be estimated as part of the unabsorbed food ^{47}Ca. Another
method of studying the absorption is to measure the radioactivity of serum
or of the whole body at selected times after administration of labelled calcium
(2 hr is suitable in normal subjects). Other more complicated methods use
two tracers: ^{47}Ca by mouth and ^{45}Ca by intravenous injection (for details see
Blau *et al.* 1957; Shimmins *et al.* 1971). ^{47}Ca of the faeces is unabsorbed food
calcium (but subject to error from immediate resecretion) and ^{45}Ca must be
secreted into the intestine. This method has been applied to patients after
removal of parts of their digestive tract and the results indicated that absorption occurs over most of the small intestine. Maximum absorption occurs
within 4 hr, and usually within 2 hr, of an oral dose.

Two non-radioactive nuclides, ^{46}Ca and ^{48}Ca, are now available and can
be used without exposing subjects to ionizing radiation. The results for
endogenous calcium by the double tracer method were between 200 and 300

mg, up to half of which was reabsorbed. Endogenous calcium is independent of the intake, suggesting that loss of calcium by this route is not a controlled excretion (Malm 1958). The digestive juice calcium has been found to be affected by the blood calcium, however (Gran 1960; Toverud 1964).

(2) ISOLATED LOOPS OF INTESTINES IN ANAESTHETIZED ANIMALS (NICOLAYSEN'S TECHNIQUE)

In anaesthetized fasting rats, loops of the intestine were sealed off from the rest of the gut by ligatures with as little interference as possible with their blood supply. A solution of a known amount of calcium chloride, or sodium phosphate, or other salt as required, was injected into the loop which was then returned to the abdomen. After 5 hr, and in some experiments 24 hr, the animals were killed and the amount of calcium or phosphate remaining in the isolated loop was estimated chemically. Since the ligatures prevented any mechanical movement of fluid into or out of the loop, any changes in the calcium or phosphate concentration must have been by absorption through the gut wall into the circulation (Nicolaysen 1937).

(3) STUDIES WITH ISOLATED INTESTINES *in vitro* (EVERTED GUT SACS)

The absorption mechanism of the small intestine is detectable in sections of intestine 2–3 cm in length, dissected from an animal and suspended in an oxygenated saline. The pieces of gut are usually turned inside out, so that the mucosal surface is on the outside, tied off at both ends and distended with saline. This ensures adequate oxygenation of the absorbing cells and the absorbed substance enters the small volume of saline inside the gut, thus allowing a relatively large and easily measured increase in its concentration. These preparations are usually referred to as 'everted gut sacs' (Wilson & Wiseman 1954). This method has shown that calcium can be absorbed by an active process in the rat (but less so, or not at all, in the chick) taking place against a concentration gradient and being inhibited by enzyme poisons (cyanide, azide). It is specific for calcium since other alkaline metals are absorbed only by simple diffusion. It occurs in two stages, absorption into the cell and a slower release into the serosa. The first stage can be studied separately by taking small pieces of intestine, incubating them with ^{45}Ca and measuring the amount of ^{45}Ca taken up. There are species differences both in the rate of absorption and in the part of the intestine which is most active. In most of the species studied, the duodenum is much more active than the rest of the small intestine but in the hamster absorption in the ileum is three times as rapid as in the duodenum (Schachter *et al.* 1960, 1961).

It is probable that some absorption of calcium takes place in those parts of the intestine where there is no active transport. Its rate seems to be slower than would be expected even from passive diffusion and Schachter *et al.* (1961) have postulated that the cells contain an active barrier which reduces passive diffusion and perhaps plays a part in preventing excessive calcium absorption (see also p. 13).

Factors controlling the absorption of calcium and phosphate

(a) Factors influencing the mucosal cells

(1) VITAMIN D AND CALCIUM ABSORPTION

There is good evidence from experiments with intact animals that one of the functions of vitamin D (also known as cholecalciferol or CC) is to favour the absorption of calcium. This conclusion was confirmed by experiments with isolated loops of intestine which showed very clearly that the rate of absorption of calcium was lower in the vitamin D-deficient rats than in the normal controls. The effect of the vitamin was specific for calcium, as the rates of absorption of neither phosphate (both inorganic and combined with sugar) nor sugars nor sodium sulphate differed in the normal and deficient rats. The effect of vitamin D on the gut mucosa is of long duration and it takes several weeks on a vitamin D-deficient diet before the reduced absorption of calcium is marked (Mellanby 1949).

The active form of vitamin D. When calcium absorption is compared in everted gut sacs from normal and vitamin D-deficient rats the absorption of calcium is much greater in the normal. Addition of vitamin D to the isolated gut sacs has no effect on calcium absorption. If large unphysiological doses of vitamin D are given to the rachitic animal an hour or so before the experiment, an increase in the powers of calcium absorption is detectable. With physiological doses, much longer intervals of up to 36 hr must elapse before calcium absorption is fully restored.

A similar delay in the action of vitamin D, the length depending on the dose, occurs when the absorption of calcium from ligated loops is studied. The explanation for this delay is now clear. Vitamin D is not the active substance but is converted in two stages to the active form (Fig. I.1). The first stage occurs mainly in the liver but also in the kidney and intestine and consists of the introduction of an OH group at the C_{25} position. The resulting 25-hydroxy cholecalciferol (25 HCC) is the main circulating substance but is relatively inactive, being bound in the plasma to an α_1 globulin of molecular weight 53 000 present at 5 μg ml^{-1}. It is further hydroxylated in the C_1 position exclusively in the kidney by an enzyme, 25-CC-1-hydroxylase, and the dihydroxy compound (1:25 DHCC) is extremely active on gut mucosa, kidney and bone. The second stage is under metabolic control (p. 43) and, in particular, is stimulated by a low calcium diet: DHCC is now usually regarded as a hormone.

The means by which 1:25 DHCC increases calcium absorption. It was

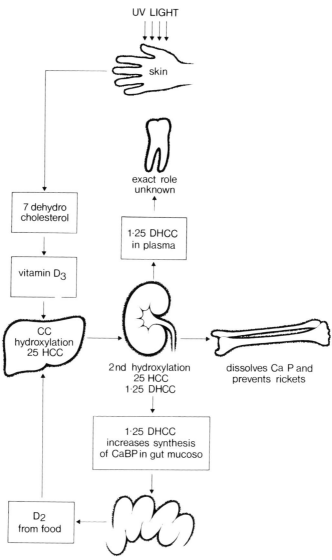

Fig. I.1 The sources, stages of hydroxylation and main sites of action of vitamin D (cholecalciferol, CC).

reported in 1964, and confirmed and extended later, that the action of vitamin D on calcium absorption was inhibited by actinomysin D, an antibiotic which stops protein synthesis by blocking transcription. This suggested that vitamin D worked via the synthesis of a protein and the converse experiment of detecting an increased formation of RNA (uptake of ^{3}H-uridine), an indicator of protein synthesis, in intestinal mucosa after feeding CC gave positive results (Norman 1966, 1974). This fits in with the observation that labelled 1:25 DHCC is located in the nucleus of the target cell. At about the same time, studies by Wasserman *et al.* (1968) demonstrated that intestinal mucosa contained a non-dialysable, heat-labile substance digested by trypsin which combined with calcium. This was identified as a protein (calcium-binding protein, CaBP) readily detectable in electrophoresis of normal mucosal extracts but absent from extracts of CC-deficient chicks. Later work has shown that, provided CC is present, the concentration of CaBP is increased by lowering the calcium of the diet (Wasserman *et al.* 1968, 1973).

Other possible actions of vitamin D are described later (pp. 18 and 20–2).

(2) EFFECT OF PREVIOUS CALCIUM INTAKE AND OF INCREASED CALCIUM NEED

Experiments on rats have established that the amount of calcium stored in the body is a factor which may influence calcium absorption. For example, Rottensten (1938) fed one group of rats a diet containing 0·15% calcium for 4 weeks, and another group the same diet except that the calcium level was 0·8%. The total calcium retained by each rat in the two groups averaged 191 and 570 mg respectively and thus the body store of calcium was much greater in the second group. During a second period which lasted 5 weeks, both groups received 0·4% calcium in their diets. The group with low calcium store absorbed about 900 mg calcium per rat and the high calcium group absorbed only 600 mg per rat. This suggests that the proportion of calcium absorbed can increase when the intake is low, a possibility which was investigated on human subjects by Malm (1958). Working on volunteers from the prisoners in Oslo gaol, he measured their calcium absorption for long periods after the intake was reduced from about 950 mg day^{-1} to between 400 and 600 mg day^{-1}. Out of twenty-seven subjects, eleven (40%) adapted to the reduced intake by increasing the proportion of calcium absorbed so that they underwent no loss of body calcium. Three subjects did not adapt their absorption at all and the remainder adapted slowly but not sufficiently to replace calcium lost while adaptation was occurring. It had already been suspected that such an adaptation could occur in the human subject by the finding in Asiatic children that calcium requirements seemed to be met by intakes far below those recommended and usually available in Western countries.

The mechanism of adaptation, formerly referred to as the 'endogenous factor', is almost certainly the control of the formation of 1:25 DHCC (p. 43).

The differences in powers of absorption of calcium according to requirements can be readily detected in everted gut sacs (Kimberg *et al.* 1961).

(3) EFFECT OF PREGNANCY AND GROWTH

Human metabolic studies suggest that the percentage of dietary calcium
absorbed increases in the later months of pregnancy. Although there is an
increase in urinary excretion also, it is smaller than the increase in absorption
so there is a net gain during pregnancy estimated at about 50 g, of which half
is in the foetus and rest is stored by the mother's skeleton, presumably as a
reserve for lactation. The effect of pregnancy on calcium absorption has been
detected in everted gut sacs.

High doses of oestrogen and progesterone for 7 weeks in one normal
human subject failed to produce the changes found in pregnancy, except for
a rise in phosphate retention. Most of the slight changes observed were in the
opposite direction to those in pregnancy. It is speculated that placental
lactogen (which has not been tested experimentally) might increase calcium
absorption and bone remodelling and that oestrogens inhibit the bone
resorption leading, presumably by a slight lowering of plasma calcium, to
increased parathyroid release which increases absorption and reduces
excretion via the urine (Heaney & Skillman 1971). Although only some of
these steps have been established by previous work, raised PTH levels have
been reported in the later stages of pregnancy.

Growing animals tend to absorb a higher proportion of their dietary
calcium than do adults and everted gut sacs from young rats have been found
to absorb calcium more actively than those from old rats. Growth hormone
has been shown to increase absorption and reduces endogenous Ca excretion
in dogs given ^{47}Ca orally and ^{45}Ca intravenously (Heaney *et al.* 1972).
Gut sacs from hypophysectomized rats absorb calcium less efficiently than
those from normal rats and pre-treatment with growth hormone reverses the
effect.

It is the active phase of calcium absorption which is affected by age,
requirements and previous intake. These factors become less important or
even quite irrelevant if the amount of calcium is adequate to meet requirements by diffusion alone.

(4) PARATHYROID HORMONE

The parathyroid hormone (PTH) favours calcium absorption because it is
one of the factors controlling the formation of 1:25 DHCC (p. 43).

(b) Factors influencing the availability of calcium in the gut

(5) EFFECT OF pH OF THE INTESTINE

The acid of the gastric juices dissolves most calcium salts and inorganic phosphates likely to be in the diet, but precipitation may occur in the small

intestine as the contents become neutralized. It has often been assumed that the absorption of calcium occurs only in the upper part of the small intestine where the pH is still well on the acid side and calcium remains soluble, but it is possible that soluble complexes may form at neutral or alkaline pH values, although their importance in absorption is debatable. On the other hand, there is good evidence that if the gut is made more acid (for example if milk is acidified with HCl before ingestion), a higher proportion of calcium is absorbed. Conversely, patients with achlorhydria or after gastrectomy tend to absorb less.

(6) THE AMOUNT OF DIETARY CALCIUM AND PHOSPHORUS AND THE Ca:P RATIO

It follows from the law of mass action that excess of, say, calcium in the gut will tend to precipitate phosphate and it might be expected therefore to reduce its absorption. In animal experiments on diets with very high or very low Ca:P ratios absorption is impaired. The Ca:P ratio is probably only important in absorption if the total concentrations of calcium and phosphate in the diet are low. The effects of the addition of moderate amounts of phosphate to the diets of *human* experimental subjects have been varied and have not always caused a reduction in calcium absorption. These contradictions cannot be explained with certainty but it is possible that in the experiments on human subjects either the total concentration of calcium and phosphate was above the level at which the ratio was important or the changes in the ratio which are permissible in human diets are not sufficiently extreme to affect absorption.

The Ca:P ratio is particularly important in the rat, a species in which vitamin D deficiency alone does not produce rickets, but requires also either a high or low Ca:P ratio in the diet. For this reason, it is necessary to be cautious in applying to the human subject the results of experiments on calcium metabolism in rats.

As the levels of calcium and phosphorus in a diet are increased the amounts absorbed also increase, but to a smaller extent. For example, in one experiment in rats, when the calcium and phosphorus in the diet were almost trebled, the amount absorbed was only about doubled, and one similar result has been reported in man. There is clearly a limit, therefore, to the beneficial effects obtainable from increasing the dietary level of these minerals (Blau *et al.* 1957).

Experiments with everted gut sacs have shown that above a certain concentration there is no further rise in active absorption. Probably the active transport system in the mucosal cells can deal with only a certain load and if this load is exceeded then the excess is absorbed more slowly by the much less efficient passive diffusion in lower parts of the gut. This may be part of the homeostatic mechanism for preventing an excessive calcium concentration in the blood and tissues where it is known to have undesirable effects.

(7) PHYTIC ACID AND PHYTATES

Sir Edward Mellanby (1921) observed in puppies that if oatmeal or whole wheat were included in a diet low in vitamin D or calcium, the severity of the rickets was increased. The anti-calcifying factor present in these foods became known as 'toxamin', since it seemed antagonistic to vitamin D. Later work showed that phytates, soluble salts (in most cases potassium salts) of phytic acid (the hexaphosphate of inositol) were the active substances and they reduced calcium absorption by forming an insoluble salt with calcium, probably containing five atoms of calcium. If magneisum ions are also present, a mixed calcium and magnesium salt is formed whose composition depends on the relative concentration of the two ions. Phytates are present in seeds where they may act as an inert store of phosphate to be broken down to inositol and inorganic phosphate by the enzyme phytase which is either present in the grain (as in wheat) or formed during germination (oats). In cereals, the phytates occur mostly in the outer part of the grain: consequently brown flour (technically known as 'high extraction flour' and usually containing 92% of the whole wheat) contains a much higher concentration of phytate than does white flour ('low extraction flour' usually containing about 70% of the constituents of the whole wheat).

The importance of phytates in the human diet has been demonstrated by several groups of workers who have shown that absorption of calcium by human subjects from diets containing brown flour is less than from white flour. The most comprehensive work has been carried out by McCance & Widdowson (1942–3), who, in addition to comparing calcium, magnesium and phosphate absorption on diets containing 70% extraction flour with those on 92% extraction flour, have also shown that the addition of phytate to white flour and its removal by enzymes from brown flour, respectively lowered and raised the absorption of calcium and magnesium. The periods on each diet were usually 3 weeks, which, although longer than in many experiments of this type, may not have been long enough to give a reliable result. The phytate does not merely immobilize the calcium and magnesium in the cereal, but may also precipitate these ions from other constituents of the diet, or, if these are low, from the digestive juices. If the latter occurs, the faeces contain more calcium than the diet and the subject is losing instead of absorbing calcium from the gut. The effect of phytate is quantitative and can therefore be neutralized by adding sufficient extra calcium to the diet to combine with it, a procedure adopted by the Ministry of Food when the National Loaf (85% extraction rate) was introduced in Great Britain in 1942.

The experiments just mentioned tend to exaggerate the effect of phytate because the calcium content of the diet was deliberately kept low, so that the amount precipitated was a substantial proportion of the total calcium present.

An important question at once arises. Many human diets do contain much phytate and little calcium, without apparently causing the disastrous interference with calcium metabolism which might be expected. Experiments by Walker *et al.* (1948) which extended over 19 weeks showed that adaptation to phytate intake can occur. During the first few weeks on a fairly high phytate diet, the expected fall in absorption of calcium occurred, but more and more calcium was absorbed in succeeding weeks throughout the experiment.

There is no proved explanation of how this adaptation to phytate is achieved but two suggestions have been made. (1) The presence of increased concentrations of phytate in the gut may favour the growth and activity of bacteria containing phytase or possibly 'induce' such an enzyme in the intestinal juices. The enzyme might be a specific phytase or some general phosphatase capable of splitting phytate. However, in the rat (a species which possesses an intestinal phytase), the phytase activity *diminishes* following an increased phytate intake (Roberts & Yudkin 1961). (2) The reduction in calcium absorption produced at first by the phytate may bring into action the mechanism by which calcium absorption becomes more efficient after a low calcium intake, i.e. the gut responds as if the animal had received a low calcium diet.

Rickets and osteomalacia have been reported among Pakistani families in Britain arising, it was suggested, from the high phytate content of the chapatis in their diet. A chapati-free diet for 7 weeks was followed by a rise in serum calcium, phosphate and alkaline phosphatase. Other workers have pointed out that rickets is more complicated than a calcium deficiency and found an improvement after vitamin D supplements, implying that this vitamin was deficient. The importance of phytate in these subjects is, therefore, controversial. In some dietary conditions phytate may also interfere with the absorption of iron, magnesium and zinc but there is no evidence that this is important under Westernized conditions.

The importance of phytate cannot be regarded as settled, but it may be concluded tentatively that if the diet contains this substance regularly it has little influence on calcium absorption. If it is suddenly introduced or increased in a diet, there may be a marked temporary reduction in calcium absorption.

The effect of phytates in reducing the solubility of teeth is referred to on pp. 456–7.

Effect of phytate on phosphate absorption. Under certain conditions, about 50% of the phosphorus of phytate may be absorbed from the human gut, indicating that a phytase, probably of bacterial origin, must be present. The higher the calcium concentration, the less phytate is broken down. Presumably calcium increases the amount of phytate precipitated and reduces the amount in a form available for splitting by phytase.

Some experiments have suggested that vitamin D favours the breakdown of phytate (Mellanby 1949). Although a direct effect on phytase has been suspected, these observations are equally well explained by supposing that vitamin D operates by favouring calcium absorption and thus indirectly favouring phytase action, as explained above.

(8) EFFECT OF OXALATES

Oxalate is another acid radical present in certain foods which makes calcium unavailable. Several vegetables contain traces of it, but spinach and rhubarb leaves contain relatively high concentrations. The free oxalate in the edible portions of these foods may precipitate significant amounts of calcium from other constituents of the diet or from the digestive juices, and in addition, the whole of the calcium contained in these foods is unavailable. The roughness of the teeth after eating rhubarb is shown by scanning electron microscopy of replicas to be caused by the deposition of crystals of calcium oxalate formed by interaction with the calcium of saliva. In rhubarb leaves (but not the stalks), free oxalic acid occurs in toxic quantities. At least one death resulted from the eating of stewed rhubarb leaves as a vegetable during the food shortage in 1917.

(9) INFLUENCE OF FAT ON CALCIUM ABSORPTION

Experiments on human subjects in which calcium absorption has been compared on different levels of fat intake (butter and lard) have suggested that these fats have no consistent effect. Animal experiments, on the other hand, have usually shown an effect but calcium absorption has sometimes been raised and sometimes reduced by increasing fat intake (Steggarda & Mitchell 1951).

The lowering of calcium absorption by fat has been explained by the formation of insoluble calcium soaps.

The feeding or injection of bile salts has been found in rats to increase calcium absorption. This has been explained in various ways such as an increased absorption of vitamin D or of complexes of bile salts, fatty acids and calcium, or by a direct effect of bile salts in increasing the slight solubility of the phosphates and carbonates of calcium which form in the intestine (Lengemann & Dobbins 1958). The calcium of bile, with a concentration equal to the ionic calcium of plasma, is an important source of the digestive juice calcium.

(10) EFFECT OF PROTEIN AND AMINO ACIDS

Experiments by McCance *et al.* (1942) in which calcium and magnesium absorption were compared in human subjects on diets as similar as possible except that one contained about three times as much protein as the other, showed that a considerable increase in calcium absorption occurred with a high protein diet. The level of protein in the diet has a marked effect on calcium metabolism but the details are still uncertain and the mechanisms almost unexplored (for references, see Walker & Linkswiler 1972). All the experiments agree that if the protein intake is increased, the calcium of the urine increases. Some workers have found that calcium absorption is also increased by the same amount as the rise in urinary calcium, retention being therefore unaffected but others report that the effect on the urinary excretion of calcium is greater than that on absorption, so that increased protein intake leads to a net calcium loss. The favourable effect on absorption had been explained by the formation of soluble complexes between calcium and amino acids tending to keep calcium in a form which could be absorbed and reducing the likelihood of forming insoluble calcium salts. If certain amino acids are added to faintly cloudy suspensions of certain insoluble calcium and magnesium salts, they become clear as soluble complexes form (Lehmann & Pollak 1942).

However, the effectiveness of different amino acids in favouring calcium absorption vary (lysine and arginine being the most active) and these variations show no relation to the ability of the amino acids to favour calcium solubility. There are also species differences (for example little effect in rachitic chicks compared with that in rats). These observations suggest that there are other mechanisms, not yet elucidated, besides the formation of complexes by which amino acids exert their effect on calcium absorption (Wasserman *et al.* 1956).

The effect of protein on urinary calcium has not been explained but since the metabolism of proteins leads to the formation of acids it has been speculated that this might encourage the removal of calcium from the skeleton, i.e. the skeleton was acting as a buffer to the acid. High protein intakes have been considered as a possible factor in osteoporosis (Johnson 1970) (see p. 27).

(11) EFFECT OF CARBOHYDRATE
When calcium absorption has been studied from diets containing different carbohydrates, it has been found with several species of animal that lactose favours calcium absorption and bone calcification (Duncan 1955). It has been suggested (though proof is lacking) that lactose is digested and absorbed more slowly than other disaccharides, and by lingering in the gut encourages the development of acid-producing organisms. Later studies have shown in the rat that several other carbohydrates, not normally contained in the diet, or their derivatives such as cellobiose, raffinose, mannitol, sorbitol, xylose, arabinose and mannose also favour calcium absorption. The idea that lactose favours calcium absorption by increasing acid production has been disproved by the finding that feeding antibiotics, which would prevent or reduce bacterial activity in the intestines, does not prevent the action of lactose on calcium absorption. Fournier (1955) suggested that these sugars were absorbed and influenced calcium metabolism by effects in the bone cells,

perhaps by being utilized for the synthesis of some bone constituent, and galactose is present in some constituents of bone. However, calcium absorption is only favoured by lactose if the lactose is present in the same segment of the intestine as the calcium, indicating either a direct interaction between calcium and lactose or some effect on the gut wall.

Although it has been shown that calcium and magnesium form unionized complexes with lactose, which could favour absorption, these complexes do not form readily under the pH and other conditions in the gut. Also, lactose is not active in dissolving or preventing the precipitation of $CaHPO_4$—the salt most likely to form in the intestine. Wasserman (1964) investigated the possibility that lactose might be changed, in the intestine, into a substance which formed a soluble complex with calcium more readily; he injected lactose into the ileum of a rat after which the ileal contents were found to decrease the precipitation of calcium phosphate. A control experiment in which saline was injected gave the same result, however; evidently the ileum normally contains one or more unidentified substances which maintains calcium in a soluble state. The evidence as a whole is strongly against complex formation as the explanation of the effect of lactose on calcium absorption.

Other common sugars (including glucose, sucrose and fructose) favour calcium absorption if they are injected into the ileum—normally they would be absorbed so rapidly that they would not reach this part of the intestine. In the rat, absorption of calcium in the ileum (where lactose and other sugars have their effect) is less than would be expected from passive diffusion: from which it has been concluded that there is an active blocking of absorption in this region (Schachter *et al.* 1961). This block depends on metabolic activity since it is reduced by enzyme inhibitors. Wasserman (1964) suggests that lactose and other polyhydric substances influence the metabolism of the cells of the ileum in such a way as to reduce the calcium block. In rats adapted to a low intake, absorption is active even in the ileum: lactose is found to enhance absorption in loops from normal but not from calcium-deficient rats supporting the idea that lactose inhibits the metabolically-dependent block.

Contradictory results have been obtained in experiments on the effect of lactose on calcium metabolism in man. In an experiment on young boys, lactose increased calcium retention, but by reducing urinary excretion and not increasing absorption (Mills 1968; Mills *et al.* 1940). No increase in calcium absorption was found by Greenwald *et al.* (1963) by balance studies in three elderly patients after feeding 50 g of lactose daily but an increase was detected in one of the patients by measurements of [45]Ca in the blood after feeding the isotope. Contrary to these results, very definite increases in calcium absorption were found in four adult volunteers by Condon *et al.* (1970) who also tested a patient with lactose intolerance (a lack of lactase resulting in diarrhoea when lactose is taken from the undigested lactose remaining in the lower intestines) and found that calcium absorption was reduced perhaps from the increased frequency of bowel action. These workers state that almost 50% of patients with osteoporosis (p. 27) have a deficiency of lactase and consequently they will have excluded milk from their diet with the possibility of a long-term calcium deficiency.

(12) SEASONAL AND UNEXPLAINED EFFECTS

In the course of their prolonged experiments on human subjects, McCance & Widdowson (1943–4) observed that in three out of six subjects large seasonal variations occurred in the absorption of calcium, but not of magnesium or phosphate. The absorption was least in February and March and greatest in July and August, and since the administration of large doses of vitamin D in March had little effect on the calcium absorption it seems unlikely that the reduced absorption in winter was caused by vitamin D deficiency. As the absorption changed with the seasons, so did the urinary excretion so that there was no seasonal change in the amounts of calcium retained by the body. This seasonal effect was confirmed by Malm (1958) in a study on calcium metabolism on 43 prisoners in Oslo gaol. The retention, as well as the absorption, was higher in the late summer and autumn (the maximum was in August) than during January–May.

Malm also found in two subjects larger variation in calcium balance which seemed to be closely related to emotional factors, the balance being negative during severe stress.

An even more remarkable change was observed in the absorption of calcium by all of five subjects who were studied continuously over the period from July 1940 to July 1942. In 1941 the absorption of calcium was less complete than in 1940 and 1942. No explanation has been suggested, nor has a year to year variation been reported by others, but very few experiments have continued for sufficiently long periods to test this point.

(13) PERSONAL VARIATION

Many workers have observed that the amount of calcium absorbed varies from individual to individual even under apparently identical conditions. There is no explanation of these variations but they may be related to previous intake and body stores of calcium, although there is no clear evidence on the point.

Phosphate absorption

In view of the formation of insoluble calcium phosphates in the intestine, the absorption of these two ions must be linked, at least partly, as explained on page 1. Those factors which favour calcium absorption will, by reducing its concentration, reduce the tendency to precipitate phosphate thus allowing more phosphate to remain soluble and available for absorption.

Phosphate absorption has usually been regarded as passive but there is evidence that it can also be an active process, although it has been much less studied than active calcium absorption. Phosphate can be absorbed against a concentration gradient (but not in the presence of cyanide) and this is reduced by vitamin D-deficiency, observations which confirm that it is an active process. Since, in the rat, vitamin D affects phosphate absorption mostly in the jejunum and calcium absorption mostly in the duodenum the effects are probably separate. This view is confirmed by the finding that phosphate absorption continues in the presence of EDTA, a chelator (p. 421) which binds calcium ions and would therefore prevent the precipitation of calcium phosphate (Kowarski & Schachter 1969; Wasserman & Taylor 1973).

No phosphate binding substance analogous to CaBP has been detected and the mechanism of vitamin D on phosphate absorption is not known.

The factors controlling calcium and phosphate absorption are summarized in Fig. I.2.

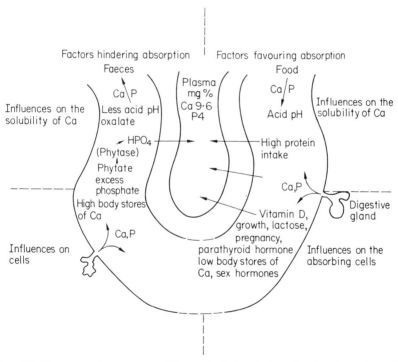

FIG. I.2. Diagrammatic summary of the main factors influencing the absorption of calcium and phosphate from the intestine.

The Role of Citrate in Calcium Metabolism

In 1941, Dickens found that bone contains up to 1% of citrate and that about 90% of the citrate of the body is located in the skeleton. This suggested that citrate might be an important intermediary in calcium metabolism. Both as a tricarboxylic acid and as a chelator (p. 421), it might be concerned in the dissolving of bone. Also, it is readily adsorbed by apatite crystals and, if it were formed by bone cells, this property would explain its presence in the bone mineral.

Further evidence for the importance of citrate in bone arises from the report of Neuman *et al.* (1956) that venous blood leaving bone has a higher citrate concentration than the arterial blood entering the bone. Other studies on the metabolism of bone (Borle *et al.* 1960) have shown, however, that lactate is the main product which accumulates, citrate amounting to little more than 1% of the acid formed. Nevertheless, there is evidence that the citrate is formed mostly by the osteoclasts and might thus be more effective in dissolving bone than its concentration would suggest.

Osteoclasts have been dissected out of bone and their composition and enzyme activities studied. The method was to transect a rat femur and apply the cut end to a glass slide, leaving an imprint of the cells on the slide. Under a microscope, the osteoclasts could be separated from the other cells and collected in sufficient quantity for analysis (Walker 1972). Their citrate concentration was about four times that in cells of the surrounding bone marrow and one hundred times greater than most other cells. The activity of aconitase, the enzyme which converts citrate into isocitrate, was one-tenth that of isocitrate dehydrogenase, a situation which would favour the accumulation of citrate.

Sources and Requirements of Vitamin D

Vitamin D (cholecalciferol, CC) is derived from two sources: D_2 arises from fat-fish, eggs and dairy produce in the diet and D_3 from the action of UV light on 7-dehydrocholesterol in the skin.

Derivatives of the two forms are both present in the blood and can be separated but the relative importance of the two has not been clear until recently. The following evidence suggests that D_3 is probably the more important.

(1) Plasma levels of the 25-hydroxy derivative of D_3 have been shown to be higher in summer and autumn than in winter in 198 normal subjects of varying ages in London (Stamp & Round 1974).

(2) In the USA where many foods are fortified with D_2 the D_3 derivative is reported to be predominant in the plasma.

(3) Daily exposure of elderly men to light increased calcium absorption although their diet was unchanged (Neer *et al.* 1971).

(4) In a group of elderly people, the dietary intake of vitamin D averaged only 64 iu per day and intake was not correlated with the calcium and phosphate concentrations of their serum but the small variation observed did correlate with hours of exposure to sunlight.

(5) When the mineral content of bone was measured in 48 post-menopausal women using the *in vivo* technique of proton absorption, which is much more accurate ($\pm 3\%$) than conventional radiological methods, significantly higher values were found in summer than in winter.

These data collected from diverse sources suggest that many elderly people may be receiving suboptimal doses of vitamin D in their diet and that unless they have a generous exposure to sunlight their calcium metabolism may be affected.

The effect of over-dosage of vitamin D

Large doses of vitamin D (for example, 5 000 iu kilo^{-1} of body weight) may produce serious symptoms and at least fourteen deaths from this cause have been reported. In certain circumstances, such as constipation or indigestion, smaller doses may be toxic. The first symptom is a feeling of well-being and an improved appetite, followed by digestive disturbances, fatigue and weakness with increased flow of urine containing high concentrations of calcium and phosphorus. Headaches and pains in the joints, muscles, jaws and teeth, have also been described.

The results of animal experiments on over-dosage of vitamin D, although very variable, perhaps because of differences in dosage, basal diet and the age of the animals, have often shown that the chemical effects in the body consist of a mobilization of calcium and phosphorus from the bones (giving a picture resembling rickets) and their deposition in the soft tissues, especially the kidneys and arteries. Deposition of excessive bone tissue has sometimes been found, however.

Although a few of the recorded cases were caused by over-dosages of fish liver oils, most of them resulted from taking the much more highly concentrated irradiated preparations which should therefore be administered with caution, especially to children.

In 1952, a disease was described in infants (idiopathic hypercalcaemia) in which the blood calcium is raised, accompanied by loss of appetite, wasting, vomiting, constipation and low muscle tone. It is strongly suspected that this condition arises from absorption of excess calcium, perhaps following over-dosage or abnormally high sensitivity to vitamin D. To prevent this condition, the concentration of vitamin D in certain infant foods has been reduced.

The Fundamental Action of Vitamin D

The overall effect of vitamin D on bone is to prevent rickets. The main features of this disease are (1) a low degree of mineralization of bone and cartilage so that in severe cases the limb bones cannot support body weight and become distorted (bow legs or knock-knees), (2) a failure of cartilage to degenerate on the epiphyseal side of a growing bone with new growth occurring normally, leading to a swelling on the bone especially noticeable in the ribs, ankle and wrist. The *overgrowth* of cartilage in a nutritional deficiency seems puzzling but a speculative explanation is as follows. Cartilage cells derive their nutrition by diffusion through the matrix which contains no blood vessels and normally, when the matrix mineralizes, diffusion is reduced and the cells degenerate. If mineralization does not occur, the cells may continue to receive nutrients and instead of degenerating, continue to produce matrix.

Vitamin D certainly plays a direct part in the absorption of calcium and of phosphorus from the intestine and the question arises as to whether this is the sole means by which this vitamin prevents rickets, or whether it has additional functions in the calcified tissues or elsewhere. The evidence is somewhat contradictory and opposite conclusions have been reached by different workers but the majority view is that bone is affected directly. The evidence is as follows:

(1) If salts containing radioactive phosphorus or calcium are *injected* into two groups of rachitic rats, one of which was partly cured by the administration of vitamin D before the experiment, it is found that the treated animals lay down 50% more radioactive element in the bones than do the untreated. Since absorption from the gut is assumed to play no part in the metabolism of injected material it is concluded that the greater uptake by bone must be due to some effect either in the bone itself or in some other tissue concerned in calcium and phosphorus metabolism. This experiment does not necessarily prove that vitamin D has caused increased *laying down of additional salts* in the bone, as the result could equally well be explained by increased *turnover* of salts without any addition. The fact remains, however, that vitamin D appears to alter bone metabolism independently of intestinal absorption (Underwood *et al.* 1951; Rasmussen 1969).

(2) Irving & Wuthier (1961) showed histologically that a lipid exists at the calcifying front in normal bone and teeth and there is evidence that it may

act as a seed in mineralization (p. 121). This lipid was reported by Irving to be absent or detectable in smaller amounts in the mineralized tissue of rachitic animals (Irving 1963). The composition of the lipids in bone undergoes complicated changes in rickets including an increase in its extractability and it is therefore possible that changes in the composition of the tissues, such as reduced mineral content had inadvertently made this lipid more easily extracted during the production of the section (Wuthier 1971). It is, however, possible that vitamin D plays some direct part in the production of the lipid.

(3) There is evidence that in vitamin D deficiency the cartilage cells fail to produce the normal changes in collagen maturation (see pp. 96–7): in rickets an increased content of hydroxylated lysine in the collagen molecule has been observed independently by two groups of workers and a reduction in the amount of cross-linking in the molecule is another effect of vitamin D deficiency (p. 96). It is presumed that these defects might alter the ability of the cartilage matrix to mineralize.

However, rachitic cartilage does mineralize readily *in vitro*, and this tissue has been very widely used in experiments on the nature of mineralization and the factors which influence it (p. 114). This mineralization *in vitro* may not be a satisfactory parallel to the processes occurring *in vivo*, however.

(4) Very high doses of vitamin D have effects almost exactly the reverse of the overall effect of small doses. Barnicot (1951) has clearly proved that these effects are at least partly caused by direct action on the bone. Crystals of vitamin D (calciferol) were attached to small pieces of skull bones of young mice and placed inside the cranium of another mouse. After 10 to 14 days, the mouse was killed and the bone grafts examined. It was found that the bone had been removed in the vicinity of the vitamin crystals and that control experiments in which cholesterol crystals were used showed no effect.

It is now fully established that even normal physiological doses of vitamin D increase acid production by bone and favour the removal of calcium and phosphate from it. This has been shown *in vivo* by Carlsson (1952): physiological doses of vitamin D increased blood calcium in rachitic animals on a diet so low in calcium that increased intestinal absorption could not have explained it. Addition of 1:25 DHCC to bone in culture increased resorption and comparison *in vitro* of the metabolism of bone from normal or vitamin D-deficient animals has shown that the normal bone releases more calcium into the medium.

Resorption of bone by vitamin D is inhibited by actinomysin D (an inhibitor of protein synthesis): resorption is therefore presumably dependent on the synthesis of a protein, which has not been identified or its function classified. Several attempts to detect CaBP in bone (which, if present, could facilitate calcium mobilization) have been unsuccessful but bone, with its small proportion of cells, obviously presents more technical difficulties for its extraction than intestine.

It has not yet been possible to reconcile convincingly the resorbing effect of vitamin D with its action in preventing rickets. It might be speculated that normally vitamin D raises the concentrations of plasma calcium and phosphate from two sources: increased absorption from the gut and mobilization from resorbing areas of bone already formed. The raised concentrations of calcium and phosphate favour the mineralization of newly-forming bone. If, as in Carlsson's experiments with animals on low calcium diets, the amount of calcium that can be absorbed from the gut is small then the main action of vitamin D is to increase the resorption from bone. On a normal calcium intake, however, absorption from the gut may be the more important effect.

The action of vitamin D on the kidney is controversial. Some experiments suggest effects on the reabsorption of both calcium and phosphate while others are negative: the kidney does contain a calcium-binding protein but it is uncertain whether it is concerned with the absorption from the glomerular fluid or whether its main effect is to control the calcium concentration in the kidney cells which is thought to be a major factor influencing the enzyme introducing the second OH group into DHCC.

Vitamin D, citrate metabolism and calcium in mitochondria

There is considerable evidence which suggests that one effect of vitamin D is to influence citrate metabolism. The level of citrate in serum and urine is reduced in vitamin D deficiency and the rate at which kidney (but not liver) mitochondria oxidize citrate is reduced if vitamin D is given to rats before they are killed (De Luca *et al.* 1956). The effect of reduced oxidation of citrate would, of course, be to raise tissue levels, which would tend to make calcium phosphate more soluble. These results support Carlsson's idea that the direct action of vitamin D on bone is to remove its calcium salts.

VITAMIN D AND BONE SOLUBILITY *in vitro*
If freshly-dissected bone is incubated in a suitable medium, calcium and phosphate dissolve into the medium as a result of the metabolic activity of the bone cells until equilibrium is reached. Bone from normal control animals reaches equilibrium at lower concentrations than those from animals pre-treated with large doses of vitamin D. This proves that vitamin D can have a local effect in making bone more soluble. The increased dissolving of bone was accompanied by an increased production of lactic acid by the bone cells. Bone heated to stop all metabolic activity, from animals which had received vitamin D, also dissolved more readily: from which it may be concluded that some change in the composition of bone, perhaps a higher citrate content,

TABLE I.1

Composition of rat femurs on various diets

	Ca %	P %	Citric acid %	
Control	24·3	12.1	0.51 ⎫	
Low Ca	19·7	9·9	0·76 ⎬ No tetany	
Low vit. D	23·5	11·6	0·46 ⎭	
Low Ca and low vit. D	19·9	9·7	0·24	Tetany

Conclusion: Ca may be readily mobilized from bone with a high citrate concentration but not from bone low in citrate. (From Hartles & Leaver 1961.)

may have increased the bone solubility although this point was not tested (Nichols 1963; Nichols *et al.* 1963).

Further evidence for changes in bone solubility related to its citrate content is provided by the experiments of Hartles & Leaver (1961). They fed groups of rats on various diets (*a*) low in calcium, (*b*) low in vitamin D, and (*c*) low in both calcium and vitamin D. The main results (Table I.1) were that the bone produced on diets low in calcium and low both in calcium and vitamin D had similar calcium concentrations but very different citrate concentrations— 0·76 and 0·24%. Corresponding with this difference was the incidence of tetany (caused by low serum calcium ion levels, see p. 33) which occurred in the animals whose bones were low in citrate (i.e. serum calcium levels were low) but did not occur in those with bones high in citrate (serum calcium levels more normal). Thus, although the two bones both had the same calcium concentration, only the bone with a high citrate level was apparently able to supply sufficient calcium to the plasma to prevent tetany.

DISTRIBUTION OF VITAMIN D IN THE BODY IN RELATION TO ITS FUNCTION

Kodicek (1963) investigated the distribution of vitamin D in the body by making autoradiographs of the tissues of animals which had received [^{14}C]-vitamin D. The vitamin localizes mainly in the liver, bones, intestines (especially the upper part where absorption of calcium is thought to occur) and kidney (in the first third of the proximal tubule where phosphate absorption is thought to take place). Surprisingly, vitamin D also accumulates in muscle and skin. In developing bone, the vitamin was in the cartilage cells concerned with matrix formation and not in the zone of hypertrophied cells where mineralization begins.

Labelled 1:25 DHCC is known from autoradiography experiments to become localized in the nuclei of cells in bone, cartilage and intestine (there is also a binding site in the cytoplasm of intestinal cells, perhaps concerned with transport of the DHCC to the nucleus), and is therefore presumably concerned with protein synthesis. This is confirmed by the observation (mentioned on p. 6) that the effects of vitamin D, both on intestine and bone, are inhibited by the antibiotic actinomycin which blocks protein synthesis.

Vitamin D and growth

When growing animals are fed a diet deficient in vitamin D, rickets develops and growth is reduced, except in the rat, a species in which a diet low in phosphate must accompany vitamin D deficiency before rickets develops. It is therefore possible in the rat to separate rickets from other effects of vitamin D deficiency: the growth of at least one type of cell—that of the duodenal mucosa—is reduced and slight hypocalcaemia occurs in this deficiency. This is shown by the reduced weight of the mucosa as a proportion of the intestine as well as by the rate of migration of cells along the villus—a process which depends on the rate of mitosis in the cells of the crypts. These effects on growth may be mediated by the action of calcium on cAMP and mitosis: attempts to test calcium and vitamin D separately have not been entirely satisfactory but tend to suggest that both are necessary for full growth. The observation that in vitamin D deficiency the mucosal cells of the intestine diminish in number introduces another complication, namely, that in vitamin D-deficient animals the absorption of several other nutrients besides calcium is less efficient than normal. Vitamin D may therefore influence growth by enhancing the absorption of nutrients generally (Wasserman & Corradino, 1973).

Calcium and Phosphorus Requirements

The concept of calcium balance

Calcium balance is the term used to describe the net gain or loss of calcium by the body over a specified period. The food calcium, minus the faecal calcium, gives the net calcium absorbed: this is compared with urinary calcium and the difference represents the amount gained (positive balance) or lost (negative balance) by the body. For example, if the diet contains 1·0 g of calcium and the faeces 0·7 g the absorption is 0·3 g. If the urine contains 0·4 g then the subject is in negative balance to the extent of 0·1 g per day.

The calcium in sweat cannot, for obvious technical reasons, be measured in long balance experiments. Short-term experiments have suggested that under minimal sweating conditions about 150 mg of calcium a day may be lost in this way, and since balance experiments usually ignore this loss, they suggest a retention higher than the true figure by this amount. This may be an overestimate, however, because with prolonged sweating the calcium concentration falls rapidly (Johnston *et al.* 1950; Duncan 1958; Leitch & Aitken 1959).

The growing child is obviously in positive balance, about 0·1 g being retained each day in the growing and mineralizing skeleton. The normal adult up to the age of about 50 is in approximate balance but the few subjects who have been studied over periods of months or years show that small daily losses of gains may persist for months without obvious causes. Resorption of the skeleton occurs but it is approximately equalled by new bone formation. After about the age of 50, a consistent tendency for negative balance arises and in the later decades this can be detected as a loss of skeletal tissue (osteoporosis, p. 27), not merely a reduction in the proportion of mineral.

The dietary requirements of calcium and phosphorus

It will be clear from what has been said that the requirements of calcium in the diet will depend, among other things, on the amount of other constituents present in the diet which favour or hinder calcium absorption.

Several methods have been used in attempts to determine the dietary requirements. One method is to collect all the published data on calcium intake in relation to calcium balance and to relate various levels of intake to the state of balance. With such a study by Leitch, on about four hundred results, the daily calcium intake on which half the subjects were in positive balance (this criterion was finally adopted since even the highest intake did not produce a positive balance in all subjects) was approximately 10 mg per kilo body weight. None of the 34 subjects whose intake was below an average of 0·13 g per day were in balance. Other estimates by similar methods agree that about 0·5 g is the minimum daily requirement.

A second method is to study the calcium balance in a group of subjects in which the calcium is deliberately placed at different levels of intake for periods preferably of several weeks, and to find at which level balance is reached. This approach to the problem of calcium requirements has been criticized on two grounds.

(1) As discussed on p. 6, there is good evidence that the intestine can adapt to a low intake by increasing absorption and the study of calcium balance may provide information, not of real requirements, but of the level of intake to which the body has become accustomed. Although it has been found possible to maintain calcium balance at low intakes (see below) it is generally felt that this is at the expense of good growth and robust health.

(2) A second reason for thinking that this method of assessing calcium requirements is unsatisfactory is that Sherman (1947), in many experiments on rats fed on a diet which is now known to be slightly deficient in vitamin A and riboflavin, found that increasing the calcium content of the diet from about 0·2% to 0·8% improved not only the growth and mineralization of the skeleton but accelerated maturity, increased reproductive powers of female animals, retarded senility and lengthened life by about 10%. Sherman suggested that a generous intake of calcium through several generations has an important influence on the health and well-being. When the basal diet was optimal in all known nutrients, raising the calcium level from 0·34% to 0·64% failed to increase reproductive powers or length of life. There is evidence that increased calcium in the diet stimulates appetite (see p. 26) and therefore the intake of other nutrients. With a good diet, full requirements may be met even if the total intake is moderate, so that in these circumstances, stimulation of appetite has little or no effect on health. These experiments have not been repeated and their significance is uncertain.

Henrikson (1968) has produced periodontal disease in dogs by long feeding of a calcium-deficient diet and provides some epidemiological evidence relating this condition in human populations to calcium deficiency a concept developed by Lutwak *et al.* (1971, 1972).

In view of the above results and of the haphazard nature of calcium absorption and the variability in absorption shown by different people, it has been customary for the figure of 0·5 g to be raised by a safety margin of about 50%. The National Research Council of the USA, and until recently the British Medical Association, agreed in recommending 0·8 g as the daily requirement for adults.

Many human diets fail to provide this intake and calcium deficiency is often considered to be widespread. A report by the World Health Organization (1962) points out, however, that no symptoms which could definitely be ascribed to calcium deficiency have ever been found in adults in any part of the world, even on an intake of only 300 mg a day, presumably because adaptation had occurred (see also Murthy *et al.* 1955). In view of these considerations, the BMA in 1969 reduced its recommended requirements to 0·5 g. The NRC retained the higher figure of 0·8 g, however, on the grounds that the high protein intake in the USA was causing excessive excretion, leading to osteoporosis. Calcium requirements are reviewed by Irwin & Kienholz (1973).

THE CALCIUM REQUIREMENT OF CHILDREN

The requirements of a growing animal for all nutrients is proportionately greater than for adults because in addition to maintaining tissues already formed, new tissue is being added by the growth processes.

The new-born child is said to contain about 25 g of calcium (0·8% of body weight), and 43 g normally accumulate between the first and tenth month, leading to 83 g at the end of the first year—the average daily retention being 0·16 g calcium and 0·10 g phosphorus. When this figure is compared with the actual intakes and absorption by breast-fed infants, it becomes clear that much less calcium is available (about 0·3 g, of which an average of about 0·07 g is absorbed) during the early months of breast feeding than is required by the infant to retain even the low level of mineralization present at birth. In other words, the skeleton grows but the new bone is under-calcified compared with the bone laid down before birth. At the age of 6 months the amount of human milk may be sufficient to allow satisfactory calcification of bone.

TABLE I.2

Two estimates of calcium requirements (g per day) at different ages

Age	Leitch's estimate	WHO estimate
6 months–2 years	0·8	0·5–0·6
2–10 years	0·9–1·0	0·4–0·5
10–15 years		0·6–0·7
slow growers	1·0–1·6	
rapid growers	1·0–2·0	
16 to adult	gradually falling to 0·8	0·5–0·6
Pregnant and lactating women	1·5–2·0	1·0–1·2

The age groups considered by Leitch and by the WHO were not quite identical but for simplicity have been approximated in this table.

Estimates by Leitch (1937) of the calcium requirements of older children, based on metabolism experiments, are given in Table I.2. These figures are somewhat higher than those suggested by others and much higher than those suggested by the WHO but they have been widely accepted on the basis that there is reason for believing that a generous intake is beneficial. The lower figures suggested by the WHO are now being increasingly accepted as being more realistic, however.

REQUIREMENTS IN PREGNANCY AND LACTATION

Calculations based on the rate at which the foetal skeleton grows and from the calcium content of the milk have suggested that the dietary calcium requirement during the latter half of pregnancy is 1·5 g per day and during lactation is 2 g per day.

In lactation, depletion of the mother's skeletal stores of calcium laid down during pregnancy appears to be a normal physiological process and it seems doubtful whether any advantage is gained by feeding such large quantities of calcium in the form of medicinal salts as to render unnecessary the use of the skeletal stores. When the stores are utilized, not only calcium, but also magnesium and trace elements in the skeleton are released and made available for the milk, which would not occur if the skeletal stores are not used.

THE ROLE OF CALCIUM IN CELLULAR METABOLISM

Calcium is known to play an essential role in many cellular properties and activities (reviewed by Wasserman & Corradino 1973). Although the outer walls of most cells have a low permeability, the walls between adjacent cells are very much more permeable and this permeability depends on calcium. The rate of mitosis of certain cells (thymus and bone marrow), both in whole animals and in cultures, is raised by increasing or reduced by lowering the calcium concentration of the environment.

There is also evidence linking growth rate of rats at different parts of their life cycle with the level of calcium ions in their plasma and the well-known regeneration of liver after partial hepatectomy was reduced by half in para-thyroidectomized rats compared with sham-operated controls. It has been known for many years that the level of calcium in the diet could be a limiting factor in the growth rate of experimental animals which was explained as an effect on the stimulation of appetite. This could be indirect, however, the real chain of events being: calcium stimulates mitosis via cAMP→growth increases→more rapid utilization of nutrients→stimulation of appetite.

THE PHOSPHORUS REQUIREMENTS

The phosphorus requirements of the body can be calculated from the calcium requirements by considering the relative amounts and functions of these two nutrients in the body.

The total calcium of the human body is estimated to represent about 2% of the body weight and the phosphorus content about 1%, although the results of the few direct analyses of cadavers which have been carried out vary widely and do not always refer to normal subjects (Forbes *et al.* 1953; Mitchell *et al.* 1945; Widdowson *et al.* 1951).

About 99% of the calcium of the body is contained in the skeleton and only 1% is present in blood and the soft tissues. The phosphorus of the skeleton is about 90% of the total since there is about 10% in the soft tissues. Since the Ca:P ratio of the body is about 2, it might be thought that the dietary Ca:P ratio should also be 2. The following considerations show that this is not so, however. In the adult who is merely maintaining his tissues but not adding to them, calcium and phosphorus are required for two functions. First, losses are incurred in the incomplete reabsorption of material secreted into the digestive juices and, secondly, the tissues of the body are maintained in a state of dynamic equilibrium (i.e. substances which form the tissues are constantly being removed and being replaced mostly by material from the diet). It has been shown, for example, that a phosphorus atom stays in the body for an average of only 30 days. To some extent, the materials released by this breakdown process can be used again for resynthesis, but losses do occur and these have to be made up from the diet.

The rate of turnover of phosphorus in the soft tissue is, however, much greater than it is in the skeleton, and about as much phosphorus is required to maintain the 10% of the total in the soft tissues as is required for the maintenance of the 90% present in the skeleton. Since 99% of the calcium is in the skeleton where the rate of turnover is slow, the requirements for maintenance are no greater than those for phosphorus in spite of the fact that the total amount present is almost double. The Ca:P ratio in the diet for the adult should therefore be about 1.

Composition of bone

The chemical composition of bone is similar to that of dentine (discussed in the next chapter), but is subject to greater variation with age and diet, and from bone to bone in the same body. The percentage of water tends to fall with age and that of the ash to rise, although the thickness of the bones may decrease with advancing years (senile osteoporosis).

Post-menopausal and senile osteoporosis

Shortly after the menopause, women go into negative calcium balance to the extent of about 15–30 mg per day. Histologically, the bone can be seen to be undergoing normal resorption but the formation of new bone is insufficient to replace it. The weakened bone leads to a ten-fold increase in bone fracture rate between the fourth and seventh decade. Post-menopausal osteoporosis is almost certainly caused by the withdrawal of oestrogen since this hormone seems to protect the bone against PTH, as revealed in tissue culture experiments. The osteoporosis also occurs after ovariectomy, even in young women.

A similar but somewhat smaller rate of calcium loss occurs in males from about the age of 60 to 65 (Nordin 1971). The cause of this change is controversial. Some workers suggest that it arises from long-term slight calcium deficiency and is one argument for maintaining a high calcium intake throughout life. Senile osteoporosis is frequently associated with osteomalacia (the presence of much unmineralized matrix, as opposed to osteoporosis, the resorption of all constituents of bone) and reduced calcium absorption, indicating a vitamin D deficiency. Calcium absorption can be increased in elderly people by a large dose of vitamin D (1000 units) suggesting that a deficiency may arise either from a reduced intake or the tendency for housebound elderly people to have reduced exposure to sunlight. It is also possible that declining kidney function may reduce the formation of 1:25 DHCC.

The possible effect of a high protein intake in favouring urinary excretion of calcium has also been considered. Other workers favour an explanation based on endocrine influences either on absorption of calcium or on bone metabolism or both but evidence on all these points is inconclusive. A high fluoride intake (50–100 mg of NaF daily) has been reported to reduce bone loss and reduce negative calcium balance in osteoporosis. Clinical opinion of its effectiveness varies. If it is effective it may work either by making the bone less soluble or by inhibiting the cells responsible for resorption (see pp. 483–90).

Calcium and Phosphorus of Blood

The calcium of blood

The average serum calcium concentration in man is 9·6 mg 100 ml^{-1} (range 9–10·2) with a daily fluctuation of less than $\pm 3\%$. Although the calcium concentration is remarkably constant, changes are detectable after calcium is absorbed from the gut and even these small oscillations seem sufficient to trigger the release of the hormones which control plasma calcium. For convenience, calcium is estimated on serum, as the calcium concentrations of serum and plasma are identical. There is no diurnal variation, nor does the level change in old age, although it does tend to be higher in the newborn than in the adult. The constancy is believed to be controlled by the parathyroid gland since an abnormal level of parathormone in the blood is one of the few factors capable of causing large changes in serum calcium. The red cells are almost free of calcium containing only 16 μmol l^{-1} of packed cells, 90% of which is bound to their surface. If red blood cells are depleted of ATP by ageing for 3–4 weeks after collection their calcium concentration increases. When incubated with a source of new ATP, the calcium was rapidly extruded, indicating the existence of an energy-dependent calcium pump.

By dialysing serum against solutions containing varying concentrations of calcium ions only between 50 and 70% of the serum calcium diffuses. The non-diffusible calcium is attached to the plasma proteins. There is an equilibrium between the amount of diffusible calcium and the amount of protein-bound calcium; if the former is lowered by dialysis or precipitation, calcium is released from the protein to restore equilibrium.

One cause of confusion has been the difficulty of estimating directly the calcium present as free ions. For some years, the only means of measuring calcium ions without disturbing the equilibrium between free and bound calcium was a biological method which depends on the fact that the amplitude of beat of a frog's heart varies according to the ionic calcium in the medium perfused through it. The estimation was made by comparing the amplitude produced by the unknown solution with those of solutions of known calcium concentration. Other methods based on different principles give similar results (Ettori & Scoggan 1959).

Some of the diffusible calcium of serum is present in an unionized form because the amount of calcium not bound to protein is slightly more than the amount found by the frog heart method to be in an ionic form. The amount of diffusible, but unionized calcium is small, probably between 6 and 12% of the total, and is thought to be present as complexes with citrate, phosphate or bicarbonate. It is known that citrate is present in serum and that this ion can form complexes with calcium. The addition of citrate to blood *in vitro* causes a rise in the diffusible calcium by splitting up of the protein-calcium complexes. Two estimates of the percentage of serum calcium in these various forms are given in Table I.3.

TABLE I.3

Two estimates of the percentage of serum calcium present in different forms

	Neuman & Neuman (1958)	Walser (1960)
Non-diffusible (combined with protein)	33	46
Diffusible (*a*) as ions	55	47
(*b*) as complexes	12	7

The phosphorus of blood

Phosphorus occurs in blood in several forms, namely inorganic phosphate (mostly HPO_4^{2-} abbreviated to P_i), esters of phosphate and sugar, phospholipids and nucleotides. The figures are usually given as milligrams of phosphorus (not phosphate) per 100 ml of blood or serum. The approximate distribution of the various forms in cells and serum of the adult are given in Table I.4.

The main points to note are (1) the small proportion of P in the inorganic form and the preponderance of this form in the serum (the concentration of P_i in the cells is so low and variable that it has sometimes been thought that it represents the amount broken down from ester P after collection of the blood), and (2) the low concentration of ester P in the serum.

TABLE I.4

Distribution of phosphorus in blood (mg P %)

	Whole blood	*Cells*	*Serum*
Total P	35–40	70–80	12–14
Inorganic P	2–3	0–2	3–4
Ester P	20–27	50	0·5
Phospholipid P	10–12	20	5–10

About half of the P_i is bound—12% to protein and 35% in complexes with calcium, magnesium and sodium (Walser 1960). The concentration of serum phosphate is much less constant than that of calcium. It falls after the ingestion of carbohydrate, following the injection of insulin or adrenalin (and presumably after the natural secretion of these hormones) and during exercise (after exercise there is usually a small rise followed by a fall). The common feature of all these events is the increased metabolism of carbohydrate which involves the conversion of carbohydrates into phosphorylated forms. A meal rich in phosphate causes a rise in the phosphate of the serum. The P_i concentration of the serum of young animals and babies is higher (5 mg%) than in the adult (3–4 mg%) perhaps from the action of the growth hormone. A seasonal variation in the P_i of serum has been observed with higher values in summer than in winter (see p. 36).

The reciprocity of serum calcium and phosphate

It is often stated that changes in the P_i of serum are accompanied by changes in the opposite direction of the serum calcium. Although it is undoubtedly true that there is a tendency for this relationship to exist, it is by no means invariable and it is only really marked in certain diseases involving calcium metabolism. Serum calcium is more constant than serum P_i and a moderate fall is usually accompanied by very slight changes in plasma calcium because hormonal controls prevent a larger change.

The question of the supersaturation of serum

Whether a salt will or will not dissolve under any given circumstances depends on the product of the concentration of the ions which form that salt. When the solution is saturated this product is referred to as the 'solubility product' and, if this figure is exceeded, precipitation occurs. For example, the precipitation of calcium phosphate may be represented as follows:

$$Ca^{2+} + HPO_4^{2-} \rightleftharpoons CaHPO_4$$

The solubility product is $[Ca] \times [HPO_4]$ where $[Ca]$ and $[HPO_4]$ represent the concentrations of these ions.

If the solubility product of tricalcium phosphate, as measured from solutions in water, is compared with the product calculated from the known concentrations of calcium ions and phosphate ions in the serum, it is found that the figure for serum is greater than can be obtained from aqueous solutions, in other words, serum appears to be supersaturated with calcium phosphate.

The presence in the serum of substances (for example protein, citrate and carbon dioxide) which can form complex ions with calcium and phosphate may alter the effective concentration (known as the 'activity') of the ions. Since reliable methods are not available for the accurate measurement of activities, solubilities are usually expressed in stoichiometric concentrations (i.e. the total concentration measured by analysis and not the smaller concentration available for reaction). If the solubility product is expressed in terms of activities it is always constant and is called the 'true solubility product' but if it is expressed in terms of stoichiometric concentrations it varies with conditions and is called the 'apparent solubility product'. In water it is possible to calculate the true solubility product whereas in serum only the apparent solubility product can be calculated.

As mentioned above, the bone crystals present such an enormous surface to the tissue fluids surrounding them that it is not surprising that the fluid is maintained in equilibrium with bone—the problem is: why is the equilibrium position an apparently supersaturated solution? Two pieces of evidence suggest that this high solubility arises because acid is produced on the surface of the bone crystals. (1) Experiments show that at pH 6·6–6·8 the solubility of bone is similar to that in the serum so that if the bone cells provided a local environment at this pH, the solubility of bone could be explained (Nordin 1957). If (as suggested on p. 30), only 50% of the serum P_i is present in the ionic state, then a pH of 7·1 would be adequate to explain the equilibrium. (2) If the solubility of living bone, dissected from a recently killed animal, and of bone killed by heating be compared over a range of pH values the living bone dissolves more readily than the heated bone above pH 6·5 but below this pH both samples dissolve at the same rate. This result suggests that living bone has the power of lowering the pH of its environment to about 6·5 and therefore dissolves more readily, but if the medium is already at or below this pH then it cannot alter the pH further and its rate of dissolving becomes the same as that of the heated bone (Schartum & Nichols 1962). It might have been expected that, once these ions left the acid environment (which the above evidence suggests surrounds the bone cells) and entered the general circulation with its higher pH, insoluble calcium phosphate would be precipitated. There is still no agreed explanation of why this does not happen but the following suggestions have been made:

(1) There are several interconvertible forms of calcium phosphate and those most likely to precipitate are either an amorphous calcium phosphate, α brushite: $CaHPO_4 . H_2O$, or octacalcium phosphate: $Ca_8(HPO_4)_2(PO_4)_4$. These substances are more soluble than hydroxyapatite (HA), the crystalline form in bone (see p. 69), but when in contact with water they become slowly converted to it. Plasma may be saturated in the sense that HA will not dissolve in it but not sufficiently saturated to allow the more soluble salts to precipitate out. This question is discussed more fully later (pp. 42–3).

(2) It is possible that the relatively high concentrations of acid or complexing agents believed to be formed by the bone cells may be necessary to dissolve bone but that the much lower concentrations of complexors in the serum may be adequate to maintain the calcium phosphate in a supersaturated solution.

The Influence of Hormones on Calcium and Phosphorus Metabolism

The role of the parathyroid glands

The stability of serum calcium and the interactions between bone, tissue fluid, gut contents and kidney function are controlled by hormones. Parathormone (PTH) and calcitonin (CT) are specifically concerned with calcium metabolism but many other hormones have an indirect influence on it.

EFFECT OF INJECTIONS OF PARATHORMONE

The part which the parathyroid glands play in maintaining blood calcium can best be pictured if the effect of injections of parathyroid hormone (PTH) or the removal of the glands are considered.

One injection of PTH into normal animals produces (1) a transient fall in plasma calcium followed by a rise within an hour or so reaching a maximum within 4–18 hr, depending on the route of the injection and lasting up to 30 hr, (2) a rise in serum citrate, (3) usually an initial fall in serum inorganic phosphate, sometimes followed by a rise with high doses, and (4) an increase in the urinary concentration of phosphate and an initial decrease in urinary calcium (sometimes followed by a rise). The initial fall in plasma calcium was at one time thought to be due to contamination of the PTH with CT but is now known to be a true effect of PTH caused by a transient influx of calcium into cells. If actinomycin, which inhibits RNA synthesis, is injected simultaneously, the effect of PTH lasts for only about 6 hr, suggesting two separate mechanisms for its action.

With repeated doses, the blood changes are followed by serious symptoms: vomiting, diarrhoea, blood in the faeces, polyuria, reduced blood volume, calcification of various tissues, for example the brain, thyroid, lung, myocardium and kidney leading to death from renal failure. Similar symptoms follow injections simultaneously of calcium chloride and *acid* sodium phosphate, suggesting that they are due to the high levels of calcium and phosphate in the blood. Calcium chloride and *alkaline* sodium phosphate do not produce symptoms or marked chemical changes in blood, probably because colloidal calcium phosphate is formed which is rapidly removed by the reticulo-endothelial system.

EFFECTS OF REMOVAL OF PARATHYROID GLANDS

When the parathyroids are removed the effects are as follows: (1) a fall of serum calcium from the normal of about 10 to about 6 mg% accompanied by a rise of inorganic phosphate and a fall in serum citrate, and (2) a fall in urinary calcium and phosphate. Tetany follows within a few days of the removal and if untreated, is fatal in many species of animal, but not in the rat unless it is on a low calcium diet. The onset of tetany cannot be related to any critical level of serum calcium but it is likely that there is a critical level of calcium *ions*, below which tetany occurs. The tetany is prevented or cured by the administration of calcium salts by injection or orally, or by the injection of parathormone.

Since the serum calcium after parathyroidectomy falls only by about 4 mg% (i.e. to 6 mg%) it is reasonable to conclude that this fraction alone is under parathyroid control, the remaining 6 mg% arising by a purely physico-chemical equilibrium with bone.

THE MODE OF ACTION OF PARATHORMONE

There is now conclusive evidence that PTH increases calcium absorption in the intestines, increases net resorption of bone and inhibits the reabsorption of P_i by the kidney tubule.

(1) EFFECTS ON ABSORPTION

By means of Nicolaysen's technique (p. 3) and also by measuring the absorption of calcium from everted gut sacs *in vitro*, several groups of workers have found that parathyroidectomy reduces calcium absorption (Talmage & Elliott 1958), although some negative results have been reported (for detailed review, see Toverud 1964).

The mechanism of this effect may be the control of the production by the kidney of 1:25 DHCC, the active form of vitamin D, which in turn affects the amount of calcium binding protein sythesized by the intestinal mucosa.

(2) EFFECTS ON BONE

Histological study of bone after parathormone injections usually shows the presence of increased numbers of osteoclasts, although this does not occur for about 6 hr after the rise in plasma calcium is well established. The rise in plasma calcium occurring within about 1 hr may be brought about either by greater activity of osteoclasts already present or by a reversal of the normal activity of osteocytes. Under conditions favouring resorption, a rarefaction of the bone surrounding osteocytes occurs which implies that these cells are also capable of resorption (osteocytic osteolysis). This role is consistent with the finding that PTH mobilizes calcium from bone deep within the tissue rather than from newly-formed bone near surfaces which are accessible to osteoclasts. This has been shown by giving ^{45}Ca for a few days followed by PTH; most of the calcium removed from bone was unlabelled indicating that the newly-formed bone was not the source of the calcium released.

The effects of PTH are readily detected when calvaria from embryonic chicks or new-born mice are cultured *in vitro* with media containing the hormone. An immediate effect is a rise in cAMP followed by the production of lactate and a rise in the calcium and phosphate in the medium. These results would suggest that PTH leads to the dissolving of bone mineral by the formation of lactate.

The effect of PTH on lysosomes is to release collagenase and other enzymes which would digest bone matrix.

When parathyroid tissue is brought into direct contact with bone (by the technique described on p. 19) local bone loss occurs proving that, at least at high concentrations, PTH affects bone directly.

Injections of PTH into rats followed by measurements of the uptake *in vitro* of [^{14}C]proline by bone has shown that its incorporation into collagen is depressed by PTH (Flanagan & Nichols 1962). This suggests that PTH may inhibit matrix synthesis as well as favour the breakdown of bone.

It must be emphasized that no calcium is mobilized from the teeth by PTH, a point discussed in more detail in Chapters V and VII.

(3) EFFECTS ON KIDNEY

It is well established that PTH inhibits resorption of P_i from kidney tubules, thus after it is injected the P_i concentrations increase in urine and fall in plasma. It was at one time suspected that this was the primary effect of PTH and that the reduced plasma P_i favoured the dissolving of bone leading to the rise in plasma calcium. PTH also increases the reabsorption of calcium, so lowering urine levels, an effect which does not require vitamin D and some workers think is the most important action in maintaining plasma calcium levels.

After an injection of PTH, the reduced urine calcium may be followed by a rise, perhaps a secondary effect of the rise in the plasma.

One of the earliest effects of PTH is to stimulate adenyl cyclase and thus to increase cAMP formation in kidney cells and it was assumed that this 'second messenger' controlled the action of the kidney on calcium. However, dibutyryl cAMP (the form which can permeate cells and so mimic the effect of endogenous cAMP) has no action on the uptake of calcium by kidney cells. These inconsistent results may be resolved by the finding that pyrophosphate (which is formed by adenyl cyclase along with cAMP but would not be present when pre-formed dibutryryl cAMP was added) does greatly increase calcium influx into cells. PTH also increases the mobilization of calcium from the mitochondria of kidney cells into the cytoplasm where it is believed to influence enzyme action and also where it becomes accessible to the calcium pump which causes its extrusion. This effect is also produced by dibutyryl cAMP so it may be presumed that this effect of PTH is mediated via adenyl cyclase.

PARATHORMONE AND CITRATE METABOLISM

There is much evidence suggesting that PTH may act by increasing citrate synthesis by bone. It has repeatedly been found that the changes in serum calcium which follow either parathyroidectomy or the injection of PTH are accompanied by changes in serum citrate, and these are greater than can be accounted for by release of citrate from the bone resorbed under PTH influence. In tissue culture of mouse calvaria, addition of PTH increased the amount of mineral and collagen dissolved accompanied by increased glucose consumption, lactate formation and a trebling of the small amount of citrate which accumulated—both an increased formation and reduced oxidation of citrate occurred. Addition of CT (and hydrocortisone) inhibited the PTH-induced resorption and reduced the citrate accumulation. There was a clear indication that the amount of calcium dissolved was more related to the citrate than the lactate accumulation but calcium release was higher than would be expected from the citrate produced. A possible explanation is that the effect on citrate is secondary to the rise in calcium because calcium is known to inhibit aconitase, the enzyme which oxidases citrate, although this seems unlikely as PTH inhibits citrate oxidation even in non-mineralized tissues where no change in calcium occurs (Nisbet *et al.* 1970). Since 1960, however, doubt has been cast on the citrate theory of PTH action by the finding that lactate, and not citrate, is the main end-product of bone meta-bolism (but see comments on p. 16). However, citrate is a chelating agent (see pp. 421–2) as well as an acid and even low concentrations of citrate might increase considerably the power of the lactate to dissolve bone. If the citrate is formed at the sites of bone resorption (for example by osteoclasts as sug-gested by Walker (1972)) it could have a large local effect even if it represented a small proportion of the total acid produced.

Forscher & Cohn (1963) suggested that PTH increases CO_2 formation from carbohydrate in bone cells, thus forming more carbonic acid which would favour the dissolving of bone by lowering the pH and perhaps also by chelating action (see pp. 421–2). They demonstrated that in animals treated with PTH increased CO_2 production is found in both the target organs of PTH (bone and kidney), but no effect is found in liver—thus proving that the effect was not merely a general stimulation of metabolism—but their hypothesis has not been followed up.

Parathormone produces very rapid effects in animals (for example changes in urine phosphate have been detected within 8 min of injection) and the rapidity of changes in blood chemistry after parathyroidectomy show that the hormone is rapidly inactivated or destroyed in the body, implying that, in order to maintain its concentration in the blood, it must be secreted continuously. The hormone is probably inactivated by the kidney but not by bone; injected PTH has a half-life of 18 min. It is not known whether inactivation occurs at the same target sites in the kidney as those that affect calcium and phosphate absorption.

Experiments reported by Iwanami *et al.* (1959) suggest that the parathyroid glands are more active in winter than in summer (possibly a temperature effect); this could account for the higher serum P_i found in summer.

These responses have been assumed to result from the release of calcium from the destruction of bone, the reabsorption of calcium from the kidney tubules and an increased absorption from the gut. Experiments by Parsons & Reit (1974) in which very low doses of parathyroid hormone were infused continuously into dogs through an indwelling cannula produced a rise in plasma calcium but no histological evidence for bone destruction and no rise in plasma hydroxyproline (a measure of breakdown of collagen of bone, see p. 86). They conclude that the effect of injected parathyroid hormone on the destruction of bone is a response to large pathological doses and that the normal function of parathyroid hormone may be to raise plasma levels of calcium via the kidney and gut and to thereby favour bone formation. This suggestion that, for many years, the effect of large toxic doses has been assumed to be the normal physiological effect might explain an old and almost forgotten observation. Selye (1932) reported that prolonged low dosage of parathyroid hormone in rats resulted in heavily-calcified bone with a small marrow cavity resembling a condition known as 'marble bone disease'.

CHEMISTRY OF PARATHORMONE

PTH is a straight chain polypeptide with 84 amino acids and a molecular weight of approximately 9500. If the terminal residue at the amino end (alanine) is removed the activity falls and is entirely abolished after the removal of the next amino acid (valine). Removal of six amino acids from the carboxylic end reduces activity greatly but does not abolish it.

CONTROL OF PARATHYROID GLANDS

Much evidence shows that the composition of the blood flowing through the gland controls the release of PTH, hypocalcaemia being a stimulus to its release.

The synthesis and release of the hormone has been studied by the culture of parathyroid tissue *in vitro*. High concentrations of calcium (and magnesium) in the medium reduce the amount of hormone leaving the gland but the relative effects of calcium and magnesium on synthesis, as opposed to secretion, have not yet been settled. The effect of calcium and magnesium is believed to be exerted through adenyl cyclase: calcium may inhibit the enzyme thus reducing the concentration of cAMP which, it is suggested, is necessary for the secretion. If these cations control synthesis as well, as some experiments suggest, it is not clear whether their effect is on the synthetic enzymes or via cAMP.

An active substance with a higher molecular weight than PTH has been detected in these *in vitro* experiments, possibly a precursor from which the circulatory hormone is split off either in the gland or immediately after secretion.

In hypoparathyroidism the concentration of cAMP in urine is abnormally low. This is found also in a condition known as pseudo-hypoparathyroidism, in which the levels of PTH in blood are normal or raised but the serum calcium resembles that of hypoparathyroidism, and is explained as a lack of sensitivity of the kidney adenyl cyclase to PTH. These findings support the conclusion that the effects of PTH in the kidney operate through cAMP.

THE DISCOVERY OF CALCITONIN

It had originally been assumed that hypercalcaemia was corrected by inhibiting PTH secretion but in 1962 Copp *et al.* showed that the effect of hypercalcaemia differs in several ways from what would be expected merely by a reduced secretion of PTH. It is now well-established that hypercalcaemia causes the release of a short acting second hormone 'calcitonin' (CT) which actively lowers the serum calcium (Copp 1969).

The evidence is as follows. The thyroid-parathyroid gland was dissected and isolated in dogs but remained attached to the circulation (Fig. I.3). The calcium of the blood flowing into the glands could be altered at will and the venous blood containing the secreted hormones then entered the general circulation where their effects could be measured by calcium estimations.

(1) Perfusion of the isolated glands with blood containing a high level of calcium led to a more rapid fall in the calcium of the systemic blood than that caused by thyroparathyroidectomy (hours -2 to 2 in Fig. I.4). A mere reduction in the release of PTH would be expected to have an effect similar to or less than that of thyroparathyroidectomy: a larger effect implies an active reduction in blood calcium. (2) After perfusing the glands with blood high in calcium, thyroparathyroidectomy was performed, and instead of the expected fall in serum calcium a rise was found (hours 8–10 in Fig. I.4). This was

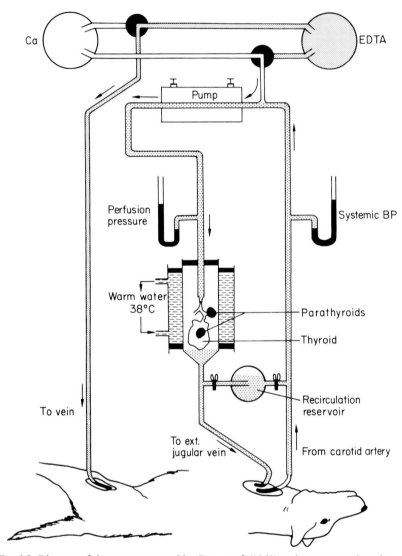

FIG. 1.3. Diagram of the apparatus used by Copp *et al.* (1962) to demonstrate the existence of calcitonin. Arterial blood is taken from the dog and either EDTA (which lowers the concentration of calcium ions) or calcium is added to it after which it is perfused through the isolated thyroid–parathyroid glands from which it takes up either PTH or calcitonin. The blood containing the hormone then enters the general circulation of the dog and raises or lowers the plasma calcium, as shown in Fig. I.4.

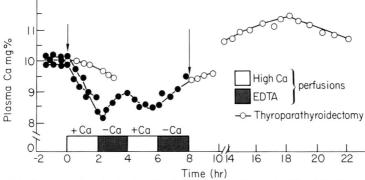

Fig. I.4. Some results obtained with the apparatus shown in Fig. I.3. Note that perfusing blood with a high calcium concentration through the thyroid–parathyroid glands results in a larger and more rapid fall in the calcium concentration of the systemic blood than occurs after thyroparathyroidectomy.

interpreted as being caused by the removal of the calcium-lowering effect of calcitonin which had been secreted in response to the high calcium of the systemic blood. (3) If the concentration of calcium ion in the blood is lowered by infusing the chelator EDTA (see p. 421) the calcium concentration returns to normal within about 2 hr. If the thyroid-parathyroid glands are removed after the infusion, the serum calcium overshoots by 1–2 mg%, presumably because of the absence of the normal effect of calcitonin in preventing an excessive rise (hours 8–18 in Fig. I.4).

EFFECTS OF CALCITONIN

Calcitonin exerts its effect direct on the skeleton where it reduces the resorption or increases the formation of bone or both. This has been shown in tissue culture and *in vivo* in rats. Its action has been observed in nephrecto-mized and eviscerated animals thus eliminating a major effect via the kidney and intestine.

Experimental administration of CT or its release from the thyroid leads to a prompt fall in the plasma concentrations of total and ionic calcium and P_i. Some workers find, but others do not, that it reduces magnesium concentra-tion also.

The response to CT occurs in rats after removal of either the kidney or the gut so that its action is not totally dependent on these organs. It acts on bone in the reverse way to PTH although it is not a direct antagonist since it is active after parathyroidectomy and its effect in suppressing resorption can be detected on bones in tissue culture. Its effect is not dependent on vitamin D. After injecting into young animals, the number of osteoclasts decreases and there are increases in the density of cortical bone and the amount of trabecular bone.

There is evidence that CT suppresses the release of destructive enzymes from lysosomes, the reverse of the effect of PTH.

The effects of physiological doses on calcium absorption are uncertain but there is evidence in rats of an inhibition of P_i absorption by CT (Tanzer & Navia 1973). It seems, therefore, that inhibition of absorption may supplement effects on bone in reducing plasma calcium.

Attempts to study effects of CT on the kidney are confused by the change in blood chemistry and possible secondary release of PTH resulting from the injections. Most experiments which have allowed for, or prevented, such effects have shown that CT has no action on the kidney.

The concentration of CT in the plasma of venous blood from the thyroid gland increases following the feeding of calcium by stomach pump in anaesthetized pigs: in some experiments, when small amounts of calcium were given, no rise in calcium of the plasma was detected although CT did rise (Munson *et al.* 1971). This suggests either that the thyroid is so sensitive to calcium levels that increased secretion occurs with changes in plasma calcium too small (less than 0·2 mg/100 ml) to detect chemically, or that the calcium level is not the only stimulus. Although a good correlation exists between the plasma concentrations of calcium and CT, injection of gastrin, the hormone released by the duodenum which stimulates the secretion of gastric juice, or of its synthetic analogue pentagastrin, is followed by CT secretion. It is possible that calcium, perhaps in the gut mucosa, releases gastrin which is the real stimulus to the release of CT by the thyroid. Pentagastrin has also a direct effect in inhibiting calcium absorption.

These experiments strongly support the idea that CT is important in controlling even the small rise in plasma calcium that might be expected from ordinary dietary sources. Slices of thyroid tissue incubated *in vitro* synthesize and secrete CT, both processes being stimulated by a high calcium concentration in, or the addition of dibutyral cAMP to, the medium (Bell & Queener 1974).

CHEMISTRY OF CALCITONIN

Calcitonin varies from species to species. The porcine hormone is a peptide with 32 amino acids and a molecular weight of 3585, and has been synthesized. A sequence of at least 25 amino acids is necessary for activity. It is a very potent hormone, 1–2 ng being enough to lower the rat blood calcium by 10%, about 1000 times as much PTH is required to produce a corresponding rise. The concentration in human blood has been estimated at approximately 0·02–0·40 ng/ml. The CT from different species varies in potency, that from the salmon being ten times more active than human and 100 times more active than porcine CT. These differences arise from variations in the rate of destruction, the half life of porcine CT being as short as 4–12 min and of salmon CT about ten times longer. Its effect is greatly increased if phosphate or pyrophosphate (PP_i) is injected along with the CT: the explanation of this effect is not known.

Although the effect of CT in lowering plasma calcium is much less in adults than in rapidly growing animals (which has been used as an argument that it inhibits bone resorption since this is more active in the young) CT remains active in adults in reducing or preventing hypercalcaemia. This suggests a role in preventing mineralization of soft tissues which tends to occur in hypercalcaemia.

In lower vertebrates CT is formed in the ultomobranchial body but in mammals this structure has become dispersed among other organs: in man it is mainly in the thyroid (C cells) in the vicinity of one of the parathyroid glands but CT-producing cells are also present in the parathyroid and thymus.

CLINICAL APPLICATION

No diseases or clinical syndromes are clearly recognized as arising from CT deficiency, perhaps because a complete deficiency in man would require abnormalities in the thyroid, parathyroid and thymus. Patients with Paget's disease, a condition in which both resorption and formation of bone are increased up to ten times in an unco-ordinated way, have been improved clinically by CT, presumably by reducing the resorption.

CALCIUM HOMEOSTASIS

The marked effects of experimental injections of PTH and CT on bone and the effect of these hormones in tissue culture has led to the wide belief that the stability of plasma calcium depends on its equilibrium with bone. The argument runs as follows. When the plasma calcium falls, the secretion of PTH rises and bone resorption then increases; conversely, if plasma calcium rises, CT is secreted which inhibits the normal release of bone mineral which was believed to occur.

However, several workers have challenged this interpretation and suggest that in normal subjects bone turnover is far too small to explain the fine control which occurs. These workers suggest that the kidney is the most important site of calcium homeostasis and that CT may inhibit and PTH stimulates the absorption of calcium by the kidney tubules. However, direct evidence of an effect of CT on the kidney is confused but tends to be negative. They agree that during active growth, or in diseases in which bone turnover is greatly increased, these hormones may act by influencing bone metabolism. This may occur to a slight extent during sleep in normal individuals when, at least in the later stages, all available calcium would be absorbed from the intestine and the bone would be the only source of additional calcium (Nordin & Peacock 1971).

The cell–fluid relationship in bone

As mentioned on p. 42, the short term maintenance of plasma concentrations of calcium and phosphate in response to such factors as dietary intake or increased utilization are probably controlled by the intestine and the kidney. The supersaturation of the plasma probably depends on the activity of the bone cells, however (Nordin 1964).

It has been realized for many years that the plasma was not in direct contact with bone crystals but that a 'membrane' consisting of the osteoblasts separated the two. The layer of osteoblasts which, the electron microscope shows, consists of cells with narrow spaces between them and with processes extending into the canaliculi, largely (but because of the small channels between the cells, not completely) prevents the tissue fluid of bone from intermingling freely with the plasma. The bone fluid would be expected, from its close contact with bone, to be in approximate equilibrium with bone salt and its calcium and phosphate concentrations will be those of the solubility products of this salt and are lower than in plasma. The osteoblasts forming the membrane evidently have the effect of pumping the additional calcium and phosphate into the plasma against a concentration gradient up to the supersaturated level, a process which requires PTH (since plasma levels fall to the solubility product after parathyroidectomy) which is ineffective in bone without vitamin D.

The calcium concentration in the cytoplasm of most cells is very low (about 10^{-7} M), high levels being toxic, and many workers consider that this low level is maintained by the temporary storage of intracellular calcium within the mitochondria brought about by a calcium pump. The pump probably receives energy from the breakdown of ATP which is stimulated by calcium. Bone alkaline phosphatase has ATPase activity and may be the enzyme which energizes the pump. Talmage speculates that a membrane-bound calcium pump is restricted to one pole of the cell, the opposite pole being relatively permeable to calcium (an arrangement which is certainly true in the intestinal mucosa). The effect of this arrangement is that the cells transport calcium— it diffuses in at one end and is pumped out at the other. Earlier work, which does not seem to have been co-ordinated with the concept of a calcium pump, provided good evidence that the bone cell transferred calcium from bone to plasma by the local production of acid (see p. 31).

The observations that the calcium concentration of mitochondria can become quite high, and even form insoluble calcium salts, suggests that some calcium may be transported via the mitochondria although there is no explanation of how it re-enters the cytoplasm before being pumped out of the cell. The concentration in the mitochondria of many cells concerned with calcium metabolism increases with PTH and is vitamin D-dependent.

It is next postulated that PTH, calcium and CT control the permeability of the appropriate side of the bone cell—these effects are known to be mediated by cAMP. The very earliest effect of PTH is a transient fall in plasma calcium following the entry of calcium into bone cells (p. 32). The entry of the calcium has two effects: it stimulates the ATPase of the calcium pump and has been shown to affect many other enzymic reactions within the cell: collagen synthesis is suppressed, the synthesis of RNA and lysosomal enzymes increased.

The Control of the Conversion of Vitamin D into its Active Form (1:25 DHCC)

It appeared at first that parathyroidectomy prevented the formation of the active form of vitamin D, 1:25 DHCC, suggesting that PTH controlled this process (Fraser & Kodicek 1973). It is well established *in vitro* that the kidney enzyme which introduces the second hydroxyl into 25 HCC (25 HCC 1-hydroxylase) is inhibited by a small rise (0·03 mM) in the calcium concentration of the medium or a larger rise (10 mM) in P_i. The production of 1:25

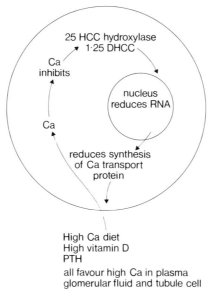

FIG. I.5 Diagram of one suggested explanation of the effects of various factors which raise plasma calcium on the hydroxylation of 25 HCC. Factors which raise plasma calcium (1) increase calcium uptake by the cells of the kidney tubule which (2) inhibits the 25 HCC hydroxylase. The increased cellular calcium also reduces the synthesis of a protein probably concerned with the transport of calcium into the cells. Thus by a feedback mechanism plasma calcium controls the formation of 1:25 DHCC.

DHCC may be controlled to meet body requirements by changes in the calcium concentration of the kidney cells (Galante *et al.* 1973) affecting the enzyme activity (Fig. I.5). It is suggested that PTH increases the calcium concentration within kidney cells (similar to the transient effect on bone, p. 43) as does vitamin D, while CT is thought to lower it. There is also evidence that a high concentration of P_i in plasma and kidney cortex cells favours the formation of the inactive derivative 24:25 DHCC and if the concentration of P_i is lowered, more of the active substance is formed.

It was later shown that factors which raise the calcium of the kidney cells (high dietary calcium, high vitamin D intake and PTH) reduce 1-hydroxylase activity, whereas a fall in the calcium content (promoted by a low calcium diet and perhaps by a high phosphate diet) increases the activity. PTH is not, therefore, essential for the production of 1:25 DHCC but is simply one of the several factors which may influence the calcium level in the kidney cells. This is confirmed by the finding that 1:25 DHCC was actively produced by thyroparathyroidectomized rats when given a diet low in calcium and vitamin D. PTH reduced the production of 1:25 DHCC in animals which had received vitamin D.

In vitamin D-deficient rats, with a tendency towards a low plasma calcium, PTH had no effect on this reaction, perhaps because the plasma calcium was already low. In contrast, Galante *et al.* (1972a) showed that PTH suppressed the formation of 1:25 DHCC and favoured the production of inactive 24:25 DHCC and the same group of workers showed that synthetic salmon calcitonin (which lowers blood calcium) increases 1:25 DHCC production and completely suppressed the 24:25 output (Galante *et al.* 1972b).

1:25 DHCC itself inhibits hydroxylation of the 25 HCC (Larkins *et al.* 1974). A possible explanation is that 1:25 DHCC stimulates synthesis of a CaBP in the kidney cells thereby increasing their powers of absorbing calcium. The higher calcium concentration that would follow would be expected to inhibit the 1-hydroxylase and thus reduce the formation of DHCC. One piece of evidence that synthesis of a protein is involved is that 1:25 DHCC does not inhibit hydroxylation in the presence of actinomysin, an inhibitor of protein synthesis.

Thus, the cells of the kidney tubules perform a dual role: (1) they control calcium excretion in the urine (by varying the amount of calcium absorbed in the tubules) and (2) the greater the amount absorbed, the more is the hydroxylase inhibited and the smaller the amount of 1:25 DHCC produced. This, by negative feedback, reduces the reabsorption. This cell is obviously strategically placed for sensing the level of calcium in the main outflow from the body fluids.

Prolactin stimulates 1-hydroxylase activity in the chick kidney and the finding that blood levels of 1:25 DHCC are greatly increased during lactation suggests that this applies also to mammals (Anonymous 1977). This activity of prolactin could explain the increased Ca absorption during lactation. Since the amino acid sequence of growth hormone and prolactin show a close similarity it has been speculated that the growth hormone may also have some influence on the formation of the active forms of vitamin D.

Sex hormones

The sex hormones may influence calcium and phosphorus metabolism in three ways. They may increase calcium absorption, stimulate the mineralization of bone, and decrease calcium excretion in the urine.

Oestradiol injected into male rats retards growth but increases the skeletal mass by inhibiting resorption. When CT and oestradiol were injected simultaneously the effect of CT on resorption was reduced but it is not known whether by direct antagonism with oestradiol or simply because if oestrogens already inhibit resorption then there is no further action which CT can take. Oestrogens have a direct effect in reducing resorption by PTH in tissue culture.

General effects of the thyroid hormone on calcium metabolism

Hyperthyroidism is accompanied by osteoporosis and the excretion of calcium and phosphorus in the urine is increased.

The thyroid hormones have a direct effect on the skeleton as both the formation and resorption of bone are greatly reduced in thyroidectomized dogs and restored to normal when thyroxine is given.

Faecal calcium is increased in hyperthyroidism indicating reduced net absorption, perhaps from increased peristalsis moving the gut contents too quickly to allow normal absorption.

Factors influencing the shape of a bone

Bone possesses an inherent growth pattern so that if, say, an embryonic femur is transplanted to an unusual part of the body, or even grown in tissue culture, it will develop into a bone of recognizable shape. It is equally clear that a bone does respond to forces applied externally. A bone will change its shape in the course of withstanding the tensions of muscles or during the remodelling of the bones in one leg after the amputation of the other.

Bassett (1964, 1965, 1968) has developed the concept that minute electric currents produced in the bone when pressure is applied may control the cells concerned with bone remodelling. It has long been known that deformation of many materials, including bone, dentine, skin and many others leads to the development of electrical potentials which are reversed in polarity when the deformation ceases (the phenomenon known as piezoelectricity). They have

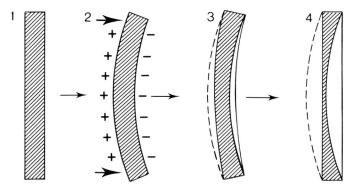

FIG. I.6 Suggested effects of deformation of a bone in producing electric currents (piezeoelectricity) which affect cellular activity resulting in changes in the shape of the bone.

been detected in the course of normal walking in living cats with electrodes implanted in the bones. Either the collagen or the collagen–apatite junction is responsible, as apatite itself has been reported to be inactive.

When currents of about the same magnitude as those recorded from the bones of living animals are passed through solutions of collagen the molecules orientate themselves at right angles to the direction of the current and remain in that position even after the current has been switched off. By adding appropriate salts (p. 89) the molecules were precipitated out as fibres. In addition to

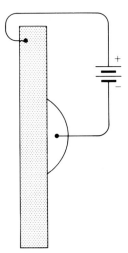

FIG. I.7 The effect of applying electric currents to bone in the living animal: new bone forms at the cathode.

this effect on collagen, it is suggested that the electrical currents would affect cellular activity as well as alter the distribution of ions and thus induce bone growth (in negative areas) and resorption (in positive areas). In an experiment in which electrodes attached to a battery were implanted in the femur of a dog so that a continuous electrical current of 2–3 μamps was applied, bone formation occurred at the cathode (in confirmation of the hypothesis) but there was no resorption at the anode (Figs II.6 & 7). It is possible that the normal piezoelectric currents formed as a result of the movements of the dog reduced at the anode the effectiveness of the current from the battery. This experiment gives partial support to the possibility that the remodelling of bones is influenced by piezoelectrical changes. Other experiments are reviewed by Marino & Becker (1977).

This concept has been applied to the acceleration of the healing of bone fractures in experimental animals. When coils were placed on the skin surrounding a fracture and pulsed with a current or with a direct current applied by electrodes implanted inside a fracture (Paterson *et al.* 1977), bone regeneration was promoted. Some preliminary success has been reported in human subjects suffering from the disease congenital pseudoarthritis in which fractures occur which refuse to heal.

Piezoelectric effects are detectable in dentine and cementum, but not enamel (Athenstaedt 1971) and are probably generated during normal mastication and, in bones, may be a factor in the greater development of the jaws with vigorous mastication (p. 528). They may also operate during orthodontic treatment.

Another suggestion is that pressure on a bone would increase the solubility of hydroxyapatite (the bone salt). There is some experimental evidence that this occurs with synthetic hydroxyapatite. The dissolving of the bone increases the local concentration of calcium ion which, in turn, may regulate the metabolism of the bone cells in such a way that they deposit or remove bone (Justus & Luft 1970).

The Excretion of Calcium and Phosphate

Faeces

From what has already been said it is clear that calcium and phosphate are both present in urine and faeces, but there is good evidence that, at least in some species (including man), negligible quantities of calcium are excreted through the wall of the large intestine. The most direct evidence was obtained by analysing the secretion from the large intestine of a subject in which it had been surgically isolated from the ileum. Thus the contents of the ileum left through a fistula and the material voided through the rectum, or obtained by washing out the isolated large intestine, could only be derived from the mucosa of the latter. It was found that negligible quantities (about 5 mg day^{-1}) of calcium and phosphorus were excreted through the large intestine (Welch *et al.* 1936).

The endogenous calcium in faeces arises mostly from the digestive juices and present evidence suggests that it is not a controlled excretion as it does not increase with increased dietary intake, although it is influenced by the concentration of calcium in the plasma.

Urine

Now that it is fully established that the calcium in faeces does not represent a true excretion it is clear that the usually smaller amount of calcium in the urine is the excretion route which is under full body control. The loss of calcium via sweat is probably influenced only by the volume of sweat secreted and is independent of the losses needed by the body to maintain the calcium

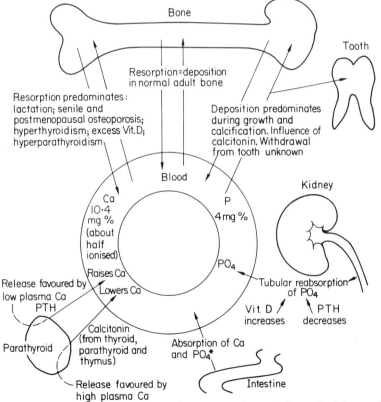

FIG. I.8. Diagram of the main factors in the general metabolism of calcium and phosphorus.

balance appropriate to the individual. Over long periods, urinary calcium reflects the relation between absorption and body requirements, for example during growth calcium is retained and a low excretion, as well as an increased absorption, both help to bring this about. However, urinary calcium does not necessarily reflect quantitatively changes in intake. For instance, in a study by Malm (1958), on fifteen adult males, a fall in daily intake from 950 mg to about half this amount resulted in an average fall in urinary calcium from 230 mg to 207 mg. As with calcium absorption, there is considerable individual variation in urinary excretion and the kidney does not necessarily maintain an individual in calcium balance. In spite of these individual variations, data from 606 normal subjects show that, on average, urinary excretion, expressed as a percentage of intake, is related to the intake per kilogram of body weight.

The calcium of urine is lowered by high P_i intake, the possible train of events being: high P in diet→raised plasma P→slightly lowered plasma Ca→increased secretion of PTH→increased reabsorption of Ca.

Urine is supersaturated with calcium and phosphate ions yet calcium phosphate does not precipitate from normal urine, even after standing. Urine contains substances which inhibit the formation of calcium phosphate precipitates acting partly by complexing the calcium: these are believed to be citrate, phosphate and sulphate which bind with 30, 10 and 10% respectively, of the calcium.

The urinary excretion of phosphate is related to the level in the plasma and has a threshold figure of between 2 and 2·4 mg 100 ml^{-1} of plasma below which urinary phosphate is virtually zero. PTH inhibits P_i absorption and thus reduces urinary P_i and raises plasma concentration.

The main factors in the metabolism of calcium and phosphorus are summarized in diagrammatic form in Fig. I.6.

References

ANONYMOUS (1977) Vitamin D and the pituitary. *Lancet* **i,** 840

ATHENSTAEDT H. (1971) Pyroelectric and piezoelectric behaviour of human dental hard tissues. *Archs oral Biol.* **16,** 495

BARNICOT N.A. (1951) The local action of parathyroid and other tissues on bone in intracerebral grafts. *J. Anat. Lond.* **82,** 233 (also **84,** 34; **85,** 120)

BASSETT C.A.L. (1965) Electrical effects in bone. *Scient. Am.* **213,** 18 (see also (1968) *Calc. Tiss. Res.* **1,** 252 (1964) Effects of electric current on bone *in vivo. Nature (Lond.)* **204,** 652)

BELL N.H. & QUEENER S. (1974) Stimulation of calcitonin synthesis and release *in vitro* by calcium and dibutyryl cyclic AMP. *Nature (Lond.)* **248,** 343

BLAU M. *et al.* (1957) Effect of intake level on the utilization and intestinal excretion of calcium in man. *J. Nutr.* **61,** 507

BORLE A.B. *et al.* (1960) Metabolic studies of bone *in vitro. J. biol. Chem.* **235,** 1206, 1211

CARLSSON A. (1952) Tracer experiments on the effect of vitamin D on the skeletal metabolism of calcium and phosphorus. *Acta physiol. Scand.* **26,** 201 (also **31,** 301, 308, 312, 317)

CONDON J.R. *et al.* (1970) Calcium and

phosphorus metabolism in relation to lactose tolerance. *Lancet* i, 1027

COPP D.H. (1969) Endocrine control of calcium homeostasis. *J. Endocrinol.* **43**, 137. Also (1962) *Endocrinology*, **70**, 638

DeLUCA H.F. *et al.* (1956) Vitamin D and citrate oxidation. *J. biol. Chem.* **224**, 201 (also *J. biol. Chem.* **228**, 469, and *Fed. Proc.* **17**, 210)

DICKENS F. (1941) Citric acid in animal tissues. *Biochem. J.* **35**, 1011

DUNCAN D.L. (1955) Physiological effects of lactose. *Nutr. Abstr. Rev.* **25**, 309

DUNCAN D.L. (1958) The interpretation of studies on calcium and phosphorus balances in ruminants. *Nutr. Abstr. Rev.* **28**, 695

ETTORI J. & SCOGGAN S.M. (1959) Ionized calcium in biological media. *Nature (Lond.)* **184**, 1315

FLANAGAN B. & NICHOLS G. JR (1962) Collagen biosynthesis by surviving bone fragments *in vitro. Fed. Proc.* **21**, 79

FORBES R.M. *et al.* (1953) The composition of the adult human body as determined by chemical analysis. *J. biol. Chem.* **203**, 359

FORSCHER B.K. & COHN D.V. (1963) *In vitro* carbohydrate metabolism of bone: effect of treatment of intact animals with para-thyroid extract. In *Mechanisms of Hard Tissue Destruction*, p. 577. Ed. SOGNNAES R.F. Amer. Ass. Adv. Sci. publ. no. **75** Washington, D.C.

FOURNIER P. (1955) Relation between utilization of structural sugars and ossification. *C.R. Acad. Sci. (Paris)* **240**, 1364 (also many other papers which can be traced through *Nutrition Abstracts and Reviews*)

FRASER D.R. & KODICEK E. (1973) Regulation of 25-Hydroxycholecalciferol-1-Hydroxylase activity in kidney by para-thyroid hormone. *Nature New Biol.* **241**, 163

GALANTE L. *et al.* (1972a) Effect of parathyroid extract on vitamin D metabolism. *Lancet* i, 985

GALANTE L. *et al.* (1972b) Effect of calcitonin on vitamin D metabolism. *Nature (Lond.)* **238**, 591. Also (1973) **244**, 438

GRAN F.C. (1960) Studies on calcium and strontium-90 metabolism in rats. *Acta physiol. Scand.* **48**, Supp. 167

GREENWALD *et al.* (1963) Effect of lactose on calcium metabolism in man. *J. Nutr.* **79**, 531

HARTLES R.L. & LEAVER A.G. (1961) Citrate in mineralized tissues. *Archs oral Biol.* **5**, 38; See also: HARTLES R.L. (1964) Citrate in mineralized tissues. *Adv. oral Biol.* 226 (a general review)

HEANEY R.P. & SKILLMAN T.G. (1971) Calcium metabolism in normal human pregnancy. *J. Clin. Endocrinol. Metab.* **33**, 661

HEANEY R.P. *et al.* (1972) Growth hormone: the effect on skeletal renewal in the adult dog. *Calc. Tiss. Res.* **10**, 14

HENRIKSON P.-A. (1968) Periodontal disease and calcium deficiency. *Acta odont. Scand.* **26**, Supp. 50

IRVING J.T. (1963) The Sudanophil material at sites of calcification. *Archs oral Biol.* **8**, 735

IRVING J.T. (1973) *Calcium and Phosphorus Metabolism.* Academic Press, New York

IRVING J.T. & WUTHIER R.E. (1961) Further observations on the Sudan Black stain for calcification. *Archs oral Biol.* **5**, 323

IRWIN M.I. & KIENHOLZ E.W. (1973) A conspectus of research on calcium requirements in man. *J. Nutr.* **103**, 1019

IWANAMI M. *et al.* (1959) Seasonal variation in serum inorganic phosphate with special reference to parathyroid activity. *J. Physiol.* **149**, 23

JOHNSON N.E. (1970) Protein and osteoporosis. *J. Nutr.* **100**, 1425 (see also **102**, 1297)

JOHNSTON F.A. *et al.* (1950) Calcium and iron in perspiration. *J. Nutr.* **42**, 285

JUSTUS R. & LUFT J.H. (1970) A mechanicochemical hypothesis for bone remodelling induced by mechanical stress. *Calc. Tiss. Res.* **5**, 222

KIMBERG D.V. *et al.* (1961) Active transport of calcium by intestine: effect of dietary calcium. *Amer. J. Physiol.* **200**, 1256

KODICEK E. (1963) Turnover and distribution of vitamin D and its mode of action. In *The Transfer of Calcium and Strontium Across Biological Membranes*, p. 185. Ed.

WASSERMANN R.H. Academic Press, London

KOWARSKI S. & SCHACHTER D. (1969) Effects of Vitamin D on phosphate transport into mucosal constituents of rat intestinal mucosa. *J. biol. Chem.* **244**, 211

LARKINS R.G. *et al.* (1974) Feedback control of vitamin D metabolism by a nuclear action of 1,25-dihydroxycholecalciferol on the kidney. *Nature*, **252**, 412

LEHMANN H. & POLLAK I. (1942) The effect of amino acids on phosphate transfer in muscle extract. *Biochem. J.* **36**, 672

LEITCH I. (1937) The determination of the calcium requirements of man. *Nutr. Abstr. Rev.* **6**, 553 (see also *Nutr. Abstr. Rev.* **8**, 1, for a correction to this review)

LEITCH I. & AITKEN F.C. (1959) The estimation of calcium requirement: a reexamination. *Nutr. Abs. Rev.* **29**, 393.

LENGEMANN F.W. & DOBBINS J.W. (1958) Bile and calcium absorption. *J. Nutr.* **66**, 45

LUTWAK L. *et al.* (1971) Calcium deficiency and human periodontal disease. *Israel J. med. Sci.* **7**, 504. Also (1972) *Fed. Proc.* **31**, 721

McCANCE R.A. & WIDDOWSON E.M. (1942–3) Mineral metabolism on diets rich in bread. *J. Physiol.* **101**, 44, 304

McCANCE R.A. & WIDDOWSON E.M. (1943–4) Seasonal and annual changes in the calcium metabolism of man. *J. Physiol.* **102**, 42

McCANCE R.A. *et al.* (1942) The effect of protein intake on the absorption of calcium and magnesium. *Biochem. J.* **36**, 686

MALM O.J. (1958) Calcium requirement and adaptation in adult man. *Scand. J. of Clin. and Lab. Invest.* **10**, Supp. 36 (contains an excellent review of calcium metabolism)

MARINO A.A. & BECKER R.O. (1977) Electrical osteogenesis: An analysis. *Clin. Orthop.* **123**, 280

MELLANBY E. (1949) Anti-calcifying action of phytate. *J. Physiol.* **109**, 488

MILLS R. *et al.* (1940) The influence of lactose on calcium retention in children. *J. Nutr.* **20**, 467

MITCHELL H.H. *et al.* (1945) The chemical composition of the adult human body and its bearing on the biochemistry of growth. *J. biol. Chem.* **158**, 625.

MUNSON P.L. *et al.* (1971) Physiological importance of thyrocalcitonin. In *Cellular Mechanisms for Calcium Transfer and Homeostasis*, p. 403. Eds NICHOLS G. JR and WASSERMAN R.H. Academic Press, New York.

MURTHY H.B.N. *et al.* (1955) The metabolism of nitrogen, calcium and phosphorus in undernourished children. 1. Adaptation to low intakes of calories, protein, calcium and phosphorus. *Brit. J. Nutr.* **9**, 203

NEER R.M. *et al.* (1971) Stimulation by artificial lighting of calcium absorption in elderly human subjects. *Nature (Lond.)* **229**, 255

NEUMAN W.F. *et al.* (1956) On the mechanism of action of parathormone. *J. Am. Chem. Soc.* **78**, 3863

NEUMAN W.F. & NEUMAN M.W. (1958) *The Chemical Dynamics of Bone Mineral.* University of Chicago Press, Chicago

NICOLAYSEN R. (1937) The absorption of calcium chloride, xylose and sodium sulphate from isolated loops of the small intestine and of calcium chloride from isolated loops of the small intestine and of calcium chloride from the abdominal cavity. *Biochem. J.* **31**, 323

NICHOLS G. JR (1963) *In vitro* studies of bone resorptive mechanisms. In *Mechanisms of Hard Tissue Destruction*, p. 557. Ed. SOGNNAES R.F. Amer. Ass. Adv. Sci. publ. no. **75** Washington, D.C.

NICHOLS G. JR *et al.* (1963) Some effects of vitamin D and parathyroid hormone on the calcium and phosphorus metabolism of bone *in vitro. Acta physiol. Scand.* **57**, 51

NISBET J.A. *et al.* (1970) Lactic and citric acid metabolism in bone resorption in tissue culture. *Clin. Orthoped.* **70**, 220

NORDIN B.E.C. (1957) The solubility of powdered bone. *J. biol. Chem.* **227**, 551 (see also **235**, 1215; **237**, 2704)

NORDIN B.E.C. (1964) The blood-bone equilibrium. *Lect. Sci. Basis Med.* **14**, 368

NORDIN B.E. (1971) Clinical significance and pathogenesis of osteoporosis. *Brit. med. J.* i, 571

NORDIN B.E. & PEACOCK M. (1971) The role of the kidney in the regulation of plasma calcium. *Acta Endocrinol. Supp.* **155,** 209

NORMAN A.W. (1966) Vitamin D mediated synthesis of rapidly labelled RNA from intestinal mucosa. *Biochem. Biophys. Res. Commun.* **23,** 335

NORMAN A.W. (1974) The hormone-like action of $1,25-(OH)_2-$ cholecalciferol in the intestine. *Vitamins and Hormones,* **32,** 326

PARSONS J.A. & REIT B. (1974) Chronic response of dogs to parathyroid hormone infusion. *Nature (Lond.)* **250,** 254

PATERSON D.C. *et al.* (1977) Electrical bone-growth stimulation in an experimental model of delayed union. *Lancet* i, 1278

RASMUSSEN P. (1969) The action of Vitamin D deficiency on bone tissue and the epiphyseal plate in rats given adequate amounts of calcium and phosphorus in the diet. *Archs oral Biol.* **14,** 1293

ROBERTS A.H. & YUDKIN J. (1961) Effect of phytate and other dietary factors on intestinal phytase and bone calcification in the rat. *Brit. J. Nutr.* **15,** 457

ROTTENSTEN K.V. (1938) The effect of body stores on the efficiency of calcium utilization. *Biochem. J.* **32,** 1285

SCHACHTER D. *et al.* (1960) Active transport of calcium by the small intestine of the rat. *Amer. J. Physiol.* **198,** 263, 269, 275; (1961) **200,** 1263

SCHARTUM S. & NICHOLS G. JR (1962) Concerning pH gradients between the extracellular compartment and fluids bathing the bone mineral surface and their relation to calcium ion distribution. *J. clin. Invest.* **41,** 1163

SELYE H. (1932) On the stimulation of new bone formation with parathyroid extract and irradiated ergosterol. *Endocrinology,* **16,** 547

SHERMAN H.C. (1947) *Calcium and Phosphorus in Foods and Nutrition.* Columbia University Press, New York

SHIMMINS J. *et al.* (1971) The measurement of calcium absorption using an oral and intravenous tracer. II. Clinical studies. *Calc. Tiss. Res.* **6,** 301

STAMP T.C.B. & ROUND J.M. (1974) Seasonal changes in human plasma levels of 25-hydroxyvitamin D. *Nature (Lond.)* **247,** 563

STEGGARDA E.R. & MITCHELL H.H. (1951) The calcium balance of adult human subjects on high- and low-fat (butter) diets. *J. Nutr.* **45,** 201

TALMAGE R.V. & ELLIOT J.R. (1958) Influence of parathyroids on intestinal absorption of radiocalcium and radiostrontium. *Fed. Proc.* **17,** 160

TANZER F.S. & NAVIA J.M. (1973) Calcitonin inhibition of intestinal phosphate absorption. *Nature New Biol.* **242,** 221

TOVERUD S.U. (1964) Parathyroid effect on intestinal absorption of calcium and on secretion of calcium with the digestive juices in vitamin D deficient rats. *Acta physiol. Scand.* **62,** Supp. 234

UNDERWOOD E. *et al.* (1951) Vitamin D in calcium metabolism. *Amer. J. Physiol.* **166,** 387.

WALKER A.R.P. *et al.* (1948) The effect of bread rich in phytate phosphorus on the metabolism of certain mineral salts with special reference to calcium. *Biochem. J.* **42,** 452.

WALKER D.G. (1972) Enzymatic and electron microscopic analysis of isolated osteoclasts. *Calc. Tiss. Res.* **9,** 296

WALKER R.M. & LINKSWILER H.M. (1972) Calcium retention in the adult human male as affected by protein intake. *J. Nutr.* **102,** 1297

WALSER M. (1960) Ion association: interactions between calcium, magnesium inorganic phosphate, citrate and protein in normal human plasma. *J. clin. Invest.* **40,** 723

WASSERMANN R.H. (1964) Lactose stimulated intestinal absorption of calcium: a theory. *Nature (Lond.)* **201,** 997

WASSERMANN R.H. *et al.* (1956) Amino acids and calcium absorption. *J. Nutr.* **59,** 371; **62,** 367

WASSERMAN R.H. *et al.* (1968) Vitamin D-dependent calcium-binding protein: purification and some properties. *J. biol. Chem.* **243**, 3978

WASSERMAN R.H. & CORRADINO R.A. (1973) Vitamin D, calcium and protein synthesis. *Vitamins and Hormones* **31**, 43

WASSERMAN R.H. & TAYLOR A.N. (1973) Physiological significance of the Vitamin-D-dependent calcium binding protein. *Triangle* **12**, 119

WELCH C.S. *et al.* (1936) Function of the large intestine of man in absorption and excretion: study of a subject with an ileostomy stoma and isolated colon. *Archs int. med.* **58**, 195

WIDDOWSON E.M. *et al.* (1951) The chemical composition of the human body. *Clin. Sci.* **10**, 113

WILSON T.H. & WISEMAN G. (1954) The use of sacs of everted small investine for the study of transference of substances from the mucosal to the serosal surface. *J. Physiol.* **124**, 116

WORLD HEALTH ORGANIZATION (1962) Calcium requirements. *Chron. Wld Hlth. Org.* **16**, 251

WUTHIER R.E. (1971) Zonal analysis of phospholipids in the epiphyseal cartilage and bone of normal and rachitic chickens and pigs. *Calc. Tiss. Res.* **8**, 36

The progress of research on calcium and phosphorus metabolism and on the physiology of the parathyroid gland and vitamin D may be followed in the successive volumes of the *Annual Review of Biochemistry*, the *Annual Review of Physiology*, and the following general reviews:

BARLTROP D. & BURLAND W.L. (1969) Eds *Mineral Metabolism in Paediatrics*. Blackwell Scientific Publications, Oxford

IRVING J.T. (1973) *Calcium and Phosphorus Metabolism*. Academic Press, New York

NICHOLS G. JR & WASSERMAN, R.H. (Eds) (1971) *Cellular Mechanisms for Calcium Transfer and Homeostasis*. Academic Press, New York

NORDIN B.E.C. (Ed) (1976) Calcium, phosphate and magnesium metabolism. *Clinical Physiology and Diagnostic Procedures*. Churchill Livingstone, Edinburgh

TALMAGE R.V. & BÉLANGER L.F. (1968) Eds *Parathyroid Hormone and Thyrocalcitonin (Calcitonin)*. Excerpta Medica Foundation, Amsterdam

CHAPTER II

CHEMICAL COMPOSITION OF TEETH

Inorganic Composition of Enamel and Dentine

The composition of enamel and dentine differ so much that it is essential to separate them before analysis if the results are to have any biological significance. The separation of the cementum from the dentine is less important because these two tissues have a similar composition and the proportion of cementum present in the normal tooth is too small to have much influence on the composition of the mixture.

The anatomical relations of the dental tissues are shown diagrammatically in Fig. II.1.

Methods of separating enamel from dentine

(A) MECHANICAL METHODS
The earliest method consisted of chipping off the enamel from the underlying dentine, a process which is greatly facilitated by first drying the tooth thoroughly by heating. Other mechanical methods consist of grinding off all the enamel with a bur leaving the dentine, or alternatively and preferably, grinding the dentine away with a bur till a hollow shell of the harder enamel is left. These methods are laborious, they do not yield pure enamel and dentine, and it is not easy to collect the ground material quantitatively because some of it may be lost as fine dust which escapes into the air, although they do avoid contact with the unphysiological fluids used in the flotation methods.

(B) FLOTATION METHODS (MANLY & HODGE 1939)
The whole tooth is ground to a fine powder in some device such as a ball-mill or a 'diamond mortar' which consists of a heavy flat pestle with which the teeth can be hammered inside a closed space that prevents loss of particles escaping into the air. The principle of the separation is that when a mixture of enamel, dentine and cementum is added to a fluid with a density of 2·70, the enamel (density 2·9–3·0) sinks, while the dentine and cementum (density

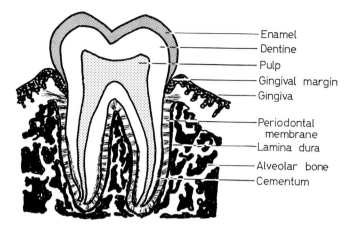

FIG. II.1. The relations of the main dental tissues.

2·14 and 2·03, respectively) float. Powdered tooth is poured into a pointed tube open at the lower end, which is fitted into a centrifuge tube containing the liquid whose density is 2·70 (Fig. II.2). A suitable liquid is 91% bromoform and 9% acetone. After thoroughly wetting the powdered tooth with the liquid, the whole is centrifuged and the enamel and dentine then form distinct layers, the enamel sinks into the outer tube and the dentine and cementum float inside the inner tube. The finger is placed over the inner tube which is removed with its contents. The dentine and enamel are then washed free from bromoform by acetone. Dentine and cementum may be separated by

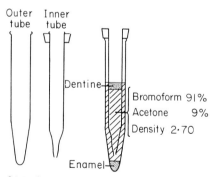

FIG. II.2. Diagram of Manly & Hodge's method of separating enamel and dentine.

treating the mixture as above, with a fluid of density 2·07, but this is rarely done as the composition of cementum (described by Neiders *et al.* 1972) is very similar to that of dentine but the ash content is lower (50%). The purity of the samples is about 97–99% and can be improved by several repetitions of the process with fluids of slightly different densities.

The effect of flotation methods on the composition of enamel and dentine has not been thoroughly studied, but bromoform-acetone removes lipids, at least partially. An aqueous solution of cadmium tungstoborate (82% w/w) has a density of 2·70 and may be used for separation without altering the lipids or, so far as is known, the rest of the organic matrix but does contaminate the inorganic fraction with cadmium (Prout & Shutt 1970b). For certain types of analyses, therefore, mechanical methods of separation may be preferable.

Manly & Hodge have also worked out the details of a very delicate test for determining the purity of the enamel and dentine, based on the optical properties of these materials. The refractive index of enamel is 1·62 and of dentine 1·56. Consequently, if a mixture of particles of enamel and dentine is placed in a fluid of intermediate refractive index (say 1·59) and studied under the microscope, as the focus is raised, a halo called the 'Becke line' appears to

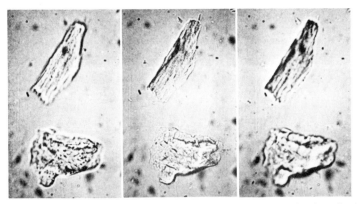

FIG. II. 3. The optical behaviour of particles of enamel and dentine in a liquid of refractive index 1·59. The upper particle is enamel and the lower dentine. The plane of focus is raised on the left, correct in the middle and lowered on the right. Note that the halo or 'Becke line' moves in opposite directions in particles of enamel and dentine.

enter the enamel particle, but moves out from the dentine particle (Fig. II.3). By examining several hundred particles the percentage purity of a mixture may be determined.

Other methods of distinguishing between particles of enamel and dentine are based on the observations that when viewed out of focus, enamel appears bluish and dentine yellowish, and the dentine, unlike the enamel, stains with periodic acid Schiff reagent and with Van Gieson's stain. Also dentine is more fluorescent in ultra-violet light than is enamel. The staining methods not only make it easier to estimate the purity of a sample but make it possible to identify the contaminating particles and, with the aid of a lens, to remove them.

The moisture of teeth and its relation to methods of recording the composition of dental tissues

When considering analytical figures of the composition of teeth, it is important to be clear whether they refer to moist, dry or ashed material. The analyses themselves are almost invariably carried out, either on 'dried' material (from which water has been removed by gentle heat), or on ashed material (i.e. from which both water and organic matter have been removed by the methods described below).

Some workers remove fat-soluble substances from the teeth by extraction with a fat solvent before analysis ('dried fat-free' samples), but the proportion of such material in teeth is so small that the effect on composition is negligible for most purposes and if the bromoform-acetone mixture is used for separation much of it will be extracted already.

Drying dentine at about 100° C does not remove all the water, since some is in a 'bound form', attached in a chemical combination, probably to the organic matrix. The published figures on the loss of weight of 'dry' enamel during ashing are also much higher than can be accounted for from its known organic constituents.

The direct estimation of the moisture in teeth is difficult, and no entirely reliable figures can be given, especially for enamel. If enamel and dentine are separated by any of the methods mentioned above, water is lost. During grinding, the heating and exposure of a large surface to the air will allow loss by evaporation and in the flotation method water will be extracted by the acetone used in washing. Most estimates of moisture have been made 'by difference', i.e. subtracting the percentage of organic matter (estimated by various ways) from the percentage loss of weight during ashing (if the temperature used is above 500° C carbon dioxide is driven off the carbonate of the tooth and this must be allowed for). Clearly such estimates are affected by the errors in determining the other constituents. Attempts have been made to determine the moisture of teeth by measuring the weight loss during the heating *in vacuo* of freshly extracted teeth split open and with their pulps removed. The results, which represent approximately the water content of dentine (since the enamel is only a small part of the whole tooth), depended on the temperature but at the highest temperature used (197° C for 23 hr) an average loss of 9·32% was found. When pieces of tooth containing dentine only were treated in this way, an average loss of weight of 12% was recorded.

When enamel or dentine, dried at 105° C, are heated strongly a loss of weight of about 5 and 37%, respectively, occurs. This could arise from the destruction of organic matter or from the evaporation of water. As mentioned later, the organic matter of enamel is probably not more than 1·3%, which leaves about 4% which might be water. By heating to different temperatures and measuring changes in weight (thermogravimetry) or birefringence (which indicate the presence of spaces in the enamel) it has been shown that water occurs in two forms—one loosely bound, probably to the organic matter, and another more tightly bound, possibly as the hydration shell round the apatite crystals. Approximate estimates on two samples of enamel (not necessarily typical but giving some idea of the order of magnitude) are 0·8% loosely bound and 3·3% tightly bound (Emerson 1962). Peaks of weight loss occur at 100° C, from loosely bound water, at 350° C, from organic matter and water bound tightly to the crystals and at 750° C from bound carbonate (Holager 1972; Komrska 1972).

When sections of enamel are exposed to an ascending series of humidities they take up water which can be estimated thermogravimetrically. When the same sections are made to loose water by exposure to descending humidity, the concentration of water at equilibrium for humidities greater than 40% is higher than the figure previously obtained, i.e. the enamel tends to retain water in pores. Calculations based on these data tended to show two clusters of pore size, one at 9 Å and the other at 25 Å—possibly representing inter- and intra-prismatic spaces (Moreno & Zahradnik 1973).

The organic matter may be removed from enamel and dentine by two methods. (1) Dry ashing. The dry tissue is heated in a crucible to a high temperature which breaks down the organic matter, but also alters the inorganic substance by liberating carbon dioxide from carbonates and changes the crystal form. (2) Wet ashing. The tissue is boiled with ethylene glycol and KOH (this mixture is more effective than aqueous KOH because it boils at a higher temperature), which removes the organic matter completely from dentine, although its action on enamel is not yet fully understood. It leaves the carbonate unaffected but apparently extracts some of the calcium and phosphorus, estimated at 0·5 and 1·5% respectively of the weight of the sample. The reagent ethylene diamine, also called 1:2 diamino ethane (not to be confused with ethylene diamine tetra-acetate (EDTA) which is a chelating agent (see p. 421) used to demineralize tissues without exposing them to acid), has been found to be a more satisfactory means of removing the organic matter without altering the inorganic matter (see Burnett & Zenewitz (1958) for a general review).

When dentine, after drying at 105° C, is treated by either of these methods of ashing, the loss of weight is made up by the organic matter *plus the bound water*. Consequently, many early analytical figures overstated the amount of organic matter in dentine and probably enamel. It is clear that analytical figures based on materials obtained by the two ashing methods will differ. Since samples ashed by heat have lost carbon dioxide, other constituents will be *proportionately* higher than in samples treated by the alkaline ethylene glycol method. Unless separate determinations of carbonate are carried out, there is no means of distinguishing, in the heat ashing method, between loss of weight due to driving off carbon dioxide from carbonate and loss due to organic matter and bound water.

Table II.1

The approximate composition of human enamel and dentine expressed in different ways

(1) As percentage of dry weight

	Ca	P	Mg	CO_2	Organic matter	Comments
Enamel	36	17	0·45	2·5	1·3	(a) Tooth material heated to about 105° C till weight constant. Some water removed but 'bound' water retained.
Dentine	27	13	1·4	3·3	20	

(b) The large differences between the figures for enamel and dentine are due to the higher organic and water contents of dentine.

(c) More analytical figures are available for this material than for others; these results can be regarded as being more fully established than are those below.

(d) Variations between results of different workers are too great to justify the calculation of accurate averages.

(2) As percentage of ash

	Ca	P	Mg	CO_2	Organic matter	Comments
Enamel	38	18	0·45	none	none	(a) Tooth material heated strongly—all water removed, organic matter destroyed and CO_2 driven off from carbonates.
Dentine	38	18	1·9	none	none	

(b) Note that in this material, the only major difference between enamel and dentine is in the magnesium content.

(3) As percentage of inorganic material

	Ca	P	Mg	CO_2	Organic matter	Comments
Enamel	37·8	17·7	0·45	2·5	none	(a) Tooth material boiled with 3% KOH in ethylene glycol which removes organic matter and water but leaves carbonates intact.
Dentine	35·5	16·7	1·8	3·9	none	

(b) In dentine, the figures given are those actually found, but they are lower than would be expected, probably because some Ca and P is dissolved by the reagent.

(4) As present in tooth of living animal (calculated)

	Ca	P	Mg	CO_2	Organic matter	Comments
Enamel	35	16·5	0·4	2.5	1·1	(a) Actual analysis of fresh tooth material is technically difficult. These approximate figures are calculated from those given in (1) above assuming:
Dentine	24	11·5	0·9	3·0	21·0	

Note that the second column of figures refers to P, and the fourth to CO_2, whereas the tooth contains PO_4 and CO_3. This explains why the figures do not add up to 100%.

(i) that enamel contains 4% of water,
(ii) that dentine contains 10% of water.

The Results of Analyses of Dental Tissues

The published results of analyses of dental tissues vary too much to warrant the calculation of exact averages, but Table II.1 gives approximate figures for the inorganic composition of enamel and dentine expressed in the three ways mentioned above. The variations found by different workers are partly caused by real differences between the composition of different teeth and partly by variations in the reliability of the methods used. The most numerous estimations have been carried out on tissues 'dried' by heating at 105° C to constant weight, and the figures on this material in Table II.1 (1) can be regarded as the most reliable. Since the organic matter has a density of about unity compared with that of the inorganic matter of about 2·9, the percentage of organic matter by volume is much greater than that by weight (see Fig. II.4).

Weatherell *et al.* (1966) developed a technique for dissecting enamel

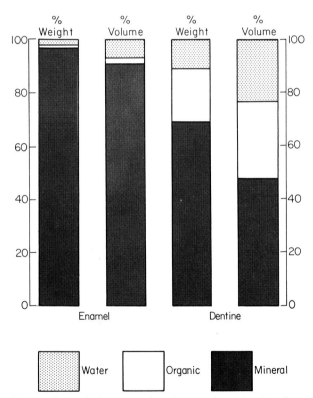

FIG. II.4. Diagram of the relative proportions in enamel and dentine of water, organic matter and inorganic matter by weight and volume.

sections into particles about 150×500 μm and analysing them in detail, thus providing information about the variability of composition in different parts of the enamel.

Sections of teeth (100–150 μm thick) were covered in nail varnish and the enamel divided into about 50 small areas by scoring the varnish with a scalpel. The section was then etched in strong acid for 15 s which dissolved away much of the enamel from the scalpel cuts and marked off separate areas which could be readily separated under a dissecting microscope with a scalpel blade or needle (Fig. II.5) and analysed.

Although the mean figures obtained for calcium and phosphorus (37·5 and 17·5%, respectively) agreed well with the figures previously reported on pooled samples, wide and rather irregular variations were found from particle to particle. The trend towards lower values for density and calcium and phosphate concentrations in samples from the interior of the enamel suggested by radiological studies, was confirmed in spite of great local irregularities (Fig. 6). In areas with relatively low mineral matter, the protein concentration was high varying by a factor of 3 from place to place (Robinson *et al.* 1971).

The enamel immediately below fissures (in molars and premolars)

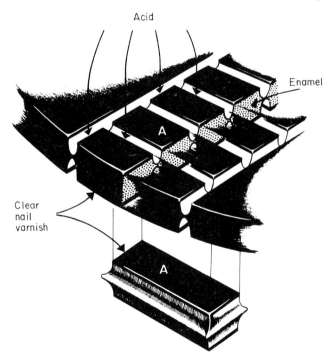

FIG. II.5. The method of Weatherell *et al.* (1966) for dissecting enamel into small pieces in order to study local variations in composition (see text).

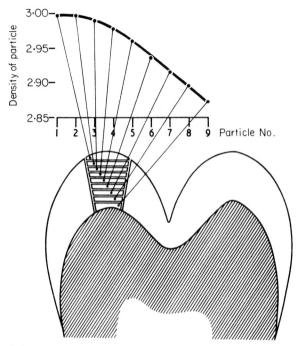

Fɪɢ. II.6. Variations in the density of enamel particles dissected at varying distances from the surface.

invariably contained a pocket of low mineral concentration whereas the enamel forming the sides of the fissure and in the mid-buccal and mid-lingual regions were often relatively high in mineral.

The density of pieces of enamel dissected from various parts of a tooth by the method described above was measured in a density gradient column. This consists of a column of liquid containing varying proportions of two liquids of different density, so that its density is higher at the bottom and falls through a regular gradient to the lowest value at the top. When small particles of known density are introduced they sink through the fluid until they reach a density equal to their own when they stop, thus making it possible to calibrate the column. The density of particles can then be determined by measuring how far they sink. Typical results of the variation of density on the surfaces or through the depth of enamel are shown in Fig. II.6. This method confirms that the density decreases from without inwards, from about 3·00 to 2·84, but did not detect an especially dense layer on the extreme outer surface reported by Thewlis (1940) (pp. 83–4) perhaps because the particles were somewhat thicker than this layer. By joining up areas of the same density 'isodens' can be drawn: they usually follow the contour

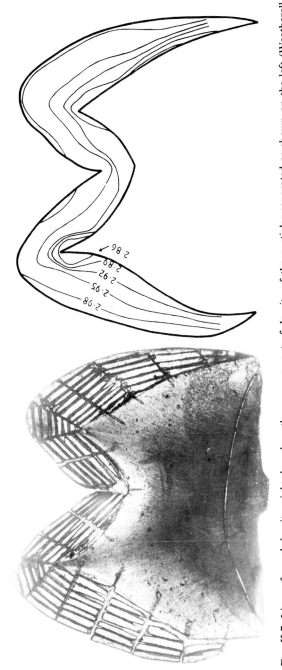

Fig. II.7. Lines of equal density, right, based on the measurement of density of the particles separated as shown on the left (Weatherell *et al.* 1967).

of the tooth but show occasional irregularities resulting either from the removal of dense layers by attrition, caries or developmental defects (Fig. II.7).

The crystalline structure of the inorganic fraction of the teeth

X-ray diffraction analysis provides an important method of studying the size, arrangement and constituents of a crystal, and has provided valuable information when applied to the teeth. The general principle of this method is that the wavelengths of X-rays are comparable with the distances between the atoms in a crystal. When a beam of X-rays meets a crystalline substance the scattering of the X-rays is in a definite pattern which depends on the arrangement of the atoms. The intensity of each part of the reflected beam depends on the nature of the atom. By study of a photograph of the reflected (or, more accurately, the 'diffracted') beam, which consists of a series of concentric circles of differing intensities, information may be obtained on these points

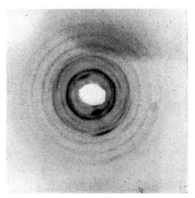

FIG. II.8. X-ray diffraction pattern from tooth substance.

(Fig. II.8). In addition, the arrangement of the crystals (whether random or orientated in a definite plan, such as all parallel) can be determined. When each circle of the diffraction pattern is uniform in intensity, the crystals are arranged randomly; if the circles vary in intensity, from one part to another, or become completely interrupted (forming arcs) then the crystals are arranged in some definite plan. The sharpness of the circles is a measure of crystal size.

The size, shape and orientation of the crystals

The electron microscope suggests the crystals consist of either ribbons, needles, or hexagonal rods ranging from 300 to 10 000 Å (averaging 6000 Å) in length and 400 to 1200 Å (averaging 500 Å) in width (for a table giving the recorded figures, see Rönnholm 1962). The wide range of these results may have arisen because the crystal size varies from tooth to tooth, since large crystals are probably formed by the growth of small crystallites and in places this growth may fail to occur. Also, small crystals may be arranged in rows placed end to end and, if the boundaries of the individual crystals are not clearly seen, the length of the row may be mistaken for the length of the crystals. Ribbons of apatite equal in length to the entire width of the enamel have been extracted from unerupted calf teeth, suggesting that the crystals of varying length previously reported are artefacts of sectioning (Simmons 1972). This is unlikely to be true of human teeth owing to the orientation of the crystals within the rods (Fig. II.19). The rods, or prisms (these synonymous terms are both in use) are the anatomical unit of enamel about 5 μm in diameter and extending through its full thickness. The crystals in enamel are about ten times larger in all directions than those of bone and dentine, probably because of their slower rate of formation. The relatively large size and, therefore, smaller surface area per unit weight of enamel crystals may have an important influence on some of the properties of enamel.

With very high magnification of crystals which had been partly damaged by the electron beam, Rönnholm (1962) and several other workers reported the presence of longitudinal lines within them; these lines could indicate that the core of the crystal which forms first differed in composition from the outer part of the crystals deposited later or they could be organic matter trapped in the crystal. Some electron micrographs have shown a serrated (or 'postage stamp') edge to the crystals, which has been interpreted as the site of fibrils of organic matter. The crystals tend to take on the shape necessary to fill the available spaces.

The orientation of the crystal has been studied by X-ray diffraction, electron diffraction, polarized light and the electron microscope. The results of different workers have varied, partly because these methods do not have the same accuracy and partly because there has been little uniformity in the types of teeth or of the areas within the enamel which have been studied.

Thewlis (1940), using X-ray diffraction patterns concluded that the crystallites could be classified into two groups, one inclined at an average of 5° and the other at 40° from the direction of the prisms (Fig. II.10). Studies with polarized light imply that the crystallites may be inclined at any angle between 0° and about 40°, with an average of about 20° (Lyon & Darling 1953). From an extension of this work, Poole & Brooks (1961) concluded that on the cuspal side of the prism the crystallites are parallel to the prism direction and on the cervical side they are inclined at between 20° and 45°, there being a gradual transition between these two extremes (Fig. II.9).

The enamel crystallites are readily seen with the electron microscope but there is no agreement about their orientation. They have been variously reported to be parallel to the prism axis, at right angles or between 20° and 40° to it, and parallel to it at the centre of the prism but at right angles at the

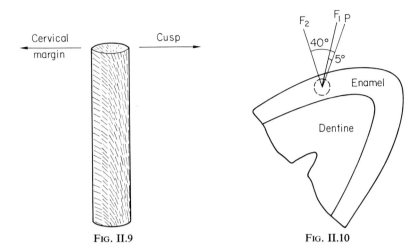

FIG. II.9.   FIG. II.10.

FIG. II.9. The orientation of the apatite crystallites within one enamel prism according to Poole and Brooks from polarized light studies (supported later by the electron micrographs of Meckel *et al.* (1965)).

FIG. II.10. The orientation of the enamel crystallites (F_1 and F_2) in relation to the prism (P), according to Thewlis from X-ray diffraction.

periphery (Kennedy *et al.* 1953; Little 1959; Frank *et al.* 1960; Rönnholm 1962).

When enamel is ground into smaller and smaller particles, the surface naturally increases very greatly as can be measured by determining the adsorption of nitrogen by the ground material. The increase is, however, greatly beyond theoretical expectations and it is concluded that grinding opens up surfaces completely closed by crystals.

The orientation of the prisms has been investigated by microphotography of thick sections of enamel at different levels of focusing so that slight deviations in successive levels are detectable. The results show that, in the inner enamel of the mid-coronal region, the prisms are arranged in a helix whose dimensions differ in different species. In man each row of prisms is inclined to its neighbours by 2°. In the outer third the rows of prisms are parallel and roughly perpendicular to the enamel surface. These changes in direction produce the optical phenomenon known as the Hunter–Schreger bands.

Wax models of the prisms based upon these optical sections show them to be wavy, the dimension of each wave corresponding to the cross-striations and, Osborn (1967) suggests, are responsible for them. Others have suggested that the striations arise because the prisms possess constrictions or varicosities. Osborn points out that the constriction of adjacent prisms are in phase, which would be expected if they are undulations but contrary to expectation if they were constrictions (the constriction of one prism would coincide with the swelling of neighbouring prisms).

The outer surface of enamel frequently lacks the normal arrangement of rods (or prisms) but is arranged either in continuous layers parallel to the surface or as 'onion-like' curves. This 'prism-less layer', usually 20–30 μm thick, was present in all of a group of 28 deciduous teeth and 70% of permanent teeth studied by Gwinnett (1967) although it did not cover the whole of the surface in most teeth, probably because it was worn away by abrasion. The apatite crystals in this layer were arranged almost at right angles to the enamel surface in contrast to those within the prisms deeper in the enamel which were inclined at an average of 26·9° to the surface in deciduous teeth (Fig. II.11). The different orientation of the crystallites in the prism-less layer

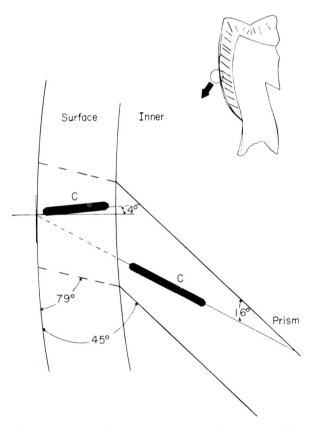

FIG. II.11. The arrangement of the apatite crystals in the prisms and the 'prism-less' layer on the outer surface of enamel. Note that in the 'prism-less' layer the crystals are almost perpendicular to the enamel surface.

and within the prisms may explain the finding of Thewlis that crystallites were inclined either at 5° or 40° to the surface.

THE SHAPE OF THE ENAMEL PRISMS

Meckel *et al.* (1965) produced convincing evidence that the most frequently observed shape of the enamel prism in human permanent teeth is like that of a keyhole with a round head or, in some places, a fish tail 5 μ in length (Fig. II.12). The tails of one row of prisms fit between the heads of the next row. The heads are orientated towards the cusp and the tails towards the cervical

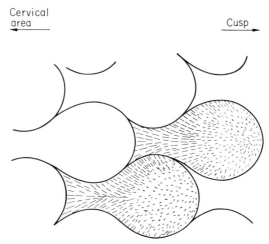

Cervical
area

Cusp

FIG. II.12. The shape of the enamel rods and the orientation of the crystallites within them according to Meckel *et al.* (1965.)

border. This general appearance can be seen in the majority of sections of enamel, but naturally, sections cut at oblique angles will distort the apparent shape of the prism.

Electron micrographs by Meckel *et al.* show that in general the crystallites are orientated in a cuspal–cervical direction in the 'tail' (cervical) end but perpendicular to this direction in the 'head' end, in broad agreement with the conclusion of Poole & Brooks arrived at by different methods.

The chemical nature of the crystals

The exact molecular form in which the various elements are present in the crystals of the calcified tissues is a highly technical controversy. Several structures have been suggested but the difficulty of choosing between them arises because the empirical formulae and properties such as solubilities, refractive indices and X-ray diffraction patterns of the various suggested substances are so similar.

The two suggested structures which have received most attention are the apatite crystal and a simple mixture.

APATITE

As discussed in more detail later (p. 76) the inorganic composition of the mineralized tissues varies from place to place in each tissue and may be affected by such factors as diet (p. 240) and age (p. 172). This suggests that the inorganic constituent must either be a mixture or a substance whose composition can vary. There is now general agreement that the main constituent is the crystalline form of calcium phosphate known as apatite with (except probably in enamel) some amorphous calcium phosphate, although many points of detail are still controversial. Apatites (from the Greek word 'deception') are a crystalline form having the general formula $Ca_{10}(PO_4)_6X_2$ sometimes reduced to $Ca_5(PO_4)_3X$, and the most widely distributed in the biological field is hydroxyapatite (HA) where X is OH.

Apatites belong to the hexagonal system of crystals characterized by a six-fold symmetry axis (the longitudinal or c axis) and three equivalent a axes (a_1, a_2, a_3). The a axes are perpendicular to the c axis and a_1, a_2 and a_3 make angles of 120° with each other. Structural details, for example location and distance of the ions in the crystal lattice, are interpreted from studies by X-ray diffraction, nuclear magnetic resonance, infra-red spectra and neutron diffraction. The lattice can be seen in electron micrographs (Fig. II.14 from Selvig 1971). Apatite structure is reviewed by Simpson (1972).

The calcium ions are arranged in two groups: one group (columnar calcium or Ca_I) forms a series of hexagons and the second (hexagonal calcium or Ca_{II}) lies within the hexagons, and the ions are arranged in triangles placed parallel to each other with adjacent triangles rotated through 60°, so if viewed along the longitudinal axis (the c axis) the calcium atoms in the two triangles would appear as a second hexagon (Fig. II.14).

The phosphates are placed in two tetrahedra (each consisting of one phosphorus atom with four oxygen atoms) between pairs of calcium ions in the outer hexagon in such a way that one phosphorus and three oxygen atoms are above the plane of the calcium ions (the fourth oxygen atom being below the plane) and the other phosphate is arranged in the reverse way (one oxygen atom above the plane of the calcium ions and the other three below it).

The hydroxyl ions are placed inside the triangles formed by the calcium ions. The hydroxyl ion, being asymmetrical, can be placed in either of two positions as HO— or as —OH along the c axis of the crystal (Fig. II.14, left). The O of these ions is either slightly (0·3 Å) above or an equal distance below the plane of the calcium triangles and the H is separated from the O by 1·0 Å (Kay *et al.* 1964). There is insufficient space to accommodate two OH groups

Fig. II.13 Electron micrograph of 3 apatite crystals ($\times 1\,600\,000$) in dentine. The regular repeating dots represent planes of projection of atoms or molecules. An internal defect in the crystal is illustrated as the number of dots between the long pair of arrows is one greater than the number between the short arrows—evidently one band ends between the two pairs of arrows.

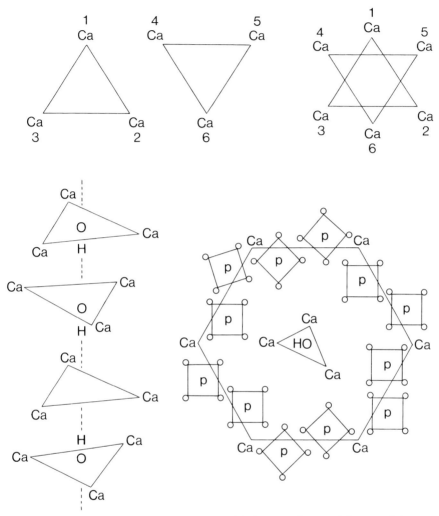

FIG. II.14 Diagram of the crystal structure of hydroxyapatite. Top left: two calcium triangles at 60 ° to each other, top right: two calcium triangles superimposed at 60 ° and viewed along c (longitudinal) axis, left: four calcium triangles viewed from the side showing the position of the OH groups and a vacancy in the third triangle from the top at the point where the direction of the OH group changes, right: the calcium triangle within the calcium hexagons showing the position of the phosphate groups (not to scale and a projection on a flat surface of ions arranged three-dimensionally).

pointing towards each other (OH HO) in adjacent calcium triangles. In order to fit the hydroxyl ions into the lattice they must either be arranged in an 'ordered column' with all the hydrogens pointing in the same direction (OH—OH—OH—OH— . . . along the c axis), or the arrangement is one of 'disordered column' with the direction reversed at various places along the c axis. Neutron diffraction data support the latter. The result of the disordered column is that occasionally along the length of the crystal, there are voids or vacancies where space prevents an OH group being placed. These vacancies can be regarded as cross over points where one orientation of hydroxyl ions (OH, OH, OH) ends and the other (HO, HO, HO) begins (Young & Elliott 1966).

Fluoride, on the other hand, can enter these vacancies where it occupies a central position in the same plane as the calcium ions (second triangle in Fig. II.14) and, in view of the relatively unstable position of the OH ions, fluoride can in addition readily replace them. The resulting crystal would be expected, for several reasons in addition to the position of the fluoride, to be more stable and less soluble than apatite without fluoride. Further confirmation of this structure is provided by magnetic resonance data of fluorapatites which show two values for the distance between F and H (2·12 and 2·18 Å). These could correspond to F ions adjacent to hydroxyls orientated in the two directions, i.e. $\dfrac{\text{F—HO}}{2\cdot12}$ or $\dfrac{\text{F—OH}}{2\cdot18}$. These concepts provide one possible explanation of how a small proportion of F ions entering apatite may have marked effects on the stability and solubility of the crystal (Young 1974, who quotes the latter figure as 2.22 Å).

BIOLOGICAL APATITES ARE NON-STOICHIOMETRIC

The Ca:P ratio of pure synthetic apatite is 2·15 (molar ratio, in the chemical not the dental sense, of 1·67) whereas the ratio in bone and teeth is lower, about 2·0. Apatites whose Ca:P molar ratio differs from the theoretical are called non-stoichiometric apatites. As the ratio is usually low, the less accurate term 'calcium-deficient' apatites is sometimes used. This has been variously explained as due to (1) adsorption of excess phosphate (as HPO_4^{2-}) on the crystal surfaces, (2) substitution of calcium by sodium and magnesium and (3) substitution of hydronium (H_3O^+) ions for two adjacent calcium ions in the crystal lattice, (4) absence of some calcium ions, electrical balance being maintained by the addition of one H^+ to a PO_4^{3-} giving HPO_4^{2-} and the absence of one (OH).

In the surface of the crystal there is a greater latitude for substitutions than in the interior, and the surface has a net electrical charge which must be balanced by ions of the opposite charge. These surface processes will be dependent upon the magnitude of the surfaces, and will therefore assume a greater importance in the small crystals of bone mineral (specific surface up to 200 m^2 g^{-1}) than for the much larger crystals of dental enamel (specific surface of 1–3 m^2 g^{-1}).

On this basis a more general formula for biologically formed apatites would be: $Ca_{10-x}(HPO_4)_x(PO_4)_{6-x}(OH)_{2-x}x\,H_2O$ where x is between 0 and 2. Normally x is a fractional number. This is characteristic for a non-stoichiometric formula. Likewise this formula takes into account the possibility that H_2O can take part in the crystal lattice.

If $x = 1$ the formula becomes:

$$Ca_9(HPO_4)^{2-} (PO_4)_5^{3-} (OH).$$

The presence of HPO_4^{2-} in the crystal can be estimated because on heating to 500–600° C it is converted to pyrophosphate $(P_2O_7)^{4-}$ (usually abbreviated to PP_i) which can then be determined:

$$2HPO_4^{2-} \longrightarrow P_2O_7^{4-} + H_2O.$$

When calcified tissues are heated to 600° C, PP_i can be detected (or an increase detected as some workers believe that traces of PP_i are normally present in the calcified tissues).

Some analyses of enamel suggest that the OH is as much as 30% below the theoretical figure which, to preserve the electrical balance, implies a deficiency of $Ca(OH)_2$ which would, of course, lower the Ca:P ratio. Another possible explanation of the low Ca:P ratio of biological apatites is that the mineralized tissues contain a mixture of apatite and some other phase such as a substance known as octa calcium phosphate (OCP) whose empirical formula is $Ca_8H_2(PO_4)_6.5H_2O$, sometimes rearranged to $Ca_8(HPO_4)_2(PO_4)_4.5H_2O$ (Ca:P ratio 1·33). Brown (1962) suggested that mineralized tissues contained layers of apatite alternating with layers of OCP but a difficulty is that OCP is not a stable substance but hydrolyses to hydroxyapatite and seems unlikely to be more than a transient constituent of the hard tissues. Brown suggested that this hydrolysis might be incomplete and the end product might be a composite crystal—OCP at one end and HA at the other, although infra-red analysis of synthetic apatites gave no evidence of an OCP phase and X-ray diffraction pattern of enamel gives no evidence of a second phase.

Two properties of apatite explain how one crystal form can have the variation in composition found in the mineralized tissues.

(a) ADSORPTION

The first means by which a stable spatial unit may change its composition is by adsorption which occurs with ions too large or with an inappropriate charge to enter the lattice (Fig. II.15).

It is often possible to desorb these ions by changing conditions such as pH without affecting the crystalline form. The citrate and magnesium, probably in the form $(MgOH)^+$, are adsorbed in biological apatite. In early caries, the magnesium and carbonate of enamel are removed preferentially to the other constituents of apatite (p. 416) which is further evidence that they are present as adsorbed ions.

(b) IONIC EXCHANGE

Ions in the crystal may undergo 'ionic exchange' with other ions in the environ-

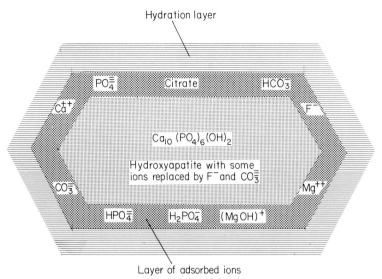

Fig. II.15. Diagram of an apatite crystal showing the hydration or layer of adsorbed water and the adsorbed ions.

ment and almost one-third of the ions in apatite can be exchanged. For example, calcium ions may be replaced by sodium, silicon, manganese, strontium, hydronium (H_3O^+) and other cations, but not magnesium; hydroxyl ions may be replaced by chloride, fluoride or other anions. This is called 'heterionic exchange'. It is also possible for one ion to be replaced by another of the same kind, for example one calcium ion may leave the crystal and another take its place ('isoionic exchange'), an exchange detectable only with labelled ions such as ^{45}Ca.

Ions of unequal charge may also exchange, neutrality being maintained by 'coupled exchange' involving more than the two ions involved in a balanced exchange. For example, the exchange of phosphate (with 3^-) and carbonate (with 2^-) might occur if a calcium and hydronium ion exchanged at the same time:

$$Ca^{2+} + 3(PO_4^{3-}) \rightleftharpoons H_3O^+ + 4(CO_3^{2-})$$

$$\text{net charge} \qquad\qquad \text{net charge}$$

$$2+ \text{ and } 9- = 7 \qquad 1+ \text{ and } 8- = 7.$$

Pure apatite contains 1.8% water but a much higher proportion is sometimes present, presumably by exchange of hydronium with calcium.

The possible compounds with an apatite structure thus form a continuous series rather than a few clear-cut substances and the particular constituents depend on conditions during the formation and subsequent treatment of the crystal.

The position of the carbonate ions is controversial. Are they in the apatite lattice, thus making the crystal a mixed carbonate hydroxyapatite (McConnell 1960), or does the crystal consist of hydroxyapatite with calcium carbonate adsorbed or is calcium carbonate present with the apatite as a simple mixture? It is agreed that no calcium carbonate crystals can be detected by X-ray diffraction patterns but this evidence is inconclusive since there is doubt as to whether the method is sufficiently sensitive to detect the 2–3% of carbonate present. When mixtures of apatite and the carbonates of magnesium or calcium are studied thermogravimetrically (p. 57) weight losses occur at 550° C and 950° C, respectively, which are absent with tooth substance. This is evidence that these salts cannot be present in the teeth at concentrations greater than 0·5 or 0·25%, respectively, the limits of detection by this method of the carbonates in a free form. Another method of investigating whether a substance is part of the lattice or is adsorbed, is by determining whether the substance can be dissolved separately from other constituents of the crystal. Since most workers have found that carbonate can be dissolved out of the calcified tissues at a greater rate than can phosphate, it is concluded that at least some of the carbonate is adsorbed on the lattice rather than being contained within it.

Studies of the infra-red spectrum of enamel by Elliott (1963) showed a more complicated pattern than can be explained by any one position of the carbonate and he concluded that part of it replaces hydroxyl ions of the apatite and the rest is adsorbed on to the crystals.

THE CRYSTALLINITY OF APATITE

All crystals are liable to contain defects such as the absence of an ion from its place in the lattice (for example the voids mentioned above) or dislocations in which a column of atoms is present in only part of the lattice (Fig. II.13). Crystals vary also in size. Large crystals with few defects are described as having a high crystallinity and vice versa. The presence of certain ions in the environment in which apatite is forming (especially magnesium and carbonate) tends to inhibit crystal growth and thus lead to the formation of crystals with a poor crystallinity: fluoride has the reverse effect and improves the crystallinity of apatite. The crystallinity may have a marked effect on certain chemical and physical properties (for example solubility and the ability to take up additional ions) and is therefore of importance in enamel. One suggested explanation of the dark line sometimes seen in electron micrographs of apatite in enamel (see p. 65) is that they are due to crystal defects.

Amorphous calcium phosphate

The intensity of X-ray diffraction of a mineral or mineralized tissue is proportional to the amount of crystalline material present and when applied to bone and dentine (but not enamel) the value obtained is less than the amount of calcium phosphate determined chemically. The inference is that some calcium phosphate is present in non-crystalline forms, a view which has gained wide acceptance. As bone ages, the proportion of crystalline material increases as estimated by X-ray refractometry, this being interpreted as a gradual conversion of the amorphous precipitate into apatite crystals (Termine & Posner 1967).

Other interpretations of these observations are possible, however (Elliott 1973). There are still uncertainties about the crystalline forms in bone and deviations from HA, other than an amorphous phase, might affect the intensity of the diffraction. Even the influence of imperfections in the crystal form of HA which might occur from trapped water or adsorbed carbonate ions could also be interpreted as evidence for amorphous calcium phosphate. It has not been clearly detected in electron micrographs but this may be because its electron density is too low to affect the electron beam.

SIMPLE MIXTURE OF $Ca_3(PO_4)_2 . H_2O$ AND $CaCO_3$

This is the oldest theory but it became eclipsed when the X-ray diffraction studies suggested so unanimously an apatite structure for the mineral phase of the calcified tissues.

The work of Dallemagne and his colleagues (1956) revived the theory and provided considerable evidence for it, although many of their observations are capable of other interpretations and their views have not been generally accepted.

Minor inorganic constituents of enamel and dentine

One of the most important findings on the lesser constituents of the enamel and dentine is that their distribution throughout these tissues is not uniform. These ions can be classified into three groups: (*a*) higher concentration on the surface of enamel than within (F, Pb, Zn, Fe, Sb); (*b*) lower concentration on surface than within (Na, Mg, CO_3); and (*c*) distribution approximately uniform (Sr, Cu, Al, K).

Ions which readily become attached to the apatite crystals tend to build up in those parts of the tooth which are exposed for the longest time to the body fluids, i.e. outer enamel, which is bathed in tissue fluid after mineralization and before eruption, and in saliva, food and drinks after eruption. The outer cementum and inner dentine are also in contact with tissue fluid throughout life and tend to concentrate trace elements in the same way as outer enamel. If, on the other hand, an ion is readily dissolved out from the calcified tissues by body fluids (Cl, CO_3, Mg, Na) then the outer and most vigorously bathed layers will be low in these constituents.

Most trace elements are present throughout the bulk of the tooth in concentrations ranging from a few parts per million to less than 0·01 ppm, although in certain places, such as the outer enamel surface, the concentration may be much higher. Only strontium, fluoride and zinc reach or exceed concentrations of 100 ppm throughout the tooth.

SODIUM

Estimates of the sodium concentration in enamel and dentine vary rather widely, but the more recent figures average about 0·7% in enamel, increasing slightly up to the amelodentinal junction with similar concentration in dentine (wet weight) but falling as the pulp is approached (Shaw & Yen 1972). The type of combination of sodium in the dental tissues is uncertain but some is probably adsorbed onto apatite or within the crystal in exchange with calcium.

The sodium concentration of enamel is higher than that of any other tissue in the body.

POTASSIUM

There have been few analyses for potassium but recent figures range between 0·3 and 0·4% (wet weight) for both enamel and dentine, the distribution being fairly uniform throughout both tissues (Shaw & Yen 1972).

MAGNESIUM

There have been many analyses for magnesium but mostly on bulk samples of enamel and dentine. Studies on its distribution show that its concentration rises from about 0·45% on the outer layer of enamel to about 0·7% in the inner enamel with still higher values in the outer dentine (1·5%) rising further to about 2% in the innermost dentine (Besic *et al.* 1969; Shaw & Yen 1972).

MANGANESE

Manganese is present in enamel at concentrations ranging from 0·45 to 1·98 ppm (outer enamel) and 0·34–0·79 for inner enamel. It is higher in mottled teeth but this may arise simply because such teeth are more permeable and may acquire manganese from foods or tea which is especially rich—150–900 ppm in tea leaves (Nixon *et al.* 1966).

CHLORIDE

Chloride has been found in both enamel and dentine and some of it can be dissolved out by water, suggesting that it originates partly from tissue fluid. The concentration in outer enamel averages about (0·6%) and falls to about 0·1% at its mid-point and remains fairly constant in the inner half. This pattern is established during tooth formation as it is present in unerupted teeth (Söremark & Grøn 1966). The dentine contains about 0·4% (dry weight) but the published figures may be low owing to loss of chloride during the preparation of the tissue.

CARBONATE

The nature of the group in the calcified tissues from which carbon dioxide may be liberated is not definitely known. Although usually referred to as 'carbonate' it may be either bicarbonate or simply carbon dioxide adsorbed as such.

The carbonate content of enamel is lower on the outermost surface (between 1 and 2%) and higher concentrations (reaching 3–4%) occur as the amelodentinal junction is approached, although some irregularities are found. The reason for this distribution is unknown but a speculative explanation is that some of the carbonate arises from the metabolic carbon dioxide of the ameloblast which may decline during the formation of the later stages of the matrix which are on the outer enamel (Weatherell *et al.* 1975).

When enamel is treated with very dilute acids, the carbonate is dissolved more readily than the phosphate. A high concentration of carbonate raises the solubility of enamel and may be a factor in lowering the resistance of a tooth to caries (see pp. 242 and 480). One suggested action of fluoride in raising the resistance of enamel to caries is that it enters the enamel crystals at the expense of carbonate and thus lowers the solubility. An alternative view is that carbonate decreases, and fluoride increases, the size and perfection of the crystals (see pp. 242 and 485).

There is a tendency for the carbonate of outer enamel to fall with increasing age which was thought to be the result of its being gradually dissolved out by acids in the plaque or exchange with fluoride. Since inner enamel exposed by attrition retains its relatively high carbonate concentration it would appear that it is more tightly bound to apatite than the carbonate in the outer layer (Little & Brudevold 1958; Weatherell *et al.* 1968a).

TRACE ELEMENTS

Several methods have been applied to the analysis of dental tissues for trace elements, and the two which have given most comprehensive information are activation analysis and spark source mass spectroscopy. In activation analysis, the sample to be analysed is exposed to bombardment by neutrons in a neutron reactor which induces radioactivity with properties characteristic of each element. By determining the nature of the induced radioactivity and its rate of decay it is possible to estimate individual elements. Some of the elements detected spectroscopically in teeth have been estimated by this method and others not previously found have been detected—for example dentine has been found to contain tungsten and gold (Söremark & Samsahl 1962). Arsenic (average concentration 0·06 ppm) has been found in mixed tooth substance (Nixon & Smith 1960, 1962).

Activation analysis is limited by the considerable chemical separation required and spark source mass spectroscopy is a more suitable and sensitive method for repetitive analyses for all elements. A small sample is vaporized and ionized by a high voltage spark producing an ion beam which is accelerated and the ions separated magnetically according to the ratio of their mass to charge, the resulting spectrum being recorded photographically. When applied to the estimation of 66 of the elements in 28 samples of young enamel (<20 years) from various parts of the USA, 35 elements were detected and 31 were absent or present in concentrations below detection (Hardwick & Martin 1967; Losee *et al.* 1974). The other elements were excluded either because their presence was already well established or, like the inert gases,

TABLE II.2

Median concentration of trace elements in enamel

	Concentrations > 10 ppm dry wt		Concentrations between 1 and 10 ppm dry wt		Concentrations between 0·1 and 1·0 ppm dry wt
Fluoride	200	Boron	2·4	Lithium	0·93
Magnesium	1550	Alumiuium	5·6	Manganese	0·26
Sulphur	270	Chromium	1·5	Copper	0·45
Chlorine	4400	Iron	2·6	Selenium	0·22
Potassium	370	Molybdenum	6·3	Bromine	0·93
Zinc	190	Barium	3·4	Rubidium	0·32
Strontium	56	Lead	3·6	Niobium	0·24
				Silver	0·16
				Cadium	0·22
				Tin	0·14
				Antimony	0·11

(Data from Losee *et al.* 1974.)

they were of no biological significance. The results are listed in Table II.2. Two elements (Si and Ni) cannot be estimated by this method but both are known, from other methods, to be present in enamel.

Little is known of the significance of most of these elements in teeth and it is likely that the presence of at least some is fortuitous and may even be due to contamination from dental fillings in neighbouring teeth. Metals from fillings and inlays, especially gold, silver and mercury, do enter the intact enamel and dentine of the teeth containing the restorations and also adjacent gingival tissues (Söremark *et al.* 1962; Bergenholtz *et al.* 1965). Although uptake by neighbouring teeth does not seem to have been definitely shown it is quite likely that some slight transfer occurs via the oral fluids.

A few points of interest about some of the trace elements in teeth will now be mentioned.

STRONTIUM

The strontium concentration in enamel varies in different geographical areas but in the USA enamel contains about 120 ppm and dentine somewhat higher concentrations, its distribution being uniform throughout the layers of the teeth. There is little change with age except in secondary dentine so that evidently strontium is not taken up significantly in the teeth after eruption.

Since the exploding of the atomic weapons from 1953 onwards, a detectable proportion of the strontium in foods, and especially milk, has been the long-lived radioactive isotope ^{90}Sr. This isotope accumulated in teeth formed after 1953, the peak of intake being in tissues formed in 1964–5, after which it began to fall, corresponding with reduced atmospheric levels. Since, if this isotope is deposited in teeth it remains there indefinitely, it forms a potentially dangerous source of radiation to the soft tissues of the mouth. Whereas the concentrations of ^{90}Sr in bone change, those in each part of the teeth remain static and indicate the levels originally present in bone formed at the same time. It enters grass, and hence cow's milk, via rain, which explains why the concentration in teeth is consistently greater in areas with highest rainfall (Starkey & Fletcher 1969).

FLUORIDE

The fluoride content of teeth is discussed in detail in Chapter XII.

SELENIUM

In view of the findings (*a*) that in parts of Oregon, USA caries incidence is related to the urinary excretion of selenium (Hadjimarkos 1960) and (*b*) injections or feeding of selenium salts increased caries in rats (Hadjimarkos 1961; Buttner 1963), the selenium concentration of teeth is of interest (see p. 453). This point has not been studied intensively but two sets of analyses (Table II.3) show a much higher concentration in deciduous than in permanent

TABLE II.3

Selenium concentration (ppm) in teeth

	Enamel	*Dentine*
Oregon, USA		
Deciduous	4·50	2·60
Permanent, under 20	1·50	0·38
Permanent, over 50	1·60	0·40
Edinburgh, UK		
Permanent	0·83 (range 0·21–1·96)	
Manchester, UK		
Permanent	0·914 (0·27–2·08)	

(Data from Hadjimarkos & Bonhorst 1959; Nixon & Myers 1970.)

teeth, no increase in the latter with age and no difference in the values for two areas of Great Britain. Distribution throughout the tooth has not been studied.

IRON

The presence of iron in human teeth has been established, but the exact concentration is still uncertain and its importance is unknown. The yellow pigment of rodents' incisors is an iron-containing compound.

LEAD

The concentration of lead in human teeth increases with age up to early adulthood and then remains constant. Published figures suggest a mean concentration of between 30 and 90 ppm in moist dentine and a similar figure in the bulk of enamel.

The distribution is rather erratic but in Birmingham, England, the highest concentration was reported to be at the amelodentinal junction and the concentration at the enamel surface was only slightly higher than this (Malik & Fremlin 1974), contrasting with reported values as high as 550 ppm at age 50 on the outer enamel in the United States in the 1950s. The reasons for these differences are quite unknown.

There is much concern about the possible toxic effects of lead ingested from the polluted urban environment. Whole deciduous teeth shed from children living in the lead belt of Philadelphia contained a significant higher average concentration of lead than in tissues from suburban residents although there was a large overlap of the values. These results not only show that lead is ingested but that analysis of shed teeth, provided enough samples are available, might be used to detect possibly dangerous intakes (Brudevold & Steadman 1956a).

COPPER

An average of approximately 20 ppm of copper has been detected spectroscopically in enamel and about half this concentration by activation analysis. It is randomly distributed and is not correlated with solubility, hypoplasia or caries (Brudevold & Steadman 1955; Nixon & Smith 1962).

ZINC

Zinc has a distribution throughout enamel similar to that of fluoride, being high on the outer surface and lower within (Nixon *et al.* 1967). Figures in the USA show variations in different geographical areas in outer enamel from 200 to 900 ppm with fairly constant values of about 200 ppm for the innermost enamel (Brudevold *et al.* 1963). The level in coronal dentine is highest on the pulpal surface but in the root both the cemental and pulpal surface levels are higher than that of the inner dentine. A high concentration is present in surface enamel from unerupted teeth and it appears to rise after eruption but too few analyses have been carried out to decide the pattern of change throughout a lifetime. The zinc concentrations of teeth vary in different geographical areas of the USA, but no figures are available from Europe.

It was stated by Cruickshank (1936) that the zinc concentration of dental tissues was higher in tubercular patients. The differences could have arisen from geographical variations as it was uncertain whether these were adequately controlled.

Zinc is readily taken up when shaken with hydroxyapatite and enamel; the mechanism is not fully known but there is evidence that it may exchange with calcium. It also binds with proteins in the body fluids and is consequently less readily available than fluoride for uptake by the tissues. Although the solubility of hydroxyapatite is reduced by zinc given after the eruption of the teeth it has not been found to reduce caries in animals. Its effect on caries incidence when given during tooth formation has not been tested.

TIN

Tin is present in enamel even in unerupted teeth. It is evenly distributed throughout the enamel and rises only slightly with age (Brudevold & Steadman 1956b) except in the vicinity of amalgam fillings. It becomes bound to the enamel after the use of a stannous fluoride dentrifice. As tin is radiopaque, its deposition in enamel may confuse the radiological scoring of caries (Glass 1967) and possibly account for some 'reversals' (a cavity present at the beginning of a trial but not detected at the end).

Factors affecting the composition of enamel and dentine

(1) POSITION IN TOOTH

Thewlis (1940) was the first to study variations in different parts of the teeth and employed quantitative microradiography. X-ray photographs (negatives) of sections of teeth 0·2–0·3 mm thick were made and the density of the shadow was measured by allowing a narrow beam of light to move along the photograph and recording, by means of a thermopile, the intensity of heat passing through the section. The greater the heat transmitted, the less dense was the shadow on the negative and the denser was the original tooth material, that is, the higher the proportion of mineral matter to organic matter and water.

The first results (Fig. II.16) suggested that the outermost 0·1 mm of enamel was denser than the rest and that the density fell gradually as the amelodentinal junction was reached (Thewlis 1940). This finding agreed with most measurements of hardness which suggest that enamel is harder on and near the outer surface than within, although this has been questioned. The apparently dense shadow of the surface could be an artefact, however, for the

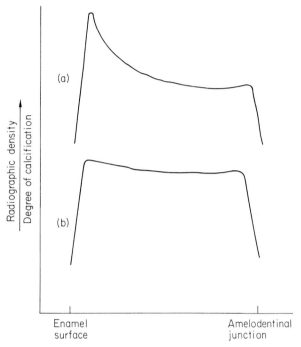

FIG. II.16. Records of the opacity of enamel to X-rays. The opacity (i.e. the density of mineral matter) in each part of the record is in proportion to the distance of the trace from the zero line. The result shows the apparent high density of the outer surface (a), the gradual decrease in density as the dentine is approached, and the low density of the outer layer of dentine. In (a), the results of Thewlis (1940) are shown which suggested that the outermost layer of enamel possessed a considerably higher density than the enamel within. In (b), more recent results are shown which failed to show a peak of high density on the surface. Both results agree that there is a slight fall in density from the outer enamel towards the amelodentinal junction.

following reason. When an object is photographed against a contrasting background, it appears to be surrounded by a halo known as the Mackie line and this phenomenon might be confused with the shadow cast by a heavily mineralized layer at the surface of enamel sections. Thewlis seemed to eliminate this artefact (Fig. II.17) by showing that the radio-density of outer enamel was greater than that of the broken edge of inner enamel (which would show a Mackie line but would not have a higher density than the rest of the section). Soni & Brudevold (1959) repeated this work with a fine-grained film (which reduces the Mackie line effect) and microradiography of enamel embedded in a medium of similar radiopacity (Baud & Lobjoie 1966) did not show a sharp peak of higher density at the surface (Fig. II.16(b)) but confirmed the original work that the density falls steadily towards the amelodentinal

FIG. II.17. Record of the density of (a) the outer unbroken surface of enamel and (b) a broken edge of inner enamel. The rise in the curve at the end of (b) is an optical phenomenon (Mackie line); the corresponding kink in (a) is much larger, indicating that it cannot be accounted for as a Mackie line but must represent a real increase in density at the surface of enamel.

junction. Present evidence is against the existence of the radio-dense surface but mostly supports the greater hardness of outer enamel. This may be associated with an outer layer about 100 μm thick which the polarizing microscope shows to be highly birefringent (p. 415) indicating that the crystals are regularly oriented, a conclusion supported by X-ray diffraction (p. 64). Enamel is less soluble at the surface than within. This has been related to the higher density of mineral matter (now in doubt), to the presence of thin layers of protein, as experiments by Darling (1943) and Meckel (1965) suggest (see p. 366), or to the presence of a high concentration of fluoride on the surface. The nature of the enamel surface and its differences from enamel as a whole is reviewed by Speirs (1971).

X-ray studies on the whole thickness of the enamel agree in showing a gradual decrease in density of calcification as the amelodentinal junction is approached, but the difference between inner and outer enamel probably does not exceed 4%.

Prenatal enamel is 3–4% less well mineralized but shows fewer irregularities than postnatal (Mortimer 1970) and the neonatal line has even lower concentration: 2–3% below prenatal enamel. Several methods have shown that the density of the enamel in the cervical region of deciduous teeth is lower than enamel elsewhere. The Ca:P ratio is high owing to a low phosphorus concentration: the excess calcium is not bound to carbonate because this is not specially high and the anion which compensates for the low phosphorus is not known. The protein concentration is higher than usual in this area.

Thewlis (1940) showed also that the outermost 0·1 mm of dentine at the amelodentinal junction is slightly less dense than the rest of this tissue (Fig. II.16a). When the density of calcification of dentine was studied throughout the crown and part of the root of a deciduous tooth, it was found that the density gradually fell in the crown till the region of the pulp was reached from which point it was almost constant along a line parallel to the pulp (Fig. II.18). This work does not seem to have been repeated or extended by more modern methods.

Differences in the distribution of individual constituents of enamel are discussed elsewhere.

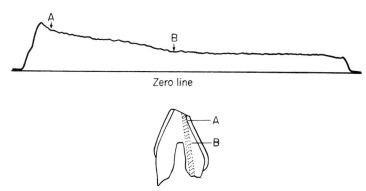

FIG. II.18. Record of the density of dentine in a deciduous tooth. The lower figure shows the location in the tooth of the dentine studied. The density falls as the pulp is approached (A)–(B), then remains constant.

(2) TYPE OF TOOTH

It is doubtful whether any group of analyses of teeth have been carried out on sufficient numbers to decide whether the different morphological types of teeth differ in chemical composition. Among the few differences reported are the fluoride on the surface of enamel (higher in incisors than in molars, see p. 478) and protein (higher in enamel from molars than from the anterior teeth).

There is little evidence of differences between the composition of permanent and deciduous teeth. This point can only be settled by the simultaneous analysis by the same workers of large numbers of the two types of teeth, and this has not yet been done on an adequate scale for all constituents. Deciduous enamel has been reported to contain a slightly higher proportion of organic matter than does permanent enamel: 0.7% in fat-free deciduous enamel and 0.6% in permanent enamel (Stack 1953).

The composition of human teeth is not found to differ in the two sexes.

(3) EFFECT OF AGE

Although it is almost certain that small changes in composition occur during the ageing of teeth to account for their decrease in permeability, there are insufficient data with which to decide their chemical nature (see p. 178). Changes in the concentration of trace elements with age have already been mentioned and those of fluoride are discussed on p. 473.

(4) DO CARIOUS TEETH DIFFER IN COMPOSITION FROM NON-CARIOUS?

This problem is in one sense insoluble because even if those parts of a tooth liable to caries differ in composition from the more resistant parts, it is not possible to predict before the disease begins which parts of a tooth will become carious, and therefore no samples of 'pre-carious' enamel can be obtained. Once the caries begins, the composition may change as a result of the disease which makes the detection of any pre-existing difference impossible. Most of the work on this problem has consisted of comparisons between the composition of non-carious teeth or enamel, and the sound part of carious teeth or enamel, but this approach is unsatisfactory because the non-carious teeth might eventually have become carious and the surviving part of the carious tooth might have resisted the disease indefinitely.

Hess & Lee (1954) stated that the proportions of some amino acids in the enamel proteins of non-carious teeth differ from those in the surviving parts of carious teeth. No explanations can be given of this finding which appears not to have been re-investigated by other workers.

The work of Sognnaes on the influence of maternal diet on the caries susceptibility of the young in several species of animals (see p. 243) provides evidence that the composition of a tooth may be related to caries resistance, but the chemical nature of the difference remains obscure. Sobel stated that by lowering the $P:CO_3$ ratio of enamel in rats by dietary means (see pp. 241–2) the teeth become more susceptible to caries, but the diets had such extreme $Ca:P$ ratios that the results are unlikely to be relevant to human caries.

The relation between fluoride in enamel and caries resistance is discussed in Chapter XII.

For a more detailed discussion of the relation between tooth structure and caries resistance see Jenkins (1961) and Ciba Symposium (1965).

The Organic Matter of Teeth

Physiology and chemistry of collagen

Collagen in the form of microscopical fibres is widely distributed and is found in areolar tissue, tendons, ligaments and the connective tissue capsules of most organs. It is also present in the matrix of bone, dentine, cementum and cartilage but in these tissues, the fibres are so fine and tightly packed that histologically their matrix appears homogeneous when stained by routine methods, although special methods, including electron micrographs, have demonstrated their fibrous pattern. It is the most prevalent single organic substance in the higher animals, since it makes up about one-third of body protein.

The composition of collagen is unusual in that one in three of the amino acids is glycine and another third is made up of alanine (12%), proline (12%) and hydroxyproline (9%)—an amino (or, more strictly, imino) acid virtually unique to collagen; estimation of the hydroxyproline in a tissue can be

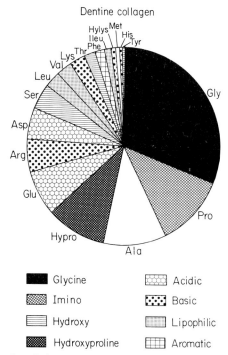

FIG. II.19. The relative proportions of the amino acids in collagen.

regarded as a measure of its collagen content. The remaining third is made up of 14 amino acids including the rare hydroxylysine (about 6%) (Fig. II.19). The amino acids of collagen from different organs show only very slight differences.

The amino acids are arranged in a triple helix as follows: the polypeptide chain is a left-handed helix with three amino acids in each turn (9·3 Å in length); this helix is also twisted into a right-handed helix with a much longer pitch of 28 Å. The complete macromolecule (known as tropocollagen) consists of three strands of the right-handed helices each containing about 1000 amino acids arranged as indicated in Fig. II.20. This arrangement is stabilized by several types of cross-links (p. 90) between the three strands and between adjacent molecules. Since every third amino acid in the polypeptide chains is glycine (the smallest amino acid), this allows the helices to come sufficiently close to form hydrogen bonds between the chains.

In bone, dentine, tendon and skin two polypeptide chains are alike but the third differs slightly in its amino acid constitution whereas in cartilage and blood vessels all three chains are identical. The molecular weight of tropocollagen is about 300 000 and its dimensions are 14×3000 Å ($1·4 \times 300$ nm).

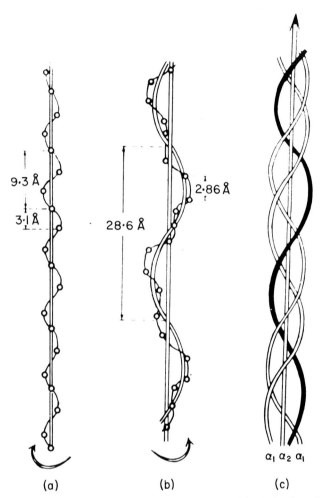

9·3 Å

3·1 Å

28·6 Å

2·86 Å

α₁ α₂ α₁

(a)   (b)   (c)

FIG. II.20. Diagram of the arrangement of the polypeptide chains in collagen.

Tropocollagen molecules readily polymerize by end-to-end and even more so by side-by-side aggregation to form collagen fibrils.

When collagen is heated with boiling water it is converted into gelatin, probably because the three chains become separated and randomly coiled. The electron microscope shows that collagen fibrils, after staining with phosphotungstic acid or uranyl nitrate, have highly characteristic regular striations at intervals of 640 Å (Fig. II.21). Their significance was first explained by the following observations (Fig. II.22).

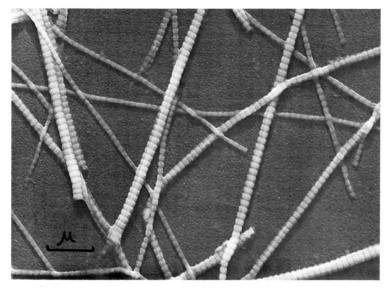

FIG. II.21. An electron micrograph of collagen fibrils from a human tendon.

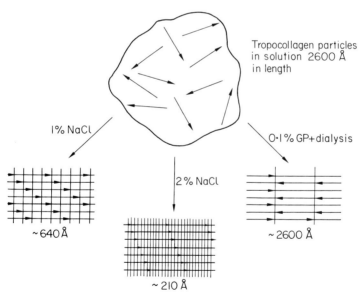

FIG. II.22. Diagram to illustrate earlier views on how tropocollagen fibrils precipitated by different reagents were thought to be arranged in different ways to give the various types of banding seen with the electron microscope. The 640 Å banding, as observed on collagen *in vivo*, is shown on the left and is made by a 'quarter stagger' of the molecules which possess a banding originally thought to be about 2600 Å.

Collagen, especially when newly formed in young tissues, dissolves in dilute acids, and if certain substances are added to the solution the collagen is precipitated as fibres which also show the banding, whilst the distances between the banding depend on the substance used to form the precipitate. With 1% NaCl as the precipitating agent, the bands correspond with the 640 Å of natural collagen. With 2% NaCl, however, the bands are only about 210 Å apart whereas with 0·1 per cent of a particular glycoprotein followed by dialysis they vary between 2600 and 3000 Å (FLS or 'fibrous long spacing' type). These findings were interpreted as follows: the smallest units of collagen were thought to have a banding of 2600 Å but in the natural form they are lying parallel (see Fig. II.22) and the individual molecules are staggered about a quarter of their length and so the bands of adjacent fibres are 640 Å apart (a 'quarter stagger'); the 210 Å bands are staggered one-twelfth of their length whereas in the FLS type the bandings are all in the same place (Glimcher *et al.* 1957).

The quarter stagger theory was revised when a new method of staining ('negative staining') was introduced. Conventional staining ('positive staining') for electron microscopy results in certain electron-dense atoms being attached to the polar groups in molecules, such as collagen, which introduce contrasts detectable by the electron microscope. Negative staining consists of surrounding the specimen by electron-dense material which is believed to

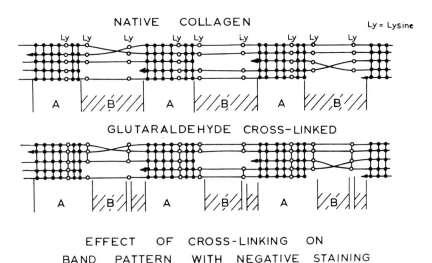

FIG. II.23. Diagram to illustrate the increased cross-linkage between lysine groups of adjacent tropocollagen molecules induced by glutaraldehyde. The crossing over of tropocollagen molecules is also illustrated.

form a rigid cast of the specimen during drying and this allows the detection of finer detail than does positive staining. This method showed that, after treatment with glutaraldehyde, which increases intermolecular cross-links, the light band of collagen increased in width from 28–34 nm at the expense of a shrinkage of the dark band from 36–30 nm to make the total of 64 nm.

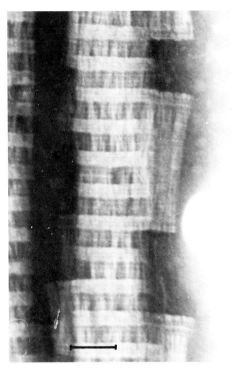

FIG. II.24. The attachment of three tropocollagen molecules (right) to an existing collagen fibre. Each newly-attached molecule spans 5 light and 4 dark bands of the collagen fibre.

This result implied that the light bands represented the sites of cross-linking, shown by other evidence to result from reaction between the glutaraldehyde and the amino groups in lysine. Negative staining also showed that the tropocollagen molecules cross each other within the fibrils (Fig. II.23) and that their length had been underestimated by about 10% and is about 2900 Å. Each tropocollagen molecule thus contains five cross-linking or bonding zones (5 × 34 nm) and four non-bonding zones (4 × 30 nm). The random aggregation hypothesis (Cox & Grant 1969) which replaces quarter stagger, suggests that any tropocollagen molecules approaching each other so that any of their bonding zones are adjacent will become attached—a process which would seem to have a much greater probability than the marshalling of tropocollagen molecules so that they were quarter-staggered. Another observation with the electron microscope which supplements the experiment with glutaraldehyde is that when a tropocollagen molecule becomes attached to an existing collagen fibre it spans five light and four dark bands clearly suggesting that the bands correspond to some link (Fig. II.24). In view of the finding that collagen molecules are 10% longer than four times the space between bands (4·4 D where D is the inter-band space) some suggested arrangements of the molecules assume there are longitudinal gaps ('holes') equal to 0·6 D (Fig. II.25) to make it possible for the bands on adjacent molecules to coincide.

This scheme runs into difficulties when considered three-dimensionally. If successive layers of collagen macro-molecules arranged in this way are packed together many of the molecules would not have a 1 D stagger with their neighbours. One of several possibilities for ensuring that the 1 D stagger occurs in all dimensions is the suggestion that the molecules are not arranged in layers but in groups of five (Fig. II.25 (b)).

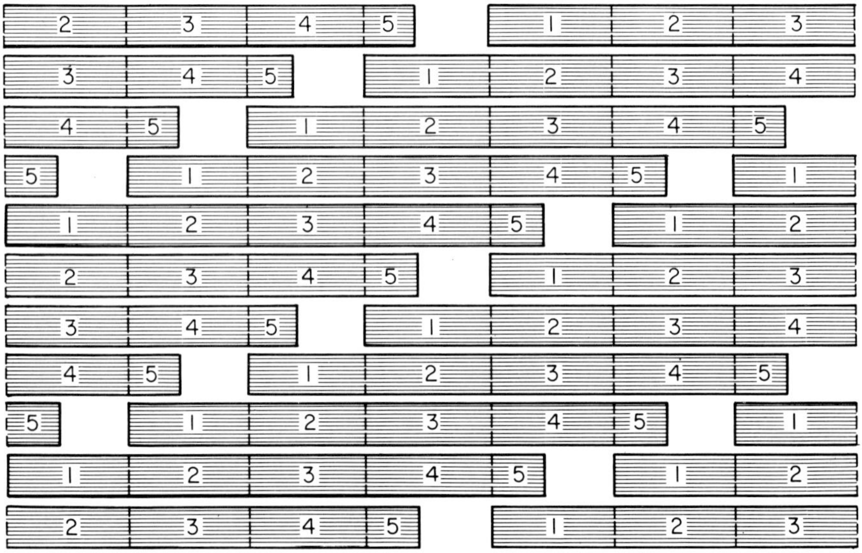

Fig. II.25. (a) Diagrammatic representation of a two-dimensional aggregate of tropocollagen molecules in 1 D stagger.

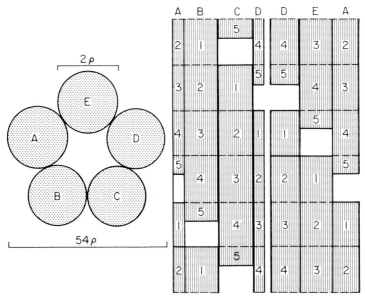

Fɪɢ. II.25. (b) Left, diagram of cross-section through a five-molecule collagen filamant. Right, this filament as it would be seen from below and from above.

Other suggested arrangements are described by Cox & Grant (1969) and Cooper & Russell (1969).

The formation of fibrous long spacing collagen by precipitation with glycoprotein or chondroitin sulphate can be speculated on this hypothesis as a binding of some of the lysine molecules with the glycoprotein, thus preventing their access to another molecule of tropocollagen and preventing the normal pattern of banding.

Densitometer tracings of the fibres show that the banded regions are more dense than the interbands, and some photomicrographs show that the whole fibre is corrugated. The increased density may arise because the fibre is thick in the banded region or the material in the fibres may be denser as well as thicker. If the banded regions are dense it has been suggested that they may contain a higher proportion of the diamino and dicarboxylic amino acids, which take up the phosphotungstic acid and uranyl nitrate respectively and are bulkier than the other amino acids present.

CARBOHYDRATE GROUPS IN COLLAGEN

Carbohydrate groups are introduced into the collagen molecule: a disaccharide containing galactose and glucose is attached to the hydroxylysine and perhaps fitted into the holes between molecules. A more bulky oligosaccharide consists of glucose, galactose and mannose (the dominant sugar), glucosamine, fucose and sialic acid. Collagen from different tissues and different species differ in the proportion of hydroxylysines to which carbohydrate groups are attached, for example, cartilage collagen contains from three to five times more carbohydrate than skin collagen. The elongated molecules of collagen are bound together into long fibrils associated with complexes of mucopolysaccharides, now known as glycosaminoglycans (GAGs) and non-collagenous proteins (ground substance). There are two main kinds of GAGs in connective tissues: (1) hyaluronic acid (a polymer of equimolecular parts of N-acetyl glucosamine and glucuronic acid) and (2) chondroitin sulphates (polymers of N-acetyl galactosamine sulphate and glucuronic acid) of which three types are known differing in solubility, optical rotation and resistance to hyaluronidase (two forms with sulphate in the 4 or 6 positions are attacked but the third form, now known as dermatan sulphate, is resistant to the enzyme).

Hyaluronic acid is found in situations where lubrication is required and may be the ground substance in which bundles of collagen fibres are embedded. This substance can be depolymerized and made less viscous by the enzyme hyaluronidase which was originally called the 'spreading factor'. This name was given because when dyes are injected into connective tissues, their rate of spread through the tissue is increased if hyaluronidase is also injected, probably because the hyaluronic acid becomes depolymerized and offers a smaller resistance to the passage of the dye in the ground substance of the tissue.

Chondroitin sulphate is found in connective tissues in which tensile strength is important. The proportion of chondroitin sulphate to collagen varies from as little as 1:20, in skin, to as much as 1:1, in cartilage. If dried cartilage is extracted with distilled water at room temperature, about one-third of the chondroitin sulphate is removed but the cartilage has to be heated gently in order to extract the remaining two-thirds. This may mean that about one-third of the chondroitin sulphate is free or loosely bound and the other two-thirds are in a more tightly-bound form.

In cartilage, the structure is probably made up as follows. Chains of between 20 and 50 GAGs are attached to protein cores (forming what is known as proteoglycans) which in turn are attached to a very long polymer of hyaluronic acid parallel to the collagen fibrils. The collagen is linked to the whole complex through an electrostatic attraction with the GAGs of the proteoglycan (Woodhead-Galloway & Hukins 1976).

BIOSYNTHESIS OF COLLAGEN

Electron micrographs of various cells forming collagen (fibroblasts, osteoblasts and odontoblasts) in conjunction with autoradiography after administering labelled proline show that polypeptides containing proline, presumably collagen precursors are, like other proteins, formed by the ribosomes on the endoplasmic reticulum. Sedimentation studies of these ribosomes, from cells actively synthesizing collagen, demonstrate that the label is associated with polyribosomes, probably aggregations of 30–40 normal ribosomes. It is possible that the aggregation occurs because the fibrous collagen precursors become ravelled with each other and engulf the ribosomes, but a more likely explanation is that the chains formed by neighbouring ribosomes interact to form larger chains, and possibly the triple helices, before being released from their ribosome. Consequently the fibrils link the ribosomes together. Neither hydroxyproline nor hydroxylysine enter the polypeptide chains as such, but the hydroxy group is inserted into proline and lysine after they have been incorporated in the polypeptide (before hydroxylation, the polypeptides are known as protocollagen). This is carried out while attached to the ribosome, by the enzymes protocollagen proline hydroxylase (which can hydroxylase both amino acids), or lysine hydroxylase (lysine only), enzymes which require molecular oxygen. This conclusion is based on the absence of an mRNA for transporting hydroxyproline and on the observation that if labelled hydroxyproline is fed it is excreted in the urine and none enters collagen; labelled proline is utilized in the polypeptide synthesis. Experiments with $^{35}SO_4$ show that at least part of the glycosaminoglycans of collagen is attached while the chains are in contact with the ribosomes. Only those proline and lysine molecules followed by glycine are hydroxylated.

The soluble precursors known as procollagens contain, at the amino end of the chain, a group of amino acids not typical of those in the rest of the molecule (for example the proportion of proline is low and of tyrosine high) representing between 1 and 4% of the molecule (the 'telopeptide' or 'registration peptide'). This terminal section of the chain is removed by the proteolytic enzyme, procollagen peptidase situated on the surface of the cell and collagen fibres then form and become insoluble.

It is possibly concerned with aligning or registering (hence the name) the procollagen chains in their correct position before forming the helix. The newly-formed helices are highly soluble and another function of the registration peptide may be to facilitate its transport. The registration peptide is removed within 20 min of the extrusion of the procollagen.

Most recent studies of collagen synthesis by electron microscopy have failed to show fully developed fibres with 640 Å banding within the cells even when they are abundant outside the cell. Numerous vesicles just within the cell wall are present, along with occasional communications between the endoplasmic reticulum and the cell wall (microtubules) and these are probably the route by which collagen precursors leave the cell and the probable site of the enzyme removing the registration peptide. Some earlier work had suggested that fully-formed fibres were present inside the cell and were thought to leave through gaps in the wall but these have not been confirmed and were probably

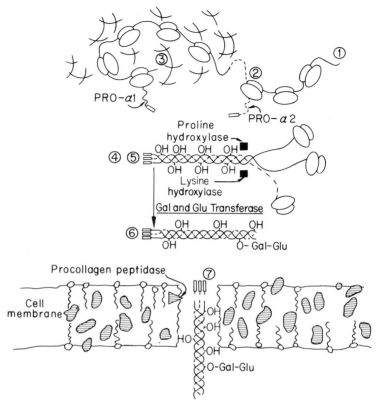

Fig. II.26. Intracellular events leading to the formation of a collagen molecule. 1. Synthesis of specific m-RNA for collagen. 2. Translation of a message by ribosomes. 3. Clustering of polysomes and association with endoplasmic reticulum. 4. Recognition and alignment of α-chains aided by registration peptides, 5. Coiling of chains and hydroxylation of specific proline and lysine residues. 7. Extrusion of the completed molecule and release of registration peptides by procollagen peptidase.

due to sectioning artefacts. If a concavity in the wall of a cell were cut across, extracellular objects might appear to be within the cell. The collagen is so insoluble that it would be difficult to transport it if it were formed within the cell.

The formation of mature insoluble collagen fibrils from the soluble precursors is usually considered to be an extracellular process involving the formation of cross-links between the chains and also between molecules. The function of the intramolecular cross-linking is uncertain, but the extramolecular links form a continuous fibrous network of great tensile strength. These links are of several types of which the following are examples: (1) between free amino and carboxyl groups of amino acids in different chains, (2) the free amino group of lysine is converted by lysyl oxidase to an aldehyde which, in a spontaneous non-enzymic reaction, combines with a similarly formed aldehyde in a neighbouring chain to form the very stable link of an aldol condensation, and (3) the links between the collagen molecules is believed to involve aldehyde groups reacting with amino groups of lysine, hydroxylysine or norleucine to form Schiff bases.

Stained histological preparations of developing connective tissue show that the fibres which form first are much finer than adult collagen fibres and differ also in that they run singly rather than in bundles and show considerable branching. These early fibres have been called 'pre-collagen' (not to be confused with pro-collagen, the precursor molecule with telopeptite still attached, see p. 95) or argyrophil fibres; the last name arises because they are stained black with silver nitrate and may be distinguished from collagen fibres which, under the same conditions, are stained a light brown. In the adult, many organs (for example lung and lymphoid tissue) contain what are called reticular fibres which appear as fine argyrophil fibres leading from the collagen fibres also present in these organs. Electron microscope studies have confirmed earlier speculations that reticular and pre-collagen fibres consist essentially of fibrils similar to those of collagen, but with fewer of them in each of the microscopically visible fibres and arranged randomly, whereas in collagen the fibrils are orientated. There is evidence that they are embedded in a membrane probably consisting of glycoprotein or GAGs. The differences in the number of fibrils in each fibre, in their orientation, and in the amount of the other non-collagen constituents in the whole complex, probably account for the differences in staining and in certain other chemical properties which have been described in collagen and pre-collagen (Little & Kramer 1952).

If these ideas become fully established then it would seem that in some conditions the pre-collagen fibres remain indefinitely in that state, but in a different part even of the same organ, pre-collagen fibres amalgamate to form the larger fibres of true collagen with changes in the nature of the associated substances.

THE ROLE OF ASCORBIC ACID AND ALKALINE PHOSPHATASE IN COLLAGEN FORMATION

In severe ascorbic acid deficiency in guinea-pigs, collagen formation does not occur, although fibroblasts survive and may even proliferate but have an abnormal appearance. The synthesis of GAGs is also defective in scurvy but the nature of the defect is uncertain—there is some evidence that the incorporation of the sulphate is prevented. The collagen content of tissues from adult animals suffering from scurvy does not decrease, suggesting that once formed, the maintenance of collagen does not require ascorbic acid with the exception of collagen in recently healed wounds, which does undergo some degeneration in scurvy. The effect of ascorbic acid is local and does not work through hormonal or systemic effects. This has been proved by injecting ascorbic acid into one area of collagen formation in a scorbutic animal and saline into another. Much more collagen was formed in areas receiving the ascorbic acid.

There is good evidence, from experiments on the concentration of labelled proline and hydroxyproline in the collagen-forming tissues of normal and scorbutic guinea-pigs, that one of the effects of ascorbic acid is concerned with the introduction of the hydroxy group into proline.

Some facts, however, cannot easily be reconciled with this role of ascorbic acid. For example, collagen synthesis occurred almost normally in cultures of chick embryonic cells which neither contained nor produced ascorbic acid. Tooth germs have formed dentine when implanted in the anterior chamber of the eye in scorbutic guinea-pigs. When $[^{14}C]$-proline was given to scorbutic guinea-pigs injected with carrageenin, a sulphated polysaccharide which induces granulomata involving rapid collagen formation, the total amount of collagen synthesized was greatly reduced compared with the controls, but $[^{14}C]$-hydroxyproline was present in the urine proving that hydroxylation of proline was still occurring. Also in scorbutic animals the large polyribosomes do not form; this could indicate a reduced tendency for the newly-formed protein chains to aggregate, possibly related to the reduced production of chondroitin sulphate.

Collagen formation is accompanied by the presence of high concentrations of alkaline phosphatase in the fibroblasts and on the fibre itself. In scurvy, neither alkaline phosphatase nor collagen appear, suggesting that collagen synthesis requires the action of phosphatase and that ascorbic acid is related to the presence of the enzyme. Nothing is known beyond this; all is speculation on what part phosphatase plays in collagen formation. From its distribution, it has been suggested that this enzyme is in some way connected with the synthesis of other fibrous proteins: for example, the keratin of hair.

HORMONES AND COLLAGEN FORMATION

Glucocorticoids of the adrenal cortex (for example, cortisone) have a marked action in inhibiting collagen formation, thus interfering with wound healing and the repair of fractured bones. Adrenocorticotrophic hormone, which causes the release of glucocorticoids, has a similar action. Mineralocorticoids (such as desoxycorticosterone), on the other hand, stimulate fibroblasts and favour collagen formation.

Other hormones have been reported to be concerned with the concentration of phosphatase or the production of mucopolysaccharides in tissues but these results cannot yet be synthesized into a consistent picture of the control of collagen formation.

THE STABILITY OF COLLAGEN AFTER FORMATION

The rate of metabolic turnover of collagen has been shown to be low, unlike that of most body proteins. When glycine containing radioactive carbon was fed to young animals, the radioactivity in their collagen rose rapidly but remained high (i.e. the collagen, once formed, does not break down rapidly), whereas in other proteins the radioactivity fell as they were broken down and replaced. In old animals, in which little new collagen would be forming, the radioactivity in collagen was low, indicating little replacement, although in other proteins the radioactivity rose and fell as in the young (Harkness 1955; Neuberger & Slack 1953). The GAGs associated with collagen do have a rapid turnover. The chondroitin sulphate of skin has an estimated half-life of about 7 days and of cartilage about 14 days (Kofoed *et al.* 1971).

An important exception to the usual stability of collagen is found in the periodontal ligament which radioactive studies have shown is replaced within a few weeks. It is possible that mechanical damage occurs to the collagen fibres during mastication and leads to their removal and replacement.

Collagenase has been detected in mammalian tissues only since 1966 and is present in gingivae and periodontal tissues. The only cells which contain a preformed active collagenase are fibroblasts and polymorphs; it can be demonstrated in other tissue such as epithelium, bone and connective tissue cells only after they have been cultured (Fullmer 1971). Presumably the fibroblasts of the periodontal ligament play a part in the collagen turnover, probably by phagocytosis (Ten Cate 1972).

In the involuting uterus, collagen is removed rapidly.

COLLAGEN AND AGEING

When collagen is heated to about 58° C the fibres shrink—this accounts for the contraction of a joint of meat during roasting. The phenomenon can be studied quantitatively by suspending weights from pieces of tendon (for example from rats' tails consisting very largely of collagen fibres running parallel) and finding the weight which just prevents the shrinkage at any particular temperature. Collagen from old rats needs heavier weights to prevent shrinkage (for example 10 g for a piece of tendon 50 mm long) than collagen from young rats (for example 3 g), i.e. old collagen can develop a greater tension during shrinkage than young collagen. The cause of the shrinking by heat is thought to be the rupturing of the cross-links between the three protein chains in collagen which keep the molecule stretched. Verzar (1963) suggested that the effect of age is probably to increase the number of cross-links. Polypeptides containing hydroxyproline and some associated GAGs are released during heat treatment of collagen and this is also affected by age: the younger the collagen the greater the amount of substance released, again indicating more numerous links in older collagen.

The ageing of collagen has been suggested as a factor, or even as a primary cause, of ageing in general but this is disputed on the grounds that invertebrates and plants undergo ageing but do not possess collagen (for review, see Sinex 1968).

Organic matter of dentine

Tomes, as long ago as 1895, stated that dentine contained 19·6% organic matter and pointed out that previous estimates were too high. The reason for the high values is that even after drying at 100° C, dentine still contains between 5 and 8% of water chemically bound to other constituents and, since this is driven off at high temperatures, it is included in the figure described as 'organic matter' when this is estimated by measuring weight loss during incineration.

Dentine contains an average of 3·4% of nitrogen and analysis of the amino acids show that about 90% of this is present as collagen, whose nitrogen content is 18·4%. The collagen content works out, therefore, at about 18% of the dentine dried to 100° C. A well-known property of collagen is its conversion into gelatin on heating and it has been estimated that a sufficiently high temperature may be reached during cavity preparation to cause some gelatin to be formed.

The collagen (estimated from the hydroxyproline) is present in higher concentrations in the outer third of the dentine (Levine 1971) corresponding with the slightly lower density of this part of the dentine.

Dentine collagen contains chondroitin sulphate which has been isolated from it in amounts stated to be about 0·6%. By chemical estimation of the constituents of chondroitin sulphate (hexosamine and hexuronic acid) the mucopolysaccharide content of dentine works out at only 0·2–0·3%. The discrepancy between the results of isolation and of estimation has not been cleared up.

The proportion of lysine which is hydroxylated is higher in collagen from dentine than from skin.

Even after very thorough demineralization, the collagen of dentine contains 0·046% phosphorus (Jones & Leaver 1974) believed to be part of a phosphoprotein linked to collagen through an oligosaccharide. This equals five phosphate groups per 1000 amino-acid residues—more than in collagen from bone and skin.

If the collagen of dentine matrix is removed by digestion with collagenase the presence of about 20 minor components can be detected (the non-collagenous matrix) equal to about 9% of the total matrix. Some of these are small, freely-soluble peptides and amino acids and two large molecules have been identified: one is a protein containing 2·5% sialic acid and the other is a proteoglycan with a similar amino-acid composition but containing much 4-chondroitin sulphate. Both proteins contain about 0·67% of phosphorus bound as phosphoserine. Some of these constituents are presumably derived from the cytoplasm of the dentinal processes. Serum albumen and immunoglobulins have been detected. The non-collagenous constituents of dentine are not identical to those of bone and deciduous dentine contains some organic constituents absent from permanent dentine.

Dentine contains a complex mixture of most types of lipids totalling 0·33% by weight (Hess *et al.* 1956; Dirksen 1963; Odutuga & Prout 1974). This was not studied extensively until recently because many analyses of the organic matter of dental tissues have been carried out on samples separated by bromoform and acetone (p. 57) which dissolves out much of the lipid, or, to make the analyses easier, lipid was removed by various solvents and discarded without analysis. If dentine, prepared so that lipid is not removed, is extracted by lipid solvents 0·22% lipid is obtained. If the treated dentine is then demineralized by acid and the organic residue thus obtained extracted again a further 0·11% (33% of the whole) can be removed. Presumably, some of the lipid is bound to, or trapped by, the mineral matter and is released when the latter is removed by acid. Some workers have reported much lower values, probably because the lipid was incompletely extracted or partly lost during the demineralization stage. Free fatty acids, mono- and diglycerides, lecithin and the polyglycerol phosphatide, cardiolipin, were extractable before demineralization. The acidic phospholipids other than cardiolipin were only extracted after demineralization (Odutuga & Prout 1974). About half the cholesterol and its esters and triglycerides were extracted before, and the other half after, demineralization, suggesting that these substances may be bound to the mineral and perhaps concerned in their deposition.

Although normal dentine does not stain with lipid stains, fat droplets can be stained in the dentinal tubules ahead of a developing carious cavity. It has been assumed that this lipid is released from bound forms present in the dentine although its distribution corresponds so well to that of the pioneer bacteria in the advancing lesions that a bacterial origin has been suggested.

Citrate is present (average 0·9%) once thought to be bound to a peptide, but as they are separable this now seems to be unlikely (Leaver 1969).

The composition of the organic matter in dentine is summarized in Table II.4.

TABLE II.4

Organic constituents of dentine (approx. percentage of dry weight)

Collagen	18	Non-collagenous matrix	%
Citrate	0·9	GAGs (mostly chondoitin	
Lipid	0·33	sulphate)	12
Non-collagenous	1·6	Glycoproteins	46
matrix		Peptides	4·2
Total	20·83	Serum proteins	2·6
		Unaccounted for	35

The organic matter of enamel

The preparation of demineralized specimens of the teeth, by exposure to strong acids, leaves almost no visible trace of any organic framework which led to the early view that enamel was wholly inorganic. Only the various layers of organic material outside the enamel (the cuticle and pellicle, see pp. 360–1) remain undissolved as a thin membrane in the vicinity of the tooth. This loss of the organic matter arises partly owing to its extreme delicacy, so that disintegration soon follows the removal of the support of the inorganic salts, but a high proportion of the unfixed organic matter is soluble in acids and therefore dissolves during demineralization. Pincus (1948) stated that pits and fissures contain a protein differing from true enamel protein which he called 'groove protein', but no one appears to have confirmed this work. These must all be removed before attempting to isolate the protein of enamel matrix.

Many workers from as early as 1870 produced evidence for organic matter within enamel (reviewed by Sognnaes 1948) but their results made little

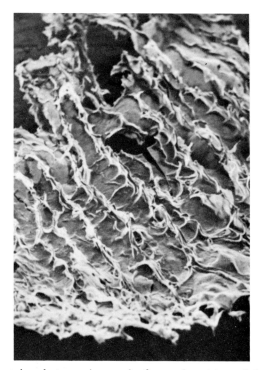

FIG. II.27. Scanning electron micrograph of enamel protein peeled off the dentine after demineralization in acid. Ribbons of protein appear to be attached to a membrane at the original amelodentinal junction.

impression until the 1920s. One method of preserving the matrix is to demineralize very slowly with very weak acid for up to 6 months but Sognnaes combined mild demineralizing agents with fixative so that the matrix was fixed and became insoluble as soon as it was exposed by the removal of the mineral.

Weatherell *et al.* (1968b) isolated the major part of the organic matter so that it could be both visualized and collected for analysis by the following method. The teeth, after fixation in 4% formaldehyde were treated with 1 mM HCl for 1 min which disolved the outer layer of enamel and ensured the removal of the adhering pellicle. The teeth were then cut in half longitudinally, placed in 3 M trichloracetic acid or 10% EDTA at pH 7·4 overnight at room temperature and transferred to water. The protein appeared as ribbons linked together by 'rings' and sometimes attached to a membrane (Fig. II.28) running along the dentine surface which could be peeled off as a continuous network: in some specimens the ribbons were obscured by fine woolly material which Weatherell *et al.* referred to as 'floss'. The ribbons were associated with the enamel tufts and were most extensive where the enamel was thick. The 'floss' was shown, on high magnification, to correspond in size and direction to rods. Chalky, amorphous deposits were occasionally seen under enamel fissures or surrounding the dentinal cornua (Fig. II.29). Lamellae, sheets of protein

FIG. II.28. Organic matter removed from half of a molar crown after demineralization with acid.

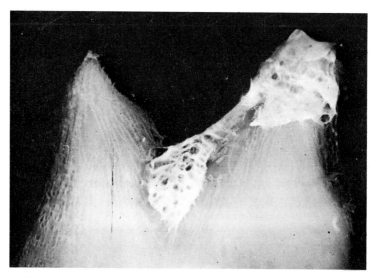

FIG. II.29. Organic matter of the enamel of permanent molar after demineralization with acid. Note the amorphous deposits round one fissure and one dentinal cornua.

reaching from the dentine to the outer surface of the enamel, were also present. The amino acid composition of all these structures was essentially the same and was rich in aspartic and glutamic acids, serine, leucine and proline (but hydroxyproline was virtually absent). The amount of organic material varies considerably from one molar to another but incisors and canines invariably contained smaller amounts than molars.

A complication of the analysis of enamel obtained by flotation is that the separation from dentine is never complete and even a slight contamination by dentine, with its protein content of about 20%, would seriously upset the result. Most analyses of enamel protein have detected hydroxyproline (Eastoe 1963) some almost certainly derived from the collagen in traces of dentine. The low hydroxyproline in the enamel structures isolated by Weatherell *et al.* shows them to be quite free from dentine. Another difficulty arises from the uneven distribution of the organic matter within the enamel. Samples from outer enamel contain much less protein (0·05% in tufts) than inner enamel containing the tufts as shown in Figs 28 and 30 (Robinson *et al.* 1971; Brudevold *et al.* 1976).

When the organic matter is obtained by dissolving powdered enamel in acid, some of the protein dissolves. This acid-soluble fraction would be removed during the demineralization of the teeth studied by Weatherell *et al.* and their analyses refer to the insoluble residue. The protein in the outer enamel, just inside the layers containing the pellicle, is almost completely soluble although, in the intact tooth, it may be present along with the insoluble protein in the inner enamel. It is soluble because it consists of peptides of molecular weight below 3500, probably left behind as protein material from the early matrix is removed. Although usually referred to as 'acid-soluble', because this is the solvent in which it has been obtained, some of it may be soluble in water. Its amino acid composition differs from that of the insoluble protein, for example serine, proline and glycine were high, glutamic acid and leucine were lower and some hydroxyproline was present. It is uncertain whether the latter arose from slight contamination with collagen or whether it is present in the enamel protein. The protein from bovine enamel separated very thoroughly from dentine contained no hydroxy-proline (Glimcher *et al.* 1964) but its presence in human enamel may arise from a species difference or from incomplete removal of collagen or its breakdown products from dentine.

Robinson *et al.* (1975) compared the amino-acid composition of the acid-soluble protein of developing and mature enamel with that of the acid-insoluble tufts. All had many similarities, but the differences suggested that the proteins were derived from each other; if the soluble developmental protein lost serine and threonine it would become less soluble and its composition would then resemble that of tufts. The soluble protein of mature teeth might be some material which failed to become insoluble. On standing in acid, the soluble protein becomes insoluble. It was speculated that the acid in a carious cavity might have a similar effect and that the precipitated protein might possibly act as a diffusion barrier which could slow up the loss of minerals from the lesion (Robinson *et al.* 1975).

Chalky enamel formed in the very early stages of caries contains three to five times the concentration of organic matter of the adjacent normal tissue. This may arise from the presence of bacteria or from an influx of organic matter from the saliva or plaque.

Contrary to wide belief, which associates caries susceptibility with a low mineral concentration in enamel, preliminary results suggest that the spread of caries seemed to be prevented or reduced by areas of enamel high in protein, i.e. relatively low in mineral (Robinson *et al.* 1971). The protein may surround the apatite crystals and either buffer the acid or act as a barrier preventing its access to the apatite.

Like most of the minor constituents, the nitrogen of enamel is not uni-formly distributed. The outer surface is high in nitrogen (presumably from the acquired pellicle (p. 360) and from deposits of salivary proteins in small defects on the surface), the inner enamel is low in nitrogen, equivalent to as little as 0.05% protein, but the concentration rises as the amelodentinal junction is reached, probably owing to the presence of enamel tufts and spindles and possibly also from the deposition of protein from dentinal fluid (Fig. II.30, and p. 168). Deciduous teeth contain higher concentrations of nitrogen in each region, except the outer surface, than do permanent teeth.

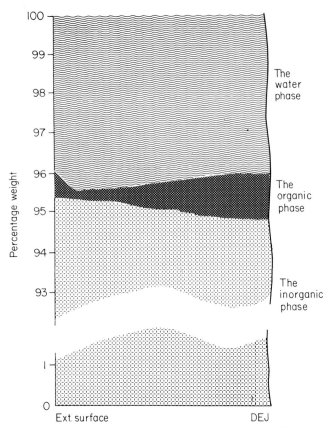

Fig. II.30. The distribution by weight of water, organic and inorganic material in fat-free enamel from the surface to the amelodentinal junction.

Some analyses suggest a steady increase of total nitrogen in enamel with increasing age while others have found no change. The only study on age changes in the nitrogen concentration of different layers of enamel showed a rise on the outer surface and adjacent to the dentine in the older teeth, presumably from protein deposits from the saliva and dentinal fluid respectively. The nitrogen in the inner enamel fell in concentration, which is difficult to explain (Savory & Brudevold 1959).

The insoluble proteins were at first thought to be keratins but amino acid analyses by modern methods have not confirmed this. They are best considered to be proteins unique to enamel for which the name 'enamelin' has been suggested (Eastoe 1971).

Both the soluble and insoluble organic matter contains bound carbohydrate groups which have been identified by chromatography as the hexoses galactose, glucose, mannose and glycuronic acid with traces of the pentoses fucose and xylose (Burgess *et al.* 1960). The total concentration averaged only 1·65 mg 100 g^{-1} of dried enamel but there is some unconfirmed evidence that variations in this fraction of the enamel may be a factor in the caries-resistance of the tooth (see p. 247).

Glimcher *et al.* (1964) stated that bovine teeth are surrounded by a thin layer of cementum (which has a collagen matrix) covering the enamel and they have reported a similar layer on unerupted human teeth after extremely careful fixation and demineralization with EDTA. The existence of this layer needs reinvestigation but, if confirmed, residual traces of it might explain the occasional presence of hydroxyproline in enamel.

The insoluble protein has usually been assumed to form·the tufts and delicate fibrous network which can be seen with an electron microscope in fixed sections of demineralized enamel (Fig. II.31). Fearnhead (1962; 1965) stated that, with certain methods of preparation, the organic matter is not in a fibrous form and he believes that the fibres do not exist *in vivo* but are produced as an artefact by the methods of fixation and demineralization usually used. He suggests that enamel protein exists *in vivo* as an amorphous gel but nuclear magnetic resonance studies of the state of water in enamel do not support this concept (Myrberg 1968). Electron micrographs of demineralized, developing rat enamel indicate that the organic matter surrounds the apatite crystals as

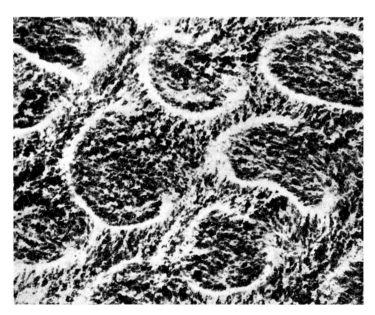

Fig. II.31. An electron micrograph of enamel matrix showing the delicate network of organic matter permeating the whole tissue. The irregular sizes and shapes of the prisms are well shown. The prism in the centre confirms the fish-tail shape described on page 68.

TABLE II.5

Organic constituents of enamel (percentage of
dry weight)
These figures can only be regarded as approximate

	Molars *Premolars*	*Incisors* *Canines*
Insoluble protein	0·3–0·4	0·2–0·25
Collagen	trace	trace
Soluble protein	0·05	0·05
Lipid	0·6	
Citrate	0·1	
Total	1·1	1·0

Analyses for lipid and citrate have not been
carried out separately for the different morphological types

double helices, at least during development (Smales 1975). Although the
possibility of artefact cannot be dismissed, the most obvious sources of
artefact were eliminated.

Most proteins contain about 16% of nitrogen and a routine method of
estimating protein in mixed material is to determine the nitrogen and multiply
by the factor 6·25 (that is, 100/16). Insoluble enamel protein was reported by
Stack (1954) to contain only about 13% of nitrogen, and the factor for this
protein is, therefore, 100/13 = 7·7; the soluble protein contains 10% nitrogen
and the factor is 10·0. There is general agreement that the nitrogen content
of enamel is about 50 mg % equivalent to between 0·3 and 0·4% protein.

Enamel has been reported to contain between 0·5 and 0·6% lipid (Odutuga
& Prout 1974; Hess *et al.* 1956) The composition is similar to that reported
for dentine (p. 101) as well as the proportions extractable before and after
demineralization. Expressed as a percentage of the organic matter, the lipid
in enamel is much higher, 42·5%, than that of the much higher proportion of
organic matter in the dentine, 1·65%. The existence of the lipid in enamel
has often been ignored because the enamel used for studying the organic
constituents is usually freed from lipid before analysis. Surprisingly strong
staining reactions for lipid have been obtained in sections of enamel with
early caries (Opdyke 1962), suggesting that in normal enamel the lipid is
masked but is released—probably by the demineralization which occurs
during the development of caries.

Citrate is present, as in all the calcified tissues, but at the lower average
concentration of 0·1%; it is higher on the surface and near the amelo-

dentinal junction than in the middle of the enamel. Lactate has also been found in human enamel with a distribution similar to that of citrate but at a lower concentration.

The approximate composition of the organic matter of enamel is summarized in Table II.5.

References

BAUD C.A. & LOBJOIE D.P. (1966) Biophysical investigations on the mineral phase in the superficial layers of human dental enamel. *Helv. odont. Acta.* **10**, 40

BERGENHOLZ A. *et al.* (1965) Studies of the transport of metal ions from gold inlays to the environmental tissues. *Acta odont. Scand.* **23**, 135

BESIC F.C. *et al.* (1969) Detailed electron probe micro-analysis of three teeth sections with early enamel caries. *J. dent. Res.* **49**, 111

BROWN W.E. (1962) Octacalcium phosphate and hydroxyapatite. *Nature (Lond)* **196**, 1049

BRUDEVOLD F. & STEADMAN L.T. (1955) A study of copper in human enamel. *J. dent. Res.* **34**, 209.

BRUDEVOLD F. & STEADMAN L.T. (1956a) The distribution of lead in human enamel. *J. dent. Res.* **35**, 430 (also **35**, 749)

BRUDEVOLD F. & STEADMAN L.T. (1956b) A study of tin in enamel. *J. dent. Res.* **35**, 749

BRUDEVOLD F. *et al.* (1963) A study of zinc in human teeth. *Archs oral Biol.* **8**, 135

BRUDEVOLD F. *et al.* (1976) Separation of human enamel structures by density fractionation. *Archs oral Biol.* **21**, 113

BURGESS R.C. *et al.* (1960) Chromatographic studies of carbohydrate components in enamel. *Archs oral. Biol.* **3**, 8

BURNETT G.W. & ZENEWITZ J. (1958) The composition of human teeth. *J. dent. Res.* **37**, 500

BUTTNER W. (1963) Action of trace elements on the metabolism of fluoride. *J. dent. Res.* **42**, 453

CIBA FOUNDATION SYMPOSIUM (1965) *Caries-Resistant Teeth.* Eds WOLSTENHOLME G.E.W. & O'CONNOR M. J. & A. Churchill, London

COOPER D.R. & RUSSELL A.E. (1969) Intra- and intermolecular crosslinks in collagen in tendon, cartilage and bone. *Clin. Orthoped.* **67**, 188

COX R.W. & GRANT R.A. (1969) Structure of the collagen fibril. *Clin. Orthoped.* **67**, 172

CRUICKSHANK D.B. (1936) The natural occurrence of zinc in teeth. *Brit. dent. J.* **61**, 530; **63**, 395; **68**, 257

DALLEMAGNE M.J. & FABRY C. (1956) In *Bone Structure and Metabolism.* Ciba Foundation Symposium. Churchill, London

DARLING A.I. (1943) The distribution of the enamel cuticle and its significance. *Proc. Roy. Soc. Med.* **36**, 499

DIRKSEN T.R. (1963) Lipid components of sound and carious dentine. *J. dent. Res.* **42**, 128

EASTOE J.E. (1963) The amino-acid composition of proteins from the oral tissues. *Archs oral Biol.* **8**, 633

EASTOE J.E. (1971) In *Tooth Enamel II.* Eds STACK M.V. & FEARNHEAD R.W. Wright, Bristol pp. 65, 119, 125

ELLIOTT J.C. (1963) Interpretation of carbonate bands in infra-red spectrum of dental enamel. *J. dent. Res.* **42**, 1081, 1115

ELLIOTT J.C. (1973) The problems of the composition and structure of the mineral components of the hard tissue. *Clin. Orthop.* **93**, 313

EMERSON W.H. (1962) Relation of thermolabile components to optical properties of dental enamel. *J. dent. Res.* **39**, 864

FEARNHEAD R.W. (1962) Recent observations on the structure of developing enamel. *Archs oral Biol. Supp.* **4**, 24

FEARNHEAD R.W. (1965) The insoluble organic component of human enamel. In *Tooth Enamel.* Eds. STACK, M.V. &

FEARNHEAD, R.W., Wright, Bristol p. 127

FRANK R.M. *et al.* (1960) Calcification of dental tissues with special reference to enamel ultrastructure. In *Calcification in Biological Systems*, p. 163. Ed. SOGNNAES R.F. Amer. Ass. Adv. Sci., Washington, D.C.

FULLMER H.M. (1971) Collagenase and periodontal disease: a review. *J. dent. Res.* **50**, 288

GLASS R.L. (1967) Radiographic evidence of tin uptake by human tooth structure. *Archs oral Biol.* **12**, 401

GLIMCHER M.J. *et al.* (1964) Coronal cementum in bovine teeth. *J. Ultrastruct. Res.* **10**, 76. See also *Science* **146**, 1676 for similar information referring to human teeth

GLIMCHER M.J. *et al.* (1957) Macromolecular aggregation states in relation to mineralization: the collagen-hydroxyapatite system as studied *in vitro*. *Proc. Nat. Acad. Sci. Wash.* **43**, 860

GWINNETT A.J. (1967) The ultrastructure of 'prismless' enamel of permanent human teeth. *Archs oral Biol.* **12**, 381, also **11**, 41.

HADJIMARKOS P.M. & BONHORST C.W. (1959) The selenium content of human teeth. *Oral Surg.* **12**, 113

HADJIMARKOS D.M. (1960) Urinary selenium and dental caries. *Nature (Lond.)* **188**, 677; also (1961) *Archs oral Biol.* **3**, 143

HARKNESS R.D. (1955) Metabolism of collagen. *Lect. Sci. Bas. Med.* **5**, 183. Athlone Press, London

HARDWICK J.L. & MARTIN C.J. (1967) A pilot study using mass spectrometry for the estimation of the trace element content of dental tissues. *Helv. odont. Acta* **11**, 62

HESS W.C. & LEE C.Y. (1954) The amino-acid composition of proteins isolated from the healthy enamel and dentine of carious teeth. *J. dent. Res.* **33**, 62

HESS W.C. *et al.* (1956) The lipide content of enamel and dentin. *J. dent. Res.* **35**, 273

HOLAGER J. (1972) Thermogravimetric experiments on tooth carbonates. *J. dent. Res.* **51**, 102

JENKINS G.N. (1961) The biochemistry of enamel in relation to caries resistance. *Archs oral Biol.* **6**, 305

JONES I.L. & LEAVER A.G. (1974) Studies on the minor components of the organic matrix of human dentine. *Archs oral Biol.* **19**, 371; also (1976) **21**, 509

KAY M.I. *et al.* (1964) The crystal structure of hydroxyapatite. *Nature (Lond.)* **204**, 1050

KENNEDY J.L. *et al* (1953) The ultramicroscopic structure of enamel and dentine. *J. Amer. dent. Ass.* **46**, 423

KOFOED J.A. *et al.* (1971) Half-life times of the glycosaminoglycan fractions in gigiva, skin and cartilage of rats. *J. dent. Res.* **50**, 171

KOMRSKA J. (1972) Derivativographic analysis of dentin. *J. dent. Res.* **51**, 148

LEAVER A.G. (1969) Studies on certain peptide fractions isolated from human dentine. *Archs oral Biol.* **14**, 503

LEVINE R.S. (1971) The distribution of hydroxyproline in sound coronal dentine. *Archs oral Biol.* **16**, 473

LITTLE K. (1959) Electron microscope studies on human dental enamel. *Proc. Roy. Mic. Soc.* **78**, 58

LITTLE K. & KRAMER H. (1952) The nature of reticulin. *Nature (Lond).* **170**, 499

LITTLE M.F. & BRUDEVOLD F. (1958) A study of the inorganic carbon dioxide in intact human enamel. *J. dent. Res.* **37**, 991

LOSEE F.L. *et al.* (1974) Natural elements of the periodic table in human dental enamel. *Caries Res.* **8**, 123

LYON D.G. & DARLING A.I. (1953) Examination of human dental enamel by polarized light. *J. dent. Res.* **31**, 731

MALIK S.R. & FREMLIN J.H. (1974) A study of lead distribution in human teeth, using charged particle activation analysis. *Caries Res.* **8**, 283

MANLY R.S. & HODGE H.C. (1939) Density and refractive index studies of dental hard tissues. I. Methods for separation and determination of purity. *J. dent. Res.* **18**, 133. (See also *Archs oral Biol.* **10**, 155 for a modification of the method)

McCONNELL D. (1960) The crystal chemistry of dental enamel. *Archs oral Biol.* **3**, 28

MECKEL A.H. *et al.* (1965) In *Tooth Enamel*, p. 160. Eds STACK M.V. & FEARNHEAD R.W. Wright, Bristol

MORENO E.C. & ZAHRADNIK R.T. (1973) The pore structure of human dental enamel. *Archs oral Biol.* **18**, 1063

MORTIMER K.V. (1970) Relationship of deciduous enamel structure to dental disease. *Caries Res.* **4**, 206

MYRBERG N. (1968) Proton magnetic resonance in human dental enamel and dentine. *Trans. R. Schs. Dent. Stockh. Umeå* No. 14

NEIDERS M.E. *et al.* (1972) Electron probe microanalysis of cementum and underlying dentin in young permanent teeth. *J. dent. Res.* **51**, 122

NEUBERGER A. & SLACK H.G.B. (1953) The metabolism of collagen from liver, bone, skin and tendon in the normal rat. *Biochim. J.* **53**, 47

NIXON G.S. & SMITH H. (1960) Estimation of arsenic in teeth by activation analysis. *J. dent. Res.* **39**, 514

NIXON G.S. & SMITH H. (1962) Estimation of copper in human enamel by activation analysis. *J. dent. Res.* **41**, 1013

NIXON G.S. *et al.* (1967) Estimation of zinc in human dental enamel by activation analysis. *Archs oral Biol.* **12**, 411

NIXON G.S. *et al.* (1966) Estimation of manganese in human dental enamel by activation analysis. *Archs oral Biol.* **11**, 247

NIXON G.S. & MYERS V.B. (1970) Estimation of selenium in human dental enamel by activation analysis. *Caries Res.* **4**, 179

ODUTUGA A.A. & PROUT R.E.S. (1974) Lipid analysis of human enamel and dentine. *Archs oral Biol.* **19**, 729

OPDYKE D.L.J. (1962) The histochemistry of dental decay. *Archs oral Biol.* **7**, 207

OSBORN J.W. (1967) Three-dimensional reconstructions of enamel prisms. *J. dent. Res.* **46**, 1412; also **47**, 217, 223

PINCUS P. (1948) Further local factors affecting dental caries: the shape and contents of occlusal grooves. *Brit. dent. J.* **84**, 25

POOLE D.F.G. & BROOKS A.W. (1961) The arrangement of crystallites in enamel prisms. *Archs oral Biol.* **5**, 14

PROUT R.E.S. & SHUTT E.R. (1970a) Analysis of fatty acids in human root dentine and enamel. *Archs oral Biol.* **15**, 281

PROUT R.E.S. & SHUTT E.R. (1970b) Separation of enamel and dentine using cadmium tungstoborate solution. *Archs oral Biol.* **15**, 559

ROBINSON C. *et al.* (1971) Variation in composition of dental enamel within thin ground tooth sections. *Caries Res.* **5**, 44

ROBINSON C. *et al.* (1975) Amino acid composition, distribution and origin of 'tuft' protein in human and bovine dental enamel. *Archs oral Biol.* **20**, 29

RÖNNHOLM E. (1962) An electron microscopic study of the amelogenesis in human teeth. I. The fine structure of the ameloblasts. *J. Ultrastruct. Res.* **6**, 229. II. The development of the enamel crystallites. Ibid., 249

SAVORY A. & BRUDEVOLD F. (1959) The distribution of nitrogen in human enamel. *J. dent. Res.* **38**, 436

SELVIG K.A. (1971) Periodic lattic images of hydroxyapatite crystals in human bone and dental hard tissues. *Calc. Tiss. Res.* **6**, 227

SHAW J.H. & YEN P.K.-J. (1972) Sodium, potassium and magnesium concentrations in the enamel and dentine of human and rhesus monkey teeth. *J. dent. Res.* **51**, 95

SIMMONS N.S. (1972) Extraction of enamel rods and apatite ribbons from embryo teeth. *J. dent. Res.* **51**, Special Issue, p. 252, abstract 819

SIMPSON D.R. (1972) Problems of the composition and structure of the bone minerals. *Clin. Orthop.* **86**, 260

SINEX F.M. (1968) In *Treatise on Collagen*, vol. 2, part B. Ed. GOULD B.S. Academic Press, London and New York

SMALES F.C. (1975) Structural subunit in prisms of immature rat enamel. *Nature (Lond.)* **258**, 772

SOGNNAES E.F. (1948) The organic elements of the enamel. A study of the principal factors involved in the histological preservation of the organic elements of enamel and other calcified structures. *J. dent. Res.* **27**, 609

SONI N.N. & BRUDEVOLD F. (1959) A microradiographic and polarizing microscopic study of sound enamel. *J. dent. Res.* **38**, 1181 (see also **39**, 233)

SÖREMARK R. & SAMSAHL K. (1962) Gamma-ray spectrometric analysis of elements in normal human dentine. *J. dent. Res.* **41**, 603 (see **41**, 596 for method)

SÖREMARK R. *et al.* (1962) Influence of some dental restorations on the concentrations of inorganic constituents of the teeth. *Acta odont. Scand.* **20**, 216

SÖREMARK R. & GRØN P. (1966) Chloride distribution in human dental enamel as determined by electron probe microanalysis. *Archs oral Biol.* **11**, 861

SPEIRS R.L. (1971) The nature of surface enamel in human teeth. *Calc. Tiss. Res.* **8**, 1

STACK M.V. (1953) Variation in the organic content of deciduous enamel and dentine. *Biochem. J.* **54**, 15; also (1951) *Brit. dent. J.* **90**, 173 & (1954) *J. Amer. dent. Ass.* **48**, 297

STARKEY W.E. & FLETCHER W. (1969) The accumulation of strontium-90 in human teeth in England and Wales—1959 to 1965. *Archs oral Biol.* **14**, 169

TEN CATE A.R. (1972) Morphological studies of fibrocytes in connective tissue undergoing rapid remodelling. *J. Anat.* **112**, 401

TERMINE J.D. & POSNER A.S. (1967) Amorphous/crystalline interrelationships in one mineral. *Calc. Tiss. Res.* **1**, 8

THEWLIS J. (1940) The structure of teeth as shown by X-ray examination *Spec. Rep. Ser. Med. Res. Coun. Lond.* No. 238

VERZAR F. (1963) The aging of collagen. *Sci. American*, **208**, 104

WEATHERELL J.A. *et al.* (1966) Sampling of enamel particles by means of strong acids for density measurements. *Archs oral Biol.* **11**, 107; also (1965) **10**, 139

WEATHERELL J.A. *et al.* (1967) Density Patterns in Enamel. *Caries Res.* **1**, 42

WEATHERELL J.A. *et al.* (1968a) Distribution of carbonate in thin sections of dental enamel. *Caries Res.* **2**, 1

WEATHERELL J.A. *et al.* (1968b) Histological Appearance and Chemical Composition of Enamel Protein from Mature Human Molars. *Caries Res.* **2**, 281

WEIDMANN S.M. *et al.* (1967) Variation of enamel density in sections of human teeth. *Archs oral Biol.* **12**, 90

WOODHEAD-GALLOWAY J. & HUKINS D.W.L. (1976) Molecular biology of collagen. *Endeavour* **125**, 73

YOUNG R.A. (1974) Implications of atomic substitutions and other structural details in apatite. *J. dent. Res.* **53**, 193

YOUNG R.A. & ELLIOTT J.S. (1966) Atomic-scale bases for several properties of apatites. *Archs oral Biol.* **11**, 699

Reviews

LAZZARI E.P. (1976) 2nd Ed. *Dental Biochemistry*. Lea & Febiger, Philadelphia

LEICESTER H.M. (1949) *Biochemistry of the Teeth*. Kingston, London (an excellent review of earlier work)

MILES A.E.W. (1967) Ed. *Structural and Chemical Organization of Teeth*, Vol. II, Chaps 16–20. Academic Press, London

WEATHERELL J.A. (1975) Composition of dental enamel. *Brit. Med. Bull.* **31**, 115

CHAPTER III

MINERALIZATION

The deposition of calcium phosphate in bone and teeth has usually been referred to as 'calcification', although most of the hypotheses suggested to explain it have involved an active participation by phosphate more than by calcium. 'Mineralization' is a more satisfactory term which does not imply any particular explanation and will be mainly used in this book—but it must be emphasized that both terms are in use and are synonymous.

The problem of mineralization can be stated thus: since blood, and presumably tissue fluid, is supersaturated with bone salt, what factors are unique in the mineralizing tissues which cause the deposition of calcium phosphate in them and in them alone? Two types of mechanism might be envisaged: (1) a 'booster' mechanism such as an enzyme activity which by raising still further the concentration of calcium or phosphate ions would, by the law of mass action, lead to precipitation and (2) the presence of a seeding or 'nucleating' substance which, because its shape resembles that of apatite, acts as a mould or template upon which the crystals are laid down (this seeding process is known as 'epitaxy') after which crystallization proceeds automatically. During the 30 years up to 1956 discussion of the first type of mechanism, based on Robison's phosphatase theory, dominated this field but in the following ten years the second possibility received most attention. The discovery in the late 1960s of vesicles, apparently budding from cells concerned with mineralization and containing substances which could participate both in boosting and seeding, suggests that both mechanisms may occur.

A problem common to both hypotheses is whether the first precipitate is apatite or whether some other calcium phosphate is formed and is converted later into apatite.

A summary of the development of the phosphatase theory

Since the theory is no longer held in any of its original forms it will only be briefly outlined here. For a more detailed account, see earlier editions of this book. The main points were as follows:

113

(1) The discovery of the enzyme alkaline phosphatase in mineralizing tissues suggested that this enzyme released inorganic phosphate from organic phosphates (for example hexose phosphates) and thus raised locally the concentration of phosphate ions, which reacted with calcium ions in the tissue fluid, leading to the precipitation of the insoluble calcium phosphate:

$$\text{hexose phosphate} \xrightarrow{\text{alk. phosphatase}} \text{hexose} + \text{phosphate ions}$$

$$3Ca^{2+} + 2(PO_4)^{3-} \rightarrow Ca_3(PO_4)_2$$

As explained on p. 32, if a precipitation of this sort occurs at all it would now be thought to take place in stages:

$$Ca^{2+} + HPO_4^{2-} \xrightarrow{} \underset{\text{phosphate}}{\overset{\text{amorphous}}{\text{calcium}}} \xrightarrow[\text{spontaneous}]{} \text{apatite}$$

It is not certain that releasing phosphate into a medium supersaturated with calcium phosphate does lead to precipitation—it is equally likely merely to increase the degree of supersaturation.

(2) When slices of cartilage, dissected from the bones of young rachitic rats, were incubated with solutions containing calcium ions and *organic phosphates* which were known to be split by phosphatase, the calcium phosphate was laid down in a way that resembled normal calcification histologically. This technique was referred to as 'calcification *in vitro*' and it provided a means of investigating the substances from which the insoluble 'bone salt' was formed. The early results suggested that organic phosphates favoured mineralization and therefore supported the phosphatase theory. The cartilaginous part of rachitic bones were used because they contained a much larger area of matrix in a calcifiable state (but which owing to being vitamin D deficient had not in fact calcified) than did normal bone. Whether the results obtained in the rachitic tissues applied to normal bone was never really investigated.

(3) It soon became clear, however, that the phosphatase theory was inadequate because (*a*) alkaline phosphatase was found to be present in tissues which did not normally calcify, (*b*) certain enzyme inhibitors which did not affect phosphatase were found to inhibit calcification *in vitro*, and (*c*) calcification *in vitro* was later found to occur in solutions containing calcium ions and *inorganic* phosphate (i.e. in the absence of organic phosphate and, therefore, presumably not involving phosphatase). Calcification did not take place in these inorganic solutions, however, if enzyme inhibitors were added, showing that even the utilization of inorganic phosphate must involve the action of some enzymes. A 'second mechanism' was postulated, possibly the synthesis of an organic phosphate in the mineralizing tissues, but even this combination was not unique to bone or teeth.

THE EFFECT OF ADENOSINE TRIPHOSPHATE

Cartier and his colleagues (1950, 1955) studied the calcification of bone slices from lamb embryos and obtained very different results from those reported by workers who had used rat rachitic cartilage. Although Cartier believes that these differences arise from his use of normal tissue, he appears to have made no direct comparison with identical techniques between the behaviour of normal and rachitic tissues. It is therefore possible that species differences (lamb versus rat) or some unsuspected difference in technique may account for the discrepancy.

In Cartier's experiments, the addition of the phosphate esters which had been found active by Robison had only a small effect in favouring mineralization. Adenosine triphosphate (ATP) was, however, extremely powerful in inducing mineralization, whereas previous workers had found it to have only weak activity. It was suggested that pyrophosphate (PP_i) was split off ATP and entered the bone where the enzyme pyrophosphatase (probably the same as alkaline phosphatase) splits most of it to form P_i. A small amount may remain unsplit which could account for the 0.5% in adult bone.

In the rare disease, hypophosphatasia—in which the alkaline phosphatase activity of bone is extremely low—growth of collagen continues or, as in rickets, may even be exaggerated in developing bone but mineralization is defective (Fraser 1957). The pyrophosphate concentration in the urine is higher than usual, a finding which supports the idea that this is the natural substrate for this enzyme and that its breakdown in involved in mineralization (Poland *et al.* 1972).

Cartier's theory has not been thoroughly investigated by others—probably because the seeding theory, which was developed shortly after, seemed more plausible and diverted attention from alternative views.

White & Hess (1956) made the surprising discovery that bone and, more especially, dentine, from which all enzymes had been destroyed or removed, still possessed the property of splitting phosphate esters. It is now established that even synthetic apatite may act as a catalyst with an action similar to that of alkaline phosphatase. Collagen fibres reconstituted repeatedly from acetic acid solutions, and therefore presumably free from non-collagenous substances, break down ATP, the phosphate released becoming bound to the collagen (Krane & Glimcher 1962). Since purified collagen thus appears to act like an ATPase, the splitting of ATP found in mineralizing tissues by Cartier could perhaps be accounted for by this action of collagen.

One of the oldest suggestions for the mechanism of mineralization was that the pH of cartilage was higher than that of other tissues which would favour the precipitation of calcium phosphate. The pH of cartilage fluid obtained by a micropuncture technique has been shown by modern methods to be about 7.58 ± 0.05, contrasting with 7.38 ± 0.04 in arterial blood measured at the same time (Cuervo *et al.* 1971). This alkalinity seems to be maintained by a secretion of bicarbonate ions promoted by carbonic anhydrase activity, since it is abolished by acetazol amide, an inhibitor of this enzyme. The importance of this reaction in mineralization has not yet been assessed.

The Seeding Theory

The seeding theory of the initiation of mineralization arose from dissatisfaction with the phosphatase theory and from the observation that if collagen fibres reconstituted from collagen solution (as described on pp. 90–1) are placed in a medium supersaturated with calcium and phosphate ions, the collagen appears to act as a seed and apatite crystals form on the fibres. Other proteins such as gelatin and fibrin do not induce crystal formation. These results suggested either that collagen or some substances closely associated with it, such as chondroitin sulphate, or a combination of collagen and chondroitin sulphate could act as a seed and form nuclei of apatite. Once the seeding nuclei are formed, crystal growth would occur until some limiting factor, possibly lack of space, prevented further growth.

THE NATURE OF THE SEEDING PROCESS

There are at least two ways in which a molecule of a particular shape could induce crystallization. (1) Regions of the molecule might have a distribution of electric charges or a spatial configuration such that calcium and phosphate ions become attached to adjacent regions and the local increase in concentration then exceeds the values at which precipitation occurs. (2) The distribution of charges or spatial configuration of the seed may encourage calcium and phosphate ions to combine with it in positions similar to those which they occupy in colloidal calcium phosphate or in some salt, such as $CaHPO_4$, which may precipitate first and then be converted into apatite. When they occupy these positions dictated by the shape of the seed they fall into place as calcium phosphate.

THE NATURE OF THE SEED

A wide variety of substances can act as a seed *in vitro* for hydroxyapatite and it is quite probable that more than one naturally occurring substance is active *in vivo*.

The following have been considered as possible seeding substances in bone.

(1) COLLAGEN

A striking observation about the seeding capacity of reconstituted collagen was made by Glimcher *et al.* (1957) who stated that only those fibres showing the 640 Å banding are mineralized *in vitro*. This was taken to indicate that the

FIG. III.1. Electron micrograph of collagen showing the 640 Å banding and the early deposition of apatite crystals mainly in the region of the bands.

group with the specific shape for seeding is not in the tropocollagen molecule but is formed by the combination of collagen molecules responsible for the 640 Å banding (pp. 90–2). Furthermore, if these fibres are swollen by exposure to acid or alkali, or shrunken by heat (i.e. their orderly structure is destroyed) they lose their power to act as seeds.

Electron micrographs show that when the crystals have grown large enough to be detected they tend to lie 640 Å apart, i.e. they show a definite relationship to the bands (Fig. III.1), so that the early crystal, at least, seems to be related to some structure having a period similar to the bands of the collagen. It is not necessarily the bands themselves which are important (although this is possible) but the existence of some repeating structure of which the bands are one manifestation. Calculation of the volume of collagen and mineral matter in the fully-mineralized tissues strongly suggests that some of the mineral must be within the collagen fibres since the spaces between the fibres are too small to accommodate the amount of mineral present. The presence of apatite inside the fibres has also been seen in electron micrographs (Fig. III.2) and it has been suggested that seeding might occur in the 'holes' in the collagen fibre (pp. 92–3).

Fɪɢ. III.2. Transverse sections of collagen fibres showing that apatite crystals are deposited inside the fibre.

Glimcher has produced evidence that phosphate may become attached to the amino acid serine in collagen where it might be expected to attract calcium ions and thus become a nucleating centre, although there is little experimental investigation of this.

Davis & Walker (1972) reported that collagen will not nucleate if its carboxylic groups are blocked by converting them into amides: presumably calcium binds to the carboxylic groups. If the remaining carboxylic groups of slightly mineralized collagen are converted to amides and the collagen is then demineralized, thus releasing the carboxylic groups previously bound to calcium, it then remineralizes when exposed to appropriate solutions. This shows that only a few carboxylic groups are needed to induce seeding.

In spite of this striking evidence that collagen is effective in seeding, there is one very great difficulty in accepting it as the seed, namely, that fibres reconstituted from solutions of collagen from skin, tendon and other non-mineralizing tissues are found to mineralize *in vitro* as readily as those from bone. In fact, owing to its insolubility (probably derived from its extensive cross-linking) bone collagen has rarely been used in experiments on mineralization. Consequently, the main problem—why do some tissues mineralize and others do not?—remains uncertain if collagen is the seed. There are several suggested explanations:

(A) VARIATIONS IN COLLAGEN STRUCTURE IN DIFFERENT TISSUES

The first suggestion is that collagen from mineralizing tissues differs from that of non-mineralizing tissues and several differences have been suggested, but their importance in mineralization is still hypothetical. But since reconstituted fibres from both mineralizing and non-mineralizing tissues are found to mineralize *in vitro* it must be supposed that in the course of reconstitution, these differences disappear.

Katz & Li (1973) concluded from X-ray diffraction and other studies that the spaces between the collagen molecules in bone and dentine average 6Å which is 3Å larger than in tendon. They suggest that this difference may explain why mineral ions enter collagen in bone and dentine but not elsewhere. The space between the molecules in tendon is smaller than the diameter of the phosphate ion, 4Å, suggesting that it could not enter tendon fibrils but could permeate the larger spaces between bone collagen fibrils and thus precipitate as apatite within these fibrils.

(B) INHIBITORS IN NON-MINERALIZING TISSUES

A second suggested explanation is that all collagens or other widely-distributed substances possess the groups needed for seeding apatite but that non-mineralizing tissues contain an inhibitor of mineralization. The evidence for this theory is as follows:

(*a*) If collagen is placed in solutions varying in calcium and phosphate concentration it is possible to find the minimum product (Ca conc) $\times$ (P$_i$ conc) at which mineralization occurs. Most collagens need a product of 35 mg 100 ml^{-1} but some mineralize with a product of 16. When plasma was included in the medium, the (Ca) $\times$ (P) product at which mineralization occurred rose, suggesting the presence of an inhibitor in plasma.

Two short-chain polypeptides have been isolated from plasma and urine which inhibit mineralization *in vitro* (Howard *et al.* 1967) and several ions at the concentrations present in plasma (HCO$_3$, SiO$_4^{2-}$, CrO$_4^{2-}$, Mg^{2+}, Zn^{2+}) have a similar effect but their importance in the living animal is hypothetical (Feagin *et al.* 1969). Plasma previously incubated with alkaline phosphatase showed no inhibitory effect. Inhibition could also be induced by certain polyphospates (for example ATP, pyrophosphate and tripolyphosphate) suggesting that such substances might be natural inhibitors of mineralization and that the role of phosphatase is to remove them and thereby allow mineralization to occur (Fleisch & Neuman 1961). This hypothesis leaves unexplained the absence of mineralization from many tissues (for example kidney and intestine) which contain both alkaline phosphatase and collagen.

(*b*) Although reconstituted collagen with the 640 Å banding readily mineralizes in solutions saturated with calcium and phosphate ions, pieces of untreated rat-tail tendon or crude collagen from skin either do not mineralize at all under these conditions or do so less readily. The most obvious difference between the crude and reconstituted collagen is that substances associated with the collagen will be largely or entirely removed during dissolving and reconstitution. Possible changes in the collagen itself during treatment cannot be dismissed, however.

(2) CHONDROITIN SULPHATE

Since a strongly acidic substance would favour attachment of calcium ions and chondroitin sulphate is the most acidic substance in the calcifying tissues it has been speculated that it might be the seed *in vivo*. This idea was supported by experiments in which substances capable of combining strongly with chondroitin sulphate (for example protamine and toluidine blue) were found to inhibit calcification *in vitro* (Sobel 1955).

The role, if any, of chondroitin sulphate in calcification *in vivo* is still unsettled but the following facts show its presence on collagen is not essential for it to act as a seed *in vitro*. Collagen fibres reconstituted from pure solution containing no chondroitin sulphate still act as seeds in calcifying solutions. Also, hyaline cartilage is one of the tissues richest in chondroitin sulphate but it does not necessarily calcify, whereas in bone the concentration is much lower.

Chondroitin sulphate, although considered by some to be the seed (either alone or bound to collagen) could perhaps be an inhibitor of calcification. These opposing effects could be brought about in the following way. The acidic properties of chondroitin sulphate suggest that it may bind calcium and, by attracting phosphate to the site, act as a seed. Alternatively, the binding of calcium by chondroitin sulphate could reduce the concentration of calcium ions below that required for mineralization and thereby act as an inhibitor. The staining properties of hyaline cartilage suggest the presence of much sulphated glycosaminoglycans and this is confirmed by chemical analysis, but as the ossifying area is approached the staining changes and analysis shows a marked fall in organic sulphate. Although several interpretations are possible, one is that glycosaminoglycans are removed near the mineralizing area. This might have two effects: it would remove the inhibitory action and might lead to the release of the calcium which was bound to the mucopolysaccharide thus raising the concentration and favouring mineralization.

(3) A LIPID SUBSTANCE ASSOCIATED WITH THE SEED

A substance which stains as a lipid with Sudan black has been detected by Irving (1960) in areas of active mineralization of bone and teeth (including enamel, one of the few factors common to enamel and other sites of mineralization). It has also been reported in areas of resorption in bone and in the dentine of resorbing deciduous roots (see p. 210). It exists in tissues in a form which does not stain but treatment with pyridine or alcohol 'unmasks' it, presumably by removing a substance which protects it from the stain (Irving 1960, 1973; Irving & Wuthier 1968).

The total lipid in developing bone in the bovine foetus rose from 1% of demineralized dry weight, in resting cartilage, to $7 \cdot 7\%$ and $8 \cdot 5\%$ of hypertrophic and mineralized cartilage respectively and in fully-mineralized bone fell to between $0 \cdot 6$ and $0 \cdot 98\%$ (Wuthier 1969). Much of this lipid could be extracted only after the tissue had been demineralized, indicating a firm bond between the calcium salts and the lipid.

Analysis of the lipids in mineralizing tissues show them to be a very complicated mixture of triglycerides, free fatty acids, and various phospholipids, about half of which contain serine or inositol. The lipid cannot be detected histologically in bone or enamel of rats deficient in vitamin D or of guinea-pigs deficient in vitamin C, but returns if these deficiencies are treated. The proportions of the phospholipids in the mineralizing tissues changed markedly in vitamin D deficiency: in general, their concentrations greatly increased (contrasting with the reduced staining of rachitic tissues) but some did decrease and some also became more difficult, and others less difficult, to extract (Wuthier 1971). Changes in extractability may account for the reduced lipid staining which Irving reported at the site of mineralization in vitamin D deficiency. These results are not easily interpreted but they provide circumstantial evidence that the lipids play a part in early mineralization.

When lipids from a variety of tissues are added to metastable solutions of calcium phosphate, a precipitate forms consisting largely of apatite but including up to $1 \cdot 9\%$ lipid. The lipid cannot be extracted from the precipitate unless the apatite is dissolved first, suggesting some form of binding. The lipid consists mostly of acidic phospholipids: when a mixture of lipids is added, the proportion of various lipids in the precipitate may be quite different from those in the mixture added—evidently only certain lipids are concerned with precipitating apatite. If the lipids are separated into various fractions and added separately to mineralizing solution, only the phospholipids precipitate apatite (Odutuga & Prout 1973; Odutuga *et al.* 1975).

(4) PHOSPHOPROTEINS

Phosphoproteins, in which a phosphate group is attached to serine, have also been proposed as seeds, particularly in dentine (see p. 158).

It is suggested that the serine groups of collagen or of a specific protein in the mineralizing tissues becomes phosphorylated by the action of an enzyme, protein phosphokinase, which transfers a phosphate group from ATP to the protein. Phosphoproteins are known to be present in the mineralizing tissues and might be expected to attract calcium and thus become nucleating centres. There is little evidence for this hypothesis, however, and one argument against it—namely that phosphoserine occurs in proteins in milk and egg yolk where mineralization does not occur.

These contrasting hypotheses may perhaps be unified by the discovery of vesicles described in the next section.

The Role of Vesicles

Electron micrographs of cartilage show groups of round or ovoid, osmophilic vesicles between 500 and 2500 Å in diameter near each cell (Fig. III.3) (Bonucci 1967, 1971; Anderson 1973). In cartilage with mineralization well advanced, these vesicles contain crystals, identified by X-ray diffraction as apatite (Fig. III.4): the clusters of crystals grow and coalesce until the whole matrix is mineralized. If the section is demineralized by EDTA or acids and treated with lead citrate or other fixatives the crystals disappear but 'ghosts' of organic matter remain—evidently the apatite crystals are closely associated with organic matter.

Later work showed the presence of two types of vesicles. Type I are round or oval, resemble lysosomes and have been shown to be extruded from the cartilage cells. They contain acid phosphatase and aryl sulphatase and presumably they breakdown the proteoglycans and glycosaminoglycans (GAGs) whose concentrations are known to fall as mineralization occurs.

Type II are irregular in shape, bounded by a trimellar membrane, sometimes contain ribosomes and have an internal structure resembling cytoplasm—serial sections show that they are pieces of the cartilage cells which have become detached. When thick slices of cartilage were treated with collagenase and the undigested residues centrifuged the Type II vesicles sedimented as a separate layer which made it possible to collect them and study their chemistry. They contain alkaline phosphatase and ATPase, enzymes characteristic of the membranes of cartilage cells, and lipids (hence their osmophilia), chiefly phosphatidylserine, a substance previously shown in the lipids of the calcifying 'front'. This substance has a strong affinity for calcium, especially in the presence of phosphate, and it is tempting to speculate that it is important in concentrating calcium ions, thus acting as a seed.

It seems that Type II vesicles may promote mineralization in several ways involving all the hypotheses proposed over the last 50 years. The alkaline phosphatase has pyrophosphatase activity (these enzymes may be identical)

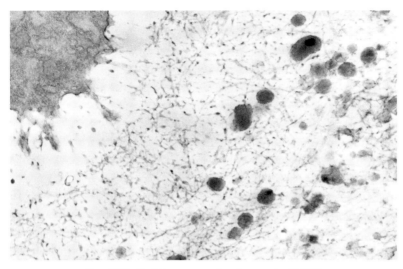

FIG. III.3. Vesicles near a chondrocyte (× 25 000)

and it converts the inhibitor pyrophosphate (PP_i) into orthophosphate thus removing its inhibitory power and simultaneously converting it into a booster by increasing the concentration of orthophosphate. The lipid may attract calcium ions, this action being favoured by the orthophosphate which, in turn, will be available to convert the calcium into calcium phosphate. An unexplained difficulty, if this is the role of lipid, is how the tightly-bound calcium becomes released from the lipid. The presence of ATPase suggests that the reactions proposed by Cartier may occur in the vesicles; alternatively, ATPase may be concerned with an energy-requiring calcium transport system as in the cells of the intestine (p. 3).

The isolation of Type I vesicles from calcifying tissues does not seem to have been made as they sediment with other cell fractions, and information on their constituents is based on histochemical observations.

The discovery of vesicles, and in particular the fact that they seem able to act both as a booster and as a seed, provided a reasonable solution to the problem of mineralization. The suggestion that collagen (or some substance associated with it) was the seed seemed unnecessary and was more or less abandoned. Some difficulties remain, however. One example is that work on vesicles indicates that apatite crystals are formed very early in mineralization and before the crystals become associated with collagen. There seems no mechanism for the formation of the amorphous calcium phosphate, which some methods of investigation (pp. 75–6) suggest is present even in fully-mineralized adult bone. Some electron micrographs of the vesicles show the presence of a non-crystalline material at early stages of mineralization, but

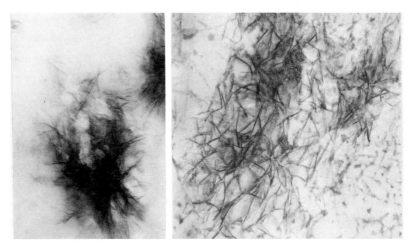

FIG. III.4. (left) Clusters of apatite crystals in a vesicle (the other structures in the vesicles are not visible) ($\times$ 90 000). (right) Crystals of apatite at the edge of mineralized cartilage ($\times$ 90 000).

whether it is amorphous calcium phosphate is not known. The possibility cannot be dismissed that the crystals seen in the vesicles are formed as an artefact during the preparation of the sections for electron micrography and that, *in vivo*, the vesicles form amorphous calcium phosphate.

The relationship of calcium phosphate formation in the vesicles to its presence within the collagen fibres is another unresolved problem.

Electron micrographs of dentine give the impression that the crystals extend beyond the membranes of the vesicles and coalesce with other crystals emerging from other vesicles, engulfing collagen in the process. Any orientation with collagen seems to be an incidental secondary process. Is the seeding *in vitro* by collagen and the formation of crystals spatially associated with the collagen fibre an artefact?

The convincing evidence that the apatite crystals are within collagen fibres but are too large to enter it as such has raised once again the possible role of collagen as a seed.

One picture of mineralization which links vesicles and collagen suggests that amorphous calcium phosphate is precipitated in the vesicle which, being more soluble that hydroxyapatite (HA), then dissolves by unknown mechanisms in the tissue fluid surrounding the cells of the mineralizing tissue. The calcium and phosphate ions then diffuse into the collagen fibre because, in the mineralizing tissues, the spaces between the fibres are large enough to permit these ions to enter, where they form HA by a seeding process (the exact nature of the seed is still unknown). In other words, the vesicles carry out a concentrating process which provides the collagen with sufficient ions to form HA crystals. This reconciles some of the contradictions but leaves unexplained the appearance of crystals bursting out of the vesicles (if they are HA they would not be so likely to dissolve) unless they are artefacts formed from the amorphous precipitates during the preparation of the tissue of the section.

The presence of vesicles in a tissue, along with collagen macromolecules surrounded by spaces sufficiently large to allow ions to diffuse between them (p. 119) provides the most reasonable interpretation of the available data to explain why mineralization occurs only in certain tissues.

It is well established that mitochondria of bone-forming cells can accumulate calcium and phosphate. The concentrations in cartilage tend to increase as the mineralization front is approached but falls at the site of mineralization (Matthews *et al.* 1970) and is less in rachitic tissues.

If the calcium phosphate in the mitochondria is concerned with mineralization as some workers suggest from the circumstantial evidence, there is no clear picture as to how it escapes from the mitochondria and leaves the cells to reach the matrix. It seems curious that the mitochondria seem to duplicate (but in a location where its function is not clear) the activity of the vesicles.

References

ANDERSON H.C. (1973) Calcium accumulating vesicles in the intercellular matrix of bone. In *Hard Tissue Growth Repair and Remineralisation*, p. 213. CIBA Foundation symposium 11. Associated Scientific Publishers, Amsterdam (see also *J. Cell Biol.* (1969) **41**, 59; *Dev. Biol.* (1973) **34**, 211)

BONUCCI E. (1967) Fine structure and early cartilage calcification. *J. ultrastruc. Res.* **20**, 33

BONUCCI E. (1971) The locus of initial calcification in cartilage and bone. *Clin. Orthoped.* **78**, 108

CARTIER P. (1950) Biochimie de l'ossification: phosphorylation et calcification. *C.R. Soc. de biol.* **144**, 311

CARTIER P. & PICARD J. (1955) La minéralisation du cartilage ossifiable. *Bull. Soc. chim. biol.* **37**, 485, 661; **38**, 697

CUERVO L.A. *et al.* (1971) Ultramicroanalysis of pH, pCO₂, and carbonic anhydrase activity at calcifying sites in cartilage. *Calc. Tiss. Res.* **7**, 220

DAVIS N.R. & WALKER T.E. (1972) The role of carboxyl groups in collagen calcification. *Biochem. Biophys. Res. Commun.* **48**, 1656

FEAGIN F.F. *et al.* (1969) Evaluation of the calcifying characteristics of biological fluids and inhibitors of calcification. *Calc. Tiss. Res.* **4**, 231

FLEISCH H. & NEUMAN W.F. (1961) Mechanism of calcification: role of collagen, polyphosphates, and phosphatase. *Amer. J. Physiol.* **200**, 1296 (also **203**, 671)

FRASER D. (1957) Hypophosphatasia. *Amer. J. Med.* **22**, 730

HOWARD J.E. *et al.* (1967) The recognition and isolation from urine and serum of peptide inhibitors to calcification. *John Hopk. med. J.* **120**, 119.

IRVING J.T. (1960) Histochemical changes in the early stages of calcification. *Clin. Orthopaed.* **17**, 92

IRVING J. & WUTHIER (1968) Histochemistry and biochemistry of calcification with special reference to the role of lipids. *Clin. Orthoped.* **56**, 237

KATZ E.P. & LI S.-T. (1973) Structure and

function of bone collagen fibrils. *J. mol. Biol.* **80**, 1 (see also *Biochem. and Biophys. Research Commun.* (1972) **46**, 1368)

KRANE S.M. & GLIMCHER M.J. (1962) Studies on the interaction of collagen and phosphate. In *Radioisotopes and Bone*, p. 419. Ed. MCLEAN F.C. Blackwell Scientific Publications, Oxford

MATTHEWS *et al.* (1970) Mitochondrial granules in the normal and rachitic rat epiphysis. *Calc. Tiss. Res.* **5**, 91

ODUTUGO A.A. & PROUT R.S. (1973) Fatty acid composition of neutral lipids and phospholipids of enamel and dentine from rat incisors and molars. *Archs oral Biol.* **18**, 689

ODUTUGA A.A. *et al.* (1975) Hydroxyapatite precipitation *in vitro* by lipids extracted from mammalian hard and soft tissues. *Archs oral Biol.* **20**, 311

POLAND C. *et al.* (1972) Histochemical observations of hypophosphatasia. *J. dent. Res.* **51**, 333

SOBEL A.E. (1955) Local factors in the mechanism of calcification. *Ann. N.Y. Acad. Sci.* **60**, 713

WHITE A.A. & HESS W.C. (1956) Phosphatase, peroxidase and oxidase activity of dentin and bone. *J. dent. Res.* **35**, 276

WUTHIER R.E. (1969) Zonal analysis of the calcification front. *Calc. Tiss. Res.* **4**, 20

WUTHIER R.E. (1971) Zonal analysis of phospholipids in the epiphyseal cartilage and bone of normal and rachitic chickens and pigs. *Calc. Tiss. Res.* **8**, 36

Reviews

IRVING J.T. (1973) Theories of mineralisation of bone. *Clin. Orthoped.* **97**, 225

NEUMAN W.F. & NEUMAN M.W. (1958) *The Chemical Dynamics of Bone Mineral.* University of Chicago Press, Chicago

SOGNNAES R.F. (Ed.) (1963) *Mechanisms o, Hard Tissue Destruction.* Washington, D.C.: Amer. Ass. Adv. Sci. publ. no. **75**

STRATES B. & NEUMAN W.F. (1958) On the mechanisms of calcification. *Proc. Soc. exp. Biol. N.Y.* **97**, 688

WEIDMANN S.M. (1957) Fractionation of phosphorus compounds in ossifying cartilage. *Nature (Lond).* **180**, 1196

The proceedings of the First International Conference on Matrix Vesicle Calcification are published in *Federation Proceedings* (1976) **35**, 104–69

CHAPTER IV

FORMATION AND MINERALIZATION OF THE DENTAL TISSUES

Enamel

Many studies have been made with the light and electron microscopes of the histological changes that occur during the development and mineralization of enamel and a fairly complete histological description of these events can now be given which can be partly correlated with chemical changes.

The dental lamina and tooth buds

During the sixth week of embryonic life in man, some of the cells of the basal layer of the oral epithelium begin to divide more rapidly than do the neighbouring cells: thus an epithelial thickening (called the dental lamina) is formed along the edges of both jaws: electron micrographs of its formation and structure have been described by Provenza & Sisca (1970). Ten swellings (the tooth buds) then develop in the lamina by similar localized increases in the rate of mitosis in positions corresponding to those of the ten future deciduous teeth. The tooth buds then become arranged into the bell-shaped enamel organ with its four layers of cells: the inner and outer enamel epithelium form the boundary within which are the stratum intermedium and the stellate reticulum (see Fig. IV.1). No details are known of the factors which control these developmental changes. The bell shape of the enamel organ encloses partially some of the adjacent mesodermal tissue which eventually differentiates into dentine and pulp as the result of an organizer in the enamel organ.

ORGANIZERS AND INDUCTION

In the development of the embryo it is often found that one group of cells causes the differentiation of a neighbouring group, a process known as induction or the action of organizers. If, for example, the cells which induce the nervous system in an embryo are made to occupy an unusual position in that embryo, the nervous system is formed (or 'induced') in that abnormal

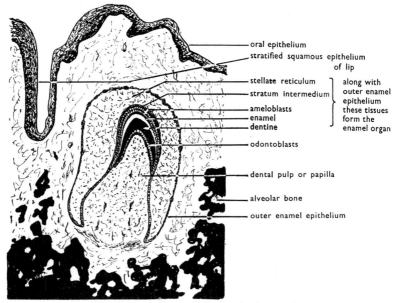

oral epithelium
stratified squamous epithelium
of lip
stellate reticulum ⎤ along with
stratum intermedium ⎮ outer enamel
epithelium
ameloblasts ⎬ these tissues
enamel ⎮ form the
dentine ⎦ enamel organ
odontoblasts
dental pulp or papilla
alveolar bone
outer enamel epithelium

FIG. IV.1. A diagram of a developing tooth.

position and the tissue which normally forms the nervous system fails to do so.

The functions of the ameloblasts

The ameloblasts perform several different functions at different stages of the development of the tooth. Each stage is associated with certain histological features in the cell and it is uncertain whether these changes are brought about by environmental influences or whether they represent stages inherent in the life cycle of the ameloblasts. In sections of tooth germs which happen to be at the right age, it is possible to observe ameloblasts at each stage. The enamel organ of the continuously growing rodent incisor contains ameloblasts at various stages throughout the whole life of the animal and provides the most suitable means of studying their various activities simultaneously in the same section.

The first function: determining the shape of the crown

The first function, performed by the very young cells of the inner enamel epithelium (not yet strictly ameloblasts) which are short columnar cells scarcely longer than their nuclei, is to determine the shape of the crown of the tooth. The position which these cells occupy at this stage becomes the amelodentinal junction of the future tooth. This function does not differ fundamentally from that of many embryonic cells whose migrations deter-

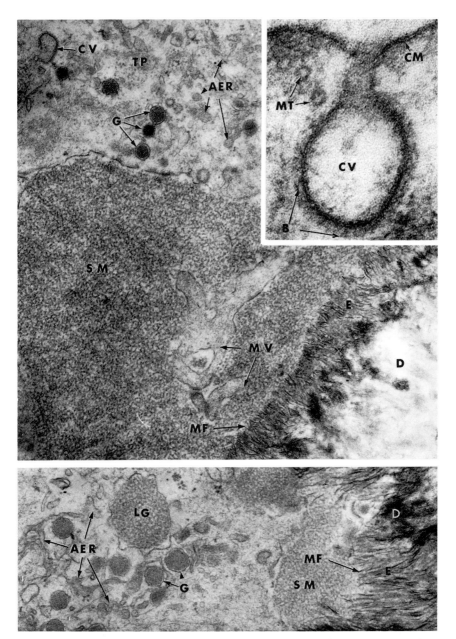

FIG. IV. 2. An ameloblast at an early stage in the formation of enamel (× 37 000). Inset: a coated vesicle (× 212 000). TP, Tomes process; SM, stippled material; E, enamel; D, dentine; G, granules; AER, endoplasmic reticulin; CV, coated vesicle; MV, microvilli; CM, cell membrane; B, bristles; MT, microtubule.

mine the position and shape of other organs. The cells in different parts of the inner enamel epithelium of molar teeth cease to undergo mitosis at different times. Division stops first in the cells of the future cusps while it continues in the 'valleys' thus leading to bending and pushing upwards of the cusps. This differential growth, whose control mechanism is not known, alters the shape of the inner enamel epithelium because it cannot expand outwards owing to the restricting effect of the dental follicle. If the follicle is removed from a tooth germ in tissue culture, the enamel epithelium occupies a larger area, but remains flat (Butler 1957). The numbers of mitoses in the cells of the inner enamel epithelium of the rat incisor, like other dividing cells, show a daily fluctuation; being highest about 10.00 hr and falling steadily till 18.00 hr. The uptake of tritiated thymidine showed a reciprocal rhythm reaching a maximum at 18.00 hr (Gasser *et al.* 1972). In addition to mitotic division, there is evidence that the increase in number of cells in the inner enamel epithelium occurs by migration of cells from the stratum intermedium (Ten Cate 1962).

Little is known about other forces which guide the movements of cells and hence the position of tissues in the embryo, but the stickiness (or 'specific adhesion') of cells may be a factor which decides whether a cell moves away from, or remains near to, its neighbours. It is possible that reactions between cell surfaces, similar to the highly specific reactions between antigens and antibodies, might account for these effects. Calcium plays some part in specific adhesion, perhaps by binding to the proteins of the cell surface and modifying their properties (Rinaldini 1958). The orientation of an extracellular matrix is believed to influence the direction of movement of embryonic cells, what Weiss (1958) calls 'contact guidance'. A phenomenon, known as contact inhibition, has been observed with fibroblasts in tissue culture. In the course of amoeboid movement, fibroblasts frequently touch each other and the reaction to this contact is movement away from the point of collision. If every pathway is blocked the cells come to a standstill (Abercrombie *et al.* 1957).

A membrane, the basal lamina, separates the first formed predentine and odontoblasts from the cells destined to become ameloblasts (pre-ameloblasts) which is penetrated by the microvilli from the pre-ameloblasts and which enter the predentine. The distal end of the pre-ameloblasts contain 'coated vesicles' at this stage—these are 110–120 μm in diameter and are surrounded by a fuzzy outer layer and, sometimes, 'bristles' (Fig. IV.2). Their wall is often continuous with the cell membrane.

The second function: organizer of odontoblasts

The second function of the ameloblasts, which they carry out after the first is complete, is that of an organizer, since the presence of ameloblasts is essential if the appropriate cells of the papilla are to become odontoblasts. This also explains the function of Hertwig's epithelial sheath which is a prolongation of the inner and outer enamel epithelium along the root where, of course, no enamel forms.

The function of the ameloblasts as an organizer has been proved by tissue culture studies. Glasstone (1939) showed that when a whole tooth germ is removed aseptically from an embryo and incubated in a sterile, nourishing medium (fowl plasma, coagulated by the addition of saline extract of chick embryo, has been found to be suitable), its development is surprisingly normal for up to 12 days. Similar results have been reported by Hay (1961) and Fisher (1971). Pulp cells develop into odontoblasts and dentine is laid down which mineralizes, and some enamel is formed from the ameloblasts. The germs of rat molars, cultured before cusp formation has begun, developed cusps approximating in size, shape and arrangement to those normally formed. When a piece of dental papilla was cultured without ameloblasts, no odontoblasts formed, but if ameloblasts were present odontoblasts were induced. Once the odontoblasts were formed, dentine was produced whether ameloblasts were present or not, though only in their presence was the dentine laid down in the normal way, as regular increments. In their absence, folded bands of dentine were laid down, which is further evidence of the importance of ameloblasts in determining the shape of the tooth (the first function).

Similar experiments in which parts of tooth germs were transplanted to the ovary of the same animal have also demonstrated the organizing function of the ameloblasts.

Ameloblasts, like many cells, exhibit polarity, that is, only one end of the cell absorbs nutrients whilst the other carries out some specialized function. Cytological changes and also observations on the direction of movement of injected dyes suggest that ameloblasts change their polarity at this stage. This change has been interpreted as follows. The young ameloblast obtains most of its nutriment from the dental papilla, but as soon as the odontoblasts are formed, and especially when a layer of dentine is laid down, this source becomes cut off and is no longer available. The ameloblasts must then receive their nutriment from the stratum intermedium, which in turn is dependent on the capillaries supplying the outer enamel epithelium—the only blood supply of the enamel organ.

The third function: matrix formation

The ameloblasts now become active in their third function which is the synthesis and secretion of matrix, the acidophilic, lightly-mineralized organic framework which, after mineralization, becomes enamel. At this stage, they are long, narrow cells, their nuclei are proximally placed (i.e. away from the

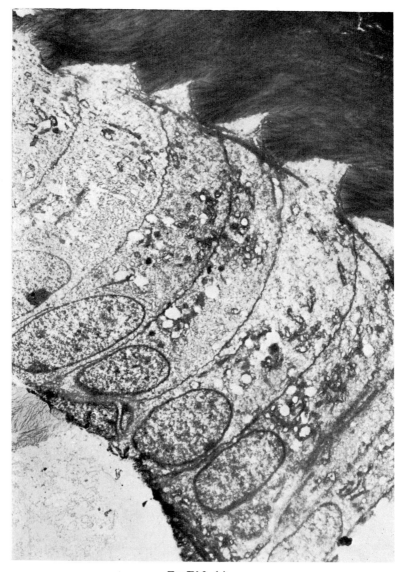

Fig.IV.3. (a)

enamel matrix) and the endoplasmic reticulum and Golgi apparatus are prominent.

No matrix is formed by the ameloblasts until after a thin layer of dentine has been laid down, i.e. dentine appears to act as an organizer on the ameloblasts and induce enamel matrix formation. Not only has this sequence been

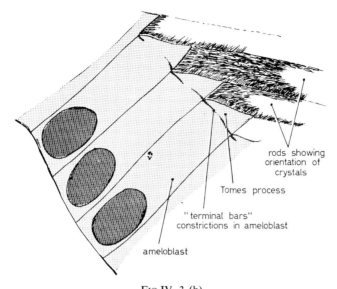

rods showing
orientation of
crystals

Tomes process

"terminal bars"
constrictions in ameloblast

ameloblast

Fɪɢ.IV. 3 (b)

Fɪɢ. IV.3. (a) Electron micrograph of developing enamel (Rönnholm 1962).
(b) Explanation of (a).

observed in histological preparations of developing enamel, but experiments on transplants have shown that, if enamel is to be formed, odontoblasts and pulp must be present with ameloblasts in the transplant. Further experimental evidence is that in the guinea-pig suffering from ascorbic acid deficiency, groups of odontoblasts die and no dentine is laid down. Adjacent to these gaps in the dentine, the ameloblasts are also quiescent, although in the circumstances of this experiment the deficiency did not alter ameloblastic activity directly. Also, removal of the dental papilla in the developing teeth of living cats has been found to cause degeneration of ameloblasts into stratified epithelium during the following months.

Rönnholm (1962) described in human developing teeth marked changes in the distal end of the ameloblast as the very first layer of matrix is formed alongside the thin layer of dentine already present. The wall of the ameloblast becomes intensely folded with long narrow processes extending towards the dentine. Between the processes filaments with the cross-banding of collagen, presumably derived from the dentine, were present. This collagen probably becomes incorporated into the innermost layer of enamel at the amelo-dentinal junction and may partly explain the presence of hydroxyproline (the imino-acid characteristic of collagen) in enamel (see pp. 86, 104).

About the time the predentine first becomes mineralized and the dental lamina is fragmented, the earliest product of the ameloblast appears in the cytoplasm within spherical granules ('dense granules'). It consists of a finely granulated material usually referred to as 'stippled material' (SM) and fills the space between the predentine, with which it may intermingle, and the ameloblasts and it immediately becomes partially mineralized. In the rat, Reith (1968) observed that mineralization occurred when the SM met the dentine some distance from the ameloblast membrane. In human teeth, on the other hand, Rönnholm found apatite crystals in direct contact with the ameloblast (Fig. IV.3). At this stage the enamel matrix is quite homogeneous, there is no sign of rods. The inner ends of the ameloblasts then become conical in shape and project into the enamel matrix, some of which, especially near the base of the process, contains stippled material, forming the Tomes's processes. They contain endoplasmic reticulum and a variety of granules and vesicles, including 'coated vesicles' described above, surrounded by a prominent membrane. The latter are thought to be concerned with transport into the cell, because they are present in cells whose function is unmistakably that of absorption. This implies that ameloblasts are involved, even at this stage, in both secretion and absorption.

The matrix does not appear fibrous except at the earliest stage of its formation when the ameloblasts are in contact with collagen fibres, presumably formed by the odontoblast. Mineralization is not associated with vesicles although lipid is present (which is associated with vesicles in other mineralizing tissues, see p. 121) and, in fixed preparations, which may not reflect the situation *in vivo*, all the mineral is crystalline there being no trace of amorphous calcium phosphate.

Osborn (1970a, b, 1973) constructed a model which imitates enamel development in several ways and with a minimum of speculation provides at least tentative explanations for many previously unco-ordinated observations. His device (Fig. IV.4) consisted of a smoke chamber with parallel rows of large (1·2 cm) screws threaded into its floor, resembling ameloblasts in position. The chamber was placed on a heating coil and smoke was introduced, which formed into a pattern of columns which could be observed through the glass

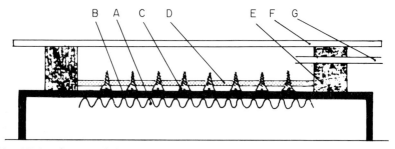

Fɪɢ. IV.4. Diagram of the smoke chamber used by Osborn to produce patterns of convection currents seen in Fig. IV.5: A, heating coil; B, metal sheet in contact with screws, C, embedded in cardboard; D and F, glass plate through which movements of smoke, admitted through glass tube, G, were observed.

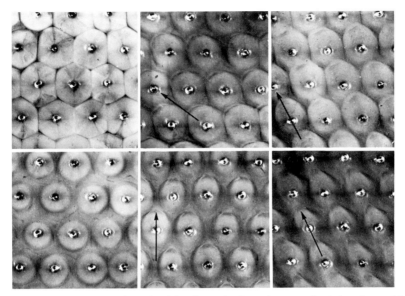

FIG. IV.5. Appearance of smoke rising from the heated screws in Osborn's model and the effect of moving the glass plate in the directon indicated by the arrows.

roof of the device and which were produced as follows. The heated screws created convection currents which propelled the smoke upward till it reached the glass when it cooled and descended to be recirculated. Looked at from above, the pattern formed first was of hexagonal shapes which became circular as the chamber warmed up; by slight shearing movement of the glass roof, distortions could be introduced resembling other shapes in which enamel prisms are found (Fig. IV.5).

The ameloblasts secrete their product (the stippled material) into the closed space between Tomes's process and the mineralized dentine thus, Osborn (1970a) postulates, developing a very small but steady pressure which, like any movement in a tube, would be expected to be laminar, i.e. more rapid centrally above each ameloblast than peripherally. The more rapidly moving material would then reflect from the mineralized front and return to the periphery of the ameloblast where, judging by the existence of coated vesicles and microvilli, absorption occurs (Fig. IV.6). This current, it is suggested, distorts the inner cell membrane into the shape of Tomes's process. At one point, there is neither absorption nor secretion, perhaps accounting for the space between the rods once thought to be occupied by unmineralized matrix but now generally considered to be the meeting-point of crystals oriented in different directions. The flow lines of matrix secretion could determine the direction of the crystallite orientation, even if the matrix is a gel with insufficient rigidity to guide the crystals.

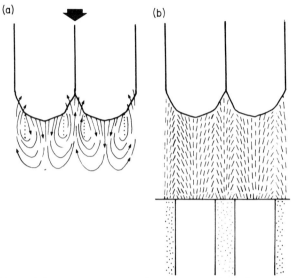

FIG. IV.6. (a) Possible movement, resembling the convection of smoke in the model of secreted material from the ameloblast towards the amelodentinal junction from which some of it is reflected and resorbed by the ameloblast. (b) The predicted orientation of the apatite crystals resulting from the flow of secreted material.

The relationship of the direction of the rods to the ameloblast as seen in the usual two-dimensional section is shown in Fig. IV.3(b) suggesting that two ameloblasts are involved in forming one rod. When considered in three dimensions and in relation to the complicated keyhole or fish-tail shapes, it must be assumed that more than two, and possibly four, ameloblasts play a part in producing one rod.

Electron micrographs show that, after the formation of matrix is complete, the ameloblasts then become much shorter, and the Tomes's processes disappear and the Golgi apparatus is smaller. Mitochondria are numerous throughout the cell with various granules, including some autophagic granules which contain the remnants of endoplasmic reticulum and other organelles and are thought to be breaking down some cell contents. The cells are evidently being reorganized before beginning their next function, the pre-absorptive stage, characterized by a more central position of the nuclei, a Golgi apparatus distal, lateral and even proximal to the nucleus (these positions are unique to this stage) and bulbous contacts both with neighbouring ameloblasts and cells of the stratum intermedium (Fig. IV.7).

At the next stage (early maturation) a striated border develops at the distal end consisting of projections towards, but separated from, the enamel by a space 400–800 Å (40–80 μm) wide, containing fine granular material which can be seen being taken into the cell by membrane invagination (absorption

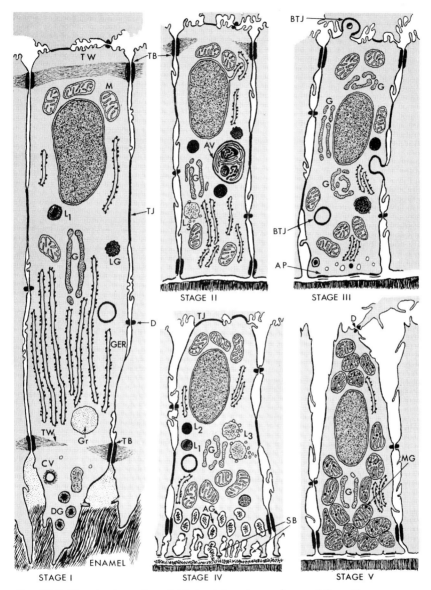

FIG. IV.7. The structure of ameloblasts at five stages of enamel formation.

Stage I, secretory stage (matrix production). Stage II, transitional stage—cell reorganization. Stage III, pre-absorptive stage. Stage IV, early maturation. Stage V, late maturation.

CV, coated vesicle; GER, granulated endoplasmic reticulum; M, mitochondria; Gr, DG, L_1 LG_1, various types of granules; TJ, tight junction; BTJ, bulb-type junction between neighbouring; G, Golgi apparatus ameloblasts seen in a different orientation half way up right-hand side of same cell; AP, attachment plaques; SB, striated border; AG, absorption granule.

granules). The cells of the enamel organ become arranged into papillae arising from the growth of capillaries into the outer enamel epithelium. An intercellular space exists between the ameloblasts and is continuous with that between the papillary cells of the enamel organ.

Other previously unexplained phenomena of amelogenesis for which Osborn's analysis provides an explanation are:

(1) As extracellular pressures develop with the accumulation of secretion, so the wall of the ameloblast will tend to be compressed: this may account for the shortening of the cell occurring at the end of the secretory stage. Once they begin to move outwards, the extracellular pressure is expended in the movement and no further change in length would be expected. The ameloblast will tend to get wider in the same way as the rods get wider. The outer surface of the enamel is larger than the inner surface but is covered by the same or a smaller number of ameloblasts (because although no new ameloblasts form, some may die). Consequently, each ameloblast must widen as the thickness of the enamel increases.

(2) The organelles tend to be arranged in a longitudinal direction because the flow of secretion and absorbed material occurs longitudinally.

(3) When secretion ends, the Tomes's processes disappear, perhaps because the pattern of pressures at the distal end of the cell will change and the forces which Osborn suggests are responsible for Tomes's process collapse.

(4) The projection of the proximal end of the ameloblast towards the papillary cells in the enamel organ also follow the flow of material.

(5) The absence of rods in early enamel reflects a disordered production of stippled material: time is needed for the development of the currents which, the hypothesis suggests, produce the rods.

The movement of ameloblasts

The ameloblasts must move away from the amelodentinal junction to make space for the matrix, the most likely motive force being the pressure generated by accumulation of the matrix (Osborn 1970b). This means that intracellular pressure must be even higher otherwise the cell would be unable to secrete its product, although the whole process is of such a small size that the absolute pressures may be presumed to be low. Osborn suggests that the hexagonal shape of the ameloblast may be produced by the slight positive pressure which may also be a factor (in addition to the current of secreted material mentioned above) in producing the Tomes's process.

He postulates a mitochondrial pump at the proximal end of the ameloblast absorbing the material which is synthesized into matrix and expelled in vesicles (not to be confused with the vesicles in bone and dentine which play a part in mineralization). Osborn (1970b) has also produced cogent reasons for believing that the pressures developed on the inner surfaces of the amelo-blast account for their changing orientation, i.e. lateral movements and consequently for the orientation of the enamel prisms they produce. An alternative explanation of these lateral movements is that the 'cell web' (a structure associated with the terminal bars of the ameloblast) acts as a con-tractile organelle (Reith & Ross 1973). These structures do resemble in some ways the myofilaments of smooth muscle.

SEEDING OF CRYSTALLITES

Apatite crystals are detectable in electron micrographs in the very earliest matrix, almost immediately after its secretion, although they occupy only a small proportion of the total space. According to Simmons (1972) the crystals span the gap between the ameloblasts and the odontoblasts and show con-tinuity with those in dentine. This suggests that the crystals originate in the dentine (Bernard 1972; Simmons 1972) and eventually fill the space left by the removal of water and protein by growth rather than by seeding of new crystals. It is, however, difficult to understand how one set of crystals seeded in the dentine could extend to the enamel and could be orientated as in Fig. II.9 (p. 66). If they do originate in the dentine, no seed is required in the enamel in which case the lipid (the one feature common to all the mineral-izing tissues) may not, after all, be important in mineralization in this tissue. No amorphous phase has been detected in enamel at any stage of develop-ment.

The arrangement of the prisms and the early crystallites in relation to the Tomes's processes according to Rönnholm are shown in Fig. IV.3(a) and (b). This shows that the orientation of groups of crystals which form first within any one prism is either parallel to the direction of the prism or oblique to it, but always approximately at right angles to the part of the ameloblast surface from which the crystals form. The space between prisms, which Rönnholm calls the 'interprismatic gap' arises from the apex of Tomes's process in Rönnholm's electron micrographs and not from a region near the base, which has been the usual view, given further support by Osborn (1970a).

Rönnholm concluded that the prism sheath did not exist in developing human enamel and that the space between the prisms is detectable merely as a change in the orientation of the apatite crystals. In bovine enamel, however, more convincing evidence of the existence of a prism sheath has been produced.

The crystallites of early matrix rapidly grow in length and become some ten times larger than crystals in bone and dentine and larger than can be obtained by precipitation *in vitro*. The reason for this large size is not known but it may be that the removal of the protein allows more space for crystal growth, which in bone and dentine would be prevented by the large bulk of collagen.

The cause of the orientation of the crystals is still controversial. Some have

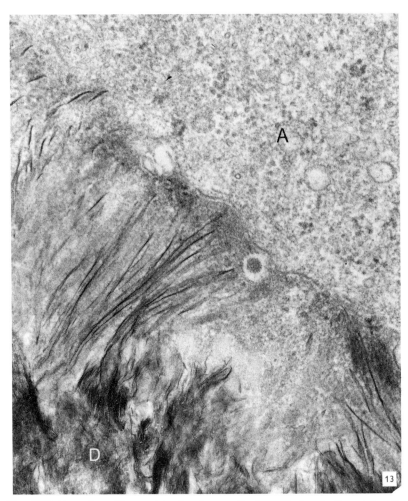

Fig. IV.8. Enamel apatite crystals showing continuity with the dentine giving the impression that they may arise from seeding in the dentine. A, ameloblast; D, dentine; ($\times$ 72 000).

suggested that it is related to the direction of the fibres frequently assumed to be present in enamel matrix—an idea given some support by Smales's finding that, at least with some methods of preparation, the organic matter is arranged in helices (pp. 107–8). If, on the other hand, the matrix is a gel, the streaming process postulated by Osborn (1970a) may orientate the crystals.

PHOSPHATASES IN EARLY ENAMEL FORMATION
The distribution of alkaline phosphatase in developing enamel was studied

quite extensively when this enzyme was believed to play an important part in mineralization. Both in man, and in several species of animal, alkaline phosphatase has been found in the outer enamel epithelium, the stratum intermedium and the stellate reticulum, and in human tooth germs Ten Cate found its activity gradient changing from no activity in the cervical loop region to intense activity near the developing cusp.

Light microscopy has given contradictory results about the phosphatase activity of the ameloblasts during matrix formation; some have found it in small areas in rat teeth near the nucleus during mineralization; only after mineralization is complete has it been reliably reported to be present throughout the whole cell. Ten Cate (1962), who examined human tooth germs, concluded that this enzyme was absent from the ameloblast but electron microscopy shows that the enzyme is present on the proximal basal membrane of the ameloblast at the beginning of matrix formation (Lunt & Noble 1972). It is reported to be absent from the matrix (Glasstone 1958a, Symons 1955). Since the function of alkaline phosphatase is still uncertain no interpretation of its distribution is possible.

An acid phosphatase differing in properties from that in lysosomes and therefore presumably not derived from them occurs in ameloblasts at the secretory stage. Its function is unknown and it is surprising that an enzyme associated with autolysis should be present in cells forming matrix (Hanker *et al.* 1972).

THE RHYTHMIC NATURE OF MATRIX FORMATION

The rate of growth of the matrix of both enamel and dentine has been measured by injecting a large dose of sodium fluoride or alizarin either (1) several times during 1–2 days which gives one ring of abnormal tissue, or (2) at the beginning and end of an interval of several days which gives two spaced rings. Measurements are then made, in histological preparations of the teeth, either of the thickness of the rings of marked tissue, or the distance between the rings produced by two injections administered at a known interval of time. Schour & Hoffman (1939) showed by these techniques that in both enamel and dentine of rodents, kittens and pups, the thickness of each increment is the same, about 16 μm per day. A lower rate (10·2–14·4 μm per day) was found by Johannessen (1961) who points out that it depends on the part of the tooth in which the growth is measured and on the age of the rat. In similar experiments on seventeen monkeys the daily rate of apposition of dentine was found to be 4 μm in the gingival third of premolars and molars with a graded difference of from 2·4 μm at the apical level to 12·2 μm in the cuspal portion.

One experiment in man suggested average daily growth rates of 3·9 μm in deciduous enamel, 3·77 μm in deciduous dentine and 2·7 μm in permanent enamel, with differences in different parts of the tooth. Measurements have also been made at different ages of the distance between the pulp and the 'neonatal line', the line of poorly formed enamel and dentine laid down at birth as a result of the metabolic disturbances occurring at this time (Rushton 1933). These measurements show for human deciduous teeth a gradient of growth rate at different levels of the tooth, being highest at the cusp, and varying for different teeth.

The fourth function: maturation

The next function of the ameloblasts is to convert the soft matrix into enamel —the hardest substance in the body containing about 95% of mineral matter. This change in enamel, which corresponds to mineralization on other hard tissues, but differs from it in some respects, has usually been called 'maturation'. The ameloblasts become slightly shorter before maturation begins and lateral spaces appear so that their distal ends are partially separated (Fig. IV.7). From this stage onwards alkaline phosphatase is present throughout the whole cell and not merely near the nucleus as it is during the earlier stages. In the rat incisor, scanning electron microscopy of the lateral surfaces of the ameloblast at the maturation stage show groups of cells with longitudinal folds running along their whole length alternating with cells without these folds but with microvilli. This suggests that each cell undergoes several cycles of activity, the activity of the folds alternating with that of the microvilli (Boyde & Reith 1976).

THE NATURE OF THE CHANGE IN ACID SOLUBILITY DURING MATURATION

In histological preparations of developing enamel, fixed for 2 days and decalcified, the more cervical parts remain undissolved while the rest disappears leaving merely an empty space (Fig. VI.9). The boundary between the acid-soluble and acid-insoluble area is fairly sharp and is approximately at right angles to the surface of the enamel. It was originally supposed that the change in acid-solubility represented a sharp transition from immature matrix to fully mineralized enamel but later work showed that there is no correlation between acid-solubility and the degree of mineralization as judged by micro-radiography (which, except near the outer boundaries, is very reliable and free from misinterpretation) or by studies with polarized light (Allan 1959; Crabb 1959). The concentration of mineral matter shows a gradual transition from matrix to the fully mineralized enamel—the boundary is not as sharp as that between the acid-soluble and acid-insoluble matrix.

The area of enamel shown radiologically to be well mineralized stains green with Papanicolaou's stain and the less mineralized areas stain red (apatite crystals and the proteins of enamel matrix also stain green and red,

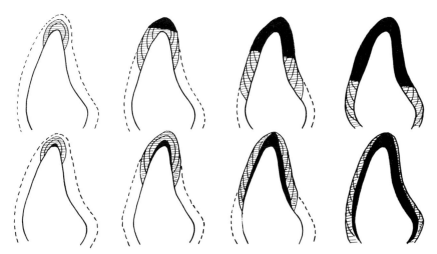

FIG. IV.9. The order in which different parts of an incisor undergo maturation (lined area—matric before maturation; black area—after maturation). The upper series (based on histological observations) shows approximately the order in which the matrix becomes acid-soluble, which was formerly believed to indicate mineralization. The lower series (after Crabb 1959 and confirmed in general in molars by Cooper 1968b) shows the changes in radio-opacity in succeeding stages of maturation; there can be no doubt that this represents an influx of mineral matter and at no stage is the boundary between high and low density transverse as in the upper (histological) series.

respectively). The boundary between the two is sharp, indicating that some critical proportion is reached: although this might suggest that maturation is a clear-cut process other evidence (mentioned below) suggests that it is gradual and continuous. The staining reaction presumably changes when the gradual influx of mineral and loss of protein reaches some critical figure.

Since the change in solubility of the matrix is not related to mineralization the question as to its real nature arises. It might be speculated that some change occurs in the matrix itself which affects its solubility, as Cooper (1968b) suggests, but which is neither dependent on nor responsible for mineralization. Alternatively, it might result from differences in permeability which affect the access of fixative: the matrix becoming insoluble only after it is fixed. Frisbie & Nuckolls (1947) stated that if pieces of enamel or matrix were fixed for 6 months then the whole matrix even of mature enamel becomes insoluble. The relationship of the solubility changes of the matrix to its mineralization has not yet been cleared up.

The order in which different parts of the enamel matrix undergo maturation has been observed radiologically in sections made from human post-mortem material (Fig. IV.9). A thin layer near the amelodentinal junction becomes radio-opaque first. Maturation then spreads from the incisal or occlusal tip of the amelodentinal junction to reach the outer surface of the enamel. It spreads laterally and cervically, the border of the calcified area being irregular —in some places parallel to the amelodentinal junction and in others parallel to the enamel surface. A thin layer of fully-mineralized enamel has been found on the outer surface even in parts where the matrix as a whole is still un-mineralized (Crabb 1959; Crabb & Darling 1962; Engfeldt & Hammarlund-Essler 1956–7). It is not known why maturation of different parts of the matrix occurs in this order.

Measurements of ^{32}P entering the developing rat incisor (Robinson *et al.* 1974) at different stages of enamel formation confirm that there is a big influx of mineral at the time of maturation and that it becomes permanently incorporated into the tooth. In about half of the animals an influx occurred at the earliest stage of matrix formation but the ^{32}P entering at this time was not present 24 hr after the injection and must have been removed although it is surprising that inorganic matter should be leaving the matrix at this stage. Fluoride also leaves the tooth during this stage of development (p. 151).

When incisors were incubated *in vitro* with ^{32}P, some was taken up at the site of the transient peak suggesting that the uptake depended on changes in the permeability of the enamel, rather than on a process controlled by cells.

There is evidence that the last stages of maturation take place after eruption by the deposition of ions from saliva (Fanning *et al.* 1953; see p. 173).

CHEMICAL DIFFERENCES BETWEEN MATRIX AND MATURE ENAMEL

A number of studies have been made of the histological and chemical changes in different parts of the same developing tooth. Weinmann *et al.* (1942) were the first to show that the organic matter of the early matrix diminished as the mineral matter increased, but their samples were too large to give information on small local variation. Cooper (1968) carried out a similar study in which he punched tiny discs weighing 10–20 μg and measuring 300 μm in diameter and 100 μm in thickness (about one-thousandth the weight of the samples of Weinmann *et al.*) from different parts of the enamel of ground sections of developing molars and analysed them for water, calcium, phosphorus and organic matter (Fig. IV.8). Unfortunately, these small samples could not be analysed accurately for water, which partly evaporated during manipulation, or for organic matter based on nitrogen determinations (because the nature of the substances present is not known). Nevertheless, the results did confirm chemically that mineral matter increased from the amelodentinal junction towards the outer enamel surface and that organic matter was removed although the removal did not follow a definite pattern (Table IV.1).

The Ca:P ratio was lower (below 2·0) in the areas of earliest mineralization and rose to 2·10–2·14 as mineralization became complete. This could be explained as a change from one crystalline form with a low ratio, for example

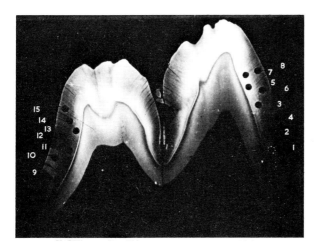

Fɪɢ. IV.10. Sections of developing enamel with samples punched out by the method of Cooper (1968). The numbers refer to the sites of the samples whose composition is given in Table IV.1.

octa calcium phosphate (see p. 32) to apatite (Ca:P = 2·15). However, the ratio was always quite near to that of apatite indicating that, even at the early stages of enamel which were sampled, most of the crystals are present in this form, as electron micrographs indicate.

During the maturation of enamel in the continuously-growing rabbit incisor, Starkey (1971) found from autoradiographs that no influx of ^{45}Ca occurred during maturation but that a shrinkage of the enamel of 8% occurred. He concluded that the loss of water incurred during the shrinkage would raise ionic concentrations and lead to the crystallization of calcium phosphate already present in the matrix. However, if the minerals are already

TABLE IV.1

The composition of developing enamel at various sites in Fig. IV.10

Location in Fig. IV.10	2	5	6	7	8	13	14	15
Density	1·52	1·78	1·48	2·07	1·58	1·55	1·18	1·28
Ca:P	2·03	2·08	2·01	2·08	1·94	2·02	2·03	2·08
Ash (g cm^{-3})	1·29	1·59	1·26	1·85	1·41	1·37	1·05	1·04
Organic matter (g cm^{-3})	0·16	0·19	0·22	0·20	0·19	0·16	0·16	0·18

in the matrix before maturation they would be detectable radiologically and the contrast between the radiodensity of matrix and mature enamel would be less marked than it is.

The lipid discovered by Irving (1963) appeared in the enamel of the rat molar only after the full width of the matrix was formed. It first appeared (at age 6 days) at the amelodentinal junction usually spreading over the next 3–4 days throughout the whole thickness and remained until the matrix became acid-soluble and was then lost (14–16 days of age). Occasionally it was present at the amelodentinal junction and near the ameloblasts but with an unstained area between. In general, the lipid staining followed the same pattern as that of the final stages of mineralization as revealed by micro-radiographs. It is clear that in enamel (unlike bone and dentine) some mineral-ization occurs in the first matrix to be formed before the appearance of the lipid.

The nature of the organic matter removed during maturation

The next point to consider is the composition of the organic matter removed. Are some constituents of the matrix removed selectively or does the fall in concentration occur because a proportion of all the organic constituents are removed indiscriminately? Comparisons by Eastoe (1963) and Robinson *et al.* (1975) of the composition of the organic matter of developing and adult enamel showed that they differ markedly, from which it may be concluded that the removal is selective. The proteins of developing enamel appeared to be unique among vertebrate proteins and contained a much higher proportion of proline, glutamic acid and histidine than did those of the mature enamel (Fig. IV.11). These features were especially marked in the 7% of the protein from develop-ing teeth which was water-soluble.

Various methods (electrophoresis, column chromatography, gel filtration, etc.) have been used to investigate the proteins of developing enamel (amelo-genins or enamelins) and the results show that they consist of very complicated mixtures; as many as six or seven major and a dozen minor constituents have been isolated from developing bovine teeth (this approach has not been attempted in human developing enamel owing to difficulty in obtaining ade-quate amounts). Some of the larger fractions have been analysed for amino acids and although different workers have obtained broadly similar results there are marked differences in detail.

Experiments by Leblond *et al.* (1955) have suggested that a glycosamino-glycan also is probably removed during maturation. They injected radioactive sulphur (as $^{35}SO_4$) into rats during enamel formation and groups of animals were killed at intervals. Autoradiographs of sections of the teeth from animals killed a few hours after showed that it was present as an intense band in the pre-enamel. Two days later, it was found in the enamel matrix spread diffusely

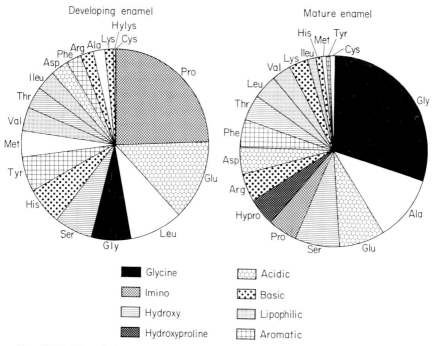

Fig. IV.11. The relative proportions of the amino acids present in enamel matrix and mature enamel. Tryptophane is also present in enamel (although absent from collagen and dentine) but is destroyed when proteins are hydrolysed by acid.

over a wide area, the new matrix formed during the 2 days was free from radioactivity. After 6 days it was absent from the matrix although still present in dentine suggesting that this sulphur-containing substance is among those removed during maturation. When ^{14}C was injected as bicarbonate (a group which can be used in the synthesis both of carbohydrates and amino acids) a small amount entered the matrix and also disappeared during maturation. The nature of the substance containing the radioactive carbon is not known. When glucose or mannose containing ^{14}C was injected (these sugars could readily be used to form GAGs (p. 94)) a much more intense reaction was found in the enamel matrix which also disappeared after a few days. It would seem likely therefore that the substance responsible for these events is a GAG, although it is apparently not chondroitin sulphate because they found that it was not removed by treating the sections with hyaluronidase.

Labelled sulphate was injected into 5-day-old rats and continued daily until some of them were 12 days old. Study of their molar teeth, showed that the label increased in the matrix at first but by the sixth day (at which time the matrix formed on day 5 is matured) was absent from the matrix but

Fig. IV.12(a)

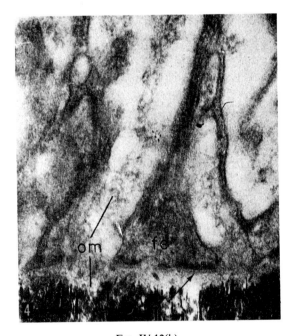

Fig. IV.12(b)

Fig. IV.12. (a) The enamel surface (E) and ameloblasts (A) after matrix formation is complete (×1200). (b) Enamel surface and ameloblasts at magnification of 63 000 showing processes on ameloblasts and 'foot-like extension' (fe); amorphous finely granular material (om) is probably protein of early matrix undergoing removal.

present in some of the ameloblasts at the absorbing stage (Reith & Cotty 1967).

As the crystal becomes larger, it can only do so by replacing other constituents of the matrix. It seems possible that the water is simply expelled by the pressure of the expanding apatite crystals although in the rat incisor the ameloblasts in the area where maturation is occurring develop thin projections with a striated border suggestive of an actively absorbing surface. Small globules containing material resembling matrix can be traced through the processes of the ameloblast into the distal end of the cell in electron micrographs (Fig. IV.12 from Reith 1963) and with the light microscope (Marsland 1951, 1952).

The ameloblasts in the stage of late maturation lose their striated border and no longer contain absorption granules but mitochondria are more numerous, indicating intense metabolic activity. The stratum intermedium cells also change their character by containing more mitochondria and larger intercellular spaces. It is presumed that both types of cell are concerned with absorption and transport of water and soluble matrix constituents. Some unconfirmed evidence suggests the presence of proteolytic enzymes in the matrix which might break down the protein into more soluble and more readily absorbed substances (Suga 1970; Beynon 1972). Lysosomes are present in the ameloblasts, including the Tomes's processes, but there is no definite evidence that their hydrolytic enzymes are released into the matrix. The presence of peptides in fully-formed enamel suggests that proteolysis does occur and that they represent part of the breakdown products which were trapped as the apatite crystals enlarged and fused. This would explain the apparently unique occurrence in enamel of peptides in a structural role.

Autoradiographs of rat molars taken at intervals after the injection of tritiated glycine have shown that the labelled product of the ameloblasts (presumably matrix protein) becomes dispersed throughout the enamel formed before the injection and it remains in the matrix during maturation. Similarly, injection of $[^{14}C]$glycine showed that the products of the ameloblasts became widely dispersed throughout the matrix (Fig. IV.13 from Young & Greulich 1963). These results imply considerable movement within the matrix but their significance is still undetermined. It could mean either that there is free diffusion of at least some of the matrix constituents so that matrix formed early may receive extra material added to it later, or, that the matrix proteins are undergoing a metabolic change, some of their original glycine being replaced by new molecules. The fact that much of the constituent containing glycine remains after maturation confirms that protein removal is selective and fits in with the higher proportion of glycine in mature enamel (Fig. IV.11).

It could be argued, however, that as the mineral salts enter, and the density rises during maturation, they merely lower the proportion of protein present

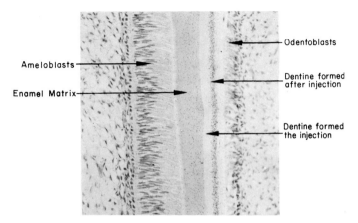

FIG. IV.13. Autoradiograph of dentine and enamel from rat killed 96 hr after the administration of [³H] glycine. Note that the protein incorporating the radioactive glycine remains in one fairly compact band in the dentine but is dispersed throughout the whole of the enamel matrix.

and that no protein is removed. This point can be investigated by studying the changes in the amount of organic matter *per unit volume*. If this falls, then it is evidence that protein must be actually removed. Two studies on these lines, by Deakins (1942) and Angmar-Manson (1971) have confirmed that the organic matter is removed. The organic matter of enamel matrix fell rapidly from 0·27 mg mm⁻³, when the matrix is very soft and its density is 1·45, to 0·05 mg mm⁻³ when the density was still as low as 1·65, and it remained at this figure as maturation proceeded. This represents a removal of 0·27 − 0·05 = 0·22 mg of organic matter mm⁻³, all of which occurred during the very early stages of maturation. Deakins stated that the water content began to change only after the removal of organic matter was complete; it fell from 0·64 to 0·12 mg mm⁻³ (a loss of 0·52 mg mm⁻³). Angmar-Manson, however, reported a steady fall in water and organic matter throughout maturation suggesting that this is a continuous one-stage process rather than being the separate removal of water and organic matter.

Weatherell *et al.* (1975) have applied their method of sampling (p. 61) and analysis to the fluoride in the developmental stages of the continuously-growing rat incisor. They found that the concentration rose during the early stages of development and, as the organic matter was withdrawn and the mineral concentration rose rapidly, the fluoride concentration dropped to levels below those of the earliest stage (Fig. IV.14). Although an obvious explanation might be that an influx of mineral matter, if it were low in fluoride, would 'dilute' the fluoride already present, this was eliminated. The most likely explanation is that fluoride is withdrawn at the same time as the organic matter and possibly bound to it; there is unconfirmed evidence for

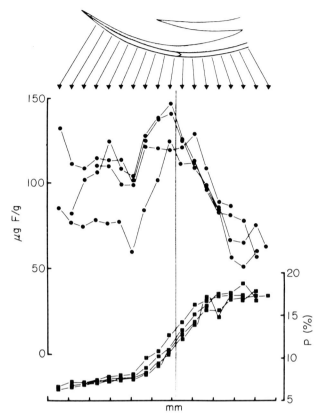

FIG. IV.14. The changes in fluoride concentration during the development of the rat incisor. The tooth is shown diagrammatically at the top, the developing apical area on the left, the incisal tip is not shown but would be on the right.

The lower curves show that as the phosphate concentration increases during mineralization fluoride is withdrawn, shown by the fall in concentration.

the presence of organically bound fluoride in enamel from old teeth (p. 478). A similar drop in fluoride occurs in pig enamel (Speirs 1975) and there are indications of it in human foetal teeth between the eighth and ninth month (Gedalia *et al.* 1961).

Crabb (1976) showed that the outer layer of enamel of unerupted premolars is more porous than normal enamel and three-dimensional replica techniques show this layer to contain a 'honeycomb' of spaces (Fig. IV.15 (a) and (b)). If this is confirmed for teeth generally, the filling in of this layer from salivary deposits may explain post-eruptive maturation, the changes (including increased resistance to caries) which enamel undergoes after eruption (p. 173).

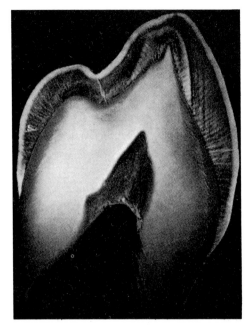

FIG. IV.15(a)

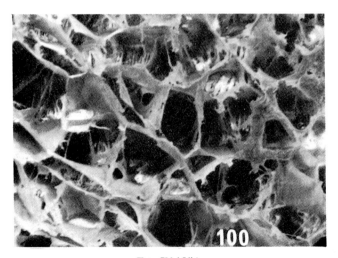

FIG. IV.15(b)

FIG. IV.15. (a) Ground section of unerupted lower first premolar showing outer 'porous enamel' ($\times 7 \cdot 5$). (b) Scanning electron micrograph of methacrylate replica of buccal enamel from unerupted premolar looking outward from the amelodentinal junction. The solid occupies the spaces in the original enamel and confirms the porous nature of outer enamal before eruption.

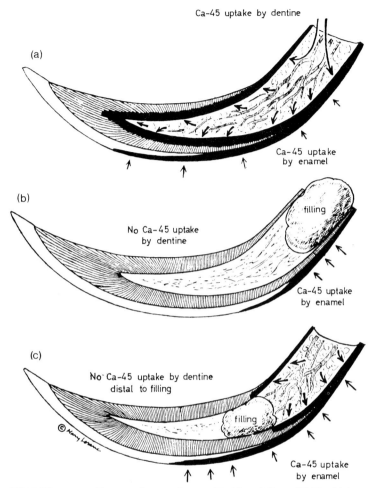

FIG. IV.16. Diagram to illustrate the experiment of Reith and Cotty (1962) which proved that calcium enters the enamel via the enamel organ and not from the dentinal side. (a) Distribution of radioactive calcium (black) in the incisor after injection into a normal rat. (b) and (c) Uptake in enamel in spite of the filling in the pulp which prevents the radioactive calcium from the entering the dentine.

THE SOURCE OF THE CALCIUM SALTS WHICH ENTER DURING MATURATION

Although it would be expected that the minerals in enamel would be secreted from the ameloblasts some early work (Shapiro *et al.* 1942; Lefkowitz *et al.* 1944, 1947) suggested that the influx of minerals during maturation came from the odontoblasts.

This was shown to be incorrect at least for the rat incisor by the following experiment. A filling was inserted into the pulp of rats' incisors followed by the administration of ^{45}Ca and autoradiography of sections showed that no deposition of calcium took place in the dentine distal to the filling thus proving that the circulation in the pulp had been arrested; enamel mineralization continued unchanged (Fig. IV.16 from Reith & Cotty 1962). Further evidence that the ameloblasts are the source of the calcium is that droplets staining specifically for calcium are present in these cells.

THE FATE OF THE AMELOBLASTS

When the enamel rods are almost completely mineralized, the ameloblasts shrink (the reduced ameloblasts) and unless stained by special methods become indistinguishable from the cells of the stratum intermedium, which is now in contact with the outer enamel epithelium, the stellate reticulum having disappeared. There is thus a layer of stratified epithelial cells covering the enamel and preventing contact between it and the connective tissue underlying the oral mucosa.

When this layer is deficient, cementum may be laid down over the enamel, or, in teeth which remain unerupted for a very long time, enamel resorption may occur. It is therefore believed that the reduced enamel epithelium may have some protective function before eruption.

Recently erupted teeth are covered by a structure known among other names as the primary enamel cuticle (see p. 361 for terminology). It consists of two layers, an inner, thin, acidophilic, 'structureless' layer (one which by ordinary histological methods shows no fibres, cells or other structural details) attached to the enamel surface (Turner 1958) and coating the apatite crystals. Outside this a cellular layer (the secondary cuticle) is usually present. This membrane can usually be obtained by placing a recently erupted tooth in 2% HCl for about 10 min when the outermost mineral layer of the enamel dissolves, leaving the membrane loosely investing the rest of the tooth. This layer when detached and spread on to a slide shows the impressions made by the projecting prism ends.

The origin of these layers is controversial. Some workers have thought that primary enamel cuticle arose from the reduced ameloblasts, either by some change in the cell bodies or, more likely, that it represented the last stage of matrix formation. The secondary cuticle has been thought to be formed from either the degenerating enamel epithelium or the cells of the oral epithelium. These two sources can be distinguished because cells derived from the oral epithelium contain no alkaline phosphatase, whereas cells from the enamel organ do (Ten Cate 1963).

Ten Cate concluded that on the non-occlusal surfaces of the teeth, the enamel epithelium degenerates before the enamel reaches the oral epithelium. On the occlusal surface, however, the enamel epithelium persists almost until the tooth makes contact with the oral epithelium. Although it is clear that the cellular layer is quite rapidly removed by friction during mastication, the fate of the primary cuticle is less certain.

If a tooth, extracted many years after eruption, is treated with acid as described above, a membrane exists over most of the enamel, except on occlusal surfaces. This observation, as well as histological studies, led to the view that the cuticle persisted throughout life. It is now realized that the membranes of developmental origin are rapidly worn off most surfaces after eruption and that the membranes on erupted teeth are deposited from saliva (p. 367).

Formation of Dentine

MATRIX FORMATION

With the light microscope the first event which is observed in dentinogenesis is the formation of a membrane between the inner enamel epithelium and the connective tissues of the dental papilla at the future amelodentinal junction of the occlusal part of the tooth. This membrane consists of argyrophil fibres from the papilla, arranged parallel to the amelodentinal junction.

The outermost cells of the papilla, which are irregular in shape and with their organelles arranged apparently randomly, then differentiate into odonto-blasts (probably the ameloblasts act as an organizer in this change) which at this stage are short, columnar cells. Later, after some matrix has formed, these cells become taller and develop various organelles including an extremely complicated endoplasmic reticulum which extends from the nucleus to the peripheral edge of, but not into, the odontoblastic process.

If tritiated thymidine, which is a source of thymine used for DNA synthesis, is given to an animal, it becomes incorporated in the nuclei of cells (i) pre-paring for mitosis, (ii) undergoing mitosis or (iii) in the daughter cells of nuclei that divided after the administration of the labelled thymidine. It is possible by autoradiography to trace the position of such cells. This method confirms that the odontoblasts arise from pulp cells and, once formed, do not divide.

The conclusion from studies with the light microscope had been that dentine matrix was not formed by the odontoblasts but from collagen fibres originating in the pulp which could be seen as coiled fibres between the odontoblasts (von Korff's corkscrew fibres, see Fig. IV.17). On this view, which is no longer held except for the layer of dentine formed first, the odontoblasts were concerned only with the mineralization of the matrix.

Throughout life, dentinogenesis occurs in two stages. First, an unmineral-ized collagenous matrix (predentine) is formed which, in the second stage, becomes mineralized at a sharp boundary (the dentine–predentine junction).

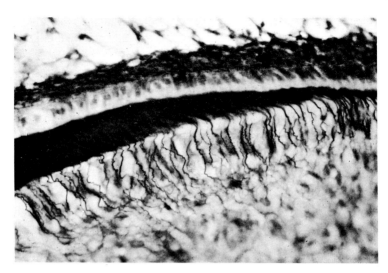

Fig. IV.17. An early stage of developing dentine showing the von Korff's fibres entering the mantle dentine. The ameloblasts are visible above the dentine but the odontoblasts are not clearly stained.

If mineralization and matrix formation are normal, then the thickness of the predentine remains constant; should mineralization be delayed without alteration in matrix formation, the predentine increases in thickness (Fig. IV.18).

The first layer of dentine to be formed is called mantle dentine in which the collagen fibres run parallel to the tubules and are formed by the pulp cells. In the rest of the dentine (circumpulpar dentine) the fibres are placed at right angles or obliquely to the tubules, and therefore approximately parallel to the inner surface of the dentine (Kramer 1951), and are formed and mineralized by the odontoblasts.

Electron micrographs have confirmed that as the odontoblasts differentiate, collagen fibres arising from pulp cells do appear between them and eventually fan out to form the first layer of predentine. Shortly after, these collagen fibres become obscured by an amorphous substance. Although most of the descriptions refer to animals, these events have been confirmed in human deciduous teeth (Sisca & Provenza 1972).

This process was thought to continue throughout the whole of dentine formation but electron micrographs indicate that after the first layer of predentine is formed, the process changes. When the odontoblasts have reached their full length, and their endoplasmic reticulum is developed, a layer of granular material containing a few very thin collagen fibrils is present near the cells. As the mantle dentine is approached the number of fibrils

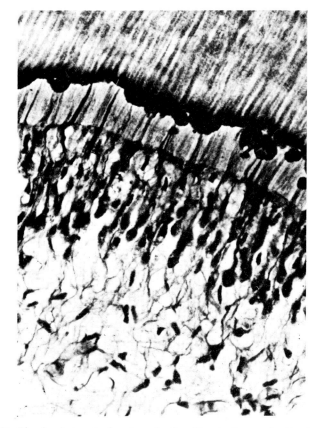

Fig. IV.18. The development of mature dentine. The dentine–predentine junction is more irregular in this section than usual.

increases and they become larger, eventually reaching a diameter of 600–700 Å. These fibres are surrounded by the unidentified amorphous substance. This change in the size of the fibre corresponds to a change in silver staining observed with the light microscope. The young predentine stains black with silver nitrate (precollagen) but the old predentine stains brown, like fully-formed collagen fibres. The different staining reactions of young and old predentine are only detectable while the primary dentine is being formed (Symons 1968) but microradiography (with ultra soft X-rays) of demineralized sections shows that old predentine contains more organic matter. The von Korff's fibres are seen to run in compact layers through the later predentine to the mantle dentine.

Injection of tritiated glycine into 6-day-old rats, followed by autoradiography of the molars from animals killed at intervals later, shows that the glycine becomes incorporated into the predentine then later into matrix and remains as a fairly well-defined layer which could be traced in the fully-formed dentine several weeks later. Unlike enamel, there is no evidence of the general diffusion of the organic products of the odontoblast throughout the matrix (see Fig. IV.12).

As the odontoblasts develop they form a fine process (Tomes's fibre or the 'odontoblastic process') which extends in length as the matrix grows and thus permeates the entire thickness of the dentine while the odontoblasts from which it arises remain alive. As the dentine becomes thicker at the expense of the pulp chamber, the inner surface of the dentine becomes smaller and is able to accommodate progressively fewer odontoblasts. This may explain why some of the odontoblasts die and their tubules become impermeable with advancing age. Alternatively, the death of the odontoblasts may be spontaneous and part of the general pulp atrophy which occurs during ageing.

MINERALIZATION OF DENTINE

The mineralization of the dentine can be observed by light microscopy as the formation of spheres of inorganic material (calcospherites) beginning in that part of the matrix which occupies the tip of the cusp and extending in conical increments throughout the crown and into the roots. These spheres normally fuse together and form a fairly homogeneous mass. In places, the fusion is incomplete owing to some interference with the mineralizing mechanism, and the spaces between the calcospherites, if extensive, are visible in ground sections as 'interglobular dentine'. Any imperfections in mineralization, such as the neonatal line, Tomes's granular layer or the contour lines of Owen, are visible by the contrast of imperfectly fused calcospherites to the more thoroughly mineralized neighbouring tissue.

At the first mineralization of the predentine, before any enamel matrix has formed or the basal lamina is removed, vesicles develop, scattered throughout the predentine but especially near the basal lamina (Eisenmann & Glick 1972; Katchburian 1973). These are similar to those in bone (p. 122) but their continuity with or origin from the early odontoblasts has not yet been demonstrated. Some of the vesicles are filled with amorphous electron dense material (amorphous calcium phosphate?), others contain fine granules while, in some, clear crystals are present. Crystals grow outward from the vesicles, and coalesce with those from neighbouring vesicles and become associated with the collagen fibres, which in the location of mantle dentine (the first 3–4 μm of dentine to form) are irregularly placed. After these 3–4 μm of dentine have formed the mineralization of circumpulpal dentine begins. Bernard (1972) suggests that this occurs by a seeding action of the crystals in the mantle dentine, thus triggering further mineralization which perpetuates itself by advancing along the collagen fibres. Dentine matrix contains about 2% of phosphoprotein (rodents teeth have as much as 11%) over half the amino acids being serine and aspartic acid to which the phosphate is attached by an ester link (Butler

1972). Proline and hydroxyproline are absent. The phosphoprotein, like chondroitin sulphate (p. 120) might favour mineralization by attracting calcium ions and leading to apatite formation or alternatively it might inhibit this process by binding calcium ions and thus lowering the ionic level. The relationship of phosphoproteins to vesicles does not appear to have been clarified. The crystals grow, as in other calcified tissues, by increasing their size and by the fusion with their neighbours. This growth of crystals fits in with two other findings: (1) that the hardness of developing dentine gradually increases from the dentine-predentine junction inwards and (2) that if ^{45}Ca is given to animals during tooth development although the greatest concentration is found at the dentine-predentine junction, some is found dispersed throughout that part of the dentine which appears to be calcified already. Although this could arise from ionic exchange it is equally likely that additional calcium enters crystals which are incompletely grown.

The crystals are smaller than those in enamel and too small to be easily seen even with the electron microscope. They have been described as flat platelets up to 1000 Å in length (Johansen & Parks 1960).

Although it is probable that mineralization begins in the vesicles, some chemical changes in the predentine matrix which were thought to be associated with mineralization were observed before vesicles were discovered. Some of these changes may occur within the vesicle. Among these changes are (1) the substance which stains as a lipid appears sharply at the site of mineralization. (2) When autoradiographs are made from sections of the teeth of animals which have received injections of radioactive sulphate, no radioactivity appears in the predentine but it is present in the predentine-dentine junction. In older animals, the dentine which had been at the junction when the injection was made showed as a band of radioactivity. Evidently some sulphur-containing substance is formed as predentine changes into dentine. Since treatment of the matrix with hyaluronidase (which, among other actions, breaks down chondroitin sulphate) abolished the band of radioactive material, it was concluded that chondroitin sulphate is formed, or at any rate the sulphate groups were introduced into the molecule, at the boundary between predentine and dentine (Leblond *et al.* 1955). Although it might have been expected that the formation of chondroitin sulphate in this region is an important factor in initiating mineralization, experiments described in the next paragraph do not support this view.

Only one series of experiments seem to have been carried out on the mineralization of predentine *in vitro* by Glasstone (1958b). She found that caps of enamel and predentine from tooth germs from which all cells had been removed by scraping, still mineralized when incubated in solutions containing calcium and inorganic and organic phosphate. Treatment of the caps with hyaluronidase did not prevent their mineralization implying that the sulphate-containing substance whose formation was demonstrated by ^{35}S (which was destroyed by hyaluronidase) cannot be concerned with mineralization in these experiments.

It is somewhat surprising that predentine should mineralize *in vitro* when it does not do so *in vivo*. The relevance of these experiments to normal mineralization must be in some doubt.

FORMATION OF THE PERITUBULAR MATRIX
The matrix surrounding the odontoblastic process (the peritubular matrix) has a different structure in human teeth (but not in the rat incisor) from that of the rest of the matrix (see p. 168 and Fig. IV.19). As already mentioned, this

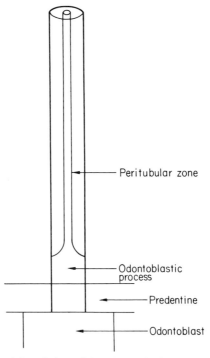

Peritubular zone

Odontoblastic process

Predentine

Odontoblast

Fig. IV.19. Diagram of the relation of the odontoblastic processes to the intertubular and peritubular matrix.

matrix undergoes a change about the same time as mineralization begins in the matrix as a whole but it becomes fully identifiable as a separate entity about 60–100 μm from the dentine-predentine junction, reaching its maximum thickness 120–200 μm from this junction (Fig. IV.19). If dentine is stained (without demineralization) with methylene blue or toluidine blue the matrix as a whole is unstained beyond a layer about 20–25 μm from the predentine, presumably because mineralization is complete and the stain cannot reach the GAGs of the matrix. The peritubular dentine does take up stain, however, in the inner dentine, which suggests that the peritubular matrix remains unmineralized (i.e. able to accept stain) for a longer time than the neighbouring inter-tubular matrix. The stains were in an acid solution, however, and some demineralization probably occurred during the staining (Weber 1971).

Microradiographs of dentine sections show that the peritubular zone is more heavily mineralized than the rest of the matrix (see p. 168).

When demineralized, the matrix of the peritubular zone is much more fragmentary than that of the intertubular areas. Electron micrographs show it to consist of sparsely distributed, very fine fibres between 250 and 500 Å in diameter showing, in favourable conditions, collagen banding, but there is evidence that other organic substances are also present. In interglobular dentine, the peritubular zone is absent (Blake 1958).

References

ABERCROMBIE M. *et al.* (1957) Social behaviour of cells in tissue culture. *Exp. Cell Res.* **13**, 276

ALLAN J.H. (1959) Investigations into the mineralization of human dental enamel. *J. dent. Res.* **38**, 1096

ANGMAR-MANSON B. (1971) A quantitative micro-radiographic study on the organic matrix of developing human enamel in relation to the mineral content. *Archs oral Biol.* **16**, 135, 147

BERNARD G.W. (1972) Ultrastructural observation of initial calcification in dentine and enamel. *J. Ultrastruc. Res.* **41**, 1

BEYNON A.D. (1972) Histochemical studies of enamel maturation in the albino mouse. *J. dent. Res.* **51**, 1234

BLAKE G.C. (1958) The peritubular translucent zones in human denture. *Brit. dent. J.* **104**, 57

BOYDE A. & REITH E.J. (1976) Scanning electron microscopy of the lateral cell surfaces of rat incisor ameloblasts. *J. Anat.* **122**, 603

BUTLER P.M. (1957) The ontogeny of molar pattern. *Biol. Rev.* **31**, 30

BUTLER W.T. (1972) In *The Comparative Molecular Biology of Extracellular Matrices*, p. 258, Ed. Slavkin H.C., Academic Press

COOPER W.E.G. (1968a) An apparatus for the removal of 25 Å diameter samples from tooth sections. *Archs oral Biol.* **13**, 835

COOPER W.E.G. (1968b) A microchemical microradiographical and histological investigation of amelogenesis in the pig. *Archs oral Biol.* **13**, 27

CRABB H.S.M. (1976) The porous outer enamel of unerepted human premolars. *Caries Res.* **10**, 1

CRABB H.S.M. & DARLING A.I. (1962) The pattern of progressive mineralization of human dental enamel, vol. 2, *Internat. Ser. Monographs Oral Biol.* (also CRABB H.S.M. (1959) *Proc. R. Soc. Med.* **52**, 118)

DEAKINS M. (1942) Changes in the ash, water and organic content of pig enamel during calcification. *J. dent. Res.* **21**, 429

EASTOE J. (1963) The amino acid composition of proteins from the oral tissues. *Archs oral Biol.* **8**, 449, 633

EISENMANN D.R. & GLICK P.L. (1972) Ultrastructure of initial crystal formation in dentine. *J. Ultrastruc. Res.* **41**, 18

ENGFELDT B. & HAMMARLUND-ESSLER E. (1956–7). A microradiographic study of the mineralization of developing enamel. *Acta odont. Scand.* **14**, 273

FANNING R.J. *et al.* (1953) Salivary contribution to enamel maturation and caries resistance. *J. Amer. dent. Ass.* **49**, 668

FISHER A.R. (1971) Morphological development *in vitro* of the whole and halved lower molar tooth germs of the mouse. *Archs oral Biol.* **16**, 148

FRISBIE H.E. & NUCKOLLS J. (1947) Caries of the enamel. *J. dent. Res.* **26**, 181

GASSER R.F. *et al.* (1972) Circadian rhythm in rat incisors. *J. dent Res.* **51**, 740

GEDALIA I. *et al.* (1961) Fluorine content of superficial enamel layer and its correlation with the fluorine content of saliva-tooth age and DMFT count. *J. dent. Res.* **40**, 865

GLASSTONE S. (1939) A comparative study of the development *in vivo* and *in vitro* of rat and rabbit molars. *Brit. dent. J.* **66**, 460, 523

GLASSTONE S. (1958a) The distribution of alkaline phosphatase in normal and transplanted rodent teeth. *Brit. dent. J.* **105**, 58 (see also *Brit. dent. J.* **165**, 256)

GLASSTONE S. (1958b) Experimental studies on calcification of tooth germs *in vitro*. *J. dent. Res.* **37**, 738

GLIMCHER M.J. *et al.* (1957) Macromolecular aggregation states in relation to mineralization: the collagen-hydroxyapatite system as studied *in vitro*. *Proc. Nat. Acad. Sci. Wash.* **43**, 860

HANKER J.S. *et al.* (1972) The formaldehyde sensitivity of acid phosphatases involved in osteogenesis and odontogenesis in the rat. *Archs oral Biol.* **17**, 503

HAY M.F. (1961) The development *in vivo* and *in vitro* of the lower incisor and molars of the mouse. *Archs oral Biol.* **3**, 86

IRVING J.T. (1963) The sudanophil material at sites of calcification. *Archs oral Biol.* **8**, 735

JOHANNESSEN L.B. (1961) Dentine apposition in the mandibular first molars of albino rats. *Archs oral Biol.* **5**, 81

JOHANSEN E. & PARKS H.F. (1960) Three-dimensional morphology of crystallites in human bone and dentin. *J. dent. Res.* **39**, 714

KATCHBURIAN E. (1973) Membrane-bound bodies as initiators of mineralization in dentine. *J. Anat.* **116**, 302

KRAMER I.R.H. (1951) The distribution of collagen fibrils in the dentine matrix. *Brit. dent. J.* **91**, 1

LEBLOND C.P. *et al.* (1955) Formation of bones and teeth as visualized by radioautography. *Ann. N.Y. Acad. Sci.* **60**, 631

LEFKOWITZ W. *et al.* (1944) Experimental papillectomy. Part II. Histological study.

J. dent. Res. **23**, 345; (1947) Experimental amelotomy. *J. dent. Res.* **26**, 151

LUNT D.A. & NOBLE H.W. (1972) Localization of alkaline phosphatase in human cap-stage enamel organs by electron histochemistry. *Archs oral Biol.* **17**, 761

MARSLAND E.A. (1951) A histological investigation of amelogenesis in rats. I. Matrix formation. *Brit. dent. J.* **91**, 252; (1952) II. Maturation. *Brit. dent. J.* **92**, 109

OSBORN J.W. (1970a) The mechanism of prism formation in teeth: A hypothesis. *Calc. Tiss. Res.* **5**, 115

OSBORN J.W. (1970b) The mechanism of ameloblast movement. *Calc. Tiss. Res.* **5**, 344

OSBORN J.W. (1973) Development of dental enamel. *Oral Sciences Reviews* **3**, 1

PROVENZA D.V. & SISCA R.F. (1970) Electron microscopic studies of human dental lamina. *J. dent. Res.* **51**, 1394 (see also *Archs oral Biol.* **16**, 121)

REITH E.J. (1963) The ultrastructure of the ameloblasts during early stages of maturation of enamel. *J. cell Biol.* **18**, 691

REITH E.J. (1968) The early stage of amelogenesis as observed in molar teeth of young rats. *J. Ultrastruc. Res.* **17**, 503

REITH E.J. & COTTY V.F. (1962) Autoradiographic studies on calcification of enamel. *Archs oral Biol.* **7**, 365

REITH E.J. & COTTY V.F. (1967) The absorptive activity of ameloblasts during the maturation of enamel. *Anat. Rec.* **157**, 577

REITH E.J. & ROSS M.H. (1973) Morphological evidence for presence of contractile elements in secretory ameloblasts in the rat. *Archs oral Biol.* **18**, 445

RINALDINI L.M.J. (1958) The isolation of living cells from animal tissues. *Internat. Rev. Cyt.* **7**, 587

ROBINSON L. *et al.* (1974) Uptake of ^{32}P-labelled phosphate into developing rat incisor enamel. *Calc. Tiss. Res.* **15**, 143; also (1975) *Archs oral Biol.* **20**, 29.

RÖNNHOLM E. (1962) An electron microscope study of the amelogenesis in human teeth. *J. Ultrastruct. Res.* **6**, 229, 249, 368

RUSHTON M.A. (1933) On the fine contour

lines of the enamel of milk teeth. *Dent. Rec.* **53**, 170

SCHOUR I. & HOFFMAN M.M. (1939) Studies in tooth development. *J. dent. Res.* **18**, 91, 161

SCHOUR I. & MASSLER M. (1940) Studies in tooth development. The growth pattern of human teeth. *J. Amer. dent. Ass.* **27**, 1778, 1918

SHAPIRO H.H. *et al.* (1942) Role of the dental papilla in early formation. *J. dent. Res.* **21**, 391

SISCA R.F. & PROVENZA D.V. (1972) Initial dentine formation in human deciduous teeth. *Calc. Tiss. Res.* **9**, 1

SIMMONS N. (1972) In *The Comparative Molecular Biology of Extracellular Matrices*, p. 286. Ed. Slavkin H.C., Academic Press.

SMALES F.C. (1975) Structural subunit in prisms of immature rat enamel. *Nature (Lond.)* **258**, 772

SPEIRS R.L. (1975) Fluoride incorporation into developing enamel of permanent teeth in the domestic pig. *Archs oral Biol.* **20**, 877

STARKEY W.E. (1971) Dimensional changes associated with enamel maturation in rabbits. *Archs oral Biol.* **16**, 479

SUGA S. (1970) Proteolytic enzyme activity in the developing dental hard tissues of the rat. *Archs oral Biol.* **15**, 556

SYMONS N.B.B. (1955) Alkaline phosphatase activity in the developing teeth of the rat. *J. Anat. Lond.* **89**, 238; also (1956) **90**, 117 & *Brit. dent. J.* **101**, 255, **105**, 27.

SYMONS N.B.B. (Ed.) (1968) The formation of primary and secondary dentine. In *Dentine and Pulp: Their Structure and Reactions.* p. 67 E. &. S. Livingstone, Edinburgh

TEN CATE A.R. (1962) The distribution of alkaline phosphatase in the human tooth germ. *Archs oral Biol.* **7**, 195

TEN CATE A.R. (1963) Acid phosphatase, non-specific esterase and lipid in oral epithelium. *Archs oral Biol.* **8**, 747, 755

TEN CATE A.R. *et al.* (1971) The non-fibrous nature of von Korff fibres in developing dentine. *Anat. Record* **168**, 491

TURNER P. (1958) The integument of the enamel surface of the human tooth. *Dent. Prac.* **8**, 341, 373

WEATHERELL, *et al.* (1975) Composition of dental enamel. *Br. Med. Bull.* **31**, 115

WEBER D.F. (1971) Peritubular matrix: A correlated radiographic and staining study. *Calc. Tiss. Res.* **8**, 7

WEINMANN J.P. *et al.* (1942) Correlation of chemical and histological investigation on developing enamel. *J. dent. Res.* **21**, 171

WEISS P. (1958) Cell contact. *Internat. Rev. Cyt.* **7**, 391.

YOUNG R.W. & GREULICH R.C. (1963) Distinctive autoradiographic patterns of glycine incorporation in rat enamel and dentine matrices. *Archs oral Biol.* **8**, 509; also (1959) **1**, 23

Review

SYMONS N.B.B. (Ed.) (1968) *Dentine and Pulp: Their Structure and Reactions.* E. & S. Livingstone, Edinburgh

An encyclopaedic work on the subject matter of this chapter is: MILES A.E.W. (1967) Ed. *Structural and Chemical Organization of Teeth*, vol. 1, Chaps 7–11. Academic Press, London

CHAPTER V

PERMEABILITY AND AGE CHANGES IN THE DENTAL TISSUES

There have been many extreme views held on the subject of the changes which a tooth may undergo after it has erupted. The controversy has been linked with the question of the 'vitality' of the enamel and dentine, i.e. the extent to which these tissues are alive and undergo metabolic changes, or can be influenced by changes in the body as a whole. Some workers have believed the tooth to be beyond the pale of general bodily changes whereas others have emphasized the possibility of circulatory channels through both enamel and dentine, and the presence of the odontoblastic processes in dentine, by means of which they postulated a metabolic control of the tooth.

The Permeability of Dentine

Experiments on teeth *in situ* in which soluble or insoluble stains have been placed within the pulp, or sealed into dentine or on the enamel, have shown (1) that the dentine is readily permeable from both the pulp and the amelo-dentinal junction, (2) that this permeability tends to fall with advancing age, and (3) that, especially in human teeth, even young enamel is very much less permeable than is dentine.

The rate of movement of stain in dentine was first estimated by Lefkowitz (1943) in living dogs by injecting argyrol (a silver stain) into the pulp through small holes bored at the necks of the teeth. The teeth were extracted at varying times after the argyrol had been introduced and sections were made. After 13 min, half the distance between the pulp and enamel had been stained and in just over 17 min the stain reached the enamel. After 28 min, about half the dentine was stained, and the area of penetration increased a little more by 38 min, after which it remained almost unchanged (Fig. V.1). A section cut transversely across the tubules showed that the stain was present in the odontoblastic process which proves that this is at least the major route of diffusion from the pulp. Similar experiments on solutions of radioactive urea,

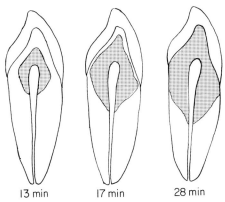

13 min   17 min   28 min

Fɪɢ. V.1. Diagram showing the time required for diffusion of stain (shaded) from pulp through dentine in living dogs (after Lefkowitz 1943).

thiourea and acetamide have confirmed that dentine is highly permeable (Wainwright & Lemoine 1950; Wainwright 1954).

It might be argued that the surgical introduction of stains into the tooth makes the dentine more permeable than normal by damaging its relation to the pulp. However, injection of Trypan blue into the blood of cats and dogs stained dentine formed before the injection, and in such experiments, the stain must enter the dentine through an undamaged pulp.

Solutions of radioactive substances have been placed inside the pulp chambers of extracted teeth kept at 37° C in a humid chamber, followed by sectioning and autoradiography which showed that small molecules such as [^{14}C]nicotinamide, [^{14}C]urea and [^{35}S]thiourea can permeate the whole thickness of the dentine (3–4 mm) within 20–30 min (Wainwright 1954). The times are so similar to those found for dyes in the tooth with blood supply intact that it shows that diffusion alone, and not tissue fluid pressure, is largely responsible for the movement of substances through the dentine.

There is evidence, based upon the movements of stains cemented into the dentine of living animals, that the diffusion in dentine occurs in both directions. The stain reaches the amelodentinal junction (and in some experiments enters the enamel) and also moves into the pulp. Parts of the dentine far removed from where the stain was introduced surgically, are also found to become slightly stained and this stain can only have been carried outwards from the pulp (Fig. V.2).

The early histological studies of dentine with the light microscope on imperfectly fixed tissues led to the conclusion that there was a space between the odontoblastic process and the walls of the tubules and some electron micrographs supported this view (Fig. V.3(a)). It was suggested that the fluid may flow from the pulp along the odontoblastic processes and was secreted

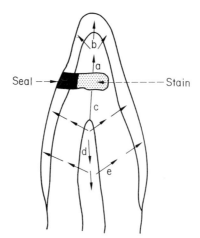

FIG. V.2. Digram showing directions of movement of stain when sealed into a cavity in the dentine (after Bodecker & Lefkowitz 1946). a—Outwards to amelodentinal junction; b—into enamel; c—inwards to pulp; d,e—to other parts of dentine.

through their walls and back into the pulp into the space which was believed to exist from which it returned to the pulp.

Electron micrographs suggest that the odontoblastic process completely fills the tubule in most places (Fig. V.3(b)) and that the space previously observed was a shrinkage artefact (Bradford 1951; Shroff *et al.* 1954). Some spaces are

(a)

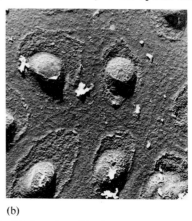

(b)

FIG. V.3. Electron micrographs of dentine. In (a) the odontoblastic process appears to be surrounded by a space. In (b) this space is absent. The reason for these different appearances are not understood but they may arise from variations in the method of preparing the sections or from real differences between dentine in different teeth. Most recent evidence supports the appearance in (b), i.e. of a process surrounded by hypermineralized solid matrix (the 'peritubular zone'). What appears to be the process in (a) might be the inner part of this zone, the outer part having been lost leaving the space.

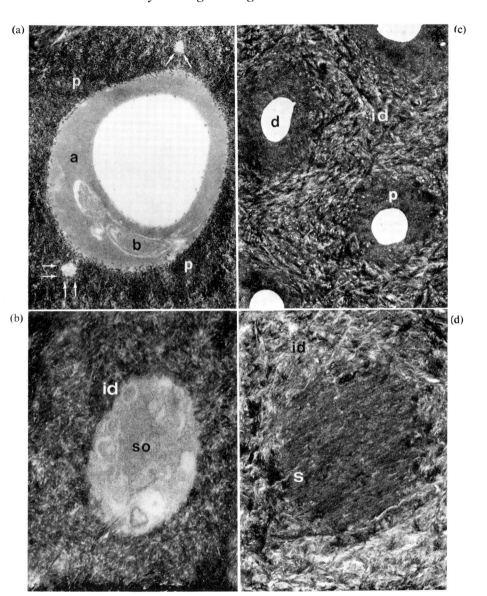

FIG. V.4. Electron micrographs of different forms of dentinal tubules: (a) hollow tubes; (b) tubule filled with granular cytoplasm (so); (c) apparent absence of process in dead tract (d) with enroaching peritubular matrix (p); (d) complete obliteration of tubule (s) (×20 000).

seen between the process and the matrix but they do not form a continuous pathway (Frank 1968). The distal part of some of the processes has been described from electron micrographs (Garant 1972; Tsatsas & Frank 1972) as either hollow (Fig. V.4(a)) or filled with finely granular cytoplasm (Fig. V.4(b)). Yet another formation seen transversely is a hollow space surrounded by a ring of organic material (Fig. V.4(c)). In older teeth the peritubular matrix becomes wider, eventually obliterating the tubule altogether (Fig. V.4(d)). Microradiography of dentine sections by Miller (1954) showed that the tissue immediately surrounding the process, the 'peritubular zone', stains differently, is more heavily mineralized and when treated with acid is more soluble and leaves a smaller residue of organic matter, than the intertubular dentine.

Examination by the scanning electron microscope of dentine treated with acid suggests that each tubule contains an inner insoluble zone (low in mineral which is soluble) and an outer very acid-soluble zone which probably has a high proportion of mineral (soluble) and a corresponding smaller proportion of organic matrix (Isokawa *et al.* 1970). The inner insoluble zone, if present in the absence of the outer zone, may be confused with the dentinal process (a possible interpretation of Fig. V.3(a)). Either it differs in composition or is less firmly arranged so that it is more easily lost during demineralization. The heavier mineralization is present in newly-erupted teeth and is not, therefore, a secondary result of mastication or attrition. Adjacent dentinal tubules are linked by occasional branches of smaller diameter than main tubules and they also possess a peritubular zone.

These views are now well established and there is no anatomical basis for a circulation in dentine. Observations on the movement of stains through the dentine could be equally well explained by diffusion of the stains through the cytoplasm of the odontoblastic process.

It has been stated that bacteria may remain alive for long periods (over a year) sealed under a dental filling. This has been established by an experiment in which infected dentine was deliberately left under amalgam fillings in cavities lined with sterilized gold reinforced with solder. After periods averaging 95 days, the cavities were reopened with stringent precautions to avoid bacterial contamination from outside the tooth and the carious residues were cultured and found to contain live bacteria. This indicates that sufficient nutrients can reach bacteria deep in dentine to remain alive but whether via the tubules or via leaks by the side of the filling was not determined (Schouboe & MacDonald 1962).

The nature of the fluid present in dentine

As mentioned on p. 57 dentine contains about 10% water and it had been supposed in the past that it consisted of a fluid often referred to as 'dental lymph'. It has also been suggested that changes in the composition of this fluid by nutritional and other systemic means might influence the dentine

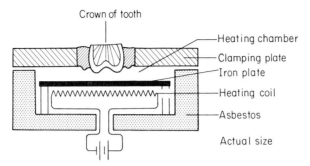

Crown of tooth

Heating chamber
Clamping plate
Iron plate
Heating coil
Asbestos

Actual size

FIG. V.5. Diagram of apparatus used by Spreter von Kreundenstein & Stüben (1955) by means of which fluid was expelled from dentine for analysis.

throughout life. Spreter von Kreudenstein & Stüben (1955) collected a fluid from dentine by the following method. The crowns of freshly extracted human molars were cut so that the roots and pulp chamber were removed, leaving a solid mass of enamel and dentine with the tubules cut across. This piece of crown was heated in a special apparatus (Fig. V.5) to about 50° C within 2 min. During the heating, tiny droplets of fluid were expelled from the cut ends of the tubules and by the end of the 2 min they had coalesced into larger drops. Another method of extracting dentinal fluid was to wash with distilled water pieces of dentine from which all pulp and enamel had been removed. Protein and twelve amino acids were found in the extract. These experiments do not, however, provide evidence of the existence of dental lymph, still less do they prove that there is any circulation in dentine. The heating method could expel liquid by thermal expansion from the cytoplasm within the processes just as easily as from a hypothetical lymph. The extraction of protein and amino acids from dentine could also be explained by the washing out of soluble constituents from the processes.

A more recent approach to this problem involved a device in which negative pressure was applied to the exposed dentine of human extracted teeth, from which liquid droplets were observed microscopically exuding from the tubules and coalescing into pools (Stevenson 1965, 1967). Another method consists of centrifuging teeth after removal of their roots, when 0·01 ml of a light yellow fluid separates per gram of tooth, which coagulated readily on exposure to air or heat. This fluid was analysed by an electron microprobe and contained 3 mEq/l of potassium, 150 of sodium and 100 of chloride (Coffey *et al.* 1970). These values are typical of interstitial fluid, indicating that the fluid was not derived from the cytoplasm and presumably arises from the discontinuous spaces in the tubule. Although there is no evidence that this fluid is circulating it is almost certainly capable of movement and must be presumed to be the source of the fluid which, at least under rather unphysiological conditions, collects on the enamel surface (p. 176). The conclusion that there is no circulating fluid does not, of course, preclude the possibility that the odontoblasts may modify the composition or increase the mineralization of the dentine—there is good evidence that this does happen (see p. 167). It is likely that these changes are brought about by direct action on the surface of the odontoblastic process and not by means of any circulating fluid. The proximal end of the process contains cytoplasm with microtubules, some endoplasmic reticulum, infrequent ribosome-like granules and mitochondria, all indicative of metabolic activity.

The Permeability of Enamel

Permeability to stains

Experiments with stains show that although enamel is much less permeable than is dentine, there is no doubt that this tissue is permeable in certain circumstances.

Fish (1933) found that stains placed in the pulp of young dogs' teeth passed right through to the surface of the enamel. In older dogs, the stain entered the enamel from the dentine but could not permeate so freely, and the outer layers and parts of the whole thickness of enamel were unstained. When the stain was placed in a metal cup cemented to the enamel surface of a young dog the stain was found to pass right through into the dentine. Again, with old dogs there was no penetration whatever through the outer surface of the enamel. Microscopic examination of sections of the teeth showed that the main channels of diffusion were the interprismatic substance, the tufts and lamellae.

Experiments with stains on human teeth *in vitro* have shown that although dentine is permeable, enamel is almost impermeable whether the stain is placed in the pulp or on the enamel surface. In only a small proportion of the teeth did the enamel take up any stain and then only in the tufts and lamellae. The permeability *in vitro* of whole teeth crowns to ^{22}Na was increased by treating with saturated urea solution or 30% hydrogen peroxide, which would denature and possibly dissolve the organic matter of enamel. Placing the crowns in boiling Ringer solution for 2 min reduced the permeability. These results suggest that the organic matter of the enamel is the route of diffusion (Arwill *et al.* 1969).

If the outer enamel is ground away, or if caries is present, the permeability to small ions is greatly increased (Hardwick & Fremlin 1959).

Berggren (1947) found that when methylene blue was placed in the dentine of a human tooth *in situ*, penetration of the pulp occurred rapidly and the rest of the dentine then received stain from the pulp. A limited amount of stain reached the enamel, especially along the tufts and lamellae and in their vicinity. The staining of the enamel was always scanty and irregular in distribution and did not reach the surface. Berggren often found a sharp, overstained line at the junction of the stained and unstained enamel clearly showing that stain accumulated at an impermeable barrier in the outer part of the enamel.

The remarkable observation has been made by Berggren that although the tooth is not permeable to tetanus toxin when applied to the enamel surface of young dogs, it becomes permeable when the toxin is mixed with strong glucose or fructose solution. These sugars were said not to affect the permeability to dyes, however. Sognnaes & Shaw (1952) on the other hand, found in living monkeys, the uptake of ^{32}P from the surface of enamel was greatly *reduced* when 20% of sucrose was also present. The results all require confirmation, but they raise the possibility that concentrated sugar solutions may influence selectively the permeability of a tooth. The effect of sugar on the permeability of the teeth is discussed further on p. 175.

Permeability to radioactive elements and their uptake by enamel

Organic dyes are fairly large molecules and experiments in which they are used might tend to suggest that the tooth is less permeable than it is to ions or smaller organic molecules.

The results of experiments with radioactive ions such as ^{45}Ca, H^{32}PO$_4$ and ^{131}I and labelled substances such as [^{14}C]urea demonstrate not only the permeability of the tooth, but also the extent to which the various tissues can retain ions which enter after eruption. The mineralized tissues acquire much lower concentrations of radioactive ions than the soft tissues, as may be seen from an experiment in which ^{32}P was injected into cats (Barnum & Armstrong 1942). The relative amounts of ^{32}P in 1 g of the ash from each tissue were as follows:

Enamel 4	Dentine 66	Diaphysis 100
Epiphysis 460	Marrow 2300	

Thus dentine contained more than enamel, in confirmation of the dye experiment which suggested greater permeability in dentine. Other experiments have shown that the dentine nearest to the pulp contains more than the outer layer, suggesting that the pulp was one source of the ^{32}P. The root dentine contained more ^{32}P than the crown dentine which is strong evidence that some entered via the cementum. Although enamel contained the lowest concentration of ^{32}P in any tissue of the body, three possible routes of entry of the element had to be considered from: (1) the pulp via the dentine, (2) the saliva, and (3) the blood supply of the periodontal membrane and cementum via the cementodentinal junction and the amelodentinal junction. These sources were differentiated by injecting ^{32}P into dogs after placing a cap on the enamel (thus eliminating access to saliva), and removing the pulp, or both (in which case the only route is via the cementum). The results show that when the pulp is removed, the uptake of the dentine is greatly reduced, and that the reduction is greater in the crown than in the root, thus confirming that the cementum is a route through which substances may enter dentine, although of much less importance than the pulp (Wassermann *et al.* 1941, Sognnaes & Shaw 1952).

Similar experiments in which autoradiographs of sections of teeth were made, show that when the pulp was removed the radioactivity was greatest at the cemento-dentinal junction. These experiments clearly indicate that root dentine may be affected chemically by the tissue fluid at both sides. The permeability of enamel to ions probably depends on its water content: when this is reduced by heating to 200° C permeability to ^{18}F and ^{24}Na falls (Joyston-Bechal *et al.* 1971). The permeability of cementum to stains is discussed on p. 192.

Sognnaes and Shaw, in one experiment which appears to have been neither repeated nor explained, found that when a tooth in a living monkey was surrounded by saliva containing ^{32}P, the uptake was, in different parts of the tooth, four to nine times greater than in an extracted tooth treated similarly from the same animal.

In experiments on living cats the absorption of ^{131}I through the canine teeth, which were dipped into vessels containing Na ^{132}I, has been demonstrated by detecting the ^{131}I in the thyroid of the animals by autoradiographs. Painting newly-extracted human teeth with solutions of radioactive substances (nicotinamide, urea, thiourea and acetamide) and placing in a humid atmosphere at 37° C followed by sectioning and autoradiography showed that (except for nicotinamide which was slower) the substances permeated the full thickness of the intact enamel within about 30 min (Wainwright 1954). A similar experiment with radioactive calcium, zinc and silver showed that these elements could penetrate defects in the enamel but not intact enamel. The surface of the teeth was found to take up the metals in a tightly bound form which could not be removed by 4 hr washing in running water (Bartelstone 1949; Wainwright 1951).

Uptake by ionic exchange

The ability of the dental tissue to take up radioactive elements does not prove the vitality of the tooth or that the total amount of mineral necessarily increases.

The ability of apatite to undergo ionic exchange and to absorb other ions is probably quite adequate to explain the changes observed in dentine and enamel without postulating enzyme activity. It seems likely that both ionic exchange and adsorption occur, but their relative importance is still undecided. The fact that radioactive phosphate and calcium can enter the fully-formed dental tissues suggests that some ionic exchange takes place without altering the composition of the teeth; for example, a calcium ion may enter the apatite lattice to replace another calcium ion which has left it. If one ion enters to replace a dissimilar ion, for example, if a fluoride ion enters to replace a hydroxyl ion which leaves, then small changes in composition will occur. This is probably the main way in which minute changes in the composition of teeth may be brought about. It is possible that such changes in teeth may have a profound effect on their properties, such as caries resistance, although with the exception of fluoride there is no convincing evidence so far that this is so.

UPTAKE BY ENAMEL DEFECTS AND THE INFLUENCE OF FLUORIDE
When teeth, either extracted or *in vivo*, are treated with radioactive ions, there is a slight uptake over the whole surface, probably by ionic exchange. Enamel defects, including very early carious lesions, take up much higher concentrations than the surface as a whole (Myers *et al.* 1952). It is probable that the removal of some of the enamel substance as a result of caries makes that area more permeable, and also exposes a greater area of crystal surface. Although this process was first detected experimentally by radioactive calcium, fluoride and phosphate, Dowse & Jenkins (1957) showed, and others have confirmed, that enamel from early cavities contains a higher concentration of fluoride than does the sound enamel from the same tooth. This finding shows that the uptake of fluoride by early carious lesions is a physiological process which occurs from the fluoride of saliva, food or drinks.

POST-ERUPTIVE MATURATION
If comparable groups of rats are fed a cariogenic diet one immediately after weaning and the other some weeks later, more caries develops over a given time in the first group than in the second (Fanning *et al.* 1953, for other references see Speirs 1967; Miller 1958). Evidently resistance to caries increases after rat's teeth have been in contact with oral fluids even for as little as 2 weeks. This increased resistance is called post-eruptive maturation and is believed to be the incorporation of additional mineral, and perhaps protein, from saliva into hypomineralized spaces still present when the tooth erupts. The increased caries resistance is paralleled by evidence of increased mineralization (reduced uptake of stain) by enamel. Inhibitors of the growth of apatite crystals or ligation of the salivary ducts in rats reduce maturation; topical applications of fluoride increase it.

The results probably have important implications in human caries. There is clinical evidence that fluoride is particularly effective in reducing caries immediately after eruption and exposure of newly-erupted teeth to sugar should be minimized although firm evidence for their high susceptibility to caries is lacking. The high permeability of outer enamel before eruption (p. 151) may be relevant.

Osmosis and permeability

Atkinson (1947) studied the behaviour of enamel as a semi-permeable membrane, i.e. one which permits water to pass but keeps back substances in solution. His method, briefly, was to dip the outer surface of an extracted tooth (with pulp removed) into water and attach the root by a short piece of rubber tubing to a glass barometer tube containing saline, fused to a capillary

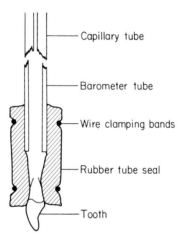

FIG. V.6. Diagram of Atkinson's method of mounting a tooth for permeability studies. The apparatus is set up so that the tooth is immersed in water or saline contained in an outer vessel (after Atkinson 1947).

tube (Fig. V.6). He found that water was drawn through the tooth by osmosis into the saline whose level consequently rose in the capillary tube. Sometimes salts were found to pass outwards through the enamel (but presumably at a slower rate than the water passed in, otherwise the osmotic pressure would become equal on both sides and the level of the saline would not have risen) but larger dye molecules did not cross the enamel. In other words, the enamel behaved as a permeable membrane to small ions but a semi-permeable membrane to large molecules.

There were great variations between the time required for detectable amounts of water to diffuse through different teeth. For example, out of a group of twelve teeth set up, the saline rose within 7 days in two of them but 30 days elapsed before diffusion occurred across all of them. Anterior teeth were found to be only about half as permeable per unit area as molar teeth. In some experiments, he tested teeth from which dentine had been completely removed (leaving a shell of enamel) and showed that they behaved in the same way as intact teeth, thus proving that it was enamel which behaves as an osmotic membrane.

Teeth from subjects of different ages were tested and it was demonstrated that permeability falls rather rapidly between the ages of 20 and 30 and then more slowly, but permanent teeth never become completely impermeable. The very great decrease in the permeability of deciduous teeth during the resorption of their roots is described on p. 212.

Fosdick *et al.* (1959) carried out similar experiments and in general confirmed the effect of age. They found that impacted old teeth, that had not been exposed in the mouth to oral fluids, were as permeable as freshly-erupted teeth thus proving that the fall in permeability with age involves deposition of material from the oral fluids.

Anions do not pass through enamel as readily as water or cations—in other words the enamel behaves as if it possessed a negative charge (Poole *et al.* 1963). Waters (1971) pointed out the selectivity of ion transport by enamel, for example, the permeability to K^+ is invariably higher than for Na^+, and concluded from measurements of the emf developed when enamel sections were placed in specially constructed cells with different solutions on either side that enamel acted as an ion exchange membrane.

The response of the pulp to very early enamel caries before it reaches the dentine (white spots without cavitation) indicates that bacterial products can diffuse through the inner enamel unaffected or only slightly affected by caries. The number of odontoblasts in the affected region was reduced and some nuclei were in the tubules. A calciotraumatic line (p. 223) on the border of the dentine was frequently observed and lymphocytes accumulated in a small area of pulp immediately under the affected odontoblasts (Brännström & Lind 1965).

After removal of the organic matter by boiling with alkaline ethylene glycol, teeth no longer behaved as osmotic membranes but became completely permeable, from which it may be concluded that the organic matter gives enamel the properties of a semi-permeable membrane.

The osmotic pressure of saliva is about half that of blood and tissue fluid, so that water tends to be drawn into the tooth. Fosdick pointed out that when the tooth surface is covered by a strong solution of sugar, the osmotic pressure on the outside may reach fifty atmospheres, i.e. about ten times that of blood. Under these circumstances, he suggested that hydrogen and other small ions would tend to be drawn into the enamel and water would be drawn outwards perhaps explaining why caries is a local penetrating lesion whereas the immersion of a tooth in acid causes a general destruction of the whole surface although this view has now been superseded (p. 423).

The flow of enamel fluid

Bergman (1963) showed that small quantities of a watery fluid are constantly passing through the enamel of extracted teeth. His first experiments consisted of attaching extracted premolars to a piece of capillary tubing similar to the arrangement used by Atkinson (Fig. V.5) and noting that water moved along the capillary at a rate equivalent to a flow through enamel of $0 \cdot 1$ mm hr^{-2}. The results were similar whether the pulp and dentine were removed or left intact. The experiments were extended by partly covering extracted teeth with immersion oil and examining the enamel surface microscopically. Bergman found that within 2–3 hr droplets of fluid, 2–4 μm in diameter, collected spontaneously under the oil. The largest droplets (20 μm after 15 hr) were in the vicinity of cracks, tufts and lamellae but most of them were generally distributed over the enamel surface (Fig. V.7). No pressure was applied to the pulp. It is thought that physical forces, such as capillarity through the narrow space between the enamel crystals, probably explain the movement of this fluid. It is obviously not dependent on blood pressure nor is it affected by enzyme poisons which suggests that it is not controlled by cell metabolism.

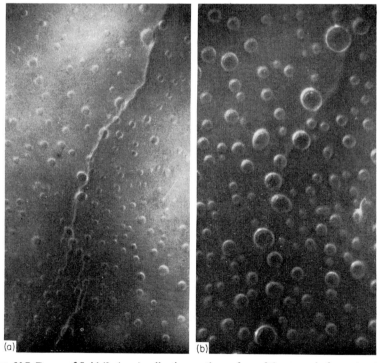

FIG. V.7. Drops of fluid (2–4 μm) collecting on the surface of the enamel of an extracted tooth covered by immersion oil, (a) after 3–4 hr, some of the drops are arranged along a lamella; (b) 12 hr later the drops are 4–8 kg/μm in diameter ($\times$ 1500).

These droplets are detectable *in vivo* in teeth covered with oil but it is not known whether they occur normally. The osmotic pressure of plaque fluid is much higher than that of tissue fluid so it would be predicted that fluid moves outwards on plaque-covered surfaces of enamel but inwards on surfaces bathed in saliva, a prediction which has not been investigated experimentally. The real value of this work is to show the existance of permeable channels in the enamel; the direction of movement within them requires further investigation.

Somewhat similar experiments by Lindén (1968) showed that in young permanent teeth the cervical area was more permeable than the rest of the crown, probably because enamel in this region is thinner and less well mineralized than elsewhere. This difference was not found in deciduous teeth which tended to have a low permeability. Teeth which had been allowed to dry and were rewetted were slightly more permeable than teeth kept moist; presumably some constituents of the enamel shrink on drying and do not resume their original shape after rewetting. Cracks and lamellae were usually more permeable although parts were impermeable, presumably some lamellae became blocked by inclusion of material from saliva and by formation of sclerotic and secondary dentine under the enamel. The reduced permeability with ageing was confirmed. In experiments with ground sections the droplets appeared first on the prism boundaries and especially in the 'tail' regions. Hypoplastic enamel was more permable and white spot caries lesions less permeable than normal enamel. If the osmotic pressure of the fluid in the pulp was increased or if the pulp chamber was dried with filter paper, the droplets rapidly withdrew.

By placing extracted teeth in a plastic bag for up to 48 hr enough fluid, averaging 0·004 μl per tooth, was collected to estimate its calcium and potassium concentration (Bergman *et al.* 1966). The means and ranges of eight samples were: calcium 9·3 mg% (1·9–22) and potassium 6·3 mg% (1·1–18). With such wide ranges little can be concluded about the possible importance of this fluid. Nevertheless, the existence of this fluid renews the possibility that the chemical composition of fully-formed enamel, as well as the progress of caries, may be affected from within the tooth by systemic changes—an old idea which had been widely rejected. Wachtel & Brown (1963) suggested that caries can be influenced by substances diffusing through the tooth from the pulp by the following experiments. When sections of teeth were exposed to acid or adequately nourished cultures of bacteria on the enamel surface, generalized dissolution resulted, not resembling the cone-shaped natural caries lesion. If, however, the bacteria were grown in solutions of vitamin-deficient media and the vitamins were placed in the pulp the lesion became a deep penetrating cavity similar to caries *in vivo*. Presumably the bacteria were attracted towards a food supply which was able to diffuse through the dentine and enamel.

Enamel as a molecular sieve

This is discussed on p. 415.

The nature of the age changes in enamel

There is still no agreement on the question of the nature of the changes occurring in enamel with advancing age which are associated with its reduced permeability. The interprismatic material is involved because this is where the reduced permeability is found. The two possibilities which have been considered are, (1) increased mineralization and (2) an influx of organic matter from saliva (see p. 365). The presence of an outer layer less soluble and probably harder (the evidence is contradictory) than the rest of the enamel indicating a higher mineral content has already been mentioned. Unerupted teeth tend to be more soluble than erupted teeth suggesting that the changes in the outer layer result from exposure to the oral fluids. The amount of mineral salts required to alter permeability probably represents a very small proportional increase in the already high mineral content, and analysis by present methods, even of large numbers of teeth from old and young individuals, would be unlikely to detect so small a chemical difference.

A gradual pigmentation of the teeth occurs with ageing. The pigmented material is less soluble in acid than the rest of the enamel and chemical analyses by Bhussry & Bibby (1957) have shown a marked increase in the nitrogen content of enamel which paralleled increased pigmentation. The pigmented layer is probably associated with the acquired enamel pellicle which was, in fact, called by Valloton the 'pigmented pellicle' (see p. 361, where other age changes on the enamel surface are described).

AGE CHANGES IN THE MANDIBLE

The age changes occurring in the skeleton as a whole are well illustrated in microradiographs of the mandible (Fig. V.8(a) and (b)). In young bone, the Haversion systems are well mineralized and both formation and resorption are equal and limited. In old age resorption is extensive and greatly exceeds formation which, from the large diameter of the Haversion canals and the low density of many of the lamellae, is incomplete (Manson & Lucas 1962). There is also a marked degeneration of the inferior dental artery so that the bone becomes increasingly dependent on the periosteal supply (Bradley 1972).

The question of the withdrawal of salts from dentine and enamel

The fact that substances can diffuse within the mineralized dental tissues raises the question: can mineral salts be removed from the tooth as they can from

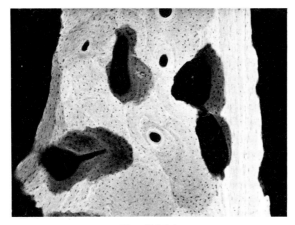

FIG. V.8.(a)

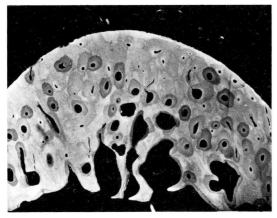

FIG. V.8.(b)

FIG. V.8(a) Microradiographs of the mandibular cortex of a 9-year-old female. Bone
is forming at the right of the large cavities; only one surface shows resorption and
the main bulk of the bone has well-mineralized osteones with narrow canals. (b)
Mandibular cortex of a 69-year-old female with many resorptive cavities and osteones
low in mineral and with wide central canals.

bone? This process would seem most unlikely in enamel, because the tissue fluid
is slight and cells absent. The greater permeability of dentine and the presence
there of the odontoblastic processes, as well as the proof that calcium and
phosphorus may enter dentine after eruption, make it seem possible that
withdrawal of salts might occur. Most experiments have, however, failed to
show any change in the mineral salt content of dentine following conditions
which might be expected to favour withdrawal, such as mineral deficiency

or parathyroid injections. It would seem established that no significant fall in mineral content can occur, although the possibility of very minute changes cannot be ruled out by present evidence. Nevertheless, it is often erroneously stated that salts can be readily withdrawn from the teeth.

Osteoclastic removal of dentine (both inorganic and organic constituents) has not been observed, except during the resorption of the deciduous teeth, or by local disease (for example, pressure from a tumour) and not by general disturbances in calcium metabolism.

Age Changes in Dentine and its Response to Irritation

If the sizes of the pulp cavities of teeth from young and old subjects are compared, it is clear that the inward growth in dentine continues, at the expense of the pulp, long after the roots are fully formed in length ('physiological secondary dentine'). When the enamel is destroyed by attrition or caries the exposed dentine is stimulated, resulting in the formation of 'adventitious secondary dentine'. This tissue is less permeable than normal dentine and thus helps, both by its reduced permeability and by its physical bulk, to protect the pulp, although irritant substances can sometimes reach the pulp through secondary dentine. Benzer (1948) found that the secondary dentine formation occurred fairly uniformly lining the whole of the primary dentine and that little was laid down after the age of 40.

It has been stated that the formation of adventitious secondary dentine in the anterior teeth begins at the incisal tip, following attrition of the enamel, and extends in a cervical direction as attrition becomes more extensive, it being implied that attrition causes this response. In molars, the thickening of the dentine has been stated to occur mostly on the floor and the occlusal surfaces of the pulp chamber, again implicating attrition, at least to explain the changes on the occlusal surface.

Philippas (1961), on the other hand, found in a radiological study that there was much less dentine thickening on the occlusal surface of the pulp chamber than on the floor and lateral walls and the thickening was therefore not a response to attrition. It is possible, however, that imperfectly mineralized secondary dentine was present but was not detected radiologically. Although the rate fell off with increasing age, the thickening of the walls continued up to the highest age studied (70). In upper central incisors, Philippas & Applebaum (1967) reported that physiological regular secondary dentine did not begin at the incisal tip but a thin layer formed fairly regularly along the walls of the pulp chamber. Adventitious (or irregular) secondary dentine formed on the coronal dentine more on the lingual than the labial walls, eventually, by age 70, almost obliterating the pulp.

In lower anterior teeth, although the amount of secondary dentine was not greatly affected by attrition its position did depend on whether attrition was mainly on the lingual or labial surfaces or was symmetrically placed. The growth of physiological secondary dentine occurs in unerupted teeth, further evidence that it is not always dependent on stimuli arising from occlusal wear. One group of unerupted molars contained, by age 30, as much secondary dentine as comparable erupted molars. Symons (1968) concluded from a study of the staining reactions in dentine of teeth over a wide age range that there are two types of physiological secondary dentine: one forms over the whole pulpal surface of the coronal dentine and is in continuity with it and the other forms at a later age (Symons suggests from the mid-twenties) only on certain parts of the dentine although not in response to any damage or irritation.

Occasionally, adventitious secondary dentine may form without gross exposure of dentine, for example under a lamella or crack in the enamel. Even very early caries affecting only the enamel (white spots or very slight cavitation) may cause a response. A reduction in the number of odontoblasts may occur, partly accounted for by 'aspiration' into the tubules (p. 185), with a hyperchromatic line in the dentine (a calciotraumatic response, p. 223) and some secondary dentine formation (Brännstrom & Lind 1965). Presumably even slight increases in enamel permeability may allow irritants to reach the odontoblasts, but intact enamel seems incapable of transmitting the stimulus to the dentine.

In a study on about 300 extracted teeth, physiological secondary dentine was present in all permanent teeth. Adventitious secondary dentine did not invariably form in response to caries, however, only 68% of ninety-eight permanent teeth with deep cavities, and as few as 36% of the teeth with shallow cavities, having formed it (Bevelander & Benzer 1943).

Corbett (1963) in a study of nearly 500 teeth found secondary dentine under carious cavities in about three-quarters of the deciduous teeth but only in about half of the permanent teeth. It was more frequent under interstitial than occlusal cavities. She considers that secondary dentine is not effective in preventing irritants from reaching the pulp as the incidence of pulpitis was greater in teeth with secondary dentine than in those without. This disagrees with the conclusion from experiments with dye or radioactive tracers which suggest that secondary dentine is an efficient seal.

A progressive decrease in staining with basic dyes detectable in demineralized sections has been reported in human dentine with increasing age especially during the decade 20–30. This is presumed to indicate increasing linkages among glycosaminoglycans reducing the number of groups available for staining (Witte & Fullmer 1967).

Experimental study of the responses of dentine to irritation

Many descriptions based on clinical material have been given of the reactions of the dental tissues to various forms of irritation. The interpretation of these studies was greatly clarified by the experimental approach to this problem by Fish (1933), Brännström (1968) and Mjör (1966, 1967). Fish prepared cavities in dogs' teeth and after allowing up to 4 months for the protective reaction to develop, the teeth were extracted and their permeability was studied by incubating the teeth for 48 hr after a stain had been placed in their pulps. By this technique it was found that either or both of two types of response might occur in most teeth but that a few did not respond at all.

(1) THE 'DEAD TRACT' REACTION AND THE 'OPAQUE ZONE'
In the first type of response, mostly to severe irritation, the odontoblasts

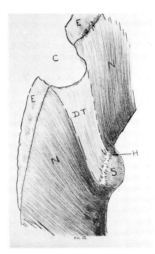

FIG. V.9. The 'dead tract' response of dentine to irritation (dog incisor). Stain allowed to permeate from pulp of extracted tooth, then ground section made. Note that no stain has entered the dead tract (DT). C—Experimental cavity made three months before; E—enamel; N—normal dentine; H—Hyaline layer of calcified, non-tubular tissue; S—secondary dentine (permeable).

of the dentinal tubules affected by the experimental cavity were killed and the tubules became sealed off from the pulp by the deposition of secondary dentine, so that this area of dentine was quite unstained (Fig. V.9). Its impermeability to stain has been confirmed by Berggren (1965) and to [^{14}C]glucose by Hardwick (1961). This zone is more radiopaque and harder than the dentine as a whole indicating that the tubules are mineralized. What appears to be the same reaction had also been described by others as 'opaque metamorphosed dentine' and 'opaque sclerosed dentine'.

Fish observed that different kinds of secondary dentine were formed at different times. That laid down immediately after an injury contained no tubules and formed a dense barrier (a 'hyaline layer'), but secondary dentine laid down later was permeable to dyes and showed clear evidence of containing tubules. He suggested that intense irritation killed or severely injured the odontoblasts and the impermeable layer of secondary dentine was formed, presumably by cells of the pulp. This has been confirmed in a detailed study of the cellular reactions to grinding of rat molars (Sveen and Hawes 1968). Immediately after the grinding, 'aspiration' of odontoblastic nuclei occurred (a movement of nuclei into the dentinal tubules, see Fig. V.12, p. 185) followed by an inflammatory reaction of the pulp cells. After 4 days, nontubular dentine was forming, probably from the spindle-shaped pulp cells which appeared under the damaged dentine. By 8 days, the inflammation had subsided and the newly-formed dentine contained some tubules and was lined by a few regular, oblong cells resembling odontoblasts. These cells were apparently formed from pulp cells in which cell division, measured by tritium-labelled thymidine, increased. The odontoblasts some distance from the damaged tubules were affected and produced thicker dentine separated from the normal dentine by a calciotraumatic response (see p. 223). This has not usually been found and the nature of the stimulus to the odontoblasts of the undamaged tubules is not clear. After an injury, odontoblasts were sometimes found to be present on the secondary dentine probably by the replacement of dead cells from undifferentiated cells of the pulp although this is still uncertain (Stewart 1963). If these cells are replacements they presumably have no processes and form non-tubular dentine thus accounting for the reduced permeability of reparative secondary dentine. If only some of the odontoblasts are killed, then the survivors produce tubules in the secondary dentine in continuity with those of the primary dentine, but there are naturally fewer of them than in a corresponding area of primary dentine because of the smaller number of odontoblasts. Other observers have found that in human teeth, the non-tubular dentine is often absent, probably because the injury inflicted is not sufficiently severe, or is too gradual, to cause the death of the odontoblasts and the consequent formation of impermeable dentine.

The deposit of secondary dentine is usually, but not invariably, confined to those tubules which are irritated and their immediate neighbours, but dead tracts frequently extend over many more tubules (for example, in lower incisors) than are affected by the attrition. Dead tracts formed in dentine exposed by attrition usually contains cracks often filled with bacteria. It is not clear why these bacteria do not produce caries; possibly they are too far removed from food supplies to metabolize actively, or that their numbers at any one site are too small to produce a sufficiently low pH.

Dead tracts are insensitive to pain, presumably because when the dentine is sealed off no stimuli can be transmitted to the nerves of the pulp.

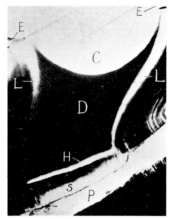

FIG. V.10. A ground section of a dog's incisor showing opaque zones (L) in uninjured tubules surrounding dentine (D) affected by experimental cavity (C). E—Enamel; H—hyaline layer; S—secondary dentine; P—pulp.

THE 'OPAQUE ZONE'

Fish found that the dead tract was sometimes surrounded laterally by tubules which were impermeable (an 'opaque zone') (Fig. V.10). Thus, both at the pulpal end and laterally, the damaged tubules were sealed off from the rest of the tooth.

It has been suggested that the opaque zone is the response in those tubules which anastomose with the more severely-affected tubules in the dead tract. Others have pointed out that since the connections between adjacent tubules seem to be rather limited the opaque zone is too wide to be explained in this way, and make the alternative suggestion that the pulp brings about this response.

(2) THE 'TRANSLUCENT ZONE' REACTION

In the second type of response, usually to less severe stimuli, a plug was formed in the *outer* end of the tubule (a 'translucent zone', so-called because it appears translucent to transmitted light but confusion may arise because it is dark and opaque to reflected light), thus sealing if off from the mouth but allowing communication to continue to the odontoblasts, which were not damaged (Fig. V.11). Fish suggested that the plug was caused by a deposition of calcium salts within the tubule and this fits in with the recent evidence (p. 168) that the peritubular zone may increase in thickness, eventually blocking the tubule, after which it becomes heavily calcified. This type of response does not seem to have been thoroughly studied in human teeth but an apparently similar change was noted by Miller & Massler (1962) in dentine of arrested carious lesions presumably caused by blocking the odontoblastic tubules by inward growth of the peritubular zone.

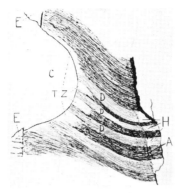

FIG. V.11. An experimental cavity to which the dentine has responded in both ways: by forming dead tracts (D) and also translucent zones (TZ) unstained as periphery but inner part of affected tubules stained and therefore in communication with pulp. E—Enamel; C—experimental cavity; H—hyaline layer; A—newly-formed dentine which is permeable.

In the unreactive teeth, the damaged tubules remained open from the mouth to the pulp which, of course, leads to pulp infection.

In caries, the dead tract response is the more frequent, probably because the toxic material in the advancing cavity prevents or removes any peripheral changes which would be required for a translucent zone response. An exception is occlusal caries in molars which, inexplicably, is more frequently associated with a translucent zone than with a dead tract.

Aspiration of Odontoblasts

In several other experiments in which very severe stimuli were applied to the

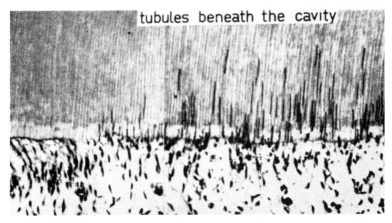

FIG. V.12. The movement of odontoblastic nuclei under those tubules which have been experimentally damaged.

dentine Brännström (1963) described movement ('aspiration') of the nuclei of odontoblasts into the tubules (Figs. V.12).

The dentine of teeth extracted 6–24 hr after desiccation (by a blast of air for 2 min on a cavity prepared before extraction) contained few nuclei and Brännström (1968) speculates that they autolyse in the tubules within this time. Predentine ceased to be formed in the vicinity of the aspirated odontoblasts for some weeks but in those teeth extracted 2–3 months after the 2 min air blast secondary dentine formed, presumably by the modified pulp cells which had taken up the positions formerly occupied by the odontoblasts.

Several hypotheses have been suggested to explain this movement such as: pumping effect owing to mechanical distortion of dentine, increased intrapulpal pressure, chemotaxis, osmosis or capillary attraction following drying of the exposed dentine. The movement of the tubule contents and even aspiration of the nuclei may occur in extracted and fixed teeth or if the teeth are cut into small pieces to improve the penetration of fixative. This finding rules out pressure and drying as explanations and the cause of the nuclear movement remains uncertain.

Mjör (1966, 1967) and Symons (1968) described variations in the radiopacity and staining reactions of the coronal dentine in the permanent teeth from young subjects. Immediately outside the predentine, the dentine is radiopaque and stains well with haematoxylin (the light zone or zone 1), outside this there is a radiolucent eosinophilic layer (the dark zone or zone 2) (Fig. V.13(a) and (b)). These zones are surrounded by the main bulk of the dentine divisible by staining reactions into two further zones, one fairly narrow taking up haematoxylin and toluidine blue (zone 3) and the other constituting the rest of the dentine (zone 4) which stains more faintly (Fig. V.13). The differences between zones 1 and 2 arise from variations in mineralization of the intertubular matrix and on the relative proportion of the areas of the tubules and of the intertubular matrix; peritubular matrix is virtually absent from these zones and does not therefore influence their properties. The light and dark zones are present in old teeth but are much less distinct than in younger teeth especially in their staining reaction. The differences between zones 3 and 4 arise mainly from the amounts and composition of the highly-mineralized peritubular matrix which is smaller in area in zone 3, but much of it remains after demineralization, whereas it is wider in zone 4 and reduces the cross-section of the processes, although little of it remains after demineralization.

The enamel and part of the dentine was ground away in young premolars and either the tooth was extracted immediately or allowed to remain in the mouth for up to three months during which it was exposed to the oral fluids and the plaque which formed on the cut dentine. Examination of the teeth after extraction showed that the immediate effects of grinding was the protrusion of some of the tubular contents (Fig. V.14), the disappearance of

(a)

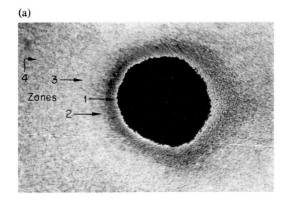

(b)

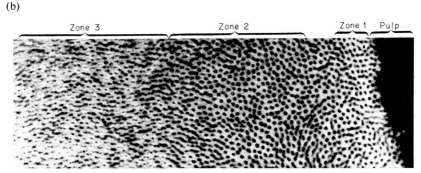

FIG. V.13(a) Microradiograph of horizontal section through pulp horn of premolar with zones 1, 2, 3 and part of 4 on the left (×48). (b) Microradiograph of dentinal tubules: radiopaque area (zone 1) probably from highly-mineralized intertubular matrix since peritubular zones are virtually absent; zone 2 (dark zone) radiolucent from high proportion tubular spaces in relation to matrix; zone 3 and the rest of the dentine is radiopaque from the high proportion of heavily-mineralized peritubular areas (×428).

zone 3 and the development of a 'spotty' staining of zone 4. The staining reaction of zone 3 returned if the teeth were exposed to the oral fluids for longer than 7 days. Even if the dentine was ground off extracted teeth which had been fixed in formalin for 48 hr, the change in zone 3 occurred.

The interpretation of these findings is still speculative. Zone 3 probably represents the early formation of the peritubular matrix and its disappearance and the protrusion of the tubules indicate a probable movement of the tubule contents so that too little remains in zone 3 to stain. The spotty staining may arise from changes in the staining reaction of the tubule contents or from its displacement following the injury. No aspiration of nuclei into the

(a)

(b)

FIG. V.14(a) Protusion of tubule contents and spotty staining of dentine after a cavity had been drilled *in vivo* (× 250). (b) Similar to (a) but with higher magnification (× 1100).

tubules was observed but Mjör believed that the protusion of tubule contents was a process fundamentaly similar to that causing nuclear aspiration. No major changes in microradiography nor any formation of secondary dentine was observed by Mjör even 3 months after grinding and he suggests that the chemical changes involved in caries may be necessary for these responses. This would not explain the results of Fish on dogs (a species which does not suffer from caries) or the formation of secondary dentine in response to attrition, and there is no acceptable explanation for the absence of secondary dentine in these experiments. The reappearance of zone 3, i.e. the renewed development of the peritubular matrix presumably indicates a recovery of the odontoblasts and a resumption of peritubular matrix formation by the odontoblastic process.

The nature of the stimulus to the odontoblasts

Although the question must still be regarded as open, most of the evidence suggests that a chemical stimulus, derived from the oral fluids, is responsible for initiating these changes in dentine. The fact that (1) dentine under cracks or other permeable defects in the enamel may produce a response when the dentine is still protected mechanically from irritation, and (2) the observation that experimental cavities which are immediately sealed with cement form secondary dentine more slowly than when left unfilled, both suggest a chemical stimulus to the odontoblasts or neighbouring pulp cells. The mechanism of the translucent zone response, which occurs at the peripheral part of the tubules some distance from the odontoblasts, is unknown, but would seem to involve an increased activity by the odontoblastic processes of the peritubular zone. Some changes similar to those observed in response to injury of dentine have been described even in unerupted teeth which are, of course, protected from external stimuli.

The dentine, especially of the apical region of the root, when viewed in sections is found to become increasingly translucent or even, in thin sections,

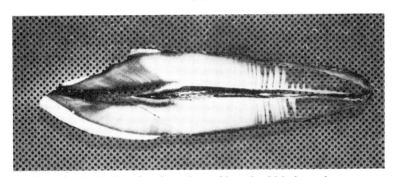

FIG. V.15. A longitudinal section through an old tooth which shows the transparency of the root dentine.

transparent with advancing age (Fig. V.15). This translucency occurs because the tubules become blocked with minerals laid down in the peritubular matrix. Light can pass through more readily because no abrupt changes in direction occur as when light is travelling through calcified dentine matrix, peritubular matrix and odontoblastic process. The term 'translucent zone' has been applied to several different types of change in dentine and some confusion has resulted. First, there are changes occurring mostly in the root and, secondly, the response to irritation mentioned on p. 184. Yet another type of change occurs in a carious cavity. The fact that translucency begins at the apex of the tooth which is least accessible to irritants suggests that this is an age change and that the formation of secondary dentine, translucent zones and dead tracts in response to irritation is perhaps to be regarded as an increase in the rate of changes already occurring spontaneously, rather than as unique changes induced only by irritation. Dead tracts have also been reported in unerupted teeth, suggesting that they, too, are spontaneous age changes not dependent on irritation.

The nature of the age changes in dentine

Three suggestions have been made to explain the reduction in permeability of dentine with age. The first is that the tubules become narrower and may eventually become completely blocked by the mineralization of the peritubular matrix. This is confirmed by chemical analysis of dentine from teeth of different ages which show a small but statistically significant increase in the mineral concentration but in the apical region only. This fits in with the fact that increases in transparency are most marked in the apical region (Fig. V.15). The water content of dentine (loss of weight at 105° C) diminishes from an average of 12.1% at age 10–20 to 9.7% at age 50–80 (Toto *et al.* 1971).

Several workers have shown histologically that the tubule contents (the odontoblastic process) become smaller and the peritubular zone becomes wider with increasing age. This change occurs first at the distal end of the tubule where the translucent zone is widest. Although the most recently formed part of the tubules (i.e. near the pulp) do not usually contain peritubular matrix it is sometimes present.

Eventually the odontoblastic process disappears and is replaced by material which is more radio-opaque (hence more heavily mineralized) than the intertubular matrix and electron micrographs (Nalbandian *et al.* 1960) show that it differs in structure from the intertubular matrix. This change occurs at different rates even in adjacent tubules since transverse sections may show some tubules completely occluded and others still containing a high proportion of odontoblastic process. The reason for some tubules remaining patent when adjacent ones become obliterated is unknown but it might be speculated that if the cell body of a particular process dies (as many do following the shrinkage of the inner surface of the dentine) the process can no longer respond to stimuli and the tubule remains patent at least for some time. The tubule from a dead odontoblast will eventually be sealed by the continued growth of matrix by the neighbouring odontoblasts.

The third suggested explanation of the reduced permeability of dentine with age is that the tubules become obstructed by gas bubbles, of unknown origin, or by deposits of lipid material. Photomicrographs have been published which suggest these changes, but interpretation is difficult and the possibility of artefact great. Older work (Rushton 1940) showed that demineralized sections of incisor teeth, with dentine exposed by attrition and containing dead tracts, stained with Sudan Black indicating the presence of fat in many of the blocked tubules, derived either from oral fluids, or, more likely, from bacteria.

Age changes in pulp

In addition to the reduction in size of the pulp with advancing age and the decline in the number of odontoblasts, which has already been mentioned, there are considerable changes in the tissue components. The number of fibroblasts is reduced and their place is taken by fibrous tissue. Blood vessels also became less numerous although, as the pulp diminishes in size, even their reduced number may appear more prominent. The blood vessels show arteriosclerotic changes from the age of 40 onwards, including the thickening of the intima by the deposition of some PAS-positive material so that it extends into the media, accompanied by calcification of the arteries starting in the aventitia and working inwards. The endo- and perineurium of the nerves also become mineralized, the minerals eventually impregnating the nerve fibre itself resulting in its obliteration so that the number of nerves is greatly diminished in later life.

Deposits of mineralized tissue known as pulp stones, or denticles, are usually formed during the ageing of the pulp. They are found either free in the pulp, or attached to, or entirely surrounded by, dentine. They are all formed in the pulp, but some become partly or completely engulfed by the dentine, as its thickness increases. Most denticles are made up of concentric layers of calcified material not resembling dentine (false denticles), but sometimes they consist of irregular dentine with traces of tubules containing odontoblastic processes (true denticles), and these must be formed by odontoblasts. The origin of the odontoblasts is uncertain; some believe that they are formed from undifferentiated mesenchymal cells in the pulp. Diffuse mineralization of the pulp, that is, the formation of many small mineralized deposits, may also occur.

Cementum

Chemical and histological structure

The chemical composition of cementum is similar to that of dentine but with slightly lower ash content: approximately 26% calcium and 13% phosphorus (Neiders *et al.* 1972).

Cementum is divided into two types: (1) primary (or cell-free) cementum which is present usually on the coronal third of the root, and contains no cells or lacunae but consists of a series of lamellae running parallel to the direction of the root, and (2) secondary (or cell-containing) cementum, which usually covers the apical two-thirds of the root and the bifurcation of the roots of multi-rooted teeth, contains cells and lacunae with canaliculi and is also lamellated. The distribution mentioned above is subject to considerable variation.

Both types of cementum contain the collagen fibres of the periodontal membrane embedded in them.

The presence of lamellae indicates that cementum is formed intermittently. It is formed by cells called cementoblasts similar to osteoblasts, which lie between the edge of the periodontal membrane and a thin layer of uncalcified 'precementum'. These cells become surrounded by the cementum they have produced and are then present in the 'lacunae'. Cementum formation continues throughout life, its average thickness from single rooted teeth increasing threefold in a linear relationship with age between 11 and 76 years (from 0·075 to 0·215 mm). The increase is greater in the apical region (0·189–0·585 mm) and least in the cervical region (Zander & Hürzeler 1958). That which forms after eruption tends to be of the cell-containing variety. The cells in the outer part of the cementum are oval in shape and contain prominent nuclei.

Occlusal stress influences both the amount of cementum laid down and its arrangement. In functioning teeth, cementum is deposited in a dense compact form, either as regular lamellae, or in some teeth, as a series of projections from the cementum already present; in both types, many periodontal fibres are embedded in the outer layers. In non-functioning teeth, however, although the cementum may be thicker than in teeth receiving occlusal stress, it is more diffuse and few fibres are attached to it. Increases in the thickness of cementum are compensated for by reductions in the thickness of the periodontal membrane and not by resorption of bone, a fact which probably explains the observation that the periodontal membrane becomes thinner in advancing age and in teeth without antagonists.

Under experimental conditions of stress, such as large doses of parathyroid hormone, cementum may be resorbed by the cementocytes in a reaction similar to osteocytic osteolysis in bone mentioned on p. 34 (Bélanger 1968). It is uncertain whether this condition ever occurs clinically in human cementum.

Permeability of cementum

Experiments in which dyes have been placed in contact with the outer surface of cementum in the living animal show that primary cementum is impermeable, except in young animals in which the whole tissue (and not any special channels) acquires the stain. In older animals, stains do not permeate either from the outer or the dentinal surface, presumably due to the deposition of an impermeable layer, thought to be of calcium salts (Stones 1934). Thus in later life primary cementum appears to be completely inaccessible, at least to molecules of stain. In young animals, secondary cementum is permeable through the intercommunicating processes of the cementum cells, both from the dentinal tubules and the periodontal membrane, but in older animals the latter route alone is important. Experiments of this type show that most of the lacunae in the inner part of the cementum do not become stained, which implies that these cells are dead and their canaliculi blocked.

When penicillin was sealed into the pulps of extracted teeth it could not be detected on the outer surface of the root except in places where the cementum was removed—in other words, it could permeate dentine from the pulp, but not cementum.

Experiments with radioactive substances have suggested that cementum is somewhat more permeable than the movements of these stains would suggest. Two possible explanations are, (1) that small ions can permate old cementum but the larger molecules of stains cannot, or (2) that both ions and large organic molecules can permeate slightly but owing to the greater sensitivity of methods of observing the presence of radioactivity, they alone have been detected.

Functions of cementum

The first function of cementum is to provide an attachment for the fibres of the periodontal membrane. As the tooth moves in eruption or in physiological mesial drift (see p. 209), groups of fibres become detached from the cementum and degenerate. New fibres are continually being formed to replace them and re-attachment is made to the layer of secondary cementum being laid down at the time.

A second function is to protect the root of a tooth when abnormal stress is applied. Pressure of a root on alveolar bone leads mainly to resorption of the bone and not of the cementum. For example, during orthodontic treatment, when lateral pressure is applied to a tooth, some shallow resorption of cementum may occur, but repair follows and the greater part of the moulding then takes place in the alveolar bone; otherwise, orthodontic treatment would cause root resorption rather than movement of the tooth.

Cementum growth can be very pronounced in the apical region of the tooth. In effect, it lengthens the root and may compensate for loss of enamel resulting from attrition.

Cementum is not dependent on the pulp and dentine for its nutrition, and therefore continues to function even if the pulp is dead. For this reason a pulpless tooth is retained because its periodontal membranes is inserted into the still vital cementum.

References

ARWILL T. *et al.* (1969) Penetration of radioactive isotopes through enamel and dentine. *Odont. Revy* **20**, 47

ATKINSON H.F. (1947) An investigation into the permeability of enamel using osmotic methods. *Brit. dent. J.* **83**, 205

BARNUM C.P. & ARMSTRONG W.D. (1942) *In vivo* and *in vitro* exchange of phosphorus by enamel and dentine. *Amer. J. Physiol.* **135**, 478 (also (1941) *J. dent. Res.* **20**, 232)

BARTELSTONE H.J. (1949) Use of radioactive iodine as tracers in study of tooth physiology. *J. dent. Res.* **28**, 658

BÉLANGER L.F. (1968) Resorption of cementum by cementocyte activity ('cementolysis'). *Calc. Tiss. Res.* **2**, 229

BENZER S. (1948) The development and morphology of physiological secondary dentin. *J. dent. Res.* **27**, 640

BERGGREN H. (1947) Experimental studies on the permability of enamel and dentine. *Svensk Tandl. Tidskrift*, **40**, No. 1B (in English) (also (1951) *J. dent. Res.* **30**, 161)

BERGGREN H. (1965) The reaction of the translucent zone of dentine to dyes and radioisotypes. *Acta odont. Scand.* **23**, 197

BERGMAN G. (1963) Microscopic demonstration of liquid flow through human dental enamel. *Archs oral Biol.* **8**, 233

BERGMAN G. *et al.* (1966) An attempt to analyse the enamel fluid. *Adv. Fluorine Res. & Dental Caries* **4**, 163; also (1965) *J. dent. Res.* **44**, 1409

BEVELANDER G. & BENZER S. (1943) Morphology and incidence of secondary dentine in human teeth. *J. Amer. dent. Ass.* **30**, 1075

BHUSSRY B.R. & BIBBY B.G. (1957) Surface changes in enamel. *J. dent. Res.* **36**, 409

BÖDECKER C.F. & LEFKOWITZ W. (1946) Vital staining of dentin and enamel. *J. dent. Res.* **25**, 357, 393

BRADFORD E.W. (1951) The interpretation of ground sections of dentine. *Brit. dent. J.* **90**, 303; (1958) The maturation of dentine. *Brit. dent. J.* **105**, 212

BRADLEY J.C. (1972) Age changes in the vascular supply to the mandible. *Brit. dent. J.* **132**, 147

BRÄNNSTRÖM M. (1964) A hydrodynamic mechanism in transmission of pain-producing stimuli through the dentine. In *Sensory Mechanisms in Dentine*, p. 13. Ed. ANDERSON D.J., Pergamon Press Ltd., Oxford.

BRÄNNSTRÖM M. (1968) The effect of dentin dessication and aspiration of odontoblasts on the pulp. *J. pros. dent.* **20**, 165

BRÄNNSTRÖM M. & LIND P.O. (1965) Pulpal response to early dental caries. *J. dent. Res.* **44**, 1045

COFFEY C.T. *et al.* (1970) Analysis of human dentinal fluid. *Oral Surg.* **30**, 835

CORBETT M.E. (1963) Incidence of secondary dentine in carious teeth. *Brit. dent. J.* **114**, 142

DOWSE C.M. & JENKINS G.N. (1957) Fluoride uptake *in vivo* in enamel defects and its significance. *J. dent. Res.* **36**, 816

FANNING R.J. *et al.* (1953) Salivary contribution to enamel maturation and caries resistance. *J. Amer. dent. Ass.* **49**, 668

FISH E.W. (1933) *An Experimental Investigation of Enamel, Dentine and the Dental Pulp.* Bale, Sons & Danielson, London

FOSDICK L.S. *et al.* (1959) Effect of age and exposure to oral environment on the permeability of teeth. *J. dent. Res.* **38**, 676

FRANK R.M. (1968) Ultrastructural relationship between the odontoblast, its process and the nerve fibre In *Dentine and Pulp.* Ed. SYMONS N.B.B., p. 115, E. & S. Livingstone, Edinburgh

GARANT P.R. (1972) The organisation of microtubules in rat odontoblast tubules revealed by perfusion fixation with glutaraldehyde. *Archs oral Biol.* **17**, 1047

HARDWICK J.L. (1961) Isotope studies on the penetration of glucose into normal and carious enamel and dentine. *Archs oral Biol.* **4**, 97

HARDWICK J.L. & FREMLIN J.H. (1959) Isotope studies on the permeability of the dental enamel to small particles and ions. *Proc. Roy. Soc. Med.* **52**, 752

ISOKAWA S. *et al.* (1970) A scanning electron microscopic observation of etched human peritubular dentine. *Archs oral Biol.* **15**, 1303

JOYSTON-BECHAL S. *et al.* (1971) Diffusion of radioactive ions into human dental enamel. *Archs oral Biol.* **16**, 375

LEFKOWITZ W. (1943) Further observations on dental lymph in the dentin. *J. dent. Res.* **22**, 287

LINDÉN L.-A. (1968) Microscopic observations of fluid flow through enamel *in vivo*. *Odont. Revy* **19**, 349; also **18**, 220, **19**, 1

MANSON J.D. & LUCAS R.B. (1962) A microradiographic study of age changes in the human mandible. *Archs oral Biol.* 7, 761

MILLER C.D. (1958) The dental caries response to rats fed cariogenic and noncariogenic diets for different periods of time. *J. Nutr.* **66**, 113

MILLER J. (1954) The micro-radiographic appearance of dentine. *Brit. dent. J.* **97**, 7

MILLER W.A. & MASSLER M. (1962) Permeability and staining of active and arrested lesions in dentine. *Brit. dent. J.* **112**, 187

MJOR I.A. (1966) Microradiography of human coronal dentine. *Archs oral Biol.* **11**, 225 (see also 1293, 1307, 1317, and **12**, 247)

MORENO E.C. & ZAHRADNIK R.T. (1973) The pore structure of human dental enamel. *Archs oral Biol.* **18**, 1063

MYERS H.M. *et al.* (1952) A tracer study of the transfer of F^{18} to teeth by topical application. *J. dent. Res.* **31**, 743

NALBANDIAN J. *et al.* (1960) Sclerotic age changes in root dentine of human teeth as observed by optical, electron, and X-ray microscopy. *J. dent. Res.* **39**, 598

NEIDERS M.E. *et al.* (1972) Electron probe microanalysis of cementum and underlying dentin in young permanent teeth. *J. dent. Res.* **51**, 122

PHILIPPAS G.G. (1961) Influence of occlusal wear and age on formation of dentin and size of pulp chamber. *J. dent. Res.* **40**, 1186

PHILIPPAS G.G. & APPLEBAUM E. (1967) Age changes in the permanent upper lateral incisor teeth. *J. dent. Res.* **46**, 1002 (see also (1968) **47**, 411, 769)

POOLE D.F.G. *et al.* (1963) The movement of water and other molecules through dental enamel. *Archs oral. Biol.* **8**, 771

RUSHTON M.A. (1940) Observations on Fish's 'dead tracts' in dentine. *Brit. dent. J.* **68**, 11

SCHOUBOE T. & MACDONALD J.B. (1962) Prolonged viability of organisms sealed in dentinal caries. *Archs oral Biol.* 7, 525

SHROFF F.R. *et al.* (1954) Electron microscope studies of dentine. *Oral. Surg., Med., Path.* **7**, 662; **9**, 432

SOGNNAES R.F. & SHAW J.H. (1952) Salivary and pulpal contributions to the radiophosphorus uptake in enamel and dentin. *J. Amer. dent. Ass.* **44**, 489

SOGNNAES R.F. & VOLKER J.F. (1941) Radioactive phosphorus in tooth enamel. *Amer. J. Physiol.* **133**, 112

SPEIRS R.L. (1967) Factors influencing the 'maturation' of developmental hypomineralised areas in the enamel of rat molars. *Caries Res.* **1**, 15 (see also (1971) *Calc. Tiss. Res.* **7**, 249)

SPRETER VON KREUDENSTEIN T. & STÜBEN J. (1955) Dentinstoffwechselstudien. *Dtsch. Zahnärztl. Ztschr.* **10**, 473, 1178; (1956) **11**, 1214; (1957) **12**, 500

STEVENSON T.S. (1965) Fluid movement in human dentine. *Archs oral Biol,* **10**, 935 (see also (1966) **12**, 1149)

STEWART J.M. (1963) Immediate response of odontoblasts to injury. *Proceedings 41st Meeting of Int. Ass. Dent. Res. Abs.* **15**, p. 36

STONES H.H. (1934) The permeability of cementum. *Brit. dent. J.* **56**, 273

SYMONS N.B.B. (1968) The formaton of primary and secondary dentine. In *Dentine and Pulp,* Ed. Symons N.B.B., p. 67, University of Dundee

SVEEN O.B. & HAWES R.R. (1968) Differentiation of new odontoblasts and dentine bridge formation in rat molar teeth after tooth grinding. *Archs oral Biol.* **13**, 1399

TOTO P.D. *et al.* (1971) Effect of age on water content in human teeth. *J. dent. Res.* **50**, 1284

TSATSAS B.G. & FRANK R.M. (1972) Ultrastructure of the dentinal tubular substances near the dentino-enamel junction. *Calc. Tiss. Res.* **9**, 238

WACHTEL L.W. & BROWN L.R. (1963) *In vitro* caries. Factors influencing the shape of the developing lesion. *Archs oral Biol.* **8**, 99

WAINWRIGHT W.W. (1951) Enamel penetration by radioactive salts of zinc, calcium, silver, plutonium, palladium and copper. *J. Amer. dent. Ass.* **43**, 664

WAINWRIGHT W.W. (1954) Penetration of teeth by radioactive materials. *J. dent. Res.* **33**, 767; (1955) **34**, 28

WAINWRIGHT W.W. & LEMOINE E.A. (1950)

Rapid diffuse penetration of intact enamel and dentine by carbon[14] labelled urea. *J. Amer. dent. Ass.* **41,** 135

WASSERMAN F. *et al.* (1941) Studies on the different pathways of exchange of minerals in teeth with the aid of radioactive phosphorus. *J. dent. Res.* **20,** 389

WATERS N.E. (1971) The selectivity of human dental enamel to ionic transport. *Archs oral Biol.* **16,** 305

WITTE W.E. & FULLMER H.M. (1967) Effects of age on dentin demonstrated with Azure A. *J. dent. Res.* **46,** 218

ZANDER H.A. & HÜRZELER B. (1958) Continuous cementum apposition. *J. dent.* **37,** 1035

CHAPTER VI

ERUPTION AND RESORPTION

Eruption

The term 'eruption' is used to refer to the movement of a tooth through the jaw tissues into the oral cavity. Eruption must be distinguished from the growth of a tooth, which means increase in size irrespective of the relative position of the tooth to its neighbouring tissues, although the growth may be one of the factors causing eruption. Eruption implies much more than the mere 'cutting' of the tooth through the gum although the term is sometimes used in this limited sense, perhaps because this is the only part of the process of which an individual is aware.

Hypotheses on the causes of eruption must take into account that the movements occurring during the eruption of different teeth differ both in distance and in direction and also that the deciduous teeth are partially, and permanent teeth completely, surrounded by bone (the dental crypt) at certain stages of their development and mineralization.

Information on which theories of eruption are based come from three sources: clinical observations on human subjects showing some abnormality of eruption, radiological and histological studies on normal subjects and experimental observations in animals. There are disadvantages in all three approaches. Observations on subjects showing abnormalities may not apply to the normal. It is not easy to procure large numbers of normal human specimens over the appropriate age range, to obtain information on an adequate statistical basis, about the histology and detailed relation of the tissues during the various stages of eruption. Animal experiments on the mechanism of eruption have almost invariably been carried out on the continuously erupting incisors of rodents and it cannot necessarily be assumed that the eruptive process in these teeth is the same as in teeth of limited growth, such as human teeth.

Consequently, it is not surprising that the question is highly controversial and that no hypothesis has yet been proposed which fits all these facts or can be regarded as a complete explanation of eruption. There is, of course, no reason to believe that only one force is at work (although much discussion does seem to have made this unjustifiable assumption) and several of the suggested mechanisms may contribute to the complicated process.

The eruption rate of the continuously growing incisor is normally balanced by the rate of attrition, so that the length of the tooth remains approximately constant. Apparent changes in eruption rate could, therefore, be a result of changes in attrition. Statistical studies by Ness (1956), Bryer (1957) and others have shown that if the distal part of one incisor is cut off, so that it is too short to be in occlusal contact with its antagonist, the eruption rate is increased about threefold and the cells in the apical region develop more quickly and become more numerous (Michaeli *et al.* 1972). Conversely, if a metal crown is cemented on to the incisor, thereby preventing attrition, then eruption ceases (Eccles 1965). Bryer has measured the effects of various dietary and surgical procedures on this 'unimpeded eruption rate' by marking the tooth with a diamond disc at the gingival level and measuring every few days the distance of the mark from the gingivae.

The various hypotheses have been reviewed by Massler & Schour (1941), Miller (1957), Ness (1964), Ten Cate (1969) and Berkovitz (1975, 1976).

Hypotheses on the cause of eruption

(1) ROOT GROWTH

The simplest theory of eruption is that the growth of the roots pushing against the alveolar bone forces the crown through the gum. Although there is a great deal of evidence which proves that root growth is not essential for eruption, and it alone could hardly explain the different directions in which the various teeth move, it is difficult to prove that under normal conditions root growth plays no part in eruption. The evidence that has been raised against the theory is as follows:

(a) The eruptive movements of some teeth, for example, the upper canines, exceed the total length of their roots.

(b) Rootless teeth are known to erupt. For example, if a deciduous tooth is extracted, its permanent successor sometimes erupts more rapidly even if its root has not yet developed. Other examples of rootless teeth are those in which the root has failed to develop, and teeth whose roots have been fractured in accidents; in such cases eruption may also occur. Occasionally the incisors are erupted in a new-born child although the roots are not yet formed; however, this is pathological but, even in the normal rat molar, movement of the germ has been stated to occur before root growth begins. In experiments by Gowgiel (1961, 1967) in which monkeys and rats were treated with X-rays in the mouth region, growth of the roots of the teeth was arrested but the rootless teeth erupted and reached functional occlusion and he concluded that eruption resulted from growth of the follicular sac.

(c) If the antagonist of a tooth is extracted after root formation is complete, 'supra-eruption' may occur (i.e. eruption beyond the normal occlusal position). This observation has been assumed to imply that the 'force' of eruption is present after the completion of root growth and is normally opposed by occlusal stress. This is not necessarily so, however, as supra-eruption may be caused, at least partly, by the elongation of the root as a result of increased growth of cementum. It is a strong clinical impression (although statistics are lacking) that when supra-eruption does occur, the clinical crown is not increased in size and this is due to simultaneous growth of bone at the alveolar crest. If the tooth should be extracted later, this bony overgrowth may lead to difficulty in denture construction

In all these examples, abnormal factors are at work and they do not *disprove* that root growth may be important in the eruption of normal teeth.

(d) When the pulp was removed from rat incisors and they were root filled, eruption ceased although changes occured in the periodontal ligament. If even 3–4 mm of pulp were left, however, eruption continued (Eccles 1965) which may explain some previous results in which eruption continued after pulp removal which had wrongly been assumed to be complete. This experiment supports root or pulp growth as a factor in eruption and is contrary to the hypothesis (discussed later) that the periodontal ligament provides the motive force.

(e) Experiments in which Hertwig's epithelial sheath was removed from one incisor in each of a group of rats (thus preventing the elongation of the root of one incisor with the other incisor acting as a control) showed that the eruption rates were the same as those of the unoperated control tooth on the other side.

(f) Experiments by Bryer (1957), Ness (1957) and Berkovitz & Thomas (1969) in which the rodent incisor was surgically fractured within the socket and the severed distal end, after a few days of reduced movement, was eventually shed also disprove root growth as the sole cause of eruption. As these experiments are relevant to other hypotheses, they are described in more detail later (p. 206). Although the pulp tissue degenerated and became avascular, the site of the fracture was inflamed and the vessels were dilated. As the distal fragment erupted, its place was taken by a vascular connective tissue. The proximal end, with the growing tissue in the apical region, continued to grow but this was shown by a folding of the wall and not by eruptive movement. Even when the proximal (growing) end was removed and its place was taken by a vascular connective tissue, the incisal end still erupted. In similar experiments by Ness (1957) the eruption rate of the severed end was much slower than in controls but eruption undoubtedly continued.

Carlson (1944) used cephalometric radiography to study the relation of root

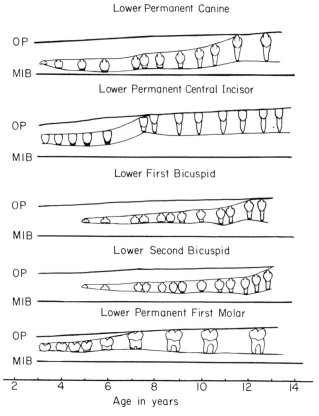

Fɪɢ. VI.1. Diagram illustrating the results of cephalometric radiography. It shows the size of certain teeth, their position in relation to the occlusal plane (OP), and the mandibular inferior border (MIB), at different ages, as revealed by radiography (after Carlson 1944).

growth to eruptive movements in children. This method consists of taking frequent radiographs of the jaws of growing children and measuring the relative positions of various landmarks, in this case the crowns and root ends of some of the mandibular teeth to the mandibular border (Fig. VI.1). Five children over the age range of 3 months to 7 years were studied, each for about 9 years. His main findings (some of which were already known) were that when root growth began there was a definite downward movement of the root of between 2 and 4 mm into the bone, showing that the effect of root growth is not always to push the crown occlusally. Following this stage there was a period of rapid eruption during which all parts of the tooth increased their distance from the mandibular border, indicating that the tooth was moving as a whole, but the crown tip showed greater movement than did the root end, suggesting that root growth was playing a part. When eruption was complete and the teeth were in occlusion, the root end moved nearer to the lower border of the mandible, so that root growth was again proceeding without causing any eruptive movement. The rate of eruption was unaltered by the emergence of the crown, which is surprising since it would have been expected that eruption would be slower when the occlusal surface of the tooth was being pushed against the resistance of the tissues. Carlson obtained quantitative evidence that there is a prolonged slow eruption of the human teeth by finding that eruptive changes had not ceased even at the age of 17 years. At the age of 12 years, after all the teeth except the third molars are in occlusion, growth still occurs at the mandibular condyle with increase in facial height. To maintain the free-way space at a constant value of 2–4 mm (see p. 516) the condylar growth is accompanied by growth of alveolar crestal bone and eruption of the teeth, but with no change in the length of the clinical crown.

This work gives no decisive evidence for any theory but is additional proof of the inadequacy of root growth as the sole force of eruption, though it gives some indirect support to the possibility that root growth may play a part.

(2) CONSTRICTION OF PULP

It has been suggested that as the odontoblasts increase the thickness of dentine in the root of the tooth, and as the pulp cavity becomes smaller, the increased pressure within is sufficient to erupt the tooth. The evidence already described based on the behaviour of rootless teeth does not support this theory, nor does the observation that teeth with extirpated pulps may erupt normally. Bryer found that in protein and calorie deficiency, which in rats produced thinner dentine and consequently wider pulps, the eruption rates were either unchanged or increased, and not decreased as the pulp constriction theory requires. In vitamin A deficiency, he found the pulp to be constricted (see pp. 255–6) as a result of the unusual dentine growth, and the pulp vessels were less numerous and narrower. Eruption rate was reduced, a result which is again contrary to this theory.

Even more striking evidence against the theory is provided by the hypophysectomy experiments in which great constriction of the pulp occurred with marked retardation of the eruption rate (see pp. 219–20).

(3) PULP GROWTH

Sicher (1942) suggested that the growth of the pulp—which must normally keep pace with the growth of the roots—may provide at least part of the 'eruptive force' in certain teeth. He showed that in a narrow zone at the apical end of the pulp, cells are in active division and that new collagen fibres are being formed and Ness & Smale (1959) has confirmed this observation and shown that two-thirds of the mitoses in pulp cells are present in the basal millimetre of the pulp. The theory has been tested by measuring the rate of eruption after the injection of antimitotic drugs. They did reduce the rate and one drug (deme-colcine) had an almost immediate effect (Chiba *et al.* 1968). Although these drugs inhibited cell proliferation in the pulp they have other effects elsewhere which might have influenced eruption so that the results were inconclusive.

Sicher described in some teeth a hammock-like 'ligament', which is anchored to the alveolar bone and surrounds the end of the root, and rests on a 'cushion' of tissue containing spaces filled with fluid. In Sicher's theory, the cushioned hammock ligament is thought to act as a relatively fixed point so that pulp growth would tend to move the tooth occlusally. The existence of the hammock ligament has not been confirmed by others (Main 1965) and his hypothesis seems unlikely.

Bryer obtained data which did not support this theory. He found that in both deficiency and overdosage of vitamin D, there was an increased pro-liferation of the pulp and it was associated with a slightly reduced rate of eruption.

(4) BONE GROWTH THEORIES

There are two ways in which bone growth has been pictured as a cause of eruption. It has been suggested that growth of the alveolar bone pulls the tooth outwards by the periodontal fibres. The theory hangs on the nature of bone growth and on the direction in which the oblique fibres run. Bone grows by apposition and not within the bone itself (interstitially). In the alveolar bone the apposition occurs on the crest and the new bone would not be expected to exert tension on the periodontal ligament inserted into bone already formed. Massler & Schour (1941) stated that in the human tooth during eruption, the fibres run in the reverse direction to what the theory requires (i.e. they give the impression that the tooth is pulling on the bone). In several species of animals, the fibres run in the same direction during erup-tion as they do in the adult, i.e. from a more cervical insertion in the bone to a more apical attachment on the tooth, which is quite compatible with the theory. In the rat molars, O'Brien *et al.* (1958) found that the periodontal fibres appeared to be parallel to the root until the tooth reaches the occlusal plane. In view of the nature of bone growth and of the uncertainties in the direction of the periodontal fibres, the theory has little support.

The second way in which bone growth may assist eruption has been sug-gested by Sicher (1942). He has found that bone may grow below the cushioned hammock ligament at the apex of certain teeth and thus provide a pressure which assists the eruptive force which he believes is mainly caused by pulp growth. In multi-rooted teeth, the bone between the roots is found to be actively proliferating during eruption and he thinks that pressure applied at this point forces the tooth towards the mouth. Sicher states that when bone is growing on the inter-radicular septum, the hammock ligament degenerates, after which time bone growth is the only force of eruption. The presence of new bone trabeculae in these places cannot be regarded as proof that they are the cause of the eruptive movement, however. If the tooth were moved by some other force, the gap it left could be filled with new bone.

Sicher emphasizes that growth of different tissues at different rates is the main factor causing eruptive movements. If madder or alizarin is fed to an animal for a period, any bone mineralized during that period acquires a permanent pink stain. This fact has been used to find out where mineralization is occurring at different stages in the growth of an animal. Brash (1926) showed by this method that some of the movements of eruption are explicable by the manner in which bone resorbs in some parts of the jaw and is deposited in others. Histological preparations show that rotating and tilting movements of teeth during eruption are accompanied by resorption of bone in front of, and apposition of bone behind, the moving tooth. Sicher & Weinmann (1944) suggest that the apposition of bone on one side of the tooth causes the opposite side to press on the bone leading to its resorption, but there seems no evidence as to whether the resorption or the apposition is the original cause of the tooth movement.

The factors controlling the growth of a bone into its final shape are not fully understood but appear to be of two main types. First, since fragments of growing femur when transplanted into other parts of the body develop into a recognizable femur, it seems clear that the cells of a developing bone possess some inherent pattern of growth. It is equally clear that the bone is sensitive to stresses applied outside itself (see p. 45).

It might therefore be suggested that eruption is partly brought about by the inherent growth pattern of the bone, especially in controlling the changes in direction of the eruptive movements, and partly by the lengthening root of the tooth which would have a direct effect in moving the tooth and an indirect effect by exacting pressures which would mould the bone by causing resorption.

Bryer found increased growth of alveolar bone or osteoid in deficiency of both vitamin A and vitamin D and in neither case was the eruption rate increased. He argues that bone growth is unlikely to be a factor in the eruption of the rodent incisor. These deficiencies promoted a growth of bone which compressed the alveolar space, however, and it is doubtful whether it can be reasonably argued from this result that *normal* bone growth is unimportant in eruption.

(5) VASCULARITY OR TISSUE FLUID PRESSURE AS A CAUSE OF ERUPTION

This theory suggests that the presence of many blood vessels in the apical region causes the formation of tissue fluid in a small closed space which exerts a steady pressure which can only expend itself by the movements of the tooth. The similar pressure in the periodontal membrane may prevent the 'leakage' of the pressure built up in the apex of the tooth. The theory could explain the supra-eruption of teeth after the extraction of the antagonists, as this force is presumably present throughout life but is normally opposed by contact with the antagonist.

Experiments on rabbits by King (1936) and on rats by Bryer showed that removal of part of the cervical sympathetic cord on one side, which cuts the sympathetic nerve supply to the teeth on that side (resulting in vaso-dilatation), is accompanied by an increased rate of eruption on the operated side as compared with the unoperated control on the other side. Bryer also found that the converse experiment—the severance of the blood vessels of the alveolar fundus—was followed by a reduced eruption rate. These experiments do suggest that changes in the blood flow may affect eruption, but provide no evidence that tissue fluid pressure is responsible. An increase or decrease in the blood flow may produce a corresponding change in the nutrients and hormones and these factors might, perhaps by affecting tissue growth, alter the rate of eruption.

Taylor & Butcher (1951) also found that cutting the inferior dental nerve (the sensory nerve to the teeth) increased eruption rates, but, contrary to the results of others, removal of the cervical sympathetic nerves had no effect. They doubted whether denervation acted through a vascular mechanism and suggested that after denervation, the incisor would be insensitive and therefore subjected to more vigorous use which had the effect of breaking off pieces from the occlusal surface. The result of this damage was similar to that of cutting the tooth, i.e. it would be out of occlusion (at least at times) and would therefore erupt more rapidly. However, Bryer concluded that vascularity is the most important factor in the eruption of the rodent incisor and thought that this also applies to the human teeth. Since changes in

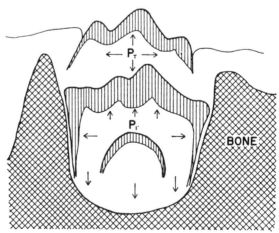

FIG. VI.2. Pressures affecting eruption. P_I is intrapulpal pressure, P_T is tissue pressure.

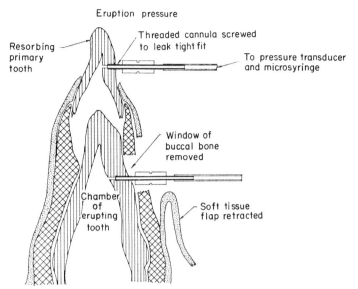

Fɪɢ. VI. 3. Diagram of the surgical procedures of Hassel & McMinn (1972) to measure the fluid pressures in the pulps of resorbing and erupting teeth.

the growth rate of the dental tissues had little effect on eruption rates he believed that the effect of the changes in blood flow influence eruption by altering local tissue fluid pressure and not by altering the supply of nutrients.

The effect of changing the blood pressure by prolonged administration of drugs has been tested by Main (1961) on the rate of eruption of the rat incisor but the results were inconclusive. Reduction of arterial blood pressure by giving hypotensive drugs for 15 days did not affect eruption rates markedly, but there was a slight fall in one experiment. The drugs used were found to *raise* capillary pressure which, on the tissue fluid theory, would be expected to increase eruption rate.

Hassel & McMinn (1972) measured in dogs the tissue fluid pressures between resorbing deciduous and erupting permanent teeth and also that within the pulp of the permanent tooth (Figs VI.2 and VI.3). In all of thirteen experiments, with precautions to avoid artefacts, the pressure difference averaging 13 mm Hg was in the direction which would promote eruption and calculation showed that the force was adequate to contribute to eruption, although this was not necessarily regarded as the only mechanism.

The Periodontal Ligament as the Source of the Eruptive Forces

The surgical procedures pioneered by Bryer were extended by Berkovitz &

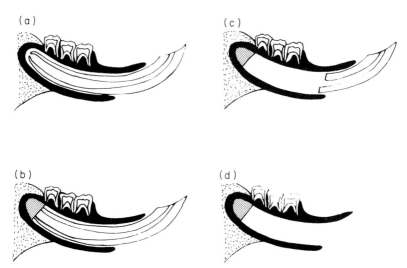

Fig. VI.4. The surgical procedures in root resection: (a) before operation; (b) proliferative odontogenic base removed; (c) continued eruption up to the alveolar crest—in some rats the tooth was retained in this position for up to 6 weeks but in others it was eventually lost, as in (d).

Thomas (1969) in experiments in which the roots of rat incisors were either resected (removal of the proliferating odontogenic base (Fig. IV.4)) or transected (the root cut into two separate parts) and the effect on the unimpeded eruption rate was measured. The results of resection were not entirely consistent as in 5 out of 16 animals, eruption virtually ceased whereas in the other 11 it slowed down at first, reached control levels by 4–7 days after the operation, remained at this rate for 12 days, then decreased when the tooth reached the alveolar crest and was lost in some rats. Complete transection showed a similar pattern. These experiments seemed to exclude root elongation, pulp and dentine proliferation (since histological study showed the pulp had degenerated after the operation) and tissue fluid pressure (since although the walls of the socket contained fluid it was not within a closed space). The only obvious eruptive mechanism is something within the periodontal ligament.

In a further experiment, the effect of a procedure which Berkovitz (1971) describes as 'partial root resection' was tested (Fig. VI.5). Those parts of the odontogenic base which form enamel were removed, leaving only the lingual tissues forming dentine and attached by the periodontal ligament. As eruption continued, the enamel-covered buccal surface was lost 24 days after the operation. Eruption continued as normal until 20 days after the operation, after which the rate declined to about one-third that of the controls. Clearly it

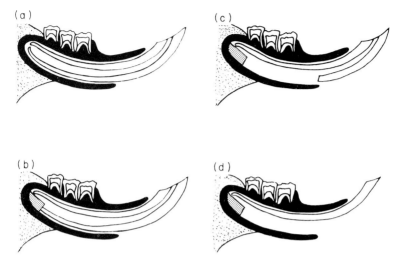

Fig. VI.5. The surgical procedures in partial root resection and its results: (a) before operation; (b) buccal region with enamel organ removed and replaced by a blood clot; (c) continued eruption moves the enamel already formed; (d) all enamel-covered part of the tooth lost but lingual part continues to erupt.

seems unlikely that tissue fluid could play any part in the eruption, since, the fluid was much less enclosed than in the previous experiment and, after shedding the enamel, again the periodontum seems the most likely source of the propulsive mechanism.

SHRINKAGE OF COLLAGEN AS A FORCE IN ERUPTION

Thomas (1964) postulated that in the course of development and maturation of collagen, the formation of cross-linkages (p. 96) might result in the shrinkage of the fibres. He suggests that if this shrinkage occurs in the fibre of the periodontal ligament it would exert a force which would lead to the eruption of the teeth. To investigate this hypothesis Thomas fed amino acetonitrile (AAN) to rats: this substance produces lathyrism, a condition in which cross-linkages of collagen do not occur. Eruption of the molars and incisors was greatly retarded although root growth continued normally.

Berkovitz *et al.* (1972) and Tsuruta *et al.* (1974) attempted to repeat the experiments of Thomas on the effect of AAN on eruption. Although the teeth became easier to extract, indicating some effect on the periodontal ligament, the unimpeded eruption rate was virtually unchanged, i.e. Thomas' previous results and his main evidence were not confirmed and this discrepancy is unexplained. These experiments did not support the periodontal hypothesis unless it was assumed that the retarding forces had been reduced to the same extent as the propulsive forces which seem unlikely when unimpeded eruption rates were not altered.

The experiments of Berkovitz *et al.* (1969, 1971) seem to eliminate most of the suggested causes except some action by the periodontal ligament. The failure to confirm an effect of AAN on the unimpeded eruption rate casts serious doubt on the hypothesis that the shrinkage of collagen is the motive force. Tsurutu *et al.* (1974) suggest that the reduction of the impeded eruption rate could perhaps be explained by the following train of events. The reduction in normal development of collagen after AAN might be expected to lead to a loosening of the teeth and consequently more movement within the socket when subjected to occlusal stress. This excessive movement might interfere with growth processes in the apical region of the tooth, although this hypothesis assumes that growth of the dental tissues is important in eruption.

The indication from the experiments of Berkovitz (1976) that the periodontal ligament produces eruption but the generally negative results with AAN suggesting that it is not shrinkage of collagen has lead to the suggestion (first speculated by Ness (1967)) that the fibroblasts in the periodontium may exert an eruptive force (Beersten *et al.* 1973, 1974). The fibroblasts are arranged in three zones in the rat incisor, one near the alveolar bone, another near the cementum and the third between the other two; the cells in the various zones differ in shape and orientation, those on the cemental side being arranged as a palisade and separated from the intermediate by a cell-free zone (Eccles 1965). The differences may arise from the amount and density of packing of the periodontal fibres.

Although there is very little direct evidence for an active role of fibroblasts in eruption (and the idea arose simply because the evidence seemed to disprove other possibilities) certain histological features of these cells have been reported by electron microscopy (microfilaments and microtubules) which are associated with motility in other cells. Such motility, in conjunction with the enmeshed collagen and oxytalan fibres might lead to tooth movement.

Eastoe (1976) speculates that if fibroblasts are concerned with both the production and phagocytosis of collagen fibrils they would be in contact with the old and new fibres. Contraction of the cell might therefore exert a tension which could be the motive force of eruption. It is by no means certain that new fibrils would retain contact with the cells since the aggregation of tropocollagen molecules into fibrils is thought to be an extracellular process.

SOME FACTORS CONTROLLING ERUPTION

Each stage of mineralization and eruption tends to occur at a slightly earlier age in girls. This difference (like the much larger differences between the ages of onset of ossification) is found before puberty and is therefore presumably controlled by the sex chromosomes rather than by sex hormones. In one survey on about 250 children, the times of mineralization and eruption, expressed as a percentage of their age, averaged 3 and 5% earlier respectively in girls than in boys. The teeth were bigger in boys by an average of 4%.

Eruption tends to occur earlier in higher socioeconomic groups, presumably owing to better nutritional conditions. Racial (i.e. genetic) factors influence eruption even more, for example permanent teeth of American children of American stock erupt an average of 7 months earlier than the corresponding teeth of white children of similar economic status (Garn *et al.* 1973).

The thyroid hormones influence the rate of eruption (Baume *et al.* 1954, pp. 215 and 221).

CONTINUOUS ERUPTION OF HUMAN TEETH

Eruption of teeth continues at a slow rate throughout adult life in man. The length of the clinical crown does not necessarily increase, since the extra eruption may merely compensate for loss of tooth substance by attrition on the occlusal surface. In western countries where attrition is slight, continued eruption leads to an increase in the vertical height of the face at a rate of about 0·4 mm per year.

Evidence for what Gottlieb (1938) called 'active eruption', that is, the actual movement of the tooth in the direction of the occlusal plane, after occlusal contact has been reached, is available from the work of Carlson, as already mentioned. It is also proved by the observation that if a tooth becomes fixed, so that active eruption ceases (for example, by ankylosis with the alveolar bone), it eventually appears to be shorter than neighbouring teeth. It is, in fact, acting as a fixed point against which the continued eruption of the other teeth may be detected. This movement of the tooth is accompanied by a change in the part of the tooth surface which is covered by the epithelial attachment. When occlusion is first reached, about one-third of the enamel is covered by epithelium, and the epithelial attachment extends approximately to the cemento-enamel junction. In late life, the whole of the enamel and a considerable area of the cementum may be exposed; and the epithelial attachment then occupies a position entirely on the cementum. This change in the position on the tooth surface of the epithelial attachment was called by Gottlieb 'passive eruption'.

Physiological Mesial Drift

As contact points between adjacent teeth in the human mouth wear, instead of a gap being left the teeth move mesially ('physiological mesial drift'). In the rat, the movement of the molars is mainly distal; in herbivores the molars move mesially and the premolars distally, so that the more general term 'approximal drift' has been suggested. Several hypotheses have been proposed to explain this drift. One is that the teeth are slightly tilted so that occlusal forces, although mainly exerted to move the tooth apically, have a horizontal component which pushes the teeth in a direction depending on whether the tilt is mesial or distal. The existence of this horizontal force was demonstrated in human subjects by Osborn (1961) who inserted orthodontic bands between the teeth and found that the force required to remove them increased when the teeth were clenched. This hypothesis was disproved by Moss & Picton (1967) who showed that the drift still occurred in monkeys even in teeth whose opponents had been extracted so that they were not subjected to occlusal forces. In these and subsequent experiments, the drift was accelerated by creating spaces between the teeth with a diamond disc and measurement was facilitated by inserting amalgam fillings in the buccal and lingual surfaces to act as markers on occlusal radiographs.

A second hypothesis, that forces from the cheeks and tongue might squeeze the teeth forward, was disproved by showing that the movement still occurred when the teeth were covered by an acrylic dome which prevented contact between the teeth and these muscular structures (Moss & Picton 1970).

In further experiments on monkeys, the trans-septal fibres of the periodontal ligament were either cut or scraped away on one side which resulted in a reduction of approximal drift compared with that on the opposite control side (Picton & Moss 1973). When the molar teeth were divided surgically so that the mesial and distal halves were separated (and the exposed pulps sealed with oxyphosphate cement) the two halves tended to drift away from each other, a movement which did not occur if the inter-dental soft tissues, including the trans-septal fibres, were damaged as before (Moss & Picton 1974). It is concluded that approximal drift arises from some force probably developed by the trans-septal fibres. Its nature is uncertain but it may be exerted by the fibroblasts as suggested for eruption.

Shedding of the Deciduous Teeth

The shedding of the deciduous teeth is preceded by the gradual removal of their roots and of the alveolar bone. The process of the removal of the root is called 'resorption' or 'absorption' but neither term is entirely satisfactory. Histological study of the stages of shedding in the human subject have been described by Furseth (1968).

The resorption of the roots is said to begin within one year of the completion of their growth. Resorption is brought about by the activity of osteoclasts (sometimes referred to in this situation as odontoclasts) which can be seen in histological sections as an almost continuous layer along the dentine at the apical end of a resorbing root and, in molars, at the bi- and trifurcations of the roots. Odontoclasts have also been reported in Howship's lacunae on the pulpal surface of the dentine, some distance from the root, in places where the odontoblasts and the predentine have disappeared, presumably by resorption (Hargreaves & Weatherell 1965). Usually, resorption begins on that part of the root adjacent to the permanent crown (for example, on the lingual surfaces of incisors and canines and between the roots of molars (Furseth 1968)). The pressure of the growing and erupting permanent successor provides an important stimulus to the resorption process. It is well known that pressure on a bone leads to the presence of osteoclasts and to its resorption, and the behaviour of the deciduous root would fit into this general pattern. There is no agreed explanation of the means by which this result is brought about, but collagenase has been detected in the granulation tissue between a resorbing deciduous root and an unerupted permanent crown and on the roots of resorbing dentine but not in most permanent teeth, when cultured *in vitro* (Morita *et al.* 1970; White & Woolley 1973). Collagenase is also detectable on the pressure side, but much less on the tension side of the periodonal ligament during experimental tooth movement (Ozaki *et al.* 1971).

Experimental evidence for the importance of pressure in root resorption is provided by the finding that removal of the germs of the permanent teeth in kittens and puppies delays the resorption of the deciduous teeth (Shapiro & Rogers 1939; Obersztyn 1963). It seems equally clear that pressure from permanent teeth cannot be the only factor involved, otherwise no resorption, rather than delayed resorption, would be the expected result of this experiment. Also, resorption is sometimes found in a part of the root which is not subject to pressure from the permanent tooth, and that resorption may begin before the permanent tooth is in close contact with the deciduous root. Clinical evidence for the existence of factors other than pressure in resorption is the observation that if the permanent germ is absent, shedding, although often delayed, does eventually occur in many cases.

A partition of bone exists at certain stages between a permanent tooth and its deciduous predecessor, and this has been raised as an objection to the pressure theory. However, resorption does not begin until the bone has been removed in the course of the remodelling which occurs during growth. In dogs, resorption of the roots does not begin until some time after the bony crypt has been enlarged and the roots are exposed (Cahill 1974). The origin of the 'odontoclasts' is uncertain: if they are osteoclasts migrating from the crypt it is difficult to understand why resorption does not begin earlier. Alternatively the odontoclasts may arise by fusion of cells in the pulp.

Obersztyn (1963) showed experimentally that two factors which greatly influence resorption of deciduous roots are trauma caused by occlusal stress and inflammation. He placed splint-bridges in dogs' mouths in such a way that the deciduous teeth received no occlusal stress; resorption of the roots ceased and repair processes began. Areas where resorption had already occurred became filled in by a bone-like tissue. In another experiment, deciduous teeth were partly ground and coated with a polymerizing resin which was known to produce severe inflammation. Resorption of the roots of the treated teeth was greatly accelerated in spite of the previous removal of the germs of the permanent teeth. It seems that these two related factors (trauma and inflammation, perhaps produced by the trauma) may explain root resorption in man.

Resorption is not a steady process but takes place in spurts alternating with periods during which new tissue (either secondary cementum or the bone-like material) may be laid down. This may explain the presence in the resorption lacunae of bone and the dentine of deciduous teeth of lipid material with staining characteristics similar to that of the lipid in mineralizing tissues (Yoshiki & Goto 1971). The cause of this lack of continuity is unknown, but is presumably related to variations in the rate of eruption and of growth processes generally.

Atkinson & Matthews (1949) discovered by comparing the permeability of deciduous teeth at different ages (see p. 117 for the method), that when they are undergoing root resorption, the permeability of their enamel decreases rapidly until, when they are shed, the permeability is virtually nil, even to water. They conclude that some substances, whose nature and origin are unknown, are deposited in enamel during resorption. Although these workers implied that this change in permeability is directly related to resorption, there is no evidence for this, beyond the fact that a larger fall in permeability of deciduous teeth occurs during the few years when resorption is active than occurs in permanent teeth in a whole lifetime.

A relation has been found between the rate of root resorption of certain teeth and the presence of dental caries (Fanning 1962). The root resorption in mandibular molars was estimated from radiographs in over 200 children and, in boys, the resorption of a root was accelerated by caries on the same side as the root by times varying between 3 and 29 months; caries on the opposite side had a smaller effect (3–17 months). In girls the trend was found but the effects were all smaller and in teeth with filled cavities the acceleration of root resorption was reduced. This effect has not been definitely explained, but in view of the results of Obersztyn, mentioned above, the accelerated resorption may perhaps result from the inflammation of the pulp following the caries.

References

Atkinson H.F. & Matthews E. (1949) An investigation into the permeability of human deciduous enamel. *Brit. dent. J.* **86**, 142

Baume L.J. *et al.* (1954) Hormonal control of tooth eruption. *J. dent. Res.* **33**, 80, 91, 104

Beertsen W. (1973) Tissue dynamics in the periodontal ligament of the mandibular incisor of the mouse: a preliminary report. *Archs oral Biol.* **18**, 61 (see also (1974) **19**, 1087, 1099)

Berkovitz B.K.B. (1971) The effect of root transection and partial root resection on the unimpeded eruption rate of the rat incisor. *Archs oral Biol.* **16**, 1033 (see also (1972) **17**, 937)

Berkovitz B.K.B. (1975) Mechanisms of tooth eruption. In *Applied Physiology of the Mouth*, p. 99. Ed. Lavelle C.L.B.

Berkovitz B.K.B. (1976) Theories of tooth eruption. In *The Eruption and Occlusion of Teeth*, p. 193. Eds Poole D.F.G. & Stack M.V. Butterworths, London

BERKOVITZ B.K.B. & THOMAS N.R. (1969) Unimpeded eruption in the root-resected lower incisor of the rat with a preliminary note on root transection. *Archs oral Biol.* **14**, 771; also (1972) **17**, 937

BERNICK S. *et al.* (1951) Role of the epithelial attachment in tooth resorption of primary teeth. *Oral. Surg., Med., Path.* **4**, 1444

BRASH J.C. (1926) The growth of the alveolar bone and its relation to the movements of the teeth, including eruption. *Dent. Rec.* **46**, 641; **47**, 1

BRODIE A.G. (1934) Present status of our knowledge concerning movement of the teeth germ through the jaw. *J. Amer. dent. Ass.* **24**, 1830

BRYER L.W. (1957) Experimental evaluation of physiology of tooth eruption. *Int Dent. J.* **7**, 432

CAHILL D.R. (1974) Histological changes in the bony crypt and gubernacular canal of erupting permanent premolars during deciduous premolar exfoliation in beagles. *J. dent. Res.* **53**, 786

CARLSON H. (1944) Studies in the role and amount of eruption in certain human teeth. *Amer. J. Orthodont. and Oral Surg.* (*Orthodontic Section*) **30**, 575

CHIBA M. *et al.* (1968) Impeded and unimpeded eruption of the mandibular incisor of the adult male rat and its stoppage by demecolcine. *J. dent. Res.* **47**, 986

EASTOE J.E. (1976) In *The Eruption and Occlusion of Teeth*, p. 249. Eds POOLE D.F.G. & STACK M.V. Butterworths, London

ECCLES J.D. (1965) The effects of reducing function and stopping eruption on the periodontium of the rat incisor. *J. dent. Res.* **44**, 860

FANNING E.A. (1962) The relationship of dental caries and root resorption of deciduous molars. *Archs oral Biol.* **7**, 595

FURSETH R. (1968) The resorption processes of human deciduous teeth studied by light microscopy, microradiography and electron microscopy. *Archs oral Biol.* **13**, 417

GARN S.M. *et al.* (1973) Negro-Caucasoid differences in permanent tooth emergence at a constant income level. *Archs oral Biol.* **18**, 609

GOTTLIEB B. & ORBAN B. (1938) *Biology and Pathology of the Tooth and its Supporting Mechanism.* Macmillan, London.

GOWGIEL J.M. (1961) Eruption of irradiation-induced rootless teeth in monkeys. *J. dent. Res.* **40**, 338; see also (1967) **46**, 1325

HARGREAVES J.A. & WEATHERELL J.A. (1965) Variation of fluoride concentration in human deciduous teeth. *Advances in Fluorine Research and Dental Caries Prevention* **3**, 247

HASSEL H.J. VAN & MCMINN R.G. (1972) Pressure differential favouring tooth eruption in the dog. *Archs oral Biol.* **17**, 183

KING J.D. (1936) Dietary deficiency, nerve lesions and the dental tissues. *J. Physiol.* **88**, 62

KRONFELD R. (1932) The resorption of the root of deciduous teeth. *D. Cosmos* **74**, 103

MAIN J.H.P. (1961) The relationship between unimpeded erupted rates and blood pressure in the rat incisor. *J. dent. Res.* **40**, 1276

MAIN J.H.P. (1965) A histological survey of the hammock ligament. *Archs oral Biol.* **10**, 343

MASSLER M. & SCHOUR I. (1941) Studies in tooth development: theories of eruption. *Amer. J. Orthodont. and Oral Surg.* **27**, 552 (a general review of the earlier work)

MICHAELI Y. *et al.* (1972) Role of attrition and occlusal contact in the physiology of rat incisors. *J. dent. Res.* **51**, 960

MILLER B.G. (1957) Investigation of the influence of vascularity and innervation of tooth resorption and eruption. *J. dent. Res.* **37**, 669

MORITA H. *et al.* (1970) The collagenolytic activity during root resorption of bovine deciduous tooth. *Archs oral Biol.* **15**, 503

MOSS J.P. & PICTON D.C.A. (1967) Experimental mesial drift in adult monkeys (*Macaca irus*). *Archs oral Biol.* **12**, 1313 (see also (1970) **15**, 979)

MOSS J.P. & PICTON D.C.A. (1974) The effect of approximal drift of cheek teeth of dividing mandibular molars of adult monkeys. *Archs oral Biol.* **19**, 1211

NESS A.R. (1956) The response of the rabbit mandibular incisor to experimental shortening and to the prevention of its eruption. *Proc. Roy. Soc. (Lond.) Ser. B* **146**, 129; (1959) *Proc. R. Soc. (Lond). Ser. B* **151**, 106

NESS A.R. (1957) Experiments on the role of the periodontal tissues in the eruption of the rabbit mandibular incisor. *J. dent. Res.* **36**, 810

NESS A.R. (1964) Movement and forces in tooth eruption. *Adv. oral Biol.* **1**, 33

NESS A.R. (1967) Eruption—a review. In *Mechanisms of Tooth Support*, p. 84. Wright, Bristol

NESS A.R. & SMALE D.E. (1959) The distribution of mitoses and cells in the tissues bounded by the socket wall of the rabbit mandibular incisor. *Proc. Roy. Soc. B.* **151**, 106

OBERSZTYN A. (1963) Experimental investigation of factors causing resorption of deciduous teeth. *J. dent. Res.* **42**, 600

O'BRIEN C. *et al.* (1958) Eruptive mechanism and movement in the first molar of the rat. *J. dent. Res.* **37**, 467

OSBORN J.W. (1961) An investigation into the interdental forces occurring between the teeth of the same arch during clenching the jaws. *Archs oral Biol.* **5**, 202

OZAKI T. *et al.* (1971) Collagenolytic activity during tooth movement in the rabbit. *Archs oral Biol.* **16**, 1123

PICTON D.C.A. & MOSS J.P. (1973) The part played by the trans-septal fibre system in experimental approximal drift of the cheek teeth of monkeys (*Macaca irus*). *Archs oral Biol.* **18**, 669

SHAPIRO H.H. & ROGERS W.M. (1939) Experiments dealing with factors influencing the shedding of deciduous teeth. *J. dent. Res.* **18**, 73

SICHER H. (1942) Tooth eruption: axial movement of continuously growing teeth. *J. dent. Res.* **21**, 201; Axial movement of teeth with limited growth. *J. dent. Res.* **21**, 295

SICHER H. & WEINMANN A.E. (1944) Bone growth and physiologic tooth movement. *Amer. J. Orthodont. Oral Surg.* **30**, 109.

TAYLOR A. & BUTCHER E.O. (1951) The regulation of eruption rate in the incisor teeth of the white rat. *J. exp. Zool.* **117**, 165

TEN CATE A.R. (1969) The mechanism of tooth eruption. In *Biology of the Periodontium*, p. 92. Ed. MELCHER A.H. & BOWEN W.H. Academic Press, London

THOMAS N.R. (1964) The role of collagen maturation in alveolar bone growth and tooth eruption. *J. dent. Res.* **43**, 947 (see also (1965) **44**, 1159; (1966) **46**, 1297)

TSURUTA M. *et al.* (1974) Effect of daily or 4-hourly administration of lathyrogens on the eruption rates of impeded and unimpeded mandibular incisors of rats. *Archs oral Biol.* **19**, 1221

WHITE P.R. & WOOLLEY D.E. (1973) Collagenolytic activity of cultured resorbing teeth. *J. dent. Res.* **52**, 979

YOSHIKI S. & GOTO Y. (1971) Sudanophil material at the edge of resorption lacunae of guinea-pig teeth and bones. *Archs oral Biol.* **16**, 823

CHAPTER VII

THE EFFECTS OF HORMONES ON THE ORAL STRUCTURES

Introduction

In the next two chapters an account is given of studies on the influence of hormones and nutrition on the oral structures. By way of introduction it may be as well to say a word about the value of these studies. Many of the experiments have thrown little light on the diagnosis of abnormalities or defects in human teeth, and indeed, superficial resemblances between the effects of various treatments in animals and conditions observed in human teeth have sometimes been misleading. It must not, however, be thought that this work has been of little value. Although many points remain to be elucidated and some new problems have been raised, there is no doubt that these studies have been of great importance in gaining an understanding of some of the fundamental mechanisms concerned in the formation and maintenance of the teeth. It is this aspect of the work which will be emphasized throughout these two chapters.

The Thyroid Hormone

No comprehensive experiments appear to have been carried out in any one species on the effects of both the removal of the thyroid and the administration of thyroid hormone on all types of teeth at different ages. A general picture of the influence of the hormone on teeth may, however, be obtained by piecing together the results of these procedures observed separately in experiments on rats, guinea-pigs, dogs and monkeys.

The actions of the thyroid hormone on calcium and phosphorus metabolism are described on page 45.

The effects of the administration of thyroid hormone

EFFECTS ON ERUPTION

Experiments on new-born rats have shown that the injection of thyroxine causes a marked acceleration in the rate of eruption of the incisor teeth. For example, in one experiment on rats treated with large doses of thyroxine, the incisors erupted within 70–80 hr after birth, whereas the controls required about 190 hr for the same degree of eruption (Karnofsky & Cronkhite 1939).

Similar results on the incisor teeth have been obtained with acetylthyroxine (see Fig. VII.1), a derivative of thyroxine which does not occur naturally and

Injected with Acetyl Thyroxine   Control

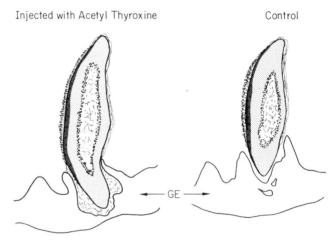

3 days after birth (one injection given)

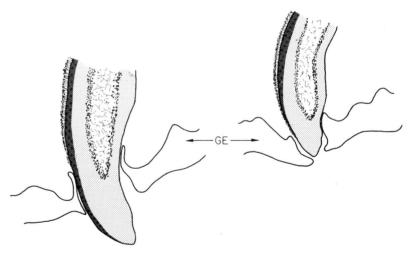

8 days after birth (several injections given)

FIG. VII.1. Effect of injection of acetylthyroxine on the rate of eruption of incisors in the new-born rat. The tip of the incisor is piercing the gingival epithelium (GE) (after Hoskins 1928).

shows the same effect *on growth* as the natural hormone but is stated to have no effect on the basal metabolic rate (Hoskins 1928).

The growth and eruption of molars were unaffected in these experiments, probably because all the animals were killed within 8 days after birth, at which age the molars are at an early stage of development. Other experiments of longer duration have shown that the eruption of the rat molar is accelerated by the thyroid hormone.

EFFECTS OF LARGE DOSES ON THE STRUCTURE OF THE TEETH
Animal experiments have shown that the rate of development as well as of eruption of the teeth is also accelerated by thyroid hormone and that these changes affect all tissues of the teeth equally, at any rate, in rats. In guinea-pigs fed large doses of the thyroid hormone for several weeks the odontoblasts were severely, but irregularly, affected in all the teeth and although in places dentine formation continued, in adjacent areas where the cells were inactive none was formed. Consequently, the inner margin of the dentine became irregular and some of the moribund cells were engulfed in the dentine formed by the more active neighbouring cells. The pulp was oedematous. The molars became loose following resorption of the alveolar bone. It must be emphasized that these changes resulted from *large* experimental doses of thyroxine (Goldman 1943).

Thyroidectomy

The importance of the thyroid hormone in the development of teeth has also been investigated by studying the effects of thyroidectomy in monkeys and rats. In monkeys, the results were a reduced rate of dentine growth, increased width of predentine (indicative of delayed mineralization) and very deficient mineralization of dentine and enamel laid down after the operation. In thyroidectomized rats, Baume *et al.* (1954) found the rate of eruption of the incisors was reduced by about 45% and the linear dimensions by about 20–25%. The enamel organ atrophied about two-thirds of the distance between the apex and the gingival margin, instead of covering the whole length of the unerupted part of the tooth; consequently, a smaller thickness of enamel was produced than in normal animals. There was a marked reduction in the vascularity of the pulp and excessive dentine formation in relation to the growth of the tooth narrowed the pulp chamber.

When thyroxine was administered to the thyroidectomized rats, there was an increase in the vascularity of the tissues and in the eruption rate, but the size of the tooth was increased to a smaller extent. Irregularities in dentine and thin hypoplastic enamel were found in a young dog fed the antithyroid drug thiouracil (English 1949).

Effect of the thyroid gland on experimental caries

Bixler *et al.* (1956, 1957) showed that decreased thyroid activity (either by graded damage to the thyroid gland by a range of doses of radioactive iodine or by feeding the antithyroid drug thiouracil) increases caries in rats, and feeding desiccated thyroid reduces it. The mechanism has not been elucidated fully, but there is evidence that it involves the salivary glands, since desiccated thyroid or antithyroid drugs have no effect on caries in animals from which the salivary glands have been removed (Haldi *et al.* 1962). The thyroid hormone probably increases the rate of flow of saliva since, although there is no information about the effect of the thyroid on the response to normal stimuli, the secretion after pilocarpine injections is increased by thyroid feeding and reduced by antithyroid drugs. The saliva from the thyroid group was thin and watery and very viscous in the group given the antithyroid drug. From these results, it would seem likely that the normal rate of flow is also affected by the thyroid hormone (Shafer & Mohler 1956).

Oral effects of some thyroid disorders in man

In hypothyroidism from birth (cretinism) the retarded growth of the skeleton is shared by the skull, giving a small dental arch. The size of the crowns of the teeth is little affected and eruption, though much retarded, is in advance of bone growth, the dental delay being approximately one-third that of skeletal delay (Garn *et al.* 1965). For example, one cretin aged 20 was found to have a dental age of 8 and a bone age of 3. The shedding of deciduous teeth is also delayed. The growth of the roots is slower than normal and the pulp canals are consequently unusually wide. The poor development of the mandible causes an open bite and a receding chin. Other causes of delayed bone growth (such as coeliac disease, anaemia and non-endocrine dwarfism) are also associated with smaller delays in dental development averaging about one-third that of skeletal growth (Garn *et al.* 1965).

Hyperthyroidism in the young subject is rare but in one case on record a 5-year-old child had a dental age of 9 and the shedding of the deciduous teeth had begun at the age of $3\frac{1}{2}$.

We may conclude that the growth and development of the dental tissues are affected, like the rest of the body, by the thyroid hormone and that excessive dosage (as used in the guinea-pig experiments) has a toxic action on odontoblasts as on other cells. It is likely that the effects on eruption follow from the general effects on growth and there seems no reason to postulate any specific effect on the teeth.

Effects of the Growth Hormone of the Anterior Pituitary

The anterior pituitary is thought to contain at least six hormones and an even larger number of effects have been reported after the injection of pituitary extracts. Some hormones can be shown to produce several actions although whether these actions are normal properties is not always known. Experiments in which the pituitary is removed or crude extracts injected can give no information about which particular hormone is responsible for any effects which may be observed. Precise information can only be obtained by studying the response to purified hormones and this has not yet been thoroughly carried out for oral effects. Indirect evidence suggests that the growth hormone is mainly responsible for the effects of pituitary extracts on the teeth but the thyroid-stimulating hormone may also play a part.

Effects of hypophysectomy on the teeth

The effects of the removal of the pituitary (hypophysectomy) on the teeth of rats have been studied by Schour & Van Dyke (1932b) and their main findings were as follows. The rates of eruption both of incisors and molars were much reduced and finally ceased altogether, but it is difficult to decide the relative importance of reductions in tooth growth, bone growth and blood supply as the cause, since all three were affected. The crowns of the molars were completely calcified when the operation was carried out and it therefore was not suprising to find that the enamel was in most places normal.

The epithelial attachment of the molars was normal near the gingivae but at the amelo-cementum junction atrophy often occurred and 'cementum spurs' were frequently found, that is, upward extensions of the cementum along the enamel, separating it from the gingival tissue. When no such layer of cementum was formed, the enamel sometimes underwent resorption (see also p. 154), the nature of which was not established. Other parts of the molar enamel were normal. The lengths of the roots of the molars were 10–15% less than normal. The dentine was virtually normal but secondary dentine production was reduced, consequently there was a smaller increase in the thickness of dentine with ageing and the pulp cavities were, therefore, larger than usual in the older animals (in contrast with the effect on the pulp in the incisors, see below). These results are illustrated in Fig. VII.2.

EFFECTS OF RODENT INCISORS

In the continuously growing incisors Schour & Van Dyke observed the effects of hypophysectomy on the formative structures of the teeth. The tooth became abnormal in shape (probably as a result of the disturbed growth of the bone) and it was smaller than in the normal, a study of sections showing that it occupied about two-thirds of the area of sections of normal teeth. The upper incisor did not always occlude with its fellow, in which case normal attrition did not occur at the incisal end.

The ameloblasts atrophied and, at the apical end, the enamel and dentine,

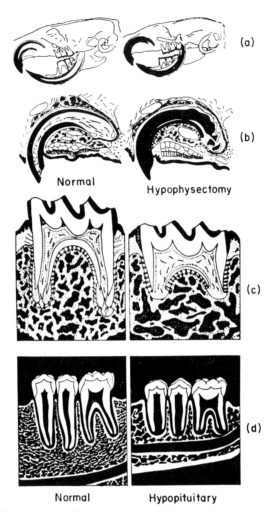

FIG. VII.2. Diagram of the effects of pituitary deficiency (right) in rats and man. (a) Radiograph of rats' skulls, the dense curved shadows represent the calcified tissues of the incisors; (b) histological section through incisors—note excessive thickness and buckling of dentine after hypophysectomy; (c) rat molars—note shorter roots and incomplete eruption but no difference in anatomical crowns; rats were 300 days old, hypophysectomized when 40 days old; (d) drawing from radiograph of human male aged 16; note shorter roots of teeth, incomplete eruption and diminished growth of bone in hypopituitarism.

with their layers of formative cells, become folded. The effect of hypophysectomy on the rat incisor has also been studied by Baume *et al.* (1954) whose findings were similar to those just described, but apical folding occurred in only 60% of their operated animals and then only some months after the operation.

They suggested that the folding resulted from the effects of masticatory stress on the unusually weak apical structures, a view confirmed by Weinreb *et al.* (1969). If folding occurred, eruption ceased completely, but in the 40% of the teeth with no folding a slow rate of eruption continued. The enamel organ and the odontogenic epithelium are especially sensitive to hypophysectomy. The formation of dentine and cementum continue without pituitary hormones, although at a reduced rate.

The dentine and pulp of the incisor showed the most characteristic and striking effects. The dentine became extremely thick at the expense of the pulp cavity which was only a tiny fraction of its normal size. The rate of dentine formation was not measured, but other workers have found in monkeys that hypophysectomy reduced it in different parts of the teeth by amounts varying between 31 and 49% of normal. In both species, this is a much smaller reduction than occurred in the rate of eruption. Consequently, the cells producing dentine, instead of having a limited life after which both they and the dentine they formed were lost in attrition, continued to form dentine in an almost stationary tooth, so that growth tended to be inwards rather than in length (Fig. VII.2). For similar reasons, the cementum was thicker than usual.

Injection experiments

Injection of crude growth hormone into hypophysectomized rats prevented the reduced rate of eruption or even caused a marked increase in the rate of eruption compared with normal controls (Schour & Van Dyke).

In experiments by Baume *et al.* (1954), pure growth hormone was injected into normal and hypophysectomized animals, in some cases in conjunction with thyroxine. It has thus been possible to decide the relative importance of the growth and thyrotropic hormones in producing the effects of hypophysectomy. It was quite clear that the growth hormone increased the size of the teeth compared with the corresponding controls in both hypophysectomized and normal rats, without altering the eruption rate. Histological studies showed that the injections had greatly increased the activity of the tooth-forming cells and their arrangement became almost normal even in those teeth which had shown apical folding. The surrounding alveolar bone also showed increased growth.

Thyroxine injections, on the other hand, increased growth, the vascularity of the tissues and eruption rate, although severe effects of hypophysectomy, such as intense folding, were not reversed. The alveolar bone showed little response to thyroxine. A combination of both hormones caused optimum eruption rate and full restoration of enamel and dentine formation.

It is concluded that thyroid hormone affects especially growth of the tooth with little effect on bone growth, whereas the pituitary growth hormone increases the size of both the dental tissues and bone.

Injection of crude growth hormone into young dogs resulted in a great increase in the growth of the skeleton, and especially of the mandible, and in addition the tongue was enlarged, due mostly to overgrowth of its connective tissue.

The effects of hypophysectomy on the supporting structure of the teeth were found to be a reduction in the vascularity and the number of osteoblasts in the alveolar bone so that the amount of bone diminished, presumably owing to failure of the normal balance between repairs and breakdown. The number of fibroblasts in the periodontal ligament diminished and the fibres showed degenerative changes. The gingivae showed inflammatory invasion with degeneration of the underlying collagen and also of the odontoblasts and pulp cells.

The oral effects of some pituitary disorders in man

In man, some indication of the part played by the pituitary in the development of the oral structures may be gained by studying clinical cases of hypo- and hyperpituitarism.

In pituitary dwarfs, the eruption and shedding of the teeth is delayed like the growth of the body generally. Even when eruption occurs it is not as complete as normal, that is, the clinical crown is smaller. Dental delay is approximately half that of skeletal delay suggesting that growth hormone is more important than the thyroid (although some patients might be deficient in thyrotrophin as well as in growth hormone). The maxilla, mandible and teeth are affected differently in pituitary dwarfs, thus leading to malocclusion. The question of the size of the anatomical crown (the area of a tooth covered by enamel) in pituitary dwarfs is uncertain. Most reports suggest that the anatomical crown is not smaller than usual, although Hamori *et al.* (1974) stated from a study of 4 dwarfs that the teeth were 10% smaller than normal. With so variable a factor as the size of the crown, it is, of course, difficult to decide whether hypopituarism has any effect, unless large numbers of measurements from dwarfs are compared statistically with figures from normal subjects. There is general agreement that the roots are shorter than normal (Fig. VII.2). In a study by Garn *et al.* (1965) of 9 pituitary dwarfs skeletal age was delayed by about 50% but dental age by only about 25%: the difference between skeletal and dental development was larger than with the other defects mentioned on p. 218. Pituitary dwarfs have a low caries rate, presumably related to the longer period of maturation and shorter exposure to sugar resulting from the delayed eruption (Nikiforuk *et al.* 1971).

When overactivity of the pituitary occurs after puberty (acromegaly), growth of the mandible is resumed causing projection of the chin (mandibular prognathism), and an abnormally long face. The mandible is one of the few bones which is capable of increased growth in later life; in fact it has been stated that growth of this bone never ceases entirely. Supra-eruption of the teeth may occur leading to overgrowth of the alveolar process and an increased size of the dental arch. The tongue becomes enlarged and this may also play some part in the prognathism. In gigantism (excess growth hormone secreted before puberty) the effects on the face and oral structures are similar to those in acromegaly.

These observations clearly demonstrate the important part which the growth hormone of the pituitary plays during the development of the oral structures.

The Calciotraumatic Response

Many different experimental procedures, for example, injections of either fluoride, strontium, calciferol, parathyroid extract or the removal of the parathyroid glands or the kidneys, cause what early work suggested was an almost identical series of changes in developing dentine and enamel which have been called collectively the 'calciotraumatic response'. The neonatal line and the contour lines of Owens have a similar pattern. Later analysis (Eisenmann & Yaeger 1969) has revealed that the response is not as uniform with different substances as was originally thought. This is a convenient point at which to describe this response even though it must be emphasized that it is not caused solely by hormones.

These changes have been studied mostly in the continuously growing rodent incisor and are usually confined to the middle third of the tooth. This means that the odontoblasts that have most recently begun the formation of dentine at the apical end of the tooth are unaffected: evidently young odontoblasts are better able to resist these disturbances than are the older cells.

Most of the early attempts to analyse the calciotraumatic response in dentine have been based on sections stained with haematoxylin and eosin, with or without previous demineralization. Experiments not concerned with the calciotraumatic response had shown that areas of undemineralized sections which stained deeply with haematoxylin were relatively opaque to Grenz-rays (or 'soft' X-rays, i.e. those with a relatively long wavelength which are especially useful for revealing fine detail) and therefore heavily mineralized: similarly, deep staining with eosin was associated with under-mineralized areas. More recent studies by radiography have failed to confirm that the heavy staining with haematoxylin is necessarily associated with hypermineralization. The reaction with haematoxylin is present in demineralized sections and was assumed to indicate changes in the matrix leading to an indirect effect on mineralization. Silver staining gives information about the matrix: precollagen stains black, collagen brown and interfibriller matrix remains unstained (Irving & Weinmann 1948).

THE THREE STAGES OF THE CALCIOTRAUMATIC RESPONSE AND THEIR POSSIBLE EXPLANATIONS

The calciotraumatic response is divided into three zones as follows (Fig. VII.3):

(1) The junction between mineralized dentine and unmineralized predentine becomes marked off by a thin line called the 'calciotraumatic line' which stains deeply with haematoxylin and for GAGs. Microradiography shows that this line is hypermineralized.

(2) The predentine formed in the 24 hr before the experiment (which would normally calcify in the 24 hr immediately following) remains un-

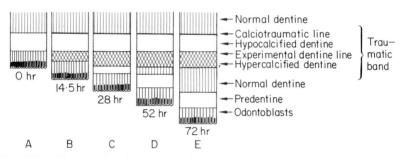

FIG. VII.3. Diagram of the Calciotraumatic Response. (A)–(E), Representation of inner part of dentine at the stated time after injection of toxic substance.

mineralized and is visible throughout the life of the dentine as a hypomineralized line. Other features of this predentine are a lighter staining reaction with haematoxylin and for GAGs. Electron micrographs by Yaeger (1963) of undemineralized sections confirm that it is hypomineralized, there being a smaller number of larger crystals. The spaces between the collagen fibres contained material which stained as protein, and since dentine contains little protein other than collagen, he concluded that it consisted of collagen which had failed to form into fibres. Yaeger suggested that the lack of mineralization might occur because the non-fibrillar material had fewer seeding sites or because it covered up the existing seeding sites. The larger size of the crystals in the hypomineralized zone might be explained by the greater size of the spaces allowing a larger crystal growth (crystal growth is normally limited by the size of the space available).

The explanation of the hypermineralized calciotraumatic line at the dentine–predentine junction is probably that this layer does not become buried in mineralized dentine (because it is adjacent to the hypomineralized zone) and has greater access to minerals and is able to take them up for a longer time. Another possibility is that it might be caused by a brief cessation of matrix formation during which mineralization proceeded normally, thus causing the calcium salts to be concentrated in a smaller bulk of matrix.

(3) With some reagents (for example usually with fluoride but not with parathyroid hormone) the predentine which was forming while the reagent was active (the layer immediately after the hypomineralized layer) becomes *hyper*mineralized

The junction between the hypo- and hypermineralized dentine represents the inner boundary of the predentine at the time the active substance was injected. This junction, called the experimental dentine line, is useful as a time-marker in analysing the effect of various agents. All tissues between the experimental dentine line and the odontoblasts must have been formed between the application of the toxic substance and the time the animal was killed and since the normal rate of formation of dentine in the rat is known to be 16 μm per day it is possible to decide whether this rate has been altered by any experimental procedure.

Eisenmann & Yaeger (1969) tested the effect of one single injection of various doses of a total of 44 cations and 20 anions on the development of enamel and dentine. In some of these ions the effect was predominantly in the enamel (for example cobalt, tin, ferrous iron, molybdate, borate), others affected predominantly the dentine (for example mercury, cadmium, uranium, copper, zinc, citrate, PO_4^{3-}, HPO_4^{3-}), whereas some affected both in a similar way (barium, strontium, chromium, magnesium, aluminium, fluoride, iodide, bromide and HPO_4^{2-}).

The response of dentine was mostly a single hypomineralized layer but some ions (for example strontium, zinc, molybdate) frequently produced a double layer of hypomineralization. The dentine formed after the immediate response was normal with ions but others occasionally produced diffuse areas and hypermineralization and with some (for example stannous ions and uranium) normal development was never resumed.

In enamel, the usual response was a single hypomineralized layer, but fluoride produced a full calciotraumatic response with both inner (first formed) hyper- and outer (later formed) hypomineralized layers, provided the dosage was sufficiently high; a low dose produced only the hypermineralization.

After fluoride, the changes in enamel were as follows. The hypermineralized band was visible in developing enamel matrix but was not detectable if the matrix was allowed to mineralize fully before the animal was killed. The hypomineralized layer remained throughout the life of the tooth. This suggests that the hypermineralized band was merely an acceleration of normal mineralization within an unmineralized matrix so that when the rest of the matrix mineralized it became invisible. The hypomineralized zone was probably formed by some change in the composition of the matrix reducing its capacity to mineralize, this would allow freer access of previously-formed matrix to tissue fluids and enable mineralization to occur for a longer time than usual in neighbouring matrix thus forming the hypermineralized layer. Alternatively, the hypermineralized layer might result from the known effect of fluoride in favouring apatite deposition.

Eisenmann & Yaeger suggested several possible mechanisms for the effects they observed. Some ions affected the growth of the rat as well as of enamel and dentine and were assumed to have non-specific effects on metabolism generally, comparable to those produced by the severe surgical procedures (removal of the parathyroid or the kidney) which lead to a calciotraumatic response. There is no explanation of the predominant effect of some ions for either enamel or dentine, but possibly some enzyme specific for matrix formation in each tissue is inhibited so that less matrix is formed or its composition is abnormal, influencing the mineralization pattern. Other possible mechanisms are inhibition of the seeding or growth of crystals or the changes in the serum concentration of calcium or phosphate. With high doses of some ions, ulceration occurred at the site of injection and a general body reaction to the resulting pain cannot be disregarded.

Influence of the parathyroid hormone

Several investigators have studied the influence of the parathyroid hormone on dental structures by observing the effects of the removal of the gland and of the injection of active extracts. Erdheim in 1911 was the first to describe the dental effects of parathyroid removal and to observe the value of the rodent incisor (which he likened to a kymograph) as a record of experimental changes in calcium metabolism. The most extensive studies have been made by Schour *et al.* (1934, 1937).

Although there is agreement about the general effects of parathyroid injections on the teeth, different workers have observed important differences of detail, the reasons for which have not been explained with certainty.

The effects of parathyroidectomy

The results of removing the parathyroids on the teeth may be stated as follows. No effects whatever are observed histologically in those parts of the teeth already formed before the experiment began, nor have any chemical changes been established, but the possibility of very small changes in composition cannot be ruled out. In the enamel of the continuously growing incisor, no effects were seen for up to 3 weeks following parathyroidectomy; in enamel formed after this period, some opaque areas were present and some spots without the usual yellow pigment. The enamel organ became disorganized and in places broke up into epithelial cysts, and the ameloblasts shortened.

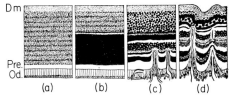

Fig. VII.4. Diagram of effect of parathyroidectomy on dentine. (a) Normal; (b) up to 20 days after parathyroidectomy showing calciotraumatic response with extensive hypermineralized zone (black); (c) long-term results of parathyroidectomy (up to 5 months); (d) effects of parathyroidectomy intensified by starving one day in seven or by repeated pregnancies and lactations; Dm—'mantle dentine', i.e. dentine near the amelodentinal junction; Pre—predentine; Od—odontoblast.

The immediate effects on the dentine are a well-marked calciotraumatic line followed by a zone of hypomineralized dentine, that is, the first two parts of a full calciotraumatic response. Later effects have been found to be more variable, however. Some workers have described the continued formation of hypomineralized dentine with progressive deterioration in its well-being. Schour *et al.*, on the other hand, found that after the initial thin layer of hypomineralized dentine was formed, the tissue laid down during the next 15–20 days was usually hypermineralized, as judged by staining with haematoxylin, in which case a full calciotraumatic response was obtained (see Fig. VII.4(b)). Schour *et al.* suggested that this difference in response may be caused by differences in diet. His animals were fed on a diet adequate in calcium, phosphorus and vitamin D, whereas other workers either used diets which were probably deficient, or else gave no details of the diets. The influence of diet on the response to parathyroidectomy was investigated by Bevelander & Hoskins (1939) and their results support the idea that the differences observed in the effects of parathyroid removal have a dietary basis.

LONG-TERM EFFECTS ON DENTINE

There is agreement about the effects of parathyroidectomy on the dentine in rats allowed to survive for up to about 6 months (parathyroidectomy is not fatal in rats as it is in man and some other species). The mineralization becomes less dense, some layers being more severely affected than others, leading to prominent but irregular stratification. The layers of dentine and the odontoblastic layer become folded and 'vascular inclusions' are present, that is, some areas of pulp tissue containing blood vessels become pinched off by the irregularities in the odontoblastic layer and eventually become embedded in the dentine (Figs VII.4 and VII.6). The odontoblasts become crowded and cease to lie in the same direction as the dentinal tubules, and the predentine is slightly wider than usual, indicating a delay in mineralization. Fractures of the teeth at weak spots in the dentine are frequently found. An unexplained observation is that the upper incisor is more severely affected than the lower and the lingual side more than the labial. These effects have, in general, been confirmed by recent work (Bernick 1969) which suggested histochemically that the protein-mucopolysaccharide complex of dentine matrix was disturbed, thus preventing normal mineralization.

The rate of eruption in animal experiments appears to be unaffected by parathormone.

These effects were more severe in two groups of the parathyroidectomized rats which were subjected to other factors known to put a strain on calcium metabolism, namely, starvation one day in seven and repeated pregnancies and lactations (see Fig. VII. 4(d)).

Injections of parathormone

The effects of injections of parathormone have been studied both in normal and in parathyroidectomized animals. In normal animals, immediately following the first injection, Schour *et al.* reported a calciotraumatic response, the hypercalcified layer of which varies in thickness with the number of injections given (Fig. VII.5). Yaeger & Eisenmann (1963) confirmed that a hypomineralized layer is formed after injecting parathyroid extracts but larger doses were required than in the early work and the later hypermineralized zone was not detected. The need for larger doses may have arisen from differences in the nature of the extracts available between the 1940s and the 1960s;

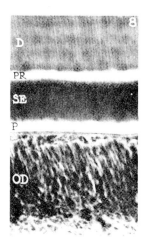

Fig. VII.5. Photomicrograph of calciotraumatic response to four injections of parathyroid extract in normal rats allowed to live 3 days after the last injection. D—Normal dentine formed before injection; PR—hypomineralized stripe; SE—hypermineralized dentine; P—predentine; OD—odontoblasts.

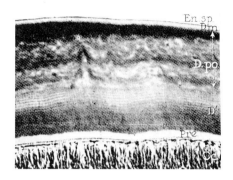

FIG. VII.6. Photomicrograph of labial dentine in upper incisor of rat killed 39 days after parathyroidectomy. One injection of parathyroid extract was given 9 days before death. En.sp.—Enamel space; Dm—mantle dentine; D′—dentine formed more regularly after injection; D.po—defective dentine (compare Fig. VII.4(c)) note folds, interglobular spaces; Pre—predentine; Od—odontoblasts.

also the later work was largely based on radiography whereas the earlier results depended entirely on the interpretation of staining reactions. It is now doubtful whether deep staining with haematoxylin does indicate hypermineralization.

The effects of parathormone administration to parathyroidectomized animals resemble the calciotraumatic response but with the difference that the layer, which in a normal animal receiving parathormone would have been hypermineralized, was usually approximately normal (Figs VII.6 and VII.7).

Schour *et al.* demonstrated that the dental effects of parathyroidectomy and of injections of parathormone, as judged by staining reactions, are essentially similar and not opposite, as might have been expected.

The mechanism of action of the parathormone in these reactions is still obscure. The dose was much larger than that required to raise plasma calcium, indicating that the effect was on matrix formation and not merely the supply of minerals. This does not explain the first hypomineralized layer, nor the fact that some workers have found that hypomineralization is the main response. It is also difficult from this theory to explain how the effect of parathyroidectomy and injections of parathormone can both produce similar effects on teeth when they have opposite effects on the composition of the blood.

Effect of the parathormone on the alveolar bone

One of the most dramatic proofs of the immunity of fully-formed dental tissues to resorption of their calcium salts is provided by comparing the histological appearances of the alveolar bone with that of enamel and dentine,

FIG. VII.7. Effect of two injections of parathyroid extract on incisor dentine of rat parathyroidectomized 136 days previously. D.po—Irregular dentine formed as a result of parathyroidectomy; D′—fairly normal dentine formed for 10 days after injection; En.sp.—enamel space; Dm—mantle dentine; Od—odontoblasts.

after a long series of parathormone injections. In the bone, progressive removal of the normal tissue by osteoclasts occurs, and fibrous tissue takes its place, but no visible changes occur in the dental tissues formed before the injections.

Oral effects of parathormone in man

Opportunities for the histological study of teeth from patients who have suffered from parathyroid disease while their teeth were mineralizing are rare. In one case on record, changes resembling very strongly those of parathyroidectomized rats were observed in three teeth extracted from a woman aged 23 who had suffered from parathyroid deficiency since the age of 12. The incremental lines were exaggerated and alternation of fairly normal bands of dentine, with bands containing interglobular spaces, were seen. Blood vessels surrounded by mineralized tissue at the pulp margin corresponded to the vascular inclusions observed in rats. The effects were apparent only in dentine mineralized after the age of 12.

In a series of five children with hypoparathyroidism studied by Hinrich (1956) it was confirmed that dental changes only occur in tissues forming during the PTH deficiency. The changes noted were defects both on matrix and mineralization of enamel and dentine with delays in eruption. This last finding disagrees with most of the animal experiments in which eruption was not delayed. A possible explanation is that in the experiments on the rat incisor, eruption was well established before parathyroidectomy and no resorption of bone was necessary for eruption to continue. In the human molar, eruption cannot occur without bone resorption and this may be diminished in hypoparathyroidism when osteoclasts are less numerous.

Loss or deficiency of the lamina dura has been reported in hyperparathyroidism and has often been suggested as a diagnostic feature; it is not specific for this condition, however, as it may occur in several other conditions and in one report on forty-two cases it occurred only in three, suggesting that the frequency of its occurrence in hyperparathyroidism has been exaggerated.

Changes in the jaws of adults suffering from hyperparathyroidism have been described, which again emphasize the sensitivity of the bone and the complete insensitivity of formed dental tissues to parathormone. Radiographs show that the alveolar bone became osteoporotic, with no change in the density of the teeth. The bone became so soft that it could be moulded with the fingers, leading to malocclusion because of the drift of the teeth as the bone changes in shape. There is a difference in opinion about whether the teeth become loose in this condition.

These observations prove the great importance of the parathyroid hormone during the mineralization of the teeth and prove the absence of gross effects in the histology and chemistry of the tooth after it has been formed.

Influence of Sex Hormones on Gingivae and Oral Mucosa

Female sex hormones and gonadotrophic hormones

Ziskin *et al.* (1941, 1946) stated that, in monkeys, oestrogens increased the keratinization of the hard palate and those parts of the gingivae which were keratinized and that ovariectomy tended to reverse these changes. This question has not been extensively studied since, but Trott (1957) from studies of human biopsies detected no changes in keratinization during the various phases of the menstrual cycle. In women over 40 years of age, however, i.e. when oestrogen secretion is diminishing, the proportion of the gingival area showing keratinization was about double that from younger subjects suggesting that oestrogens reduced keratinization.

More recent experimental results have confirmed that the female sex hormones influence the growth of the oral epithelium but have produced little evidence that they increase keratinization. They also dilate the blood vessels in the underlying tissue and increase their permeability. The details are as follows.

The effect of oestrogens on the oral mucosa has been studied in ovariectomized squirrel monkeys some of which were given oestriol by intramuscular injection. Certain measurements were made of the vaginal and oral epithelia which indicated their response: the length of the basement membrane (as a measure of its folding), the number of basal cells per mm of basement membrane (indicating their size) and the percentage of cells labelled by [³H] thymidine injected 1 hr before the animals were killed (indicating their rate of mitosis). The animals treated with oestrogen had larger and much more active cells in their vaginae and similar but much smaller differences were found in the buccal epithelium; the gingival epithelium showed only a slight tendency towards larger cells (Litwack *et al.* 1970). This proves that the oral epithelium is a target organ for oestrogens but is much less sensitive than that of the vagina. This was confirmed by the finding that quite high concentrations of injected [^{3}H]oestradiol were detectable in extracts of strips of buccal mucosa and gingiva, indicating that the hormone was bound to the oral tissues. In one experiment in rats higher concentrations accumulated in the oral tissues than in the more obvious target in the uterus.

The permeability of blood vessels in the hamster cheek pouch, as shown by the leakage of dyes bound to protein or the escape of Indian ink particles, increased after the local placing of oestrogen and progesterone. Electron micrographs of endothelial cells of rabbits' gingivae after injection of progesterone provide direct evidence of increased permeability of capillaries and venules to the electron-dense markers, ferritin and thorotrast. Reversible gaps appeared between the cells and in the diaphragms of fenestrated capillaries (Mohamed *et al.* 1974).

Gingival changes related to menstruation

There is a slight tendency for gingivitis to increase at puberty but this condition tends to recede between the ages of 11 and 17 (Sutcliffe 1972).

The flow of exudate from the gingival crevice (p. 324), as measured in a group of seventeen young women by placing strips of filter paper within the crevice, is at its lowest during menstruation (average 0·8 mm in 3 min) and rose (to 1·2 mm in 3 min) about the time of ovulation; control measurements in 7 males over the same time showed no difference but varied randomly from 0·8 to 1·0 (Lindhe & Attström 1967). In another study, by Holm-Pedersen & Löe (1967), the gingival exudate was measured by placing filter paper over the crevice, as opposed to within it, in subjects undergoing well-controlled oral hygiene and, as a result, with gingivae free from inflammation. No flow, or the merest trace (0·05 mm), was detected in the majority of measurements (448 out of 576) at any stage of the menstrual cycle, nor was any change in the gingival condition observed. These workers did find that a higher proportion of gingivae had measurable exudate during pregnancy (out of 79 crevices studied, 38 showed no exudate, 25 a trace and 16 a moderate flow).

The explanation of these apparently discrepant results may arise from the different methods used. Only when the paper was put in the crevice thus causing some inflammation was the flow affected by menstruation, suggesting that the hormones affected pre-existing inflammation, but did not initiate it. This conclusion was supported in an experiment on dogs made free from gingivitis by frequent scaling and polishing and feeding a hard diet, which also showed little or no exudate when measured by extra-crevicular methods and no increase occurred after oestrogen and progesterone. In dogs with gingivitis, on the other hand, a considerable rise occurred within 10 days of injecting oestrogen and progesterone.

In human females, receiving a contraceptive pill with a progestational effect, a slight but statistically significant increase in the flow of crevicular fluid has been reported (Lindhe *et al.* 1969).

In a study of the activity of the enzyme hyaluronidase in the saliva of twelve young women, in nine it rose during menstruation. Two forms of this enzyme are present in saliva, one of bacterial origin and one from the oral tissues, probably from the lysosomes. The concentration of tissue hyaluronidase decreases at menstruation and the bacterial enzyme either rises or is unchanged (Speirs 1961; Prout & Hopps 1973). Progesterone is believed to decrease the stability of lysosome membranes and since it is least active at menstruation it causes least release at that time. The rise in concentration of bacterial hyaluronidase, when it occurs, may result from an increase in bacterial numbers following the shedding of more epithelial cells at menstruation.

PREGNANCY GINGIVITIS
In pregnancy, changes in the gingivae may occur ('pregnancy gingivitis'). Some clinical surveys suggest that it is present in all pregnant women, others that its incidence is as low as 30%. Löe & Silness (1963) reported that an increased incidence of gingivitis was noticeable from the second month of pregnancy, increasing up to the eighth month after which a decrease occurred. The incidence fell rapidly after parturition. Adams *et al.* (1974) confirmed the occurrence of significantly higher gingivitis scores in the incisor region among pregnant than among non-pregnant women, in spite of evidence of superior oral hygiene among the pregnant group. The difference was greater in the maxillary teeth and did not reach significance in the mandibular incisors. The characteristic changes are bleeding and oedema of the gingivae and a deepening of their colour, indicative of a poor circulation. Biopsy specimens showed the following histological changes: loss of keratin in the alveolar gingivae, hyperplasia (increased number of cells) of the stratum germinativum, the rete pegs (the papillae of connective tissue which project into the epithelium) become elongated and frequently split, with nuclear degeneration of the epithelial cells. Slight inflammatory changes occur in the lamina propria.

Gingivae which are completely healthy do not change during pregnancy but in those which are inflamed, the usual relationship between the amount of plaque and the intensity of the gingivitis (p. 397) is less evident. This suggests that the sex hormones which increase during pregnancy do not initiate the inflammation but increase the sensitivity of the gingivae to irritants.

It may be tentatively concluded that the main effect in pregnancy gingivitis is increased permeability of blood vessels produced by progesterone (itself inactive in the absence of oestrogen) and that the oestrogens have a small additional effect in stimulating the growth of the oral epithelium. Contrary to the findings of Ziskin (1946) recent results suggest that oestrogens reduce keratinization.

The increased mobility of the teeth during pregnancy is described on p. 511. The explanation is uncertain but a possible clue is the finding that pregnancy reduces the rate of incorporation of proline into the periodontal ligament of rats. The replacement of the collagen fibres is presumably impaired thus affecting the anchoring of the tooth.

The hormone 'relaxin', which relaxes the pubic ligaments during pregnancy, was also shown to affect the periodontal tissues of mice and hamsters in a similar way. The fibres became more loosely arranged and less dense with increased spaces between them which were filled with oedema fluid (Rice 1962). There was no effect on the gingivae or oral mucosa suggesting that this hormone plays no part in pregnancy gingivitis. Whether these changes occur in the human subject is not known.

In cases of sexual precocity from adrenal tumours in human subjects, bone growth is greatly accelerated (averaging 70% in one series of twelve patients) but dental development is advanced much less (an average of 9%). In one example, a girl aged 2·8 years had a skeletal age of 7·5 (an advance of 4·7 years) and a dental age of 3·3 (an advance of 0·5 year) (Garn *et al.* 1965).

Sex differences and effects of pregnancy on dental caries

It has often been stated that the incidence of dental caries is increased during pregnancy, hence the expression 'Every pregnancy costs a tooth'. It was once widely believed that during pregnancy the withdrawal of mineral material occurred from the teeth into the blood, as it does from bone. This belief was regarded as the 'explanation' of the alleged increase in caries. Statistical surveys on large groups of women have failed to show that caries is more prevalent during pregnancy than it is among non-pregnant women of the same age.

In rats and hamsters, male animals tend to be more susceptible to dental caries than females (Keyes 1949; Shaw 1950; Bixler *et al.* 1955) although this has not invariably been found (Granados *et al.* 1950). Removal of the testes lowers caries susceptibility and the administration of male hormone has usually increased it.

It had been supposed that the effect of male hormones on caries was exerted through the salivary glands but in experiments by Bixler *et al.* (1955) rats were castrated and their salivary glands were removed, and the effects of castration on caries were still apparent. It would seem, therefore, that contrary to earlier beliefs, saliva is not the main route by which castration influences caries in the rat, and the explanation is unknown.

Data on the incidence of dental caries in human subjects of both sexes suggest that girls are slightly more susceptible than boys, partly (but not wholly) because the teeth erupt at an earlier average age in girls (see p. 208) and they are therefore exposed to caries-producing influences for a longer time (Mansbridge 1959). The fluoride concentration of the surface of enamel averages 10% higher in boys than in girls, probably as a result of the longer interval between the formation of enamel and the eruption of the teeth during which fluoride is acquired by the enamel surface (Aasenden 1974).

Effect of adrenal steroids and sex hormones on the supporting structures of the teeth

A well-known effect of cortisone and ACTH is to favour osteoporosis in bone generally, probably by interfering with the synthesis of new protein required in bone remodelling but possibly also by an accelerated breakdown of existing bone matrix. Androgens and oestrogens oppose these effects and it is thought that the maintenance of the skeleton may depend on the balance between these two antagonistic groups of hormones. Large differences exist between the sensitivity of different species—the mouse being more sensitive than other species of laboratory animals. Cortisone treatment or ovariectomy of young mice results in osteoporosis of the alveolar bone, reduction in the height of the bone in relation to the teeth, and degenerative changes in the periodontal membrane. When oestradiol and cortisone were given simultaneously, these changes did not occur. In rats, growth hormone also opposes the osteoporotic action of large doses of cortisone. In a further experiment, ovariectomy was carried out in a group of young mice (4–6 weeks old) and in a group 1 year old. The changes occurred only in the young group; they became apparent 3 months after ovariectomy and became more pronounced with time. Oestradiol alone produced an increased number of cells in the periodontal ligament and increased bone formation for about 5 weeks, but after 10 weeks dosing this change was reversed and even the bone formation normally occurring was absent (Glickman & Shklar 1955). In general, the effect of oestrogens in bone is to inhibit growth but increase the size of the trabeculae which fuse together forming a more solid bone with a smaller marrow cavity. The relevance of these experiments, usually with high doses of hormones, to human disorders of the supporting structures is still uncertain but is worth further study.

References

AASENDEN, R. (1974) Fluoride concentrations in the surface tooth enamel of young men and women. *Archs oral Biol.* **19**, 697

ADAMS D. *et al.* (1973/74) Pregnancy gingivitis: a survey of 100 antenatal patients. *J. Dent.* **2**, 106

BAUME L.J. *et al.* (1954) Hormonal control of tooth eruption. *J. dent. Res.* **33**, 80, 91, 104

BERNICK S. (1969) Histochemical study of dentin in parathyroidectomized rats. *J. dent. Res.* **48**, 1251

BEVELANDER G. & HOSKINS M.M. (1939) A comparison between dietary and hormonal factors in the development of dentine. *J. dent. Res.* **18**, 533

BIXLER D. *et al.* (1955) The effects of castration, sex hormones and desalivation on dental caries in the rat. *J. dent. Res.* **34**, 889

BIXLER D. *et al.* (1956) The effects of testosterone, thyroxine and cortisone on the salivary glands of the hypophysectomized rat. *J. dent. Res.* **35**, 566

BIXLER D. & MUHLER J.C. (1957) Fluoride and thyroid activity in caries incidence. *J. dent. Res.* **36**, 304 (see also **36**, 571, 709, 880, 883, 886)

EISENMANN D.R. & YAEGER J.A. (1969) Alterations in the formation of rat dentine and enamel induced by various ions. *Archs oral Biol.* **14**, 1045

ENGLISH J.A. (1949) Experimental effects of thiouracil and selenium on the teeth and jaws of dogs. *J. dent. Res.* **28**, 172

GARN S.M. *et al.* (1965) Endocrine factors in dental development. *J. dent. Res.* **44**, 243

GLICKMAN I. & SHKLAR G. (1955) The steroid hormones and tissues of the periodontium. *Oral Surg., Med., Path.* **8**, 1179

GOLDMAN H.M. (1943) Experimental hyperthyroidism in guinea pigs. *Amer. J. Ortho. and Oral Surg. (Oral Surg. Section)* **29**, 665

GRANADOS H. *et al.* (1950) Differences of sex in caries susceptibility. *J. dent. Res.* **29**, 194

HALDI J. *et al.* (1962) Relationship between thyroid function and resistance to dental caries. *J. dent. Res.* **41**, 398

HAMORI J. *et al.* (1974) Tooth size in pituitary dwarfs. *J. dent. Res.* **53**, 1302

HINRICH E.H. (1956) Dental changes in idiopathic juvenile hypoparathyroidism. *Oral Surg., Med., Path.* **9**, 1102

HOLM-PEDERSEN P. & LÖE H. (1967) Flow of gingival exudate as related to menstruation and pregnancy. *J. periodont. Res.* **2**, 13

HOSKINS M.M. (1928) The effect of acetyl thyroxin on the development of the teeth. *J. dent. Res.* **8**, 85

IRVING J.T. & WEINMANN J.P. (1948) Experimental studies in calcification. *J. dent. Res.* **27**, 669 (an analysis of the calciotraumatic response)

KARNOFSKY D. & CRONKHITE E.P. (1939) Effect of thyroxine on eruption of teeth in newborn rats. *Proc. Soc. exp. Biol. N.Y.* **40**, 568

KEYES P. (1949) The effect of gonadectomy and testosterone propionate on caries activity. *J. dent. Res.* **28**, 653

LEVINE R.S. & KEEN J.H. (1974) Neonatal enamel hypoplasia in association with symptomatic neonatal hypocalcaemia. *Brit. dent. J.* **137**, 429

LINDHE J. & ATTSTRÖM R. (1967) Gingival exudation during the menstrual cycle. *J. periodont. Res.* **2**, 194

LINDHE J. *et al.* (1969) The influence of progesterone on gingival exudation during menstrual cycles. *J. periodont. Res.* **4**, 97

LITWACK D. *et al.* (1970) Response of oral epithelia to ovariectomy and estrogen replacement. *J. periodont. Res.* **5**, 263

LÖE H. & SILNESS J. (1963) Periodontal disease in pregnancy. I. Prevalence and severity. *Acta odont. Scand.* **21**, 533.

MANSBRIDGE J.N. (1959) Sex differences in the prevalence of dental caries. *Brit. dent. J.* **106**, 303

MOHAMED A.H. *et al.* (1974) The microvasculature of the rabbit gingiva as affected by progesterone: an ultrastructural study. *J. Periodontol.* **45**, 50

NIKIFORUK G. *et al.* (1971) Increased caries resistance in the primary dentition of children with growth hormone deficiency. *J. dent. Res.* **50**, 518

PROUT R.E. & HOPPS R.M. (1973) Changes in hyaluronidase in human saliva during the menstrual cycle. *J. periodont. Res.* **8**, 86

RICE H.B. (1962) Effect of relaxin on periodontal tissues. *J. dent. Res.* **41**, 351

SCHOUR I. *et al.* (1937) Changes in the teeth following parathyroidectomy. *Amer. J. Path.* **13**, 945, 971

SCHOUR I. & HAM A.W. (1934) Action of vitamin D and of the parathyroid hormone on the calcium metabolism as interpreted by studying the effect of single doses on the calcification of dentine. *Arch. Path.* **17**, 22

SCHOUR I. & MASSLER M. (1943) Endocrines and dentistry. *J. Amer. dent. Ass.* **30**, 595, 763, 943 (a general review giving many early references)

SCHOUR I. & VAN DYKE H.B. (1932a) Effect of replacement therapy on eruption of the incisor of the hypophysectomized rat. *Proc. Soc. exp. Biol. N.Y.* **29**, 376

SCHOUR I. & VAN DYKE H.B. (1932b) Changes in the teeth following hypophysectomy. I. *Amer. J. Anat.* **50**, 397. II. *J. dent. Res.* **14**, 69

SHAFER W.G. & MUHLER J.C. (1956) The effect of desiccated thyroid, propylthiouracil, testosterone, and fluorine on the submaxillary glands of the rat. *J. dent. Res.* **35**, 922

SHAW J.H. (1950) Gonadectomy and dental caries activity. *J. dent. Res.* **29**, 798

SPEIRS R.L. (1961) Salivary hyaluronidase and the menstrual cycle. *Brit. dent. J.* **110**, 204

SUTCLIFFE P. (1972) A longitudinal study of gingivitis and puberty. *J. periodont. Res.* **7**, 52

TROTT J.R. (1957) An histological investigation into keratinization found in human gingivae. *Brit. dent. J.* **103**, 421

WALTON R.E. & EISENMANN D.R. (1975) Ultrastructural examination of dentine formation in rat incisors following multiple fluoride injections. *Archs oral Biol.* **20**, 485

WEINREB M.M. *et al.* (1969) Role of attrition and occlusal contact in the physiology of the rat incisor. *J. dent. Res.* **48**, 120

YAEGER J.A. (1963) Strontium response in dentin. *J. dent. Res.* **42**, 1178

YAEGER J.A. & EISENMANN D.R. (1963) Response in dentin to injected agents. *J. dent. Res.* **42**, 1208

ZISKIN D.E. & APPLEBAUM E. (1941) Effects of thyroidectomy and thyroid stimulation on growing permanent dentition of rhesus monkeys. *J. dent. Res.* **20**, 21

ZISKIN D.E. & NESSE G.J. (1946) Pregnancy gingivitis. *Amer. J. Ortho. and Oral Surg.* (*Oral Surg. Section*), **32**, 390

CHAPTER VIII

THE INFLUENCE OF DIET ON THE ORAL STRUCTURES

Mineral Metabolism and the Teeth

As with experiments on the oral effects of hormones, the results of nutritional deficiences are not necessarily relevant to clinical conditions in man, but may provide information about the factors controlling tooth formation.

Effect of total mineral deprivation on teeth

A few experiments have been reported in which the effects of feeding diets low in all mineral salts have been studied on rats' teeth. Such experiments are not of great value partly because reduced salt intake greatly reduces appetite and therefore the intake of all nutrients, and partly because it is not possible to say which of the several deficiencies present are responsible for the observed effects. The weights of the incisors in the rats receiving the diet deficient in all minerals were lower than in control animals and the percentages of ash were reduced and of water increased. The ash content of the incisors fell by 7·9%, a much smaller fall than occurred in the ash of bone (24·2%), thus suggesting that teeth have priority over bone when minerals are deficient (Clarke & Smith 1935). Another important difference between the behaviour of bone and teeth was that when a diet with a normal salt content was fed to animals which were deficient in minerals, the ash content of the bone returned to normal but that of the teeth formed during the deprivation period remained unchanged, although secondary dentine formed during the second period was normal.

Calcium and phosphorus deficiency

Some of the experiments on the effects of calcium and phosphorus deficiency on teeth were carried out to find out whether the minerals of bone and teeth are equally available during a deficiency of either element. The results agree that whereas a diet with a low calcium or phosphorus content may cause considerable removal of minerals from bone, virtually none occurs from teeth already formed. Slight changes in composition of molars observed in adult experimental animals on various dietary regimes are believed to be related to differences in the structure of secondary dentine laid down during the experiment, rather than to the removal of minerals from tissue already formed. Even teeth developing while the deficient diet is being fed may be almost normal although bone forming at the same time is grossly defective.

Gaunt & Irving (1940) fed diets varying both in the Ca:P ratio (0·5, 1·0 and

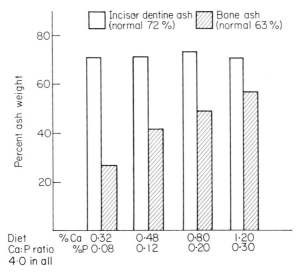

Fig. VIII.1. Effect of level of calcium and phosphorus in diets all with Ca:P ratio 4·0 on the ash content of bone and incisors on rats. Note that the incisors are hardly affected by the dietary level of calcium and phosphorus whereas the ash content of bone is much reduced. The ash of the tooth is, however, slightly reduced by low dietary calcium and phosphorus with a Ca:P ratio of 0·5 (not shown in diagram) but on this diet also the effect on the teeth is smaller than it is on bone.

4·0) and in the percentage of calcium and phosphorus (shown in Fig. VIII.1) and studied the effects on the weight, composition and histological structure of the bones and teeth. The results were somewhat complex but the main conclusions were: (1) The teeth were much less affected than the bones and were not affected at all if the diet contained more than 0·4% of calcium and phosphorus. (2) The bones were better able to tolerate a low Ca:P ratio (that is a relative calcium deficiency) and the tooth a high Ca:P ratio (that is a relative phosphorus deficiency). This fact has not yet been fitted into theories of the mineralization of bone and dentine. A possible explanation of the apparent priority afforded to the teeth may be that, unlike bone, no mineral is removed from them in dietary deficiency. For early work see Karshan & Rosebury (1932).

Histologically, the changes noted by Gaunt & Irving in the teeth from animals on the lower intakes of calcium and phosphorus were increased width of predentine (indicating a longer time between the formation and calcification of the matrix) and imperfect fusion of the calcospherites leading to interglobular dentine. 'Vascular inclusions' (blood capillaries) were also present in the predentine which are a common feature of imperfect dentine formation. It must be emphasized that these experiments had no direct relevance to the caries-resistance of the teeth. Similar results were reported by Ferguson & Hartles (1963) who studied the effects of calcium and phosphorus deficiency with or without an accompanying vitamin D deficiency on the

TABLE VIII.1

Effects of various deficient diets on the weights and percentage of ash in rats humeri and incisors

| | Humeri | | | | Incisors | | | |
| | Weight | | Percentage ash | | Weight | | Percentage ash | |
Group and diet	Young	Adult	Young	Adult	Young	Adult	Young	Adult
1. Control	100	100	100	100	100	100	100	100
2. Low calcium, vitamin D normal	50	78	69	97	86	96	97	99
3. Low vitamin D	120	92	101	100	97	94	98	99
4. Low calcium, low vitamin D	47	83	68	95	58	86	73	98
5. Low phosphorus, vitamin D normal	55	72	60	93	67	97	98	100
6. Low phosphorus, low vitamin D	56	78	52	92	63	92	96	99

(Data from Ferguson & Hartles 1963.)

humeri and incisors of growing and adult rats. They found (Table VIII.1) that a lack of calcium was associated in the continuously growing incisor with smaller changes in weight and ash content than in bone and a low phosphate intake had almost no effect on the incisors of adult rats, contrasting with a drop of more than 25% in the humeri weight and a 7% fall in the ash. The histological effects on the alveolar bone were more marked than on the humeri. Vitamin D deficiency did affect the incisors especially when combined with calcium deficiency but, even then, the effect was smaller than on bone.

The presence of vitamin D with a deficiency of either calcium or phosphorus reduced the bone weight and ash content presumably because vitamin D itself mobilizes bone mineral (p. 19). The effects on adult bones were confined to influencing re-modelling and were naturally smaller than in young animals in which new tissue was being added rapidly. Low calcium diet reduced the amount of dental tissue formed but its ash content was approximately normal, whereas diets low in phosphorus affected more the percentage of ash and the histological appearances of dentine rather than the amount of tissue formed. (See Harrand & Hartles 1971 for review).

In the young animal the combined effect of deficiencies of calcium and vitamin D produces the most severe effects in the incisor.

Diets very low in calcium (0·026%) led in rats to marked loss of tissue from the interior of the alveolar bone leaving a thin shell with few trabeculae; if vitamin D was deficient as well, there was little additional effect (the rat is resistant to vitamin D deficiency). The number of fibres in the periodontal ligament was reduced resulting in more intervening space. This probably arose from reduced masticatory stress owing to the loss of supporting structures providing fewer stimuli than usual to the developing collagen (Oliver *et al.* 1969).

EFFECT OF CA:P RATIO OF THE DIET ON THE COMPOSITION OF THE TEETH IN RELATION TO CARIES-RESISTANCE

Sobel *et al.* (1948, 1958, 1960) fed diets with great extremes in the Ca:P ratio (for example 10·4 and 0·123) and reported that the concentration of carbonate of the calcified tissues (expressed as CO_2 in Table VIII.2) varied. The effect is even more striking if the ratios of phosphate to carbonate (usually expressed as $PO_4:2CO_3$ ratio) are compared—but for simplicity this has not been done in Table VIII.2. This observation can perhaps be explained as follows. Since the levels of calcium and phosphorus in the serum were found to vary with these

TABLE VIII.2

Percentage composition of calcified tissues in relation to Ca:P ratio of diet

Ca:P ratio of diet	10·4				0·123			
	CO_2	Ca	P	Ca/P	CO_2	Ca	P	Ca/P
Serum	49·1	11·9	3·6	3·3	56·1	6·3	11·0	0·57
Enamel	3·73	35·1	17·5	2·0	2·84	35·1	18·2	1·94
Dentine	4·25	28·2	14·1	2·0	2·93	26·6	13·9	1·91
Bone	3·22	17·4	8·7	2·0	2·58	17·2	9·40	1·83

(Data from Sobel & Hanok 1958.)

diets, it follows that the ratio of phosphorus to CO_2 in the serum also varied even though the concentration of CO_2 itself did not vary greatly. The proportion of phosphate and carbonate entering newly formed calcified tissues may depend on the proportions of these ions in the plasma. If, therefore, a diet with a high Ca:P ratio is fed (i.e. with a relative deficiency of phosphorus), the plasma phosphate falls and, even if there is no change in the plasma CO_2, the ratio between phosphate and CO_2 falls (equivalent to a *relative* rise in CO_2). Bone and dental tissues forming when the plasma has this low $P:CO_2$ ratio will then contain a higher carbonate concentration.

The conclusion from this experiment is that very wide variations in the Ca:P ratio of the diet have only a small effect on the Ca:P ratio of the bone and teeth but a marked effect on their carbonate content and consequently on their phosphate to carbonate ratio.

Although the variations in the Ca:P ratios of the diets greatly exceeds those likely to be found in human diets, these experiments do establish that the composition of the mineral part of the teeth depends on the composition of tissue fluid and therefore on the diet eaten during mineralization.

Sobel *et al.* (1960) stated that animals bred on a diet with a high Ca:P ratio, and therefore forming enamel with a high carbonate content, are more liable to caries than are control animals. One possible explanation is that, in the early stages of caries, the carbonate of enamel is released preferentially, perhaps resulting in weakened crystals or more permeable enamel. An alternative and more probable explanation of the effect of carbonate on enamel is that the concentration of carbonate present in the medium from which apatite crystals are forming influences their 'crystallinity' (the size of the crystal and number of defects in it). Excess carbonate, by becoming adsorbed on the growing crystal, blocks the sites on which other ions would normally be deposited and thus leads to small crystals with many defects. This effect of carbonate is the opposite of that of fluoride, which is believed to improve the 'crystallinity' of apatite. If enamel is high in carbonate it might be expected to be damaged more readily by acid than would enamel low in carbonate (Grøn *et al.* 1963). The point has not been fully investigated in relation to caries in man (but see pp. 480–1), but variations in the Ca:P ratio of rats' diets of a magnitude more comparable with those likely to occur in man (from 2:1 to 1:3) were found not to affect the carbonate of teeth significantly (Wynn *et al.* 1956, 1957). Conversely, McClure & McCann (1960) confirmed the effect of the Ca:P ratio of the diet during tooth formation on the carbonate concentration of teeth in the rat, but they did not find that enamel high in carbonate was more susceptible to caries.

It is possible that, even after formation, the composition of bone may be altered by changes in the $P:CO_3$ ratio in the tissue fluid and such changes could conceivably occur in the outer surface of enamel by ionic exchange if the $P:CO_3$ ratio of the surrounding saliva alters.

The 'war-time diet' effect on children's teeth

Another line of evidence has suggested that tooth structure and chemical composition may be affected by diet.

Observations on the incidence of dental caries among European children during both World Wars showed that a fall occurred presumably related to alterations in diet. An analysis by Sognnaes (1948) of the data revealed that the greater part of the fall in 5-year-old children seemed to occur some years after rationing began, suggesting that the effect was working through an increased resistance of the teeth, a conclusion supported by others. If the rationing worked through local effects in the mouth, for example, by a reduction in sugar intake lowering acid production on the surface of the tooth, Sognnaes considered that the fall would be expected to have been detected immediately after rationing was introduced. This conclusion has been questioned by Parfitt (1954), however, on the following grounds. It is the *rate* of development of caries which alters with changes in the environment of the tooth and in clinical surveys the total number of decayed, missing or filled teeth (the DMF score) which is usually measured. It is argued that the rate of caries might have to be reduced for several years before changes in the total DMF became sufficiently different to be detected. The figures on caries during the war were based on routine examinations, not research surveys, and are relatively crude. It is quite possible that the effect of a dietary change would only be convincingly detected 2 or 3 years after it began and this might be interpreted as a delay. Although most of the alleged delay can perhaps be explained on this basis, other figures confirm that the effect was partly real. For example, Toverud (1955–7) has shown that the rate of increase in caries in 12- to 13-year-old children did not rise immediately after sugar in the diet approached the pre-war level after 1945. The younger age groups showed a much more rapid response to the post-war rise in sugar intake. Marthaler (1967) examined many of the data on caries rates during and after the war and concluded that the 'war-time diet' effect was caused exclusively by the local effects of low sugar intake. The greater delay in the increase in caries in the older children as sugar consumption rose after the war could be explained as an effect on post-eruptive maturation (p. 173). Data from other experiments suggest that newly-erupted teeth are very prone to caries when exposed to sugar but develop a resistance to it after they have had contact with the oral fluids before excessive sugar ingestion. After the war the teeth of 7- to 8-year-old children would have erupted under conditions of increasing sugar consumption while the teeth of the older children had erupted some years before when sugar was severely rationed.

The evidence as a whole suggests that the major factor of the war-time diet did produce changes in the *rate* of caries, indicating an environmental effect, but, some workers believe that a structural change occurred as well. There are good grounds for supposing that the main environmental factor was the reduced sugar intake but other effects may have contributed. Among the recognized effects of rationing were a lowered sugar intake and an increased proportion of unrefined carbohydrates (for example potatoes and high extraction flour) in the diet, but many other changes may have occurred which have escaped detection. In Britain, the Welfare Foods Scheme of the Ministry of Food provided expectant and nursing mothers and young children with extra milk and vitamins but it is doubtful whether these groups received satisfactory diets in other European countries.

Animal experiments on the influence of diet on caries incidence

Sognnaes (1947) followed up his conclusions that the war-time diet effect was structural rather than environmental by conducting animal feeding experi-

TABLE VIII.3

Effect of maternal diet during pregnancy and lactation on the caries susceptibility of the offspring's teeth

Animal	Maternal diet during pregnancy and lactation	Offspring's diet after weaning	Duration of experiment after weaning (months)	Average caries score	Number of animals
Hamsters	Natural*	Refined†	4	6·1	6
	Refined†	Refined†	2	48·0	3
Rats	Natural*	Refined†	4	0	12
	Refined†	Refined†	2	2·7	10
Mice	Natural*	Refined†	4	0	15
	Refined†	Refined†	2	0·5	21

* The natural diet was well balanced and contained natural food constituents.
† The refined diet contained purified protein (casein), 67% pure sucrose, pure vitamins and mineral salts.

(Data from Sognnaes 1947.)

The results show (1) that hamsters suffer from caries if fed on a high sugar diet for 4 months even if bred on a good natural diet (line 1).

(2) If *bred* on a synthetic, high sugar diet, the caries score only 2 months after weaning is eight times that of the control after 4 months (line 2) although the numbers of animals in these groups were small.

(3) Rats and mice do not suffer from caries if bred on a natural diet even if fed the high sugar diet after weaning (lines 3 and 5).

(4) Rats and mice do suffer from caries if bred on the synthetic, high sugar diet, although the incidence is low.

ments. He fed diets of refined constituents, including 67% of sucrose, to pregnant and lactating hamsters, rats and mice and compared the incidence of caries in the offspring with that of animals fed a balanced diet of natural, unrefined foodstuffs. The young from the parent animals fed on the refined, high sugar diet were much more susceptible to caries than were the offspring of the controls on the natural diet. In fact, mice and this strain of rat are not normally susceptible to caries at all on the sugar diet, but these litters showed slight susceptibility to the disease (Table VIII.3). It should be noted that the great increase found with hamsters was based on a very small number of animals, but other workers have obtained similar, if less dramatic, results and the general idea that caries susceptibility may depend partly on maternal diet can now be regarded as proved, although some negative results have been obtained (for references, see Speirs 1964). It has also been found that feeding this refined, high sugar diet during lactation has a similar but smaller effect on caries susceptibility. When lactating mothers are fed a particular diet the young will have access to it from an early age so that some effects might result from direct contact between the refined diet and the newly-erupted teeth of the young which seem to be especially susceptible to caries as mentioned elsewhere (pp. 173 and 243). Unfortunately, there was a considerable number of differences between the two diets in Sognnaes's experiments (for example, the type and percentage of carbohydrate, the total percentage and relative amounts of minerals and trace including elements, calcium, phosphorus and fluorine, as well as unknown factors, perhaps present in natural foods, but removed from refined foods) and it is quite impossible at present to decide which of these differences caused the increased susceptibility to caries.

THE EFFECT OF THE HIGH SUGAR CONCENTRATION OF THE DIET ON CARIES SUSCEPTIBILITY

Some workers have suggested that the level of sugar itself produced a systemic influence on the caries-susceptibility of the teeth and, although this seems a less likely cause than other differences between the diets, some experiments have strengthened this possibility but, for various reasons, they were indecisive. In one by Buxbaum *et al.* (1957), hamsters were bred on the high sugar, caries-producing diet used by Sognnaes, and other groups received diets with medium and low proportions of sugar. The diets were fed for 100 days, after which the teeth were scored for caries and the carbohydrate contents of the whole teeth (not separated into enamel and dentine) were estimated and expressed as 'glycoprotein' although carbohydrate only was estimated without reference to its bound form. The results (Table VIII.4) show that both the caries susceptibility and the carbohydrate of the teeth were greatly increased by the high sugar feeding.

TABLE VIII.4

Effect of sugar-rich diet on caries score and 'glycoprotein' content of hamster teeth

Generation	Diet	No. of animals	Average caries score	Glycoprotein content of teeth (mg/g. tooth)
1st	Control	4	2·4	0·269
2nd	Control	6	3·0	0·162
1st	Sugar-rich	13	23·3	0·599
2nd	Sugar-rich	2	36·0	0·8235

(Data from Buxbaum *et al.* 1957.)

The result implies that the concentration of carbohydrate within the tooth may be a factor in determining its caries resistance, although an alternative possibility seems to have been overlooked, namely, that the carbohydrate entered the tooth after the caries began. It is quite conceivable that the carbohydrate of the enamel might be utilized by the attacking bacteria, and that high carbohydrate would be associated with a low resistance. It is, therefore, unfortunate that the analyses were carried out on the whole teeth and not on the separated enamel and dentine. If the high concentration of carbohydrate observed were in the dentine it would be unlikely to influence the number of cavities which, presumably, depends on enamel, although it might increase the rate of spread of caries through the dentine.

In the second series of experiments (by Steinman & Haley 1957) groups of rats, 2 or 3 days old, were fed 20% solutions of various carbohydrates (sucrose, lactose, starch, mixtures of glucose and fructose, and a control group received water) three times a day from a dropping pipette, and after weaning were all put on to a high sugar, caries-producing diet. The caries score after 13 weeks showed that early feeding of carbohydrates greatly increased caries susceptibility (see Table VIII.5) and that lactose had the least effect. Although no attempt was made in the experiment to relate the caries to tooth composition there is a strong implication that the early feeding of carbohydrate influenced the caries susceptibility by this means. It is also possible, however, that this procedure may have led to the infection of the mouth with cariogenic bacteria at an earlier age than is usual.

Two similar experiments have failed to confirm these results. In one, sugars were injected intra-peritoneally to rats from the age of 10 to 19 days (Brown & Bibby 1970) and in another sucrose and lactose were given in a more physiological way (by stomach tube) and over a longer period of tooth development, from birth to 21 days (Crossland & Holloway 1971) but caries susceptibility was not influenced significantly in either experiment.

TABLE VIII.5

Effect of carbohydrate supplements given to
suckling rats on their final caries score

Substance given	No. of rats	Total caries score
Water	9	12·8
20% sucrose	6	32·8
20% lactose	7	8·1
20% starch	8	52·6

(Data from Steinman & Haley 1957.)

These results could hardly explain the effects of pre-natal feeding, however, because enamel formation in the rat does not begin until after birth. What these four experiments really show is the possibility of modifying the composition of the tooth by dietary means. It is to be hoped that these experiments will be repeated on a larger scale.

H. Egyedi (1953) reported that the carbohydrate concentration of teeth from natives of Indonesia, who had a high resistance to caries, was lower than in teeth from inhabitants of Holland whose caries resistance was much lower. He produced no dietary evidence that the carbohydrate intake was greater in Holland than in Indonesia (the reverse would be expected from the usual nature of European and Asiatic diets although total food intake is less in Asia) so that the significance of this work is uncertain. Analyses of enamel from Liberians and natives of Amsterdam failed to show any difference in the carbohydrate content and therefore did not support this theory (P. Egyedi 1973).

Although the question is still unsettled, the most careful experiments suggest that an intake of excess carbohydrate during enamel formation does not affect caries susceptibility—but whether this is because the enamel carbohydrate is unchanged or because enamel carbohydrate does not affect caries has not been adequately investigated. Contact of a recently-erupted tooth with excess sugar does favour caries (see p. 173).

OTHER EFFECTS OF THE DIET ON CARIES SUSCEPTIBILITY

In addition to this inconclusive evidence that the carbohydrate of the diet used by Sognnaes may influence the composition of the tooth, there is also reason for believing that its mineral content is important in this respect. Sognnaes & Shaw (1954) in one experiment, found that if the natural diet was ashed, and the ash (including, of course, the trace elements) was fed to groups of rats (1) during pregnancy and lactation, or (2) to the young rats after weaning, that

TABLE VIII.6

Effect of the ash of a natural diet on caries in rats when fed with a caries-producing (high sugar) diet before or after weaning

| | Diet fed | | |
No. of rats	During pregnancy and lactation	After weaning	Average caries score
47	High sugar	High sugar	6·2
50	High sugar + ash of natural	High sugar	4·2
13	High sugar + ash of natural	High sugar + ash of natural	1·4

(Data from Sognnaes & Shaw 1954.)

caries-susceptibility was lowered in each case with the greatest effect in group 2, and the least in group 1 (see Table VIII.6). This experiment indicates that one or more of the mineral constituents of the diet, probably trace elements, can affect the composition of the teeth and increase their caries-resistance. The effect of the ash when given after weaning (which is presumably on the environment of the tooth and not directly on its structure) may not resemble that of the original diet, however, because when food is ashed the inorganic residue differs from the inorganic constituents of the original diet. Not only are organic phosphates broken down to inorganic salts but the phosphate in the ash is largely converted into pyrophosphate, which has been found to reduce caries in rats—an effect which is perhaps explained because pyrophosphate lowers the solubility of teeth *in vitro* and also inhibits acid production by salivary organisms.

It is not known whether effects on the carbohydrate or minerals of the tooth played any part in the war-time reduction in caries.

An experiment (by Holloway *et al.* 1961) consisted of comparing the size, shape and caries susceptibility of rats teeth on diets fed to mothers during pregnancy and lactation in which the protein (casein) and sucrose varied reciprocally (67% sucrose and 24% casein compared with 19% sucrose and 72% casein). The teeth formed on the high sucrose diets were smaller (owing to shorter distances between the outer borders of the dentine rather than to differences in the enamel thickness) and in many of the rats certain cusps of the teeth were missing and the caries susceptibility was greater.

These differences could have been related either to the excess sugar or to variations in the protein intake which, since casein (a phosphoprotein) was the protein used, also involved variations in the phosphorus content of the diet. It was concluded that protein and not phosphate was important in altering the morphology of the tooth but phosphate was a factor in controlling the caries resistance. This experiment clearly proves the importance of dietary factors other than minerals in the structure and caries resistance of rats teeth, even though the differences between the diets were more extreme than are likely to occur in human diets.

An experiment in which diets containing either 8 or 25% protein were fed either during pregnancy or lactation or both showed that protein deficiency only during lactation had a marked effect on body weight, tooth size or caries scores (Navia *et al.* 1970). It must be borne in mind that some of the diets used in these experiments were so unbalanced (for example 67% of sugar) that the general health of the animals was impaired.

Luoma (1961) injected glucose or fructose solutions into rats while their teeth were forming, a procedure that would be expected to lower plasma phosphate since it is needed to metabolize the sugar. The carbonate of the enamel was raised and the $PO_4:2CO_3$ ratio was significantly lowered by the sugar injections which, in view of the results of Sobel (1955) (p. 241), would be expected to increase caries susceptibility, although this was not studied.

The whole position may be summed up as follows: the war-time diet effect was undoubtedly mostly caused by changes in the environment of the tooth, sugar rationing being probably the most important factor, which may also explain the possible effect on the resistance of some teeth by increasing post-eruptive maturation. Animal experiments have shown that the diet during enamel mineralization can influence its composition and its caries resistance. This apparently may occur in two ways: possibly through the carbohydrate content of the tooth and through the mineral matter, probably involving unidentified trace elements. Finally, the relevance of the animal experiments to the war-time effect or to the question of building up resistance to caries in man is not known.

EFFECT OF DEPRIVATION OF ESSENTIAL FATTY ACIDS

Groups of rats 2 weeks old were fed either a high-sugar fat-free diet or the same diet supplemented with essential fatty acids until the age of 16 weeks. In the deficient rats the ameloblasts at the secretory stage lost their acidophilic-staining zone and the basal end showed vacuolar distensions into the stratum intermedium. The ameloblasts at the resorbing stage accumulated an acido-philic material which displaced the nuclei which were pyknotic. The matrix showed a coarse irregular structure in contrast to its normal homogeneous appearance. This may be related to an unusual 'honeycomb' structure of the enamel observed in these deficient animals (Prout & Tring 1971, 1973). In the molar, but not the incisor, the periodontal tissues were also affected. The odon-toblasts lost their identity and became indistinguishable from the pulp cells and space appeared between them, and much interglobular dentine was present.

The lipid composition of mixed enamel and dentine is affected slightly by the carbohydrate of the diet. With a starch diet, the palmitic acid was high and the unsaturated fatty acids lower than with a sucrose diet (Alam & Harris 1972). When a cariogenic diet was fed, the composition of the lipid in the teeth changed, the concentration of fatty acids (which some reports suggest constitute about 50% of the lipid in rats teeth) was reduced.

Trace elements

Fluoride has a powerful influence on the teeth, especially their resistance to caries, and there is somewhat confused evidence suggesting that other trace elements are also implicated. For example, as mentioned on p. 247 Sognnaes & Shaw (1954) found that the ash of their natural diet when fed during tooth formation increased caries resistance. Corn and milk produced in New England promoted greater caries activity in hamsters than similar foods from Texas and contained less than half the concentration of several trace elements.

Trace elements associated with caries in human populations are dealt with on p. 453.

MIXTURES OF TRACE ELEMENTS

Kruger (1959) studied the effect on caries in the rat of injections, during tooth formation, of salts containing certain trace elements either alone or in combination. The main results were that (1) the salts of fluoride, boron, vanadium and molybdenum and, to a lesser extent, copper injected separately all reduced caries; (2) fluoride was more effective by itself than when injected with a mixture of four salts containing boron, copper, manganese and molybdenum, i.e. the four salts reduced the effect of fluoride; and (3) aluminium and iodine were without effect.

EFFECTS OF TRACE ELEMENTS ON THE SIZE AND MORPHOLOGY OF TEETH

Kruger (1962) found by a mathematical analysis of the shapes of the occlusal fissures in the teeth of rats which had received boron, fluoride and molybdenum that these trace elements tended to make the occlusal fissures wider and shallower. The trace elements were injected over three different stages of formation of the first mandibular molar namely at ages 3–6 days, 7–10 days and 11–14 days. The period 7–10 days was the most sensitive and boron and fluoride caused the production of teeth with wider and shallower mesial fissures. In approximately one-fifth of the animals injected with boron the fissure was eliminated altogether. With fluoride, the teeth were described as flatter and when it was given in the last period were smaller than the controls. Injections of molybdenum also resulted in wider but not shallower mesial

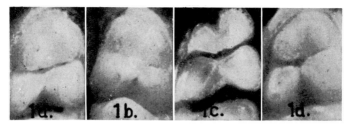

FIG. VIII.2. Mesial fossa of mandibular molars of rats given varying supplements of trace elements during enamel formation; (1a) control; (1b) boron; (1c) fluorine; (1d) molybdenum.

fissures. In some cases, these effects were so marked, that they could be detected in photographs (Fig. VIII.2).

These changes in shape and size of teeth would tend to reduce the extent to which food remains trapped in and around the teeth, and thereby would be expected to reduce the susceptibility to caries. This is not necessarily the only possible way in which these trace elements reduce caries as they might also influence the composition of the tooth. Injection in very large doses of strontium, molybdenum and boron with or without fluoride into rats during tooth formation increased caries (Hunt & Navia 1975).

The size and shape of the fissures in human molars are difficult to study because reliable results are only obtainable from sections of newly-erupted teeth. Sections are necessary because the fissures are so narrow that their depth cannot be measured from outside by probes; sometimes the neck of the fissure is deceptively narrow and then leads into a wider terminal portion where size cannot be estimated in the intact tooth. Newly-erupted teeth must be studied because caries, which destroys the shape of the original fissure, occurs so rapidly in these sites. Probably for these reasons, few data exist on the shape of the fissures of human teeth in relation to diet. Cooper & Ludwig (1965) have reported, however, more rounded cusps in teeth from Napier (high molybdenum) in confirmation of Kruger's animal experiments. Data on the effect of fluoride on the overall dimensions and certain other morphological features of the teeth are discussed on p. 481.

Magnesium deficiency

Irving (1940) studied the effects of magnesium deficiency on both the chemistry and histology of the incisors of young rats. In experiments lasting up to 12 days, the rate of growth of the teeth was only slightly reduced and the absolute amount of magnesium they contained remained steady or even increased slightly (Fig. VIII.3). The maintenance of the magnesium at a

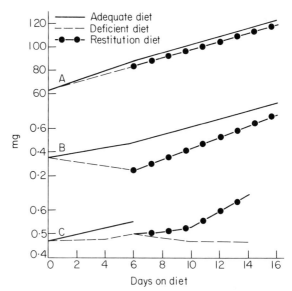

FIG. VIII.3. Effect of magnesium deficiency on bone and teeth. (A) Mean weight of incisors; (B) mean magnesium content of femur; (C) mean magnesium content of incisor.

The result shows (1) that the magnesium content of the incisor (C) remains steady when that of bone is falling (B); (2) when magnesium is restored to the diet its concentration in both bone and incisors rises and eventually becomes normal.

constant level in an actively growing incisor implies that magnesium is entering the newly-formed tissue in the root at the same rate at which magnesium is being lost by the attrition of the dental tissues on the incisal surface. This result contrasted strongly with the changes in bone in which the level of magnesium fell sharply within 6 days to about two-thirds of normal. This is further evidence of the inability of a tooth to yield up its minerals and of the priority the tooth seems to have during a nutritional crisis.

When magnesium was restored to the diet of the deficient rats, the amounts laid down in both teeth and bone exceeded the normal rate so that within 4 days the concentration in the tooth had reached the normal level (Fig. VIII.3). The rate of growth is progressively reduced if the deficiency is prolonged and, after about 20 days on a magnesium deficient diet, may be only one-third that of normal.

The histological effects of magnesium deficiency were as follows. At a point about 3 mm from the basal part of the tooth, the predentine suddenly doubled in width and if the deficiency were sufficiently prolonged it trebled at a point farther away still from the root, thus the dentine–predentine junction was in different positions at different levels of the tooth (Fig. VIII.4). This

FIG. VIII.4. Photomicrograph of incisor dentine of rat on a magnesium-deficient diet for 6 days showing 'predentine step' but the stratifications are only faintly visible.

phenomenon, which Irving who described it called the 'predentine step', appears to be unique for magnesium deficiency. The calcified dentine beyond this step showed a series of faint lines running parallel to the dentine–predentine junction ('stratification') very uniformly about 27 μm apart corresponding with 2 days' output of dentine; their cause is unknown (Trowbridge *et al.* 1971). The dentine also stained less intensely with haematoxylin, although the interpretation of this is uncertain. With prolonged deficiency, the dentine was more seriously affected in the labial part of the tooth (that is, under the enamel), thus distorting the shape of the pulp (contrast with vitamin A deficiency in which the lingual part was most severely affected, see pp. 255–7). The odontoblasts gradually atrophied on the magnesium deficient diet, their length changing from the normal of about 50 μm to 33 μm after 23 days and in places the cells failed to recede from the predentine and became embedded in it. The odontoblastic layer and the dentine became folded after a long deficiency. Similar results were reported by Trowbridge & Seltzer (1967) who concluded that the impaired matrix formation was the main effect resulting from reduced activity of magnesium-dependent enzymes. They showed histochemically that alkaline phosphatase was less active and that less proline and sulphate were incorporated into the matrix.

The enamel organ also showed degeneration, the ameloblasts became a low cubical epithelium filled with calcareous granules but this effect was not unlike other forms of degeneration of the enamel organ, such as in hypophysectomy and vitamin A deficiency (Fig. VIII.5).

In experiments in which the magnesium deficiency has lasted as long as 186 days, complete atrophy of the enamel organ of the incisal area has been observed, the cells being replaced by a thin non-cellular structure. In the apical part of the tooth, the enamel organ disappeared completely and there was direct contact between connective tissue and the outer surface of the

(a)   (b)

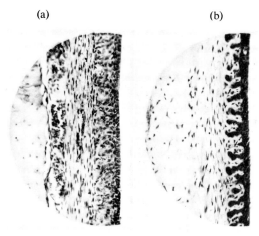

FIG. VIII.5. Effect of magnesium deficiency on enamel organ of rat incisor. (a) Normal;
(b) 23 days on magnesium deficient diet (compare with vitamin A deficiency, Fig.
VII.6(b)).

dentine. Recovery of the odontoblasts from a short deficiency occurred
rapidly when magnesium was restored to the diet except for those most
distally placed, which failed to recover.

In one of the earliest studies on magnesium deficiency in rats (Klein *et al.*
1935) symptoms resembling chronic periodontal disease were observed
(hypertrophy of the gingivae and loosening of the teeth) but in later work
these points were not followed up. Eruption rates of rat incisors were considerably reduced in magnesium deficiency lasting 16 weeks and longer
(Kusner *et al.* 1973). The results on matrix formation and mineralization
probably arises from reduced activity of enzymes requiring magnesium as a
co-factor.

Whether the presence of magnesium in the calcified tissues confers any
special properties on them, or whether it merely enters them accidentally is
not known. The fact that magnesium enters the tooth when it is being removed from bone might suggest some special function in the tooth but could
occur simply because, unlike bone, there is no mechanism for removing it.
Magnesium is widely distributed in foods and a deficiency is unlikely in human
diets.

Vitamins and the Oral Tissues

Vitamin A deficiency

THE FUNDAMENTAL ACTION OF VITAMIN A
One of the most widespread symptoms of vitamin A deficiency which occurs

in all species studied is the hyperplasia (increased number of cells) and keratinization of most epithelial cells (liver and kidney tubule cells are exceptions). Wolbach & Bessey (1942) suggest that vitamin A is needed for the normal maintenance of most epithelial cells and in its absence they become keratinized, which leads to the multiplication of the basal cells in an attempt to replace those that die. Apparently, whatever the original function of the cell, the final picture of stratified epithelium is identical in this deficiency.

Another effect of vitamin A which is relevant to dental problems is its control over osteoclasts. Sir Edward Mellanby (1942–3) found that osteoclasts are inactive in vitamin A deficiency and that bone may be laid down by osteoblasts at sites where it would normally be removed, thus leading to a thickening of the bone. In certain parts of the skeleton the increased thickness of bone may damage nerves by exerting excessive pressure on them, leading to the nerve degeneration which is a symptom of vitamin A deficiency. In tissue culture, vitamin A increases the permeability of lysosome membranes leading to the release of proteolytic enzymes.

EFFECTS OF VITAMIN A DEFICIENCY ON THE RODENT INCISOR

For a complete understanding of the effects of vitamin A deficiency on the rodent incisor, it is important to make clear the unusual development of this tooth. It develops from an elliptical epithelial structure at the apical end of the tooth which proliferates throughout the life of the animal. This tissue, known as the odontogenic epithelium, has three functions similar to those of the enamel organ in human teeth: (1) it determines the shape of the amelo–dentinal and cemento dentinal junctions, (2) it has an organizing influence on the mesenchyme causing the cells to differentiate and promotes the formation of dentine, and (3) the cells of the labial third (as viewed in transverse section) become the enamel organ. In spite of its name, the odontogenic epithelium is not concerned only with odontoblasts and dentine.

The effect of vitamin A deficiency on the rodent incisor has been thoroughly established by several groups of workers whose main conclusions are in good agreement (Wolbach & Howe 1933; Baume *et al.* 1969).

After about 30 days on a deficient diet the enamel loses the yellow pigment normally present in this tissue in rodents and becomes chalky white; the tooth becomes more brittle and shares the reduced general growth of the skull and skeleton, which is typical of 'avitaminosis A' (i.e. vitamin A deficiency). The first effect noted in histological sections is the degeneration of the ameloblasts and the conversion of the other cells of the enamel organ into a stratified epithelium which may become keratinized (Fig. VIII.6(b)). This change does not occur at the extreme apical end, where, although the enamel organ is buckled, the constituent cells may be almost normal. Groups of degenerating ameloblasts sometimes become detached from the enamel organ and form calcified droplets in the connective tissue and may even enter the pulp in

(a)

(c)

(b)

(d)

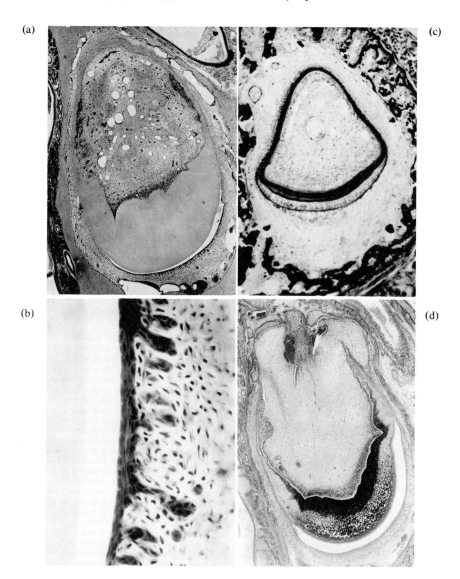

FIG. VIII.6. Effects of vitamin A deficiency on rat incisors. (a) Transverse section of incisor of rat on the deficient diet for 101 days; note the great thickening of the dentine and its thinness at the lingual end; (b) high power of enamel organ in same rat; (c) normal control; (d) rat was on deficient diet 170 days followed by 14 days with vitamin A restored to diet.

Note the poor mineralization of the dentine formed during the deficiency and its improvement after the vitamin was given and, on the left, the irregular dentine, probably formed in the vicinity of cells of the odontogenic epithelium which have entered the pulp through gaps in the defective dentine.

places where, owing to the deficiency, dentine is absent. The response of the enamel organ to the deficiency is similar to that found in other epithelial structures, namely, the conversion of epithelial layers into keratin regardless of their normal function. It is possible that changes in the shape of the alveolar bone following reduced action of osteoclasts may interfere with the blood supply of the enamel organ and thus contribute to its degeneration. The degeneration of the enamel organ leads to hypoplastic enamel.

The most striking histological finding is that the odontoblasts on the mesial and lingual (that is, cementum covered) sides of the tooth become less active and eventually atrophy and the dentine becomes much thinner than usual and may be folded or pleated and lined by pulp connective tissue cells. Dentine may be absent altogether in places. On the labial side, which is covered by enamel, the odontoblasts become *more* active and the dentine becomes abnormally thick although it is poorly calcified with many inter-globular spaces. Consequently in transverse sections of the tooth the pulp cavity is seen to be pushed towards the lingual side (Fig. VIII.6(c)). In a prolonged deficiency, however, even the labial odontoblasts eventually degenerate, but only after the enamel organ has atrophied. Adjacent odonto-blasts do not degenerate simultaneously so that if an isolated group of cells ceases to form dentine while their neighbours remain active the inactive cells become surrounded by dentine ('cell inclusions').

There is no satisfactory explanation of the differences in response of the labial and lingual odontoblasts to vitamin A deficiency. It is remarkable that the former should increase dentine production at a stage of the vitamin deficiency at which other odontoblasts have completely disappeared and the body as a whole is losing weight.

EFFECT OF VITAMIN A DEFICIENCY ON RAT MOLARS
If young rats are fed a vitamin A-deficient diet at weaning, the crowns and most of the root of the molar teeth are formed before the vitamin A reserves of the animal are exhausted and consequently most of these tissues are normal. The third molar, however, which is developed last, shows irregular root formation and degeneration of some of the odontoblasts.

The only way of demonstrating the full effects of vitamin A deficiency on molar teeth of rats is to breed animals from vitamin A-deficient mothers. This approach is limited by the fact that very severely deficient rats are unable to give birth to live litters and will not survive to reproductive age if on a diet completely free of vitamin A. With young born to mothers fed on diets low in vitamin A for 13 weeks, no effects were noted on the teeth up to the age of 5 weeks, at which age the vitamin A stores in the young rats' livers were found to be exhausted. The molars of rats born to mothers which had been on the deficient diets for longer than 15 weeks showed defects similar to those described above for the incisors, namely, badly mineralized and irregular dentine (but of approximately normal thickness) ossifying cells in the pulp, and degeneration of the enamel organ with larger areas of dentine than normal unprotected by enamel (in rats' molars some parts of the occlusal surface are normally not covered by enamel). The results on the incisors of both mothers and young were in good confirmation of those obtained by previous workers but they showed that the teeth of the young suffered more severely than did those of the mothers.

RECOVERY FROM VITAMIN A DEFICIENCY

When vitamin A is given to a deficient animal the enamal organ recovers first, followed shortly after by the odontoblasts underlying enamel and later by the lateral and lingual odontoblasts. Irregularities in the dentine are filled in and the epithelial inclusions in the pulp become surrounded by dentine, they presumably exert their normal organizer action on pulp cells and convert them into odontoblasts (Fig. VIII.6(d)). Predentine is formed before the odontoblasts have become morphologically normal, the latter process being complete in about 19 days. The odontoblasts appear to be formed anew from pulp connective tissue cells which happen to be in contact with the dentine and not necessarily through the regeneration of the atrophied odontoblasts.

EFFECT OF EXPERIMENTAL VITAMIN A DEFICIENCY ON THE SOFT TISSUES OF THE MOUTH

In vitamin A deficiency the gingivae and ducts of the salivary gland share in the hyperplasia and keratinization which occur in mucous membranes generally and, in rats, degeneration of the secretory cells of the salivary gland has been described. The salivary ducts may become almost blocked by keratin formed from what is normally a simple epithelium. In one experiment, by Salley *et al.* (1959), in which vitamin A-deficient hamsters were put on to a cariogenic diet, the caries score was about three times greater than that of control animals receiving vitamin A. They attributed this result to the reduced salivary flow which followed the degeneration of the gland.

Lady Mellanby (1929) found that vitamin A intake during the growth period in dogs had an influence on the well-being of the gingival epithelium throughout their lives. If the diet was deficient in vitamin A during growth, the gingival epithelium was hyperplastic and the periodontal ligament became infected (Fig. VIII.7), and although feeding the vitamin in later life reduced the severity of the symptoms, these tissues never became quite normal. If, however, a generous intake was allowed during early life, the gingival and periodontal tissues resisted infection and even a subsequent vitamin A deficiency was less marked in its effects. Owing to the storage of vitamin A in the body, deficiencies must be prolonged and severe to produce dramatic symptoms both in the teeth and in the supporting structures.

Similar results have been reported in rats (King 1940; Miglani 1959). A

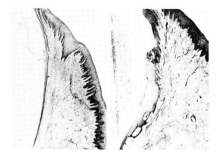

FIG. VIII.7. Effect of vitamin A deficiency (right) on the gingival epithelium of dog compared with normal (left). Note the hyperplasia of the epithelium particularly adjacent to the enamel space.

calcification and narrowing of the periodontal ligament due apparently to a distortion of the alveolar bone which showed increased osteoclastic, and reduced osteoblastic, activity has been described (Miglani) but with more severe deficiency (rats born to deficient mothers) the periodontal ligament was *widened*. The mineralization in the periodontal ligament led to fusion between the root of the tooth and the bone (ankylosis).

ORAL EFFECTS OF VITAMIN A DEFICIENCY IN MAN

From the relatively few cases of uncomplicated vitamin A deficiency that have been reported in children, the impression is gained that human teeth are less sensitive to this deficiency than might have been expected from animal experiments. For example, Bloch (1930) described the macroscopical structure of the teeth in sixty-four patients aged between 8 and 12 who were so severely deficient that they were blind as a result of xerophthalmia. Nineteen showed rachitic changes also and their dental defects might therefore have been complicated by the multiple deficiency. Of the remainder, six had perfect teeth, though they had suffered from xerophthalmia during their first year when, of course, dental mineralization was in progress. Only twenty-one of the children showed slightly hypoplastic deciduous incisors and of these only ten had been severely deficient while these teeth were being mineralized. Conversely, of the twenty-four children with normal incisors, thirteen did have xerophthalmia during the mineralization of their incisors. The condition of the dentine was not known, but it is clear that no gross disturbance of the enamel organ had occurred in spite of the severe vitamin A deficiency.

The changes in the tooth germ of the first permanent molar have been described in one case of possible vitamin A deficiency in a $3\frac{1}{2}$-month-old child who died from pre-natal syphilis. The enamel organ was atrophied and enamel formation had ceased; predentine was wide and mineralization had occurred only under the small cap of enamel and was very defective. The evidence for vitamin A deficiency was provided by the finding of the usual epithelial changes in the trachea and elsewhere. Nevertheless, this baby had received cod liver oil, although little food of any kind had been assimilated because of persistent vomiting and it cannot be regarded as certain that the dental defects were caused by a vitamin deficiency (Boyle 1933).

Clinical observations on nine subjects known from estimations of serum vitamin A and carotene to be suffering from vitamin A deficiency did not show evidence of damage to the periodontal membrane (Russell *et al.* 1961). An experimental deprivation of vitamin A in adult human subjects showed no oral symptoms even after 25 months (Hume & Krebs 1949).

It is generally agreed that vitamin A deficiency is rarely responsible for human enamel hypoplasia, presumably because the deficiency has to be so severe before marked dental effects are produced. There is no evidence that the commoner diseases of the supporting tissues in man are caused by vitamin A deficiency, at any rate, in western countries.

Effects of vitamin D deficiency

The dental effects of vitamin D deficiency were studied very thoroughly in dogs by Lady Mellanby (1929), who later confirmed her results on rats and rabbits.

EFFECT ON DENTINE

The main results of vitamin D deficiency on the dentine are a widening of the predentine (indicating a delay in calcification), irregularity of the boundary between dentine and predentine, and interglobular spaces in the dentine itself (Fig. VIII.8). These defects all indicate impaired mineralization but the dentine is thinner than usual in a vitamin D-deficient animal, implying that matrix formation is affected. That the reduced matrix production was caused specifically by a deficiency of vitamin D, and not by some secondary deficiency, was proved by an experiment in which an animal on a vitamin D deficient diet was irradiated by ultra-violet light which permitted the formation of dentine of approximately normal thickness. The only known physiological effect of irradiation likely to influence the teeth is that of vitamin D formation in the skin. There has been little comment on the reduction in matrix formation in vitamin D deficiency but it fits in with Kodicek's finding (see p. 21) that in cartilage vitamin D is localized in cells concerned with matrix formation rather than with mineralization and with the effects of vitamin D on general growth (p. 22).

Some workers have reported degeneration of the odontoblasts but this finding has not been invariable and may possibly be due to deficiencies other than vitamin D which were present simultaneously.

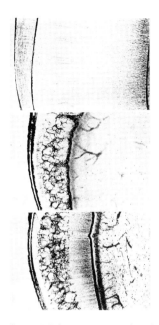

Fig. VIII.8. Effect of vitamin D deficiency on enamel and dentine of dogs' teeth. (a) Normal; (b) deficient; (c) deficient at first, later given vitamin D. Note extreme thinness of enamel and dentine and the imperfections in their structure in (b) and (c).

EFFECT ON ENAMEL

There is less agreement about the effect of vitamin D deficiency on the enamel and the great discrepancies observed remain uncertain. Lady Mellanby (1929) found that the enamel of vitamin D-deficient dogs tended to be thinner than normal indicating faulty matrix formation, and was also poorly mineralized (Fig. VIII.9). The surface was irregular and pigmented, effects which were easily observed in the living animal. In very severe deficiency no enamel whatever was formed over parts of the dentine. Other workers have made similar observations and in addition it has been stated that the normal change of the ameloblasts from columnar to cubical epithelium occurred prematurely, an effect which would be expected to reduce matrix formation (believed to be carried out when the cells are columnar) and accelerate maturation. The latter process is presumably made more difficult in vitamin D deficiency by the shortage of minerals in the tissue fluid. Weinmann & Schour (1945), however, reported that enamel is unaffected in rats by vitamin D deficiency lasting up to 56 days. Since vitamin D stores take a considerable time to deplete, these results might be explained by variations in the amount of vitamin stored before the experiment began.

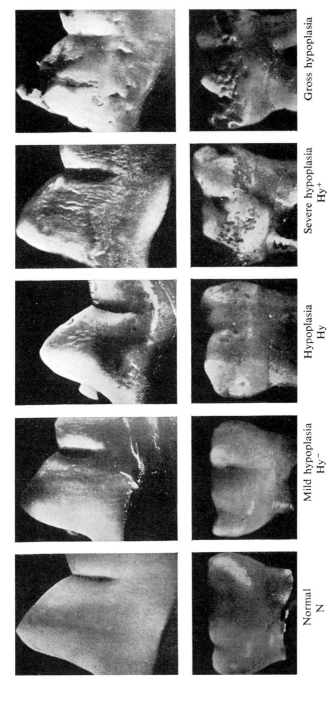

Fig. VIII.9. Comparison of human deciduous teeth showing different grades of hypoplasia (lower row) with the teeth of vitamin D-deficient dogs (upper row).

Normal
N

Mild hypoplasia
Hy⁻

Hypoplasia
Hy

Severe hypoplasia
Hy⁺

Gross hypoplasia

SITE OF ACTION OF VITAMIN D

Although the direct effect of vitamin D on bone is well established (p. 19) and, surprisingly, consists of a removal of mineral there is little information on the nature of the direct effect of vitamin D on dental tissues or on which cells are affected. Kodicek's method of locating [^{14}C]vitamin D in tissues has not been applied to the teeth.

EFFECT OF MATERNAL DIET ON THE MINERALIZATION OF THE TEETH OF THE YOUNG

Lady Mellanby (1929) showed that the intake of calcifying factors by the mother had a marked effect on the structure of those teeth of the young which were mineralized before birth or during lactation. When a defective diet was given to the young, the effects were less severe if the mother had received ample vitamin D than if the mother had been deprived of the vitamin during pregnancy and lactation. The eruption of the deciduous teeth of puppies born of a deficient mother was delayed and observations (limited to eight puppies) suggested also that the eruption of the permanent teeth was delayed slightly even if the puppies received vitamin D after weaning.

DENTAL DEFECTS IN MAN AND THEIR RELATION TO DENTAL CARIES

The results of vitamin D deficiency which Lady Mellanby observed on dogs' enamel closely resembled the condition known in human teeth as hypoplasia. Lady Mellanby (1936) followed up her work on the effects of vitamin D deficiency in animals with an inquiry on the incidence and histology of hypoplasia in human teeth and its relation to the susceptibility of the teeth to caries. Her conclusions on this work, unlike those on the effects of vitamin D deficiency on the structure of dogs' teeth, are controversial and many points remain unsettled. It must be emphasized that her experiments on dogs gave no direct information about the influence of vitamin D on caries because dogs do not suffer from this disease.

The macroscopic structure of human teeth in the mouth was studied by rubbing a probe lightly over them and judging the degree of roughness by their 'feel'; examination with a hand lens also revealed any irregularities present. With extracted teeth, graphite was rubbed over the surface which showed up irregularities clearly. By these means, teeth were graded either as 'normal' (N) (meaning 'perfectly formed', not meaning 'as usually found'), 'slightly hypoplastic' (Hy−), 'moderately hypoplastic' (Hy) or 'severely hypoplastic' (Hy+). The term hypoplasia was already in use to refer to severe defects comparable with the grade Hy+, and to avoid confusion, the term 'hypoplasia (M)' is used when teeth are being classified according to Mellanby's scheme and 'hypoplasia (G)' (gross) refers to the condition previously known simply as hypoplasia. Examples of human teeth in each grade are shown in Figs VII.9 and VIII.10.

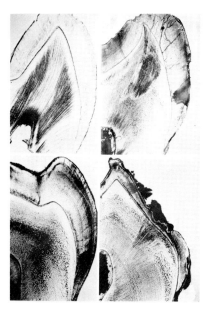

Fig. VIII.10. Histological structure of human deciduous teeth with different grades of hypoplasia, illustrating the correlation between internal structure and external appearance. Upper left: N, enamel not cracked or pigmented; no interglobular spaces in dentine. Upper right: Hy−, enamel cracked and pigmented; numerous small interglobular spaces in dentine. Lower left: Hy+, similar, but defects more severe. Lower right: HyG, enamel extremely thin and irregular; very numerous interglobular spaces in dentine. In these specimens dentine of Hy+ is more severely affected than in HyG.

THE INCIDENCE OF HYPOPLASIA

About 1500 extracted human teeth were graded into the four types of hypoplasia by the above methods and ground sections were made. The histological structure of enamel was then graded according to thickness, irregularities, pigmentation and the presence of tufts and other markings. Dentine was classified according to the number and size of the interglobular spaces.

A high correlation was found between the macroscopic and histological grading, so that it was thought possible to predict the histological grading of a tooth in the mouth from its macroscopical appearance (Fig. VIII.10). The resemblance between the characteristics of human hypoplastic teeth and of the teeth of vitamin D-deficient dogs is striking (Fig. VIII.9) and this led Mellanby to the hypothesis that hypoplasia of human teeth is also caused by vitamin D deficiency.

The incidence of hypoplasia among English school children was high and was correlated with economic status. Table VIII.7, taken from the many detailed figures in her report, shows the higher incidence and greater severity

TABLE VIII.7

Percentage of extracted deciduous teeth from different sources showing varying degrees of hypoplastic dentine

	No. examined	Normal	Hy−	Hy	Hy+	Percentage showing some degree of hypoplasia
Private sources	380	40·3	28·4	17·4	13·9	59·7
Public elementary schools	880	13·0	12·8	29·5	44·7	87·0

(Data from Mellanby 1936.)

of hypoplasia in dentine (judged histologically) from teeth extracted from elementary school children, compared with those obtained from private practitioners treating patients mostly from higher income groups.

IS VITAMIN D DEFICIENCY THE CAUSE OF HYPOPLASIA?
It is important to consider the validity of the hypothesis that hypoplasia of human teeth is caused by vitamin D deficiency. If the hypothesis be true it might be expected that the incidence of rickets would be comparable with that of hypoplasia, unless the amount of vitamin D required to prevent rachitic bones is less than that required to prevent hypoplasia in teeth. As already stated, the evidence seems to indicate that teeth have a priority for calcifying factors and are more resistant than the bones to deficiencies. This raises the question of the incidence of rickets among English children. Even in the 1920s, when this work was done, the incidence of severe rickets was much lower than that of severe hypoplasia. However, in a histological study of bones obtained *post mortem* from over 200 children who died between the ages of 2 and 14 years, 46·5% showed signs of mild rickets of which only five had been detectable during life. This work suggests that rickets was more widespread than had been realized, although the children studied in this survey were clearly in less robust health than the average.

Marshall Day (1944) failed to show any relation between the occurrence of clinical rickets and of dental hypoplasia. He studied 200 Indian boys who had received diets low in calcifying factors during the whole of the period in which their teeth were calcifying, and found the percentage with hypoplastic teeth was about the same among those with and without clinical signs of rickets (Table VIII.8).

In a survey involving forty-six rachitic and forty non-rachitic children between the ages of 6 and 10, hypoplastic permanent teeth were present in ten of the rachitic (22%) and only one (2·5%) of the non-rachitic children. This

TABLE VIII.8

Incidence of caries and hypoplasia in relation to degree of clinical rickets

Degree of clinical rickets	No. of boys examined	No. of teeth present	Percentage showing hypoplasia	Average no. of cavities per mouth
No rickets	113	3019	67	1·52
Slight rickets	64	1782	62	1·70
Moderate to severe rickets	23	656	61	1:39

(Data from Marshall Day 1944.)

and other surveys have therefore supported the belief that vitamin D deficiency may be one cause of enamel hypoplasia, but that this defect is by no means invariably present even in children suffering from frank rickets. Also, other causes may produce hypoplasia even if the vitamin D intake is adequate.

Sarnat & Schour (1941, 1942) studied the clinical history of sixty subjects whose teeth showed *gross* hypoplasia. Only ten of these subjects had a clinical history of rickets and in about half the subjects it was impossible to relate the hypoplasia to any illness. The exanthematous illnesses (scarlet fever, measles, chicken-pox and smallpox which result in peeling of the skin) did not appear to be connected with the hypoplasia, as in many cases the hypoplastic enamel had been formed before the illness occurred.

It is clear that there are only a limited number of ways in which enamel may respond to defective conditions and it is likely that many types of interference, whether dietetic, environmental or from disease, might influence the development of the teeth, and especially the enamel, in similar ways. It may be concluded, therefore, that the hypoplasia so frequently present in human teeth, cannot necessarily be regarded as evidence of vitamin D deficiency, in spite of its resemblance to the effect of lack of vitamin D in animals.

HYPOPLASIA AND CARIES

The next point to be considered is whether hypoplastic teeth are more liable to caries than are well-formed teeth. Lady Mellanby correlated the degree of hypoplasia (as indicated by dentine structure) of 1500 teeth with their degrees of caries and concluded that hypoplastic teeth are more liable to the disease. For example, 77·9% of well-calcified deciduous teeth were found to be free from caries and 74% of very hypoplastic teeth showed advanced caries. The results of an examination of 275 sectioned permanent teeth were in agreement with this conclusion. Similar results were obtained when the extent of caries was correlated with surface structure of the intact tooth or with hypoplasia of enamel judged histologically.

Three other, less extensive, surveys carried out independently by Allen (1941), Bibby (1943), Carr (1953) and Davies (1939) supported this view. McCall & Krasnow (1938) found it to be true in deciduous, but not permanent teeth while Staz (1944) reported that hypoplastic teeth in a group of seventy-three Indian children were *more resistant* to caries than were well-formed teeth. It is clear that the bulk of the evidence favours the view that hypoplasia and caries are related.

Lady Mellanby's conclusion was that only 168 (11%) of the teeth in her collection did not show the correlation between structure and resistance to caries. Of these, seventy-seven well-formed teeth had become carious and ninety-one hypoplastic teeth had resisted the disease. Since she thought that the quality of the *secondary dentine*, as well as that of the original structure of the teeth, might be related to the resistance to caries (the 'second hypothesis') ground sections of these teeth were then examined for the presence and quality of secondary dentine. Thirty-two of the 168 teeth could not be readily classified, either because so much resorption of the root had occurred that any secondary dentine formed had been removed, or because no secondary dentine had formed. Thus out of 168 exceptions to the conclusion that structure and resistance to caries are related, 136 were available to test the hypothesis that the structure of secondary dentine could reverse the effect of the primary structure on caries resistance. The results (Table VIII.9) show that

TABLE VIII.9

Secondary dentine in teeth with no direct association between original structure and caries

| | Structure of secondary dentine | | | | Total |
	Good	Absent	Poor	Absorbed	number
'Normal' primary structure with caries	10	12	52	3	77
Hypoplastic primary structure with little or no caries	26	26	22	17	91

(Data from Mellanby 1936.)

52 out of the 77 teeth with 'normal' structure but with caries had poor secondary dentine (and 12 had none) whereas 26 of the hypoplastic teeth without caries had good secondary dentine (26 had none). These 78 teeth supported the hypothesis that the quality of secondary dentine could reverse the effect of the primary structure.

It must be concluded that only slightly more than half of a rather small number of teeth supported the second hypothesis. Even if future work should put this hypothesis on a sounder footing there remains the difficulty of explaining the mechanism by which secondary dentine can affect resistance to caries. It is difficult on present theories of caries, to explain how secondary dentine can alter the resistance of the surface of enamel and especially difficult to picture a mechanism by which absence or poor quality of secondary dentine could reduce the resistance of well-formed enamel and primary dentine to the initial attack of caries. However, an hypothesis must not be rejected because it cannot be explained, but only if it fails to correspond with facts (see also concluding paragraph of this section on p. 269).

Study of the ground sections of the whole collection of 1500 teeth showed that teeth with well-formed primary tissues did not necessarily produce well-mineralized secondary dentine and vice versa. This occurred presumably because the quality of tissue formed depended on the nutritional condition prevailing at the time of its production as Mellanby showed in animal experiments.

The question of the relations between hypoplasia, secondary dentine formation and caries must still be regarded as unsettled.

THE EFFECT OF VITAMIN D SUPPLEMENTS ON CARIES

Experiments have attempted to determine whether vitamin D supplements reduce the incidence of hypoplasia and caries in children. Although some results have been completely negative, most have suggested that some reduction in caries can be effected by generous doses of vitamin D, especially if given before the eruption of the teeth. Some experiments have indicated the reduced rate of the extension of cavities which had formed before the administration of vitamin D had begun ('arrested caries').

Animal experiments have also led to inconclusive results. None of Mellanby's dogs suffered from caries even when severely deficient in vitamin D but this fact is of little significance because the dog is a species which is caries free.

The possible mechanisms of action of vitamin D in caries reduction are obscure. When given before eruption it might improve the structure of the tooth and hence its resistance to caries. There is no proved explanation of the low resistance to caries which some workers believe to be shown by hypoplastic teeth although a 'common sense' explanation that the uneven surface may provide a large number of sheltered areas where bacteria can grow and attack the tooth. The mechanism of the possible 'arrest' of caries under the influence of vitamin D is not understood. The only form of arrested caries which is readily explained is quite independent of vitamin D and occurs when the sides of a cavity collapse under masticatory stress and the area becomes self-cleansing. Similarly, if one of a pair of carious teeth which share a contact point is extracted, the surviving tooth may become self-cleansing and the caries may become arrested.

The statistical evidence that the structure of a tooth or of secondary dentine is related to its power to resist caries does not, of course, *prove* that differences in structure are the cause of differences in resistance. It may be that the factors which promote the development of sound tissues, also, by some independent mechanism, reduce the tendency to caries. For example, one experiment suggested that salivary concentrations of calcium and phosphorus were raised by taking extra vitamin D, an effect which might be expected to reduce the solvent action of acid on the teeth. These results have not been confirmed, but they illustrate one type of indirect mechanism that might explain the action of vitamin D on caries.

Effects of over-dosage of vitamin D on the oral structures

In the dental tissues, the effects of over-dosage of vitamin D in animal experiments have shown variable results. The dental effect of one large dose in rats is to produce a calciotraumatic response in the incisor dentine. Effects which have been reported in one experiment on a small number of dogs over-dosed with vitamin D for several months included increased deposition of alveolar bone at the expense of marrow cavity, pathological calcification in the periodontal ligament, increased thickness of cementum, or the deposit of some cementum-like substance on the roots leading to fusion (ankylosis) between the bone and the root, and the formation of pulp stones. These effects were less severe if high doses of vitamin A were administered along with the vitamin D (Becks 1942).

Somewhat similar results have been found after a series of large doses spread over 5 months, followed by a 5 months' recovery period during which normal doses only were fed, thus showing that prolonged, or possibly permanent, effects on the mineralized tissues may result from over-dosage of vitamin D. Although in these experiments, the over-dosage was far more prolonged than would ever be likely to be administered to human subjects, they emphasize again the importance of avoiding high doses of vitamin D, especially in synthetic preparations in which it is unaccompanied by vitamin A.

Vitamin K and quinones

No changes in the growth or structure of the teeth have been observed either in vitamin K-deficient animals, or in animals receiving large doses of vitamin K for other experimental reasons.

Fosdick and his collaborators (1948) discovered that vitamin K was a powerful inhibitor of acid production by salivary bacteria, suggesting that it might have anti-caries effects which were tested by the use of a chewing gum containing vitamin K; a promising result was obtained but the value of vitamin K is limited by its unpleasant taste.

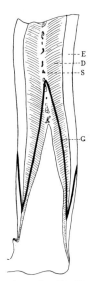

Fig. VIII.11. Diagram of a guinea-pig molar. E—Enamel; D—dentine; S—secondary dentine formed at point where tooth becomes solid; G—line joining points which were formed simultaneously.

The effects of ascorbic acid deficiency

As discussed on p. 97 one of the fundamental actions of ascorbic acid is to promote the formation of collagen fibres and probably to maintain the specialized function of odontoblasts and osteoblasts.

Only three types of animals (guinea-pigs, monkeys and man) are known to require this vitamin in their foods (others can synthesize it in their own tissues) and most experimental work has been done on the guinea-pig. In this species, the molars as well as the incisors are of continuous growth and it has therefore been possible to study the effects of the deficiency on both types of teeth. In the molars, the odontoblasts and presumably the pulp cells which are concerned with matrix formation, are carried towards the occlusal end by the growth of the tooth. Thus the dentine becomes thicker as the occlusal end is approached and the inner surface of the dentine naturally becomes smaller resulting in the death of most of the odontoblasts. Secondary dentine is then formed (presumably by the odontoblasts or pulp cells which survive) causing the tooth to become almost solid (S in Fig. VIII.11).

EFFECTS IN DENTINE

The most obvious dental changes occurring in ascorbic acid deficiency are, as would be expected, on the mesenchymal parts of the tooth, namely, the

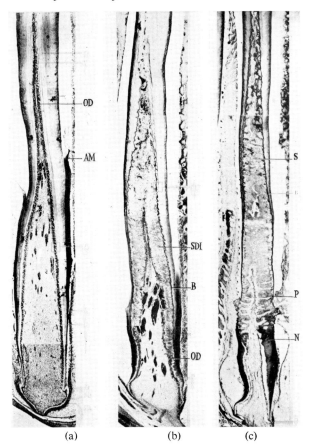

(a)   (b)   (c)

FIG. VIII.12. Photomicrographs of guinea-pigs' molars. (a) Normal; (b) sub-scurvy (i.e. inadequate intake of ascorbic acid but not complete deficiency); (c) complete deficiency, followed by cure for 10 days before death.

OD represents the point at which the odontoblasts begin to degenerate. AM represents the transition between insoluble enamel matrix (below) and soluble mature enamel which occupied the space above.

Note in (b) that the odontoblasts begin to degenerate earlier and that the dentine is consequently thinner but is lined by a calcific barrier (B). The upper part of the pulp is filled with irregular secondary dentine (SDI)—this is absent in completely deficient animals.

In (c) note the thin dentine in the upper part of the tooth (formed during the early part of the deficiency) and the absence of enamel and virtual absence of dentine immediately below the point marked P. The normal, thick dentine (N), and probably the secondary dentine (S) (which, as mentioned above, is absent from animals killed during a complete deficiency) were formed during the 10 days' recovery period, but no primary dentine was formed in the earlier part of the tooth even during the recovery period, presumably because the odontoblasts or other cells concerned in dentine formation were killed.

periodontal fibres, dentine and pulp. Experiments in which alizarin (a substance laid down in growing bone and dentine and is therefore used as a marker for new tissue) was injected at intervals into guinea-pigs showed that the growth rate of dentine is reduced after 1 week on a deficient diet. The odontoblasts become reduced in length, atrophy earlier than usual, become disorientated and fail to recover when a severely-deficient animal is given ascorbic acid. The growth of dentine is reduced, and may cease before it has formed the solid mass present in normal teeth so that the tooth has a thinner wall (Fig. VIII.12). The odontoblasts atrophy in dentine already formed, but this tissue is not changed morphologically although it is sealed off from the pulp by a thin layer of secondary dentine (the usual pulpal response to injury, pp. 180–1).

The effects, both on the growth rate of dentine in the incisor and on the length of the odontoblast, show such accurate quantitative responses to the intake of ascorbic acid over the range 0–5 mg per day, that their measurement has been suggested as a method of assay of ascorbic acid (Fig. VIII.13).

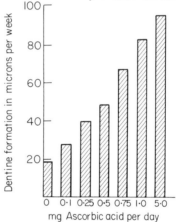

Fig. VIII.13. The relation between rate of dentine growth and intake of ascorbic acid (after Boyle *et al.* 1940).

If the deficiency is not too severe or prolonged, the pulp becomes more and more filled with a mineralized material variously known as pulp stones, osteodentine or calcific scar tissue (Fig. VIII.12) corresponding to the premature formation of the secondary dentine eventually formed in the solid part of the normal guinea-pig molar (Fig. VIII.12(b)). The interpretation of the production of this material suggested by Fish & Harris (1935) is as follows: the degeneration of the odontoblast and its process causes the death of the dentine and as a protective response the pulp cells attempt to lay down what these workers call 'calcific scar tissue' which, if the deficiency is not severe, may almost completely fill the pulp (Fig. VIII.12(c)). In complete deficiency this response is confined to a narrow layer immediately inside the dentine, probably because the pulp cells, as well as odontoblasts, are unable to form more of this tissue in the absence of ascorbic acid.

The cells of the pulp also show degeneration, and haemorrhages may occur, probably owing to the weakness of the cement substance between the endothelial cells of the capillaries (which is believed to be the cause of the petechiae or small haemorrhages found in the skin and elsewhere in scurvy).

If ascorbic acid is given to a guinea-pig after a deficiency severe enough to cause the death of the odontoblasts, no new dentine is formed on the inner surface of that part of the tooth which developed during the deficiency. Dentine formation may, however, be almost normal in the apical part of the tooth which is formed after the cure of scurvy begins, and the pulp may recover sufficiently to form scar tissue. If the deficiency is less severe, so that the odontoblasts do not degenerate completely, they may recover when ascorbic acid is fed and a new layer of dentine may be deposited inside the defective layer formed during the partial deficiency. In monkeys the effects of ascorbic acid deficiency on bone and dentine were compared; bone and osteoblasts were much more severely affected than the odontoblasts (Messer 1972).

EFFECTS ON THE ENAMEL

During the early stages of ascorbic acid deficiency, or in incomplete deficiency, the ameloblasts and enamel remain normal so far as can be judged from histological appearances. This fact accounts for a characteristic of ascorbic acid deficiency in guinea-pigs, namely, the high ratio between the width of enamel and dentine. In the normal tooth, the ratio is about 3:4 but in ascorbic acid deficiency the impaired growth of dentine may alter the ratio to 3:1 or even

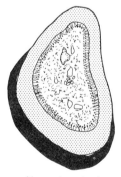

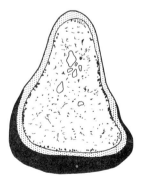

Normal control   Ascorbic acid deficient

FIG. VIII.14. Transverse sections of guinea-pig incisors showing effects of ascorbic acid deficiency. Note (1) that enamel is unaltered in this experiment, (2) that dentine is thin, thus altering the ratio of the thickness of enamel to dentine, and (3) the degeneration of the odontoblasts and pulp cells.

4:1 (Fig. VIII.14). In complete deficiency, however, the enamel organ may degenerate and this causes local gaps in the enamel. The ameloblasts do not recover even when the vitamin is restored to the diet. Fish & Harris believe this to be a direct effect of the deficiency on the ameloblasts, which is quite feasible, because although ascorbic acid deficiency affects mainly mesodermal structures, at least two epithelial tissues, namely skin and hair follicles, become abnormal in experimental deficiency. Boyle (1934) has suggested, on the other hand, that the enamel organ degenerates if it is damaged by excessive tooth movement following degeneration or haemorrhage in the periodontal ligament, and points out that in the guinea-pig, masticatory stresses have to be borne by the periodontal membrane while enamel formation is continuing. This contrasts with most other teeth in which amelogenesis is complete before eruption and therefore before stresses are applied to the periodontal region.

EFFECT OF ASCORBIC ACID DEFICIENCY ON THE ALVEOLAR BONE
AND PERIODONTAL LIGAMENT

In bone, ascorbic acid is necessary for the differentiation of osteoblasts and the formation of the collagen matrix. In ascorbic acid deficiency, the osteoblasts revert to fibroblasts and since bone, unlike dentine and enamel, is normally in a state of flux and depends for its maintenance on the constant

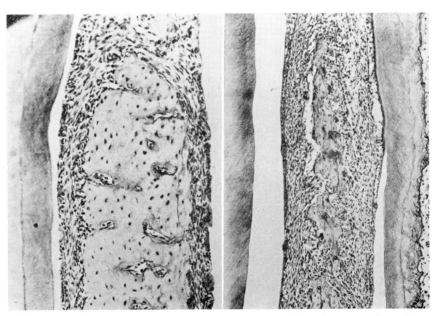

FIG. VIII.15. Left—normal periodontal membrane and bone between guinea-pig molars. Right—scorbutic animal; note resorption of bone and degeneration of periodontal ligament (Glickman 1948).

formation of new material to replace that which is removed, the deficiency causes the atrophy of bone which was formed before the deficiency began (Fig. VIII.15). In scurvy, both in human subjects and in guinea-pigs, atrophy of the alveolar bone has been observed, and when it occurs in those parts of the bone in which the periodontal fibres are inserted, the fibres may become detached.

The periodontal ligament consists of collagen fibres, and in the guinea-pig, they are constantly being renewed as the teeth erupt. In the scorbutic animal this renewal becomes difficult or impossible with two consequences. First, the support of the tooth becomes weakened and the teeth may very easily be extracted (the detachment of the fibres from the degenerating bone may also contribute to this). Secondly, the weakened periodontal ligament is less able to carry out its normal role of converting pressures on the tooth (which, if applied to the bone would tend to cause resorption) into tensions (which favour bone growth). This lack of tension may contribute to the atrophy of the alveolar bone. Haemorrhage in the periodontal ligament may accompany these changes. Loosening of the teeth is one of the classical symptoms of clinical scurvy as well as being observed in scorbutic guinea-pigs and it is somewhat puzzling that Crandon (1940), who lived on a diet free from ascorbic acid for 6 months, found little or no looseness of the teeth. He did observe, radiographically, interruptions in the lamina dura, however.

DENTAL EFFECTS OF ASCORBIC ACID DEFIENCY IN MAN

In a study of the histology of teeth from human adults suffering from scurvy Westin (1925) found, as would be expected, that enamel changes were absent, odontoblasts were degenerated and that the pulp was hyperaemic and oedematous, with widespread calcific scar tissue.

In two fatal cases of infantile scurvy, showing typical bone changes, the tooth germs were examined by Boyle (1933). In one patient aged 11 months, the germs were completely normal and in the other aged 8 months there were found minute haemorrhages and cysts in the enamel organ and occasional haemorrhages interrupting the odontoblasts. The size, arrangement and development of the various parts were quite normal. Boyle suggested that the absence in these human subjects of the effects observed in deficient guinea-pigs might be related to the slower rate of growth in man compared with that in the guinea-pig and also to the absence of occlusal stress during the formation of human teeth compared with its presence during the formation of teeth in the guinea-pig which occurs while the occlusal surface is functioning.

ASCORBIC ACID DEFICIENCY AND THE GINGIVAE

In 1772, Lind stated that the symptoms of scurvy included bleeding, soreness and sponginess of the gums but he was careful to state that gingival symptoms were not invariably found, a point which has been overlooked by many who have quoted his work. When gingivitis does occur, the capillaries of the gingivae become enlarged and dilated which causes swelling and gives them a deep red, shiny appearance. This begins on the interdental papillae and spreads over the whole surface. Haemorrhage follows the slightest irritation and, in severe deficiency, may be spontaneous. Ulceration and infection may occur at this stage. In young children suffering from scurvy, the gingivae are so swollen that they may cover completely the partly erupted teeth.

In scorbutic guinea-pigs, the gingivae are more susceptible than normal tissues to the effects of irritants. In clinical scurvy it would seem that the gingival symptoms are caused by injury, infection or the simultaneous presence of other deficiencies, superimposed on a lack of ascorbic acid.

Crandon & Lund (1940), even at the end of their experiment on a scorbutic diet found only a 'slight bogginess' in the gingivae which did not bleed even after toothbrushing. Small pieces of tissue surgically removed for histological study (biopsy) showed no abnormality.

A study was conducted in Britain by the Medical Research Council on groups of volunteers, ten of whom received no ascorbic acid for varying periods up to about 6 months, eight received 10 mg a day and three controls received 70 mg a day. Although slight gingivitis and bleeding was found in most of the subjects, those on the ascorbic-free diet showed quite marked oral symptoms, contrary to the findings of Crandon and Lund, mentioned above. The first scorbutic changes in the gums were seen after 30 weeks' deprivation and took the form of a slight reddening and swelling of the tips of the interdental papillae with haemorrhage a week or so later. The whole swollen area became purplish and the surface layer degenerated producing a slimy whitish film and some ulceration. All but one of the deficient group showed some gingival symptoms. Dosing the scorbutic subjects with 10 mg of ascorbic acid produced improvement within 1 or 2 weeks, but 12 weeks were needed for full recovery. No mention was made of the condition of the alveolar bone. The subjects receiving 10 mg throughout showed no scorbutic symptoms.

The common occurrence of some degree of gingivitis is sometimes ascribed to a sub-clinical ascorbic acid deficiency. There is evidence that some cases of gingivitis are caused by such a deficiency and can be cured by the administration of this vitamin although caution is required in accepting some of the claims because of the difficulty of estimating quantitatively what constitutes a 'cure'. It is, of course, equally certain that there are other causes of the condition (see p. 397) since some cases do not improve with ascorbic acid treatment.

Campbell & Cook (1942) reported that the rate of healing of gingival tissue after dental extractions is accelerated when large doses of ascorbic acid are taken before and after the extractions but this finding does not seem to have been investigated further.

The vitamin B complex

DEFICIENCY OF VITAMIN B₁

No convincing evidence of the influence of vitamin B_1 (thiamine or aneurin) on oral structures has yet been published. Statements have been made that a 'marked sensitivity' of the oral tissues occurs in human patients suffering from aneurin deficiency. Changes in the voice have also been described which were thought to be caused by a neuritis of the tenth nerve (neuritis is a recognized symptom of aneurin deficiency in animals). Another report describes the occurrence of 'pin point' vesicles on the buccal mucosa, under the tongue and on the palate which are said to have healed after the administration of aneurin. None of these symptoms were found in the several experiments in which human volunteers had lived up to 6 months on diets containing very low levels of aneurin, and it seems likely that the oral changes described above were not caused by aneurin deficiency.

RIBOFLAVIN DEFICIENCY

Up to 1938, no symptoms which were definitely related to riboflavin deficiency were known in man. The results of an experiment on eighteen women, who were fed on a diet deficient in riboflavin, clearly showed that riboflavin deficiency caused lesions in the oral tissues. Within 94–130 days, ten of the women developed 'cheilosis' (lesions on the lips). At first, a pallor of the lips appeared, followed by fissures at the angle of the mouth (angular stomatitis) then the lips became unusually red and shiny owing to denudation of the epithelium. Desquamation occurred also in other parts of the face. These lesions cleared up in most of the subjects within a few days following daily doses of 1–2 mg of synthetic riboflavin. Although cheilosis undoubtedly occurs in riboflavin deficiency, this is not the only cause of this symptom as some patients do not respond to riboflavin treatment but do when pyridoxin (vitamin B_6) is administered.

A specific type of 'glossitis' (inflammation of the tongue), in which the tongue becomes a magenta colour with enlargement and flattening of the tips of the papillae, has also been described in riboflavin deficiency.

Riboflavin is required by the tissues as a constituent of flavoproteins which are important in tissue oxidation. There is no explanation of why deficiency of flavoproteins in the tissues (as will occur in riboflavin deficiency) produces the symptoms mentioned above and considering that flavoproteins are widely distributed in the body it is surprising that the symptoms are so localized.

Young rats born to mothers deficient in riboflavin suffer from dentofacial anomalies. It appears that riboflavin is important for the proper multiplication of mesenchymal cells about the thirteenth day of uterine life. In a deficiency in rats, various skeletal defects occur some of which affect the face and teeth.

NICOTINIC ACID (NIACIN)

Deficiency of nicotinic acid is known to have oral symptoms in man. The tongue becomes swollen and presses against the teeth causing indentations in it, with the development of painful, fiery-red areas of inflammation. In acute stages the inflammation extends to the whole oral mucosa, including the gingivae which are painful, feel scalded and readily become infected. Salivation is excessive. A dramatic cure follows dosage of nicotinic acid.

The disease pellagra is believed to be a combined deficiency of nicotinic acid, riboflavin and aneurin and may be partly caused not only by real dietary deficiencies but also by the presence in the diet of 'antivitamins', i.e. substances which interfere with the utilization of vitamins. Consequently, the above symptoms rarely occur alone but are usually associated with the cheilosis and stomatitis caused by riboflavin deficiency.

In dogs, deficiency of nicotinic acid causes the disease known as 'black tongue' which resembles human pellagra, the symptoms being glossitis, stomatitis, typical skin lesions and diarrhoea. The discovery that black tongue is cured by nicotinic acid suggested the use of this vitamin in the treatment of human pellagra.

PANTOTHENIC ACID DEFICIENCY

Pantothenic acid deficiency in dogs, on a diet which also caused deficiency of unknown members of the vitamin B complex, produced degeneration of the oral epithelium so complete in places that the underlying connective tissue was exposed. Osteoporosis of the alveolar bone was also noted. When pantothenic acid was fed to the dogs, so that only the unknown substances were deficient, similar, but much less severe epithelial degeneration and bone atrophy were observed. In spite of the severity of the symptoms of pantothenic acid deficiency, there is little inflammation present. The results of experiments in which several deficiencies occur are, of course, difficult to interpret and must be treated with caution. If a nicotinic acid deficiency were induced as well, a severe inflammation of the gingival tissues was superimposed on the above symptoms. Similar results have been observed in rats but no symptoms of pantothenic acid deficiency, either in the mouth or elsewhere, are known in man.

PYRIDOXIN (VITAMIN B_6)

There is no information on the effects of a clinical deficiency on the oral structure except that, as mentioned above, a form of cheilosis has been found which responds to pyridoxin. By injecting the antivitamin desoxypyridoxin (which prevents pyridoxin from exerting its normal function) to eight human subjects skin lesions and erosions at the angle of the mouth developed which were rapidly cured by pyridoxin but unaffected by other vitamins. Some of the subjects developed sore, swollen tongues and lesions of the oral mucosa which were cured by pyridoxin specifically. This vitamin, like others of the vitamin B complex is, therefore, presumably concerned with the well-being of the oral tissues.

Experiments on rats (Steinman & Hardinge 1958) and monkeys (Rinehart & Greenberg 1956) have shown that vitamin B_6 has an influence on caries. Daily doses of 20 mg (about ten times the normal dietary intake) given to pregnant women over a period of about 6 months was reported to reduce the caries rate especially when sucked as lozenges bringing the vitamin into contact with the oral bacteria (Hillman *et al.* 1962). An effect on the caries rate of children has also been reported (Strean *et al.* 1958). These large doses are believed to influence caries by altering the proportions of different bacteria in the mouth but all this work on vitamin B_6 requires confirmation and extension.

VITAMIN B_{12}

In pernicious anaemia (failure to absorb vitamin B_{12}), some patients suffer from soreness of the tongue and in severe cases the painful lesions spread throughout the oral mucosa. Like the other symptoms of the disease, they clear completely with doses of vitamin B_{12}.

EROSION OF TEETH BY ACID DRINKS OR SWEETS

Many drinks, fruit juices and sweets (such as acid drops) have a low pH and would be expected to dissolve enamel if taken regularly. Experiments in which these materials were given to dogs and rats in their drinking water have resulted in enamel erosion—a fairly generalized superficial demineralization of enamel quite different from the highly localized penetrating lesion of caries. Fruit squashes, solutions of acid sweets, black currant juice, melted 'iced lollipops' all had an erosive effect, but the results varied with different products. Holloway *et al.* (1958) found that sweetened solutions of citric acid were more damaging than unsweetened. Their suggested explanation is that the sweetened juices are held in the mouth longer but, since the intensity of the acid taste is reduced by the sugar, they are less effective stimuli to saliva than acid alone. This conclusion was supported by their finding that sugar did not influence demineralization of teeth in test-tube experiments and in the animal experiments sucrose and saccharine (at the same level of sweetness) had a similar effect although saccharine is not converted into acid by bacteria.

In man, the effect of occasional acid drinks is unlikely to be important but frequent consumption of products which are held in the mouth for some time (such as acid drops, iced lollipops or undiluted fruit juices placed on babies' dummies or in their feeding bottles) are damaging.

Methods of preventing the erosion are: the inclusion of calcium phosphate or fluoride in the product, or ensuring that the pH is not below 3·5.

The effect of the physical consistency of the food on the oral tissues is described on p. 528.

Conclusion

The position with regard to the influence of dietary factors on the oral tissues may perhaps be summarized as follows. Animal experiments have clearly shown the importance of vitamins A, D and C and of minerals in the development of teeth and have yielded important information about the fundamental nature of some of the developmental processes. It can also be concluded that the teeth seem to be less sensitive than most other tissues implying that they have some measure of priority for deficient materials. This is probably one of the resons why there are so few proved effects of dietary deficiencies on human teeth; another point is that many influences (dietary, hormonal and general bodily health) may affect the teeth in similar ways, thus making it difficult to assess the relative importance of diet. No effects have been observed in the mineralized dental tissues formed before a deficient diet was fed.

There is no doubt that *severe* dietary deficiencies may affect the well-being of the soft tissues of the mouth but the role of nutrition in causing the frequently observed minor disorders of the oral mucosa and periodontal membrane is still uncertain.

References

ALAM S.Q. & HARRIS R.H. (1972) Effects of nutrition on the composition of tooth lipids and fatty acids in rats. *J. dent. Res.* **51,** 1474

ALLEN I. (1941) A survey of nutrition and dental caries in 120 London elementary school children. *Brit. med. J.* **i,** 44

BAUME L.J. *et al.* (1969) Progressive atrophy and expulsion of upper rat incisor after prolonged Vitamin A deficiency. *J. dent. Res.* **48,** 330

BECKS H. (1942) Dangerous effects of vitamin D overdosage on dental and paradental structures. *J. Amer. dent. Ass.* **29,** 1947

BIBBY B.G. (1943) The relationship between microscopic hypoplasia (Mellanby) and dental caries. *J. dent. Res.* **22,** 218

BLOCH C.E. (1930) Vitamin A deficiency and dental anomalies in man. *Acta Paediat.* **11,** 535; *Amer. J. Dis. Child.* **42,** 263

BOYLE P.E. (1933) Manifestations of vitamin A deficiency in a human tooth germ. Case report. *J. dent. Res.* **13,** 39

BOYLE P.E. (1934) The tooth germ in acute scurvy. *J. dent. Res.* **14,** 172

BOYLE P.E. *et al.* (1940) Rate of dentine formation in incisor teeth of guinea pigs on normal and on ascorbic acid-deficient diets. *Arch. Path.* **30,** 90

BROWN J.P. & BIBBY B.C. (1970) Effect on rat caries of sugars administered before tooth eruption. *Caries Res.* **4,** 56

BUXBAUM J.D. *et al.* (1957) The effect of diet on the deposition of glycoprotein in the teeth and its relationship to dental caries in the Syrian hamster. *J. dent. Res.* **36,** 173

CAMPBELL H.G. & COOK R.P. (1942) The use of ascorbic acid (vitamin C) in the treatment of tooth extraction wounds. *Brit. dent. J.* **72,** 6

CARR L.M. (1953) Correlation between

Mellanby hypoplasia and dental caries. *Dent. J. Aust.* **25**, 158

CLARKE M.F. & SMITH A.H. (1935) Deficient saline diet and development of teeth. *Amer. J. Physiol.* **112**, 286

COOPER V.K. & LUDWIG, T.G. (1965) Effect of fluoride and of soil trace elements on the morphology of the permanent molars in man. *N.Z. dent. J.* **61**, 33

CRANDON J.H. & LUND C.C. (1940) Experimental human scurvy. *New Eng. J. Med.* **222**, 748 (see also *New Eng. J. Med.* (1940) **223**, 353 and *J. Amer. Med. Ass.* (1941) **116**, 663)

CROSSLAND L.M. & HOLLOWAY P.J. (1971) A technique for tube-feeding newborn rats, and the effects of administration of various carbohydrate solutions on their subsequent caries susceptibility. *Caries Res.* **5**, 144

DAVIES J.H. (1939) An investigation into the relationship between dental structure and dental caries in children attending public elementary school. *Brit. dent. J.* **67**, 66

DAY C.D.M. (1944) Nutritional deficiencies and dental caries in Northern India. *Brit. dent. J.* **76**, 115, 143

EGYEDI H. (1953) Experimental basis of the glycogen theory of enamel caries. *Dent. Items* **75**, 113, 971

EGYEDI P. (1973) A caries study in Liberia from the point of view of the glycogen theory. *Ned. Tijdschr. Tandheelkd.* **80**, 142

FANNING R.J. *et al.* (1953) Salivary contribution to enamel maturation and caries resistance. *J. Amer. dent. Ass.* **49**, 668

FERGUSON H.W. & HARTLES R.L. (1963) Effect of vitamin D on the bones of young rats receiving diets low in calcium or phosphorus. *Archs oral Biol.* **8**, 407

FISH E.W. & HARRIS L.J. (1935) The effects of vitamin C deficiency on tooth structure in guinea-pigs. *Brit. dent. J.* **58**, 3

FOSDICK L.S. (1948) The degradation of sugar in the mouth and the use of chewing gum and vitamin K in the control of dental caries. *J. dent. Res.* **27**, 235

GAUNT W.E. & IRVING J.T. (1940) The influence of dietary calcium and phosphorus upon tooth formation. *J. Physiol.* **99**, 18

GLICKMAN I. (1948) Acute vitamin C deficiency and periodontal disease. *J. dent. Res.* **27**, 9

GRØN P. *et al.* (1963) The effect of carbonate on the solubility of hydroxylapatite. *Archs oral Biol.* **8**, 251

HARRAND R.B. & HARTLES R.L. (1971) The effect of vitamin D in rats maintained on diets with different mineral content but with the same calcium to phosphorus ratio of unity. *Br. J. Nutr.* **24**, 929 (see also (1967) **20**, 59; (1969) **22**, 43)

HILLMAN R.W. *et al.* (1962) The effects of pyroxidine supplements on the dental caries experience of pregnant women. *Amer. J. clin. Nutr.* **10**, 512

HOLLOWAY P.J. *et al.* (1958) Fruit drinks and tooth erosion. *Brit. dent. J.* **104**, 305

HOLLOWAY P.J. *et al.* (1961) Effects of various sucrose:casein ratios in purified diets on the teeth and supporting structures of rats. *Archs oral Biol.* **3**, 185

HUME E.M. & KREBS H.A. (1949) Vitamin A requirements of human adults. An experimental study of vitamin A deprivation in man. *Spec. Rep. Ser. med. Res. Coun., Lond.* **264**

HUNT C.G. & NAVIA J.M. (1975) Pre-erupted effects of Mo, B, Sr and F on dental caries. *Archs oral Biol.* **20**, 497

IRVING J.T. (1940) Influence of diets low in magnesium on histologic appearance of incisor teeth of rat. *J. Physiol.* **99**, 8

KARSHAN M. & ROSEBURY I. (1932) Correlation of chemical and pathological changes in teeth of rats on rachitic and non-rachitic diets. *J. dent. Res.* **12**, 437 (see also **10**, 267; **11**, 64; **13**, 10, 305)

KING J.D. (1940) Abnormalities in the gingival and subgingival tissues due to diets deficient in vitamin A and carotene. *Brit. dent. J.* **58**, 349

KLEIN H. *et al.* (1935) The effects of magnesium deficiency on the teeth and their supporting structures in rat. *Amer. J. Physiol.* **112**, 256

KRUGER B.J. (1959) The effect of 'trace elements' on experimental dental caries in the albino rat. *University of Queensland Papers* **1**, 1

KRUGER B.J. (1962) Trace elements and dental morphology. *University of Queensland Papers* **1**, 181 (see also *J. dent. Res.* (1962) **41**, 215)

KUSNER W. *et al.* (1973) The role of attrition and occlusal contact in the physiology of the rat incisor Part VI. Impeded and unimpeded eruption in hypophysectomized and magnesium deficient rats. *J. dent. Res.* **52**, 65.

LITTLE K. (1959) Electron microscope studies on human dental enamel. *Proc. Roy. Mic. Soc.* **80**, 199

LUOMA H. (1961) The effect of injected monosaccharides upon the mineralization of rat molars. *Archs oral Biol.* **3**, 271

McCALL J.O. & KRASNOW F. (1938) The influence of metabolism on teeth. *J. Paediat.* **13**, 498

MARTHALER T.M. (1967) Epidemiological and clinical dental findings in relation to intake of carbohydrates. *Caries Res.* **1**, 222

McCLURE F.J. & McCANN H.G. (1960) Dental caries and composition of bones and teeth of white rats: effect of dietary mineral supplements. *Archs oral Biol.* **2**, 151

MEDICAL RESEARCH COUNCIL (1953) Vitamin C requirements of human adults. *Spec. Rep. Ser. med. Res. Coun., Lond.* **280**

MELLANBY M. (1929) Diet and the teeth. Part I. Dental structure in dogs. *Spec. Rep. Ser. med. Res. Coun., Lond.* **140**

MELLANBY M. (1936) Diet and dental structure in man. *Spec. Rep. Ser. med. Res. Coun., Lond.* **191**

MELLANBY E. (1942–3) The effect of bone dysplasia (overgrowth) on cranial nerves in vitamin A-deficient animals. *J. Physiol.* **101**, 408

MESSER H.H. (1972) Dentin and bone formation in scorbutic monkeys. *J. dent. Res.* **51**, 1106

MIGLANI P.C. (1959) The effect of vitamin A deficiency on the periodontal structures of rat molars with emphasis on cementum resorption. *Oral Surg.* **12**, 1372

MILLER C.D. (1958) The dental caries response of rats fed cariogenic and noncariogenic diets for different periods of time. *J. Nutr.* **66**, 113

NAVIA J.M. *et al.* (1970) Effect of undernutrition during the perinatal period on caries development in the rat. *J. dent. Res.* **49**, 1091; also: Evaluation of nutritional and dietary factors that modify animal caries. 1213

NIZEL A.E. & HARRIS R.S. (1955) Effects of ashed foodstuffs on dental decay in hamsters. *J. dent. Res.* **34**, 513

OLIVER W.M. *et al.* (1969) Calcium deficiencies and collagen synthesis. *J. peridont. Res.* **7**, 29

PARFITT G.J. (1954) The apparent delay between alterations in diet and change in caries incidence: a note on conditions in Norway reported by Toverud. *Brit. dent. J.* **97**, 235

PROUT R.E.S. & TRING F.C. (1971) Effect of fat-free diet on ameloblast and enamel formation in incisors of rats. *J. dent. Res.* **50**, 1559

PROUT R.E.S. & TRING F.C. (1973) Dentinogenesis in incisors of rats deficient in essential fatty acids. *J. dent. Res.* **52**, 462

RINEHART J.F. & GREENBERG L.D. (1956) Vitamin B$_6$ deficiency in the Rhesus monkey with particular reference to the occurrence of atherosclerosis, dental caries and hepatic cirrhosis. *Amer. J. clin. Nutr.* **4**, 318

RUSSELL A.L. *et al.* (1961) Periodontal disease and nutrition in Eskimo scouts of the Alaska National Guard. *J. dent. Res.* **40**, 594, 604

SALLEY J.J. *et al.* (1959) The effect of chronic vitamin A deficiency on dental caries in the Syrian hamster. *J. dent. Res.* **38**, 1038

SARNET G.B. & SCHOUR I. (1941) Enamel hypoplasia (chronologic enamel aplasia) in relation to systemic disease. *J. Amer. dent. Ass.* **28**, 1989; (1942) **29**, 67

SCHOUR I. & MASSLER M. (1945) The effect of dietary deficiencies upon the oral structures. *Physiol. Rev.* **25**, 442. Also in *J. Amer. dent. Ass.* (1945) **32**, 714, 871, 1022, 1139 (a comprehensive review with many references)

SOBEL A.E. (1955) Local factors in the mechanism of calcification. *Ann. N.Y. Acad. Sci.* **60**, 713 (discusses the carbonate content of teeth in relation to caries in experimental animals)

SOBEL A.E. & HANOK A. (1948) Calcification of teeth. I. Composition in relation to blood and lymph. *J. biol. Chem.* **176**, 1103 (see also *J. biol. Chem.* (1952) **196**, Introductory page, for correction to this paper)

SOBEL A.E. & HANOK A. (1958) Composition of bones and teeth in relation to blood and diet in the cotton rat. *J. dent. Res.* **37**, 631; (1960) **39**, 462

SOGNNAES R.F. (1947) Caries-conducive effect of a purified diet when fed to rodents during tooth development. *J. Amer. dent. Ass.* **37**, 676

SOGNNAES R.F. (1948) Analysis of war-time caries reduction in European children, with special regard to observations in Norway. *Amer. J. Dis. Child.* **75**, 795

SOGNNAES R.F. & SHAW J.H. (1954) The effect of a natural salt mixture on the caries-conduciveness of an otherwise purified diet. *J. Nutr.* **53**, 195

SPEIRS R.L. (1964) The systemic influence of carbohydrates on teeth. *Proc. Nutr. Soc.* **23**, 129

STAZ J. (1944) Hypoplastic teeth and dental caries. *J. dent. Res.* **23**, 230

STEINMAN R.R. & HALEY M.I. (1957) Early administration of various carbohydrates and subsequent dental caries in the rat. *J. dent. Res.* **36**, 532

STEINMAN R.R. & HARDINGE M.G. (1958) The effect of pyridoxine and injected

carbohydrate on incidence of caries. Dentinal circulation related to diet. *J. dent. Res.* **37**, 874

STREAN L.P. *et al.* (1958) The importance of pyroxidine on the suppression of dental caries in school children and hamsters. *New York State Dent. J.* **24**, 133

TOVERUD G. (1955–7) Influence of war and post-war conditions on the teeth of Norwegian school children. *Millbank Mem. Fund Quart.* **34, 35, 37**

TROWBRIDGE H.O. & SELTZER J.L. (1967) Formation of dentin and bone matrix in magnesium-deficient rats. *J. periodont. Res.* **2**, 147

TROWBRIDGE H.O. *et al.* (1971) Histochemical studies on the dentin of magnesium-deficient rats. *J. periodont. Res.* **6**, 130

WEINMANN J.P. & SCHOUR I. (1945) Experimental studies in calcification. *Amer. J. Path.* **21**, 821, 833, 857, 1047, 1057

WESTIN G. (1925) Scorbutic changes in the teeth and jaws of man. *Dent. Cos.* **67**, 868

WOLBACH S.B. & BESSEY O.A. (1942) Tissue changes in vitamin deficiencies. *Physiol. Rev.* **22**, 233

WOLBACH S.B. & HOWE P.R. (1933) The incisor teeth of albino rats and guinea-pigs in vitamin A deficiency and repair. *Amer. J. Path.* **9**, 275

WYNN W. *et al.* (1956) Dental caries in the rat in relation to the chemical composition of the teeth and of the diet. *J. Nutr.* **58**, 325; (1957) **63**, 57

CHAPTER IX

SALIVA

Composition of Saliva

Before summarizing present knowledge of the composition of saliva it is important to emphasize the difficulties of investigating this problem. First, saliva is produced by three pairs of large glands and the smaller glands of the oral mucosa (labial, lingual, buccal and palatal), whose secretions differ in composition and whose relative contribution to the mixed saliva present in the mouth varies with conditions. Saliva may also contain fluid from the gingival pocket (gingival, or crevicular, fluid; see p. 324). Since little is known about the factors which decide the relative secretion rates of each source, this variable is difficult to control. The composition of the saliva produced from any one gland varies with the rate of flow which itself varies with the type, intensity and duration of stimulus used for obtaining the sample. Consequently, the composition of saliva may vary with changes in the stimulus. Although much more reproducible results are obtained by analysing the secretion of separate glands, rather than mixed saliva, even then variations are found, such as changes at different times of the day or differences related to meals. Secondly, the presence of suspended matter (mostly bacteria, epithelial cells and mucin) raises the question whether or not saliva should be centrifuged before analysis. Centrifuged saliva gives lower figures for some constituents than does uncentrifuged; if on the other hand, the suspended matter is not removed it frequently interferes with the analytical techniques. Thirdly, the presence of living bacteria in saliva and the spontaneous loss of CO_2 after collection cause changes in the composition on standing, hence the accuracy of some analyses depends on the length of time elapsing between collection and analysis. Fourthly, some analytical methods which have been worked out for other biological fluids have sometimes been used on saliva, although later work has shown that for accurate results with saliva, the methods need modification. Fifthly, it is difficult to collect saliva under conditions which are physiological; saliva stimulated by chewing wax or rubber bands which is so frequently used, may differ from that produced in response to food.

Saliva varies greatly in different individuals and in the same individual under different circumstances, and few average figures for its composition can be obtained which have any meaning or significance unless large groups of, say, several hundred people are studied under standardized conditions.

For these reasons it is impossible to give a satisfactory quantitative account of the composition of saliva in man, but some of the more reliable figures are collected in Table IX.1. These must be regarded merely as a general guide. No complete list of the constituents of saliva (or any other biological fluid) can be compiled as a large number of substances are present in traces and have not been estimated. Comprehensive tables of the published data on the constituents of saliva (but including some single estimations of uncertain accuracy) are presented by Mason & Chisholm (1975).

METHODS OF COLLECTING SALIVA FROM THE DIFFERENT GLANDS
Since the composition of the products of the various glands differs, it is clear that the nature of mixed saliva will depend on the relative activity of each gland. In man, although direct cannulation of the parotid duct has been used, a far more convenient method for separating parotid saliva from that of the other glands is by means of the cannula (Fig. IX.1), usually named after Lashley, but more correctly called the Carlson–Crittenden cannula after the real inventors. This consists of two concentric rings of metal or plastic attached to a disc about half an inch in diameter. Tubes are inserted (1) so that the outer space between the two rings may be evacuated, and (2) from the inner space which is placed over the parotid duct to lead the saliva away into a receptacle placed outside the mouth. The design has been modified by rounding off the sharp edges which irritated the mucosa after prolonged use, so that the shape approached that of a hemisphere rather than the disc illustrated. Another modification was introduced by Curby (1953) (the 'Curby cup'). A third tube is included through which air bubbles can be released from the central chamber and suction of air from the outer space is effected by a rubber pipette ball fixed to a hypodermic needle inserted into the polythene tubing (see Fig. IX.2).

For the separate collection of saliva from the submandibular and sublingual glands a device has been designed by Schneyer (1955) (Fig. IX.3(a)) basically similar to one introduced by Pickerill (1912) (a 'segregator'). It has to be specially made for each donor and consists of an acrylic appliance with three separate chambers: a central one which is placed over the duct of the submandibular gland and two lateral ones which cover the numerous ducts of the sublingual glands. Polythene tubing leads the secretion to collecting vessels outside the mouth. In some subjects it is impossible to use this device owing to anatomical peculiarities in the position of the ducts. Another disadvantage of Schneyer's apparatus is that it cannot be used for mechanical stimuli as it projects into the lower surface of the tongue. A device designed by Henriques & Chauncey (1961) avoids this difficulty. Truelove *et al.* (1967) suggested further modifications (Fig. IX.3(b)).

TABLE IX.1
Composition of saliva (mg/100 ml)

	Resting		Stimulated	
	Mean	Range	Mean	Range
Whole (mixed)				
Total solids	500	300–860	530	400–900
Ash			250	170–350
Organic constituents				
Protein	220	140–640	280	170–420
Amino acids			4	
Amylase	38		?	
Lysozyme	22		11	0·4–62
IgA	19			
IgG	1·4			
IgM	0·2			
Glucose	1·0		1·0	0·5–3
Citrate			Trace	
Lactate			Trace	
Ammonia			3	1–12
Urea	20	12–70	13	0·6–30
Uric acid	1·5	0·5–3	3	1–21
Creatinine	0·1	0·05–0·2	?	?
Cholesterol	8	2·5–50		
cAMP	7		50	
Inorganic constituents				
Sodium	15	0–20	60	
Potassium	80	60–100	80	
Thiocyanate—smokers	9	6–12	?	
non-smokers	2	1–3	?	
Calcium	5·8	2·2–11·3	6	
Phosphate (P)	16·8	6·1–71	12	
Chloride	50		100	
Fluoride (ppm)	0·028	0·015–0·045	0·011	0·007–0·021
Parotid				
Total solids			700	500–900
Organic constituents				
*Total protein	100	?	200	100–300
Amylase	60		120	?
Lysozyme			2·3	0·5–8
IgA			4	1·7–6·3
IgG			0·4	0–0·1
IgM			0·4	
Amino acids				?
Urea	26		13	10–16
Ammonia	0·9		0·3	
Uric acid	4		7	?
Free carbohydrate			3	2–5
Total carbohydrate			24	15–33
Glucose	1		0·2	?
Lipid			2·8	1–5

TABLE IX.1 (*cont.*)

	Resting		Stimulated	
	Mean	Range	Mean	Range
Inorganic constituents				
Sodium	55	12–72	800	115–2600
Potassium	120	100–320	100	48–125
Calcium	5·0	2–8	5·7	2–10
Magnesium	0·3	0·2–1·5	0·04	0·02–0·80
Chloride	85	60–140	100	35–175
Bicarbonate	6	3·30	120	30–360
Phosphate (P)	28	12–60	9	6–15
Thiocyanate	30		18	
pH	5·8	5·2–6·2	7·4	6·5–8·0
Fluoride ions (ppm)	0·02		0·01	

Submandibular

Organic constituents				
*Total protein	50	30–80	76	30–150
Free carbohydrate			1.4	0–4
Total carbohydrate			10	4–19
Lysozyme			1·5	0·5–4·2
Amylase	25			
IgA	1·6		?	
Urea	10·5	?	20	?
Ammonia	0·9	?	0·08	?
Uric acid	3·3	?	1·3	?
Lipid	—		2·0	

Inorganic constituents				
Sodium	6		60	20–120
Potassium	60		60	20·80
Calcium	6		8	6–12
Magnesium	0·17		0·08	
Chloride	42		98	35–140
Bicarbonate	13		150	18–200?
Phosphate (P)	15		7	0·6–42
pH	6·6		7·5	6·1–7·5

Minor Glands

Protein	296	145–560	258	145–355
Sodium	32	6–86·25	85·8	25·3–225·4
Potassium	75·3	39–113	67·5	43–97·5
Calcium	9·2	6·5–13	8·1	6·4–10
Magnesium	1·6	0·96–2·9	1·3	0·96–1·92
Chloride	110	56–189	198	66·5–381·5
Phosphate (P)	1·9	0·77–3·41	1·4	0·62–1·86

* Estimated by the biuret method which ignores bound carbohydrate in the protein

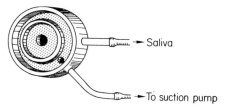

FIG IX.1. A diagram of the original Lashley cannula. In more recent designs the shape has been made more rounded (see text). The inner circle is placed over the parotid duct and the lower tube is attached to a suction pump thus evacuating the outer space and causing the cannula to adhere firmly to the cheek. The saliva flows along the upper tube.

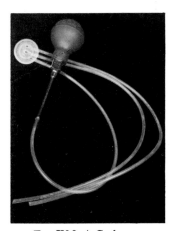

FIG. IX.2. A Curby cup.

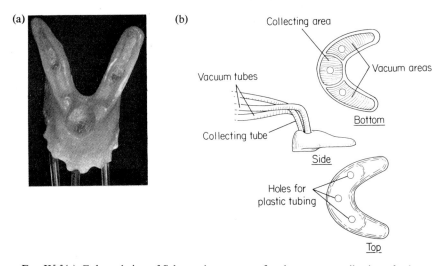

FIG. IX.3(a). Enlarged view of Schneyer's apparatus for the separate collection of sublingual and submandibular saliva. (b) Its modification by Truelove *et al.*

MINOR SALIVARY GLANDS

The minor glands are widely distributed throughout the mouth except for the gingivae and the anterior region of the hard palate (Fig. IX.4). The proportion of saliva derived from them has been estimated by comparing the rate of flow of mixed saliva (either stimulated or unstimulated) draining from the open

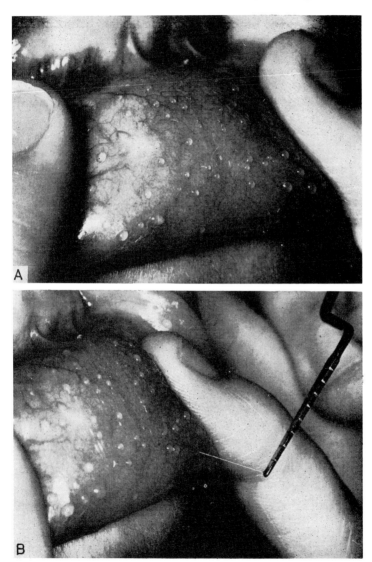

FIG. IX.4. (a) The secretion from the small salivary glands on the inner surface of the lower lip; the droplets formed in about 3 min. (b) A demonstration of the spinnbarkeit (see p. 316) of the mucous secretion of the oral glands.

mouth in a given time with the sum of the volumes collected from the major glands when cannulated. A more refined method (Dawes & Wood 1973a) consists of collecting the parotid saliva outside the mouth through a Lashley cannula and anaesthetizing the lingual nerve, which abolishes secretion from the submandibular and sublingual glands. Under the circumstances any secretion draining from the mouth can only be from the minor glands. These methods have been applied only to small numbers of subjects; the average contribution was somewhat less than 10% of the whole saliva.

Organic constituents

THE PROTEINS OF SALIVA

The total protein content of human saliva averages about 300 mg per 100 ml but may vary widely. The concentration in parotid is higher than in submandibular saliva and the results depend on the method of analysis, since they all estimate different characteristics of the protein, such as nitrogen (Kjeldahl method), peptide links (biuret method) or the amount of tyrosine and tryptophane (absorption at 280 nm). Clearly, these different methods may give widely different results even with the same proteins.

Several proteins recognized first from their properties (and discussed later in relation to their function) are present in both parotid and submandibular saliva and have been isolated and studied individually. These proteins are amylase (p. 338), higher in the parotid; lysozyme (p. 342), higher in the submandibular; glycoproteins (those in saliva were formerly known as mucins); IgA combined with secretory piece (p. 393) and traces of blood proteins. Staining sections of human parotid glands with fluorescent antibodies to these proteins shows that amylase is produced by the acinar and intercalated duct cells, lysozyme by groups of cells in the striated ducts and IgA from plasma cells mostly along the intralobular ducts (Kraus & Mestecky 1971).

The proteins detected, but not isolated and fully examined, include many enzymes in low concentration (see p. 296) and about 1% of salivary proteins appear to be blood proteins including albumin, IgG, IgM, transferrin and lipoproteins. Detailed reviews of the proteins of saliva, known from electrophoresis to number between thirty and forty in the parotid (Hay 1975), have been published by Levine & Ellison (1973) and by Mandel (1974). The secretions of the sublingual and minor glands have not been fully investigated.

Saliva contains a mixture of glycoproteins which were formerly referred to as mucin or mucoids and are characterized by containing carbohydrate side-chains. Glycoproteins are resistant to proteolytic enzymes (hence their protective effect on the wall of the digestive tract) because the carbohydrate side-chains prevent the enzymes from reaching the protein core (Fig. IX.5). Saliva treated with pepsin to remove proteins other than glycoproteins, was used by Schrager & Oates (1971) to isolate what they thought was the main glycoprotein of mixed saliva, probably of submandibular origin. It contains a protein

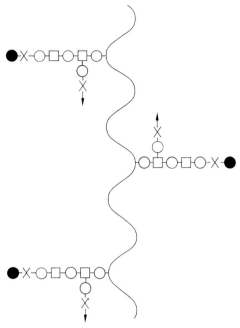

FIG. IX.5. A diagrammatic representation of the structure of a glycoprotein (not necessarily identical to those of human saliva). The wavy line represents the polypeptide helix and the carbohydrate side-chains are made up with the following constituents:

●—sialic acid, ×—D-galactose, ○—N-acetylglucosamine, □—mannose, △—fucose. Sulphate is also present in some salivary glycoproteins.

core with up to 75–85% of the molecule as carbohydrate side chains with an average of eight residues per chain and containing galactose, glucosamine and galactosamine in the ratio of 4:3:1. Other groups in some of the molecules are fucose (a methyl pentose), sulphate and sialic acid (N-acetyl neuraminic acid, acid, or NANA, which can be regarded as a condensation product of pyruvic acid and an amino sugar, usually mannosamine). Some of these constituents are arranged in the same order as the blood group substances and their presence confers blood group activity on the glycoproteins. Threonine and serine make up 45–50% of the amino acids and another 30% consist of proline and alanine.

Earlier work gave very different results but the methods used failed to separate the proteins effectively and the results were consequently based on complex mixtures (McCoombe *et al.* 1961; Mandel *et al.* 1964. Previous work suggested that sialate, with its strong negative charge, was the terminal group of the side chain (Gottschalk 1961) but Schrager & Oates concluded that sulphate is the main end group although its concentration is very variable.

A sulphated protein of low isoelectric point has been detected in the sublingual saliva of the *Macaca irus* monkey after injection of $Na^{32}SO_4$ and was also detected in the secretion from pieces of the gland incubated *in vitro* (Sönju & Rölla 1974). It has a strong affinity for apatite (see p. 368).

The chief glycoprotein of the parotid has been isolated and represents between 8 and 12% of the dry weight of the stimulated saliva. About 80% of its amino acids are made up of proline, glycine and glutamic acid. Its carbohydrates consist of approximately equal proportions of N-acetyl glucosamine, mannose, galactose and fucose with a much smaller amount of sialate. When rapidly secreted, the protein core is present without its carbohydrate chains; presumably it is secreted before there is time for all the carbohydrate groups to be attached (Levine *et al.* 1973).

A major portion of the other parotid proteins also have about three-quarters of their amino acids made up of proline, glycine and dicarboxylic acids. The number of proteins of this type is uncertain but four major and approximately eight minor constituents can be detected (Hay & Oppenheim 1974). Three have been isolated: they have a low molecular weight (12 000), contain no carbohydrate or sialate and have a strong affinity for hydroxyapatite. Considerable variation in the structure of these proteins occurs among salivas from different individuals. About 1% of the parotid protein consists of a small, strongly basic molecule, resembling a protamine, in which about 60% of its amino acids are made up of lysine, histidine and arginine (Balekjian *et al.* 1972). An acidic protein (m.wt 4500) containing much aspartic acid and histidine is also known. The parotid protein with the greatest affinity for apatite described so far is a small acidic protein (m.wt about 5000) containing much glutamic acid, tyrosine and proline with no carbohydrate (Hay 1973).

In view of their low molecular weights, many of the proteins of saliva (about one-third of those in the submandibular and one-tenth of the parotid proteins) are dialysable. The isoelectric point of salivary proteins covers a wide range from about 3 to 9.

Both of the major salivary secretions contain a high molecular weight protein (about 15 mg 100 ml^{-1}) which causes clumping of certain salivary bacteria (p. 378) and binds to apatite. It contains 33% protein, 19% carbohydrate and 3% sialic acid, the other constituents being unidentified (Hay *et al.* 1971). It may play an important part in plaque formation.

The difficulty of collecting submandibular saliva from the duct, and its physical properties, have limited the detailed study of its proteins. They are in lower concentration but of greater complexity than those of the parotid, consisting of the same proteins as in the parotid (from the serous cells) and additional proteins from the mucous cells. Only the proteins of low molecular weight have been examined because the larger molecules do not enter the gels used for electrophoresis. One protein (m.wt 12 000), representing 10–20% of the total, contains phosphate and is precipitated by calcium and may be a constituent of plaque (p. 376).

Some of the proteins of submandibular and sublingual saliva are unstable and readily precipitate by shaking, on contact with foreign surfaces or spontaneously. In some subjects, stimulated saliva is cloudy even when collected from the ducts.

Sublingual saliva is secreted in small volumes (about 5% of the total) and is difficult to collect separately. However, a protein of molecular weight 562 000 and an isoelectric point of 3 has been isolated. Its composition varies in different people, for example, in 'secretors' (subjects whose saliva possesses blood group activity) the fucose and amino sugars are in higher concentration.

Histochemical staining of human salivary glands reveals that the neighbouring cells in one acinus may contain different glycoproteins or, less often, all the cells in one acinus may give a different glycoprotein staining than the cells in an adjacent acinus. For example, the acinar cells in the sublingual gland may contain groups containing sulphate or sialate whereas cells of the submandibular gland contain acid or neutral glycoproteins and much lower concentrations of sulphur-containing products. This suggests that different cells produce each type of glycoprotein although conceivably the differences in staining might have arisen from different stages in the synthesis of the same glycoprotein or variations in the degree of secretory exhaustion (Eversole 1972).

The IgA of saliva differs from that of serum in having a higher molecular weight. The IgA enters the salivary gland from the plasma, or may be synthesized by plasma cells in the gland, and an additional protein ('secretory' or 'transport piece') is synthesized in the gland and attached to two molecules of IgA and the whole is secreted in that form (Tomasi *et al.* 1965). The secretory piece which is itself antigenic and migrates like a globulin, may be present in saliva in an unbound form in most children and some adults, if the γ globulins are absent. For example, a new-born baby's serum contains no antibodies; the latter increase in concentration up to puberty following exposure to infection and presumably bind increasing proportions of the secretory piece (South *et al.* 1966).

IgA is present in parotid saliva in the highest concentrations, that of IgM and IgG being extremely low (less than 0·2 mg 100 ml^{-1}). Their concentration falls with increased rates of flow. Traces of albumin are also present (0·6 mg 100 ml^{-1} is a typical figure). Some proteins (for example horse radish peroxidase) are secreted into rat submandibular saliva when injected into the blood.

The immunoglobulins of gingival fluid are present in similar proportions to those of plasma and its IgA contains no secretory piece.

OTHER NITROGENOUS CONSTITUENTS

The amino acid content of saliva has been studied chromatographically and by microbiological methods, but as yet too few subjects have been studied to give a complete picture as to which amino acids are present, their concentrations, or how they vary under different conditions. Eighteen amino acids have been detected in whole saliva—of these nine have been found consistently and nine were sometimes present. The total is about 4 mg% and, except for glycine (about 0·8 mg%), the concentration of most individual amino acids is less than 0·3 mg%. Comparison of salivas from the parotid and submandibular glands showed that the amino acid concentration of parotid saliva was lower than that of the submandibular secretion and that fewer amino acids were present—six regularly, in the parotid and twelve in the submandibular (Battistone & Burnett 1961). Other workers have reported the presence of fourteen amino acids mostly at concentrations less than 0·1 mg% varying from glutamic acid 0·44 mg% to lysine 0·024 mg%.

Peptides are present and there is evidence that they act as co-factors in the metabolism of salivary bacteria (Kröncke *et al.* 1958; Molan & Hartles 1971; Kleinberg *et al.* 1973).

Urea, creatinine, uric acid and ammonia are present in saliva but their significance, if any, is unknown. The concentration of urea is closely related to plasma levels but varies also with the rate of flow (although detailed findings are contradictory). Virtually all the ammonia is formed by bacteria from urea and amino acids (p. 395). Saliva contains cyclic AMP and its concentration increases during and after stimulation from a typical resting value of 5 pico mole/ml^{-1} up to 50 pico mole/ml^{-1} (Nistrup Madsen & Badawi 1976).

GLUCOSE

Lundqvist (1952) showed that sugars in a free form are present only in traces in fasting saliva (about 0·5–1·0 mg 100 ml^{-1}). The carbohydrate part of glycoproteins is readily split off from the protein by ill-defined bacterial enzymes (sometimes referred to as 'mucinase') in saliva thus liberating reducing sugar, which cannot readily be distinguished from sugar being secreted by the salivary gland. If sufficiently accurate methods of analysis are used, minute changes in the glucose of parotid saliva are detectable which parallel those of blood when glucose solution is perfused (for example it rose from 1·03 to 2·06 mg 100 ml^{-1} when the blood sugar changed from 83 to 188 mg 100 ml^{-1}).

Similar estimations on diabetic patients also showed a relation to blood values, but consistently higher than in normals (from 1·61 to 3 mg 100 ml^{-1} when the blood sugar was 141 (fasting) and 263 mg 100 ml^{-1} respectively).

Much higher concentrations of sugar may persist in mixed saliva after eating carbohydrate. Lanke (1957) compared the effect of different foods on salivary sugar and found that starchy cereal foods (especially the more highly-refined types) raised it for between 27 and 38 min, sweets for 22–25 min, and potatoes for only 15 min. Movement of the lips and tongue after eating greatly increase the rate of sugar clearance.

OTHER ORGANIC CONSTITUENTS

Citrate has been found in saliva in concentrations ranging from 0·2 to 2·0 mg 100 ml^{-1}. If the saliva stands for about an hour almost the whole of its citrate disappears, presumably by bacterial action.

Lactate is present in very variable quantities since it is one of the main products of bacterial degradation of carbohydrates by salivary bacteria. After a meal, tenfold increases in concentration up to 50 mg% have been found. Traces of lactate (18–40 μg ml^{-1}) and pyruvate (2–4 μg ml^{-1}) are present in parotid duct saliva.

The agglutinogens A, B and O which are polysaccharides which may be present in the side-chains of the salivary glycoproteins, are found in the saliva of about 80% of people ('secretors'), whose cells contain them; they have been isolated in yields of about 3 mg 100 ml^{-1}. The activity in the saliva of 'secretors' is several hundred times greater than that of the red blood corpuscles, a fact which is of medico-legal importance, because it may make it possible to determine an individual's blood group from, say, a recently used drinking vessel or a discarded cigarette end. In 'non-secretors' (subjects whose blood corpuscles contain agglutinogens, but whose saliva is inactive) similar chemical substances can be isolated but they do not possess agglutinating activity. The blood group substances in secretors are present in highest concentrations in saliva from the minor and sublingual glands, lower in submandibular and completely absent from the parotid saliva of some secretors but traces are sometimes present.

Experiments with anti-A labelled with fluorescein have showed histologically that the A substance is present only in mucous cells. The M, N and Rh factors are not present in any of the salivary secretions. The content of blood group substances in each type of saliva may be related to the number of mucous cells in the glands; the parotid usually contains only serous cells, but some glands have a few mucous acini, perhaps accounting for the occasional presence of these substances in parotid saliva. The submandibular saliva of secretors contains more bound carbohydrate, especially fucose, than that from non-secretors.

Water-soluble vitamins have been estimated in mixed saliva by microbiological methods but widely different results have been reported (Table IX.1). Their presence in duct saliva does not seem to have been investigated. Part of the vitamin content of saliva is synthesized by oral bacteria, another part may be present from food debris, but the relative importance of these sources is not known (Glavind *et al.* 1948; Disraely *et al.* 1959).

Saliva is also stated to contain apoerythein, a substance related to the 'intrinsic factor' concerned in the utilization of vitamin B$_{12}$.

Chromatography of parotid and whole saliva has detected the presence of many lipids, including cholesterol and cholesterol esters, fatty acids, glycerides and phospholipids, but they are present in very low concentration (Dirksen 1963). The major fatty acids are C$_{20}$ with five double bonds (40% of the whole) and C$_{22}$ with four or six double bonds. These are very different from the fatty acids of blood and suggest that the human salivary glands synthesize fatty acids (Mandel & Eisenstein 1969).

Corticosteriods (mostly cortisol and cortisone) are present in parotid and submaxillary saliva after ACTH injection and, although the concentrations $(1-2 \mu g 100 ml^{-1})$ are much lower than those of blood, they run parallel to them and are independent of the rate of flow (Shannon *et al.* 1962). They are not present as glucuronides, the form in which they are excreted in the urine. Since cortisone is almost absent from the plasma, the salivary glands presumably produce it by dehydrogenating cortisol—the appropriate dehydrogenase has been detected in salivary glands (Katz & Shannon 1969).

It has been suggested that determinations of certain substances (for example urea and corticosteroids) in saliva collected at controlled rates of flow might be a more expeditious way of investigating plasma levels, while diagnosing disease, than the taking of blood samples.

THE ENZYMES OF SALIVA

Although salivary amylase is the only enzyme sufficiently active in the mouth to play any significant part in human digestion (p. 338) it is not the only enzyme present, as is often stated.

Parotid saliva, collected by cannula, contains variable concentrations of acid phosphatase, esterases, choline esterase, aldolase, lysozyme (see p. 342), β-glucuronidase, succinic dehydrogenase, peroxidase, carbonic anhydrase and kallikrein (see p. 329). Lipases have been reported but not confirmed in duct salivas when tested on specific substrates—presumably some non-specific esterases of saliva can break down lipids (Pritchard *et al.* 1967). Other enzymes may also occur which have not yet been detected. Additional quantities of some of these enzymes (for example acid phosphatase) and a great range of others arising from the flora of the mouth or the oral tissues include alkaline phosphatase, catalase, hyaluronidase, proteinases, urease and deaminases, the enzymes concerned in converting carbohydrates to lactic acid and many others (see Chauncey 1961). Some of these enzymes may play an important part in processes which occur slowly and are highly localized (such as dental caries) but they may be ignored as far as the digestion and utilization of food are concerned.

Inorganic constituents

CALCIUM AND PHOSPHORUS

The most extensive survey of the calcium and phosphorus concentrations of saliva was carried out by Becks & Wainwright (1934, 1937). Becks estimated the calcium of resting saliva from over 600 subjects and found an average of $5 \cdot 8$ mg 100 ml^{-1}, ranging from $2 \cdot 2$ to $11 \cdot 3$ mg%. Wainwright analysed the same samples for phosphate concentration (as P) which averaged $16 \cdot 8$ mg

100 ml^{-1} (range 6·1–71·0 mg%) but more recent figures, while giving similar average values, do not show such wide variation. Ericsson (1949) published figures on small groups varying in age, caries susceptibility and diet.

Becks & Wainwright found that the unstimulated saliva of slow secretors (less than 20 ml hr^{-1}) contained slightly higher calcium and considerably higher phosphate concentrations than that of rapid secretion. When the total *amounts* (as opposed to concentrations) of calcium and phosphate secreted per hour were calculated (that is, milligrammes per 100 ml multiplied by number of milligrammes secreted per hour) it was found that the slow secretors secreted very much less of both calcium and phosphate than did the members of the other group (Table IX.2).

TABLE IX.2

Effect of rate of flow on calcium and inorganic phosphorus contents of unstimulated saliva

	Av. rate of flow (ml hr^{-1})	Av. conc. of Ca (mg%)	Av. amount of Ca (mg hr^{-1})	Av. conc. of P (mg%)	Av. amount of P (mg hr^{-1})
Slow secretors	13·4	5·99	0·80	17·0	2·21
Rapid secretors	39·6	5·66	2·26	11·8	4·42

(Data from Becks & Wainwright 1941.)

Samples were also collected from the same subjects several times over a period of 1–2 years and it was found that the output from the slow secretors showed the greater variation.

With stimulated mixed saliva, the calcium and phosphate concentrations were lower in both groups than in unstimulated saliva and the differences between the groups were smaller in stimulated than unstimulated. The amount secreted per hour naturally rose in both groups because the rate of flow increased very considerably. The effect of stimulation in reducing the calcium and phosphate of mixed saliva is exceptional but has been well established. The fall in calcium concentration arises from an increase in the proportion of parotid saliva (pp. 311–2) but the change in phosphate concentration is a real reduction in the secretion from the glands.

The phosphate of mixed saliva is present in several forms including about 10% as organic compounds (mostly phosphorylated carbohydrates, phospholipids, nucleotides such as ATP, and nucleoprotein). It has been stated that up to 10% is present as pyrophosphate (Vogel & Amdur 1967; Sawinski & Cole 1965) which, as an inhibitor of the precipitation of calcium phosphate, could be a factor influencing calculus production. Its presence in saliva has not been confirmed (Edgar & Jenkins 1972). Between 6 and 24% of the phosphate is complexed, much of it being non-dialysable. It has often been assumed that this was in the form of colloidal calcium phosphate but Grøn (1973) found only 1–2% in this form. It is more likely to be bound to the low molecular weight protein, rich in basic amino acids (lysine, histidine and arginine) isolated by Balekjian *et al.* (p. 292).

On the assumption that salivary proteins had the same binding power as plasma proteins, and on the basis of ultrafiltration experiments, Dreisbach (1960) concluded that most of the bound calcium of saliva is complexed by unidentified small molecules. Some calcium is also present as complexes with carbon dioxide as can be shown by the observation that removal of much CO_2 from saliva by bubbling air through it may cause the precipitation of about one-third of the calcium originally present. This is a much greater effect than can be accounted for merely by the fact that CO_2 removal causes a rise in pH, and emphasizes that CO_2 plays a special part in maintaining the calcium levels in saliva. A glycoprotein has been isolated from saliva, however, which combines with approximately 8 mg of calcium g^{-1} at neutrality (i.e. about 16 times the binding power of plasma proteins) and releases much of it at pH 5·0 (Rölla & Jonsen 1967) which suggests that this is the nature of the bound calcium in saliva. These contradictory results have not been reconciled.

The concentrations of calcium and phosphate in saliva, even more than in plasma, suggest supersaturation with respect to most forms of calcium phosphate (tricalcium phosphate, octa calcium phosphate but less often to dicalcium phosphate dihydrate, $CaHPO_4 \cdot 2H_2O$) with the exception of unstimulated parotid saliva which may sometimes fail to be saturated.

The pH and concentrations of calcium and phosphate are higher in un-stimulated submandibular than parotid saliva and can be regarded as super-saturated with respect to hydroxyapatite by a factor of 2. When stimulated the pH rises dramatically (p. 301), calcium concentrations rise slightly and the phosphate level falls but the proportion as HPO_4^{2-} increases so the level of supersaturation rises reaching almost 3. Resting parotid saliva with an average pH, as emerging from the duct, of below 6 and possibly even as low as 5·3, is sometimes slightly unsaturated with respect to hydroxyapatite and even less so to enamel which, probably owing to its carbonate and magnesium content, is more soluble than pure hydroxyapatite. It becomes saturated as its pH increases on losing CO_2 when exposed to air and on stimulation, the pH and calcium concentrations rise and phosphate concentrations fall reaching supersaturation level of about 2 (Grøn 1973).

When dicalcium phosphate dihydrate ($CaHPO_4 \cdot 2H_2O$) is allowed to stand in water at about pH 7·0 for 24–48 hr the pH falls and much of it is converted into hydroxy apatite and other forms of calcium phosphate. When this salt stands with saliva, however, this change does not occur (Grøn 1973). Also when solutions of calcium salts and phosphates are mixed in concentrations which lead to slight precipitation, addition of saliva prevents the precipitation (Grøn & Hay 1976). The substance(s) responsible for this activity in saliva (and plaque) are associated with the tyrosine-rich acidic proteins of low molecular weight mentioned on p. 292 (Grøn & Hay 1976). This activity may be important in maintaining the environment of the tooth saturated with calcium phosphate. It could also be a factor in reducing remineralization in caries thus opposing the effect of fluoride in favouring remineralization (pp. 418 & 485).

The saturation of saliva by calcium phosphate is believed to be important in (*a*) dental caries and (*b*) calculus formation.

(*a*) *Relation of calcium and phosphate of saliva to caries—the concept of 'critical pH'*. The rate at which apatite dissolves in acid depends on several factors of which the most important are the pH and the concentration of calcium and phosphate ions already in solution. The pH affects the amount dissolving for the following reasons. Although apatite contains phosphate in the form of PO_4^{3-} ions, this ion cannot exist in solution at physiological pH values except in very minute concentration. If this ion is released, as apatite dissolves into a physiological medium, it is immediately converted into HPO_4^{2-} which in turn mostly becomes $H_2PO_4^-$ if the pH is reduced below about 3·0.

$$PO_4^{3-} \underset{-H^+}{\overset{+H^+}{\rightleftharpoons}} HPO_4^{2-} \underset{-H^+}{\overset{+H^+}{\rightleftharpoons}} H_2PO_4^-$$

If the pH falls, the tendency for these reactions to occur will increase thus lowering the concentration of PO_4^{3-} and encouraging more PO_4^{3-} ions to leave the solid apatite.

The concentrations of calcium and phosphate influence the rate at which apatite dissolves, by the law of mass action. From what has been said above it is clear that the concentration of ions needed to prevent apatite from dissolving depends on the pH. In the presence of calcium and phosphate ions at salivary concentrations, calcium phosphate is insoluble at neutrality but if the saliva becomes acid a particular pH will be reached at which the apparent solubility of calcium phosphate (see p. 31) becomes so high (because most of the PO_4^{3-} ions have been changed to HPO_4^{2-}, as described above), that the concentrations of ions in the solution will fail to saturate it. This is a reason, additional to those mentioned on p. 31, for distinguishing between apparent and real solubility. The pH at which any particular saliva ceases to be saturated is referred to as the 'critical pH' and below this value, the inorganic material of teeth may dissolve in it (Fosdick & Starke 1939; Ericsson 1949).

Experiments with saliva and buffer solutions saturated with calcium phosphate have confirmed that tooth substance dissolves in saliva below a pH varying from saliva to saliva (depending on their calcium and phosphate concentrations) but usually between 5·5 and 6·5.

Other factors which, in test-tube experiments, influence the amount of calcium phosphate dissolving in buffer solutions are as follows:

(1) Since the critical pH is controlled by the activity of calcium and phosphate ions any substances which form complex ions with calcium or phosphate will lower the activity and thereby lower the degree of saturation. If complexing substances were present in sufficient concentration to complex all the calcium at neutral or alkaline pH values, then the solution would be unsaturated and apatite would dissolve over a wide range of pH and the concept of a critical pH, above which apatite did not dissolve, would be invalid. This is one of the basic ideas in the proteolysis-chelation theory of dental caries (pp. 421–2).

(2) The strength of the buffer (for example an $M/1$ buffer at any particular pH will dissolve more than an $M/10$ buffer at the same pH).

(3) The amount of solid present (for example if 2 g of apatite are shaken with 10 ml of buffer more will dissolve than if 1 g is shaken). With most substances, the solubility is independent of the amount of solid per millilitre (the solid:solution ratio) but this is not true of apatite because it can react with ions in solution and the extent of this reaction increases with increases in the solid:solution ratio.

(4) The 'ionic strength' (which is a measure of the influence of all the ions present) can alter solubility but this is probably the least important of the factors mentioned.

The importance of these additional factors in controlling the amount of enamel dissolving in saliva or plaque is not known.

It must be emphasized that the critical pH applies only to saliva or other solutions saturated with calcium phosphate. There is no pH value above which tooth substance will not dissolve if calcium and phosphate ions are absent. Teeth will dissolve in distilled water at neutrality although at a very slow rate.

In dental caries it is probably the equilibrium between enamel and the fluid phase of the inner surface of plaque which is important. Although information is accumulating about the composition of the 'plaque fluid' as a whole, nothing is known about how it varies in different parts of the plaque.

In view of the many factors which influence it, the critical pH cannot be calculated with precision, and some workers doubt whether the concept of a critical pH is valid at all. Comparisons between the pH changes in plaque from caries-active and caries-free subjects do support this concept and suggest that caries occurs only if the pH falls below 5·2.

(*b*) *Calculus formation.* The instability of salivary calcium and phosphate means that local changes in the concentration of substances (such as CO_2), which are concerned in maintaining the calcium phosphate in solution or the effect of seeding substances (p. 116) may cause it to precipitate as calculus or tartar (discussed more fully on pp. 402–4).

OTHER INORGANIC CONSTITUENTS

The following ions are present in saliva in readily detectable amounts: sodium, potassium, magnesium, chloride, sulphate and thiocyanate. Minute traces of fluoride, iodide, bromide, nitrite, iron and tin are present and some samples of mixed human saliva contain other trace elements, those most commonly detected are zinc, lead, copper and chromium (Dreizen *et al.* 1970).

The average concentration of thiocyanate is about 13 mg 100 ml^{-1} with a wide range (3–27 mg 100 ml^{-1}), and the concentration appears to be lower with high rates of flow. An old finding that its concentration is higher in the saliva of smokers has been confirmed in stimulated parotid saliva (smokers approximately 7 mg 100 ml^{-1} and non-smokers 4·5 mg 100 ml^{-1}). Results with whole saliva are less clear-cut because the thiocyanate is oxidized and forms antibacterial factors (p. 342). Thiocyanate itself can inhibit bacteria but, in most experiments, only at concentrations greater than those in saliva.

The fluoride content of saliva is of interest in connection with the important effect of fluoride in reducing dental caries. The concentration found by earlier chemical methods is about 0·1–0·2 ppm but results with the fluoride electrode suggest much lower figures between 0·01 and 0·05 ppm (mostly in ionic form with very little bound). When doses of between 1 and 10 mg of fluoride as sodium fluoride were given the concentrations in saliva rose but not significantly with 1 mg (Yao & Grøn 1970; Shannon & Edmonds 1972) no comparisons have been reported so far in areas with and without fluoridated water. It is uncertain whether these low concentrations can influence the tooth directly but the fluoride in saliva may be the source of the very much higher levels of fluoride in dental plaque (see p. 486). The fluoride concentration of resting saliva is higher than that of stimulated but does not vary with the strength of the stimulus, a finding that has not yet been explained.

HYDROGEN ION CONCENTRATION

Saliva loses CO_2 after collection and consequently the pH will rise on standing unless the sample is collected under oil. Unless very great precision is required, this precaution is unnecessary (at least for unstimulated samples), provided that the samples are tested for pH within a few minutes of collection.

The pH of saliva is extremely sensitive to the rate of flow especially under resting conditions, and results are of no value unless this factor is controlled. Fig. IX.6 shows the wide range of pH of parotid saliva at different rates of flow. It also shows that the nature of the stimulus is unimportant. If two different stimuli are given, matched in intensity so that they produce the same rate of flow, then the pH will also be the same. The pH value of submandibular saliva is affected in the same direction by flow-rate but to a smaller extent.

Oster *et al.* (1953) found with an electrode placed under the tongue that the

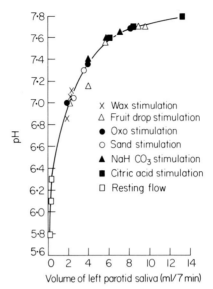

X Wax stimulation
△ Fruit drop stimulation
● Oxo stimulation
○ Sand stimulation
▲ NaH CO₃ stimulation
■ Citric acid stimulation
□ Resting flow

Volume of left parotid saliva (ml/7 min)

Fig. IX.6. Effect of the flow-rate of parotid saliva, induced by several different stimuli, on the pH value.

average of 385 pH determinations on the resting saliva of 195 subjects was 5·97 (range 5·73–6·15) and similar figures have been obtained by other workers when readings were made on saliva very near to the duct and before the pH had risen as a result of the loss of carbon dioxide. Submandibular saliva has a higher resting pH than that from the parotid gland. Schmidt-Nielsen (1946) found an average in 40 adults of 5·81 for parotid resting saliva (range 5·45–6·06) and 6·39 (range 6·02–7·14) for submandibular saliva.

Most workers agree that the pH of saliva varies throughout the day and this is probably controlled by the rate of flow although this is not certain. During sleep the pH falls presumably because the rate of flow is almost zero (although plaque pH is high during sleep owing to alkali production). During eating the pH rises—because the rate of flow increases. After a meal, the pH has almost invariably been found to fall below the fasting level to which it returns within 1–2 hr.

The pH of the saliva is higher in animals than in man; values of 8·5 or even 9·0 have been recorded for the rat, sheep and dog.

THE SECRETION OF THE MINOR GLANDS
Sufficient secretion for analysis was collected by Dawes & Wood (1973b) from four subjects by applying suction to a micropipette placed over the glands after secretion. Among their main findings were: a pH of about 7·0 which was independent of flow-rates, suggesting the absence of bicarbonate

(p. 307), confirmed by direct analysis, the virtual absence of amylase and the presence of blood group substances in secretors at much higher concentrations than in submandibular saliva. The concentration of phosphate is about one-tenth, but that of calcium about the same, as in submandibular saliva; both fell with increased rates of flow and the degree of saturation with respect to hydroxyapatite is uncertain. The concentration of protein was similar to that in other secretions but its effect on viscosity was very much greater (Table IX.1).

Although their influence on the saliva as a whole may be small these glands may have a considerable effect on the environment of the teeth as their secretion is probably in contact with them for long periods, undiluted by saliva from the major glands when these are unstimulated.

THE CELLS OF SALIVA

Microscopical examination of saliva shows that epithelial cells (buccal squames) are always present in addition to leucocytes—mostly polymorphs— which enter the mouth through the gingival crevice since they are absent from saliva collected from the ducts and very few are present in saliva from infants before the eruption of teeth or from edentulous adults (Wright 1964). The majority of the leucocytes are disintegrating and those which are intact have a swollen appearance, presumably owing to the low osmotic pressure of saliva. Even healthy gingivae allow some leucocytes to enter the mouth, the numbers increasing four- to five-fold between waking and mid-day. The number increases with inflammation (Schiott & Löe 1970). The leucocytes in the gingival fluid are mostly neutrophils (95–97%) with 1–2% of lymphocytes and 2–3% monocytes (Attstrom 1970). Some of these cells are viable and some phagocytosis probably occurs in the gingival crevice but once they are propelled into the mouth further activity is unlikely. Disrupted leucocytes release enzymes into the saliva and, because of their large size compared with the bacteria, may contribute a considerable proportion of the extracellular enzymes.

The number of bacteria in the saliva is of the order of 10^8 ml^{-1} and even larger numbers are present in mechanically-stimulated saliva, presumably by dislodging plaque or bacterial deposits from the mucosa. The species present have been reviewed by Morris (1953), Bisset & Davis (1960), Hardie & Bowden (1974) and Nolte (1973). Owing to the great variations in conditions in which the oral flora live, it is difficult to culture all the species present, or obtain information about the total number. If any one species is considered it can only be expressed as a proportion of 'total cultivatable organisms'. Most of the bacteria are of the facultative types: strict aerobes and strict anaerobes are relatively few. Yeasts are almost always present and sometimes certain protozoa (for example *Amoeba salivarius*). The cells and bacteria are largely responsible for the cloudy appearance of saliva.

Many bacteria adhere to the epithelial cells but salivary proteins which agglutinate bacteria (p. 378) reduce this adherence. The counts decrease after a meal and gradually increase between meals—evidently the removal by swallowing saliva does not keep pace with the growth in the mouth (Geddes & Jenkins 1974).

THE GASES DISSOLVED IN SALIVA
Like all body fluids, saliva contains nitrogen, oxygen and carbon dioxide in solution. The oxygen and nitrogen contents are stated to be between 0·18 and 0·25 vol. % and about 0·9 vol. % respectively.

Unstimulated saliva contains 10–20 vol. % of carbon dioxide and vigorously stimulated saliva up to 150 vol. %. About 25% of it is combined with protein as a carbamino compound (Wah Leung 1961) and most of the remainder is present in an equilibrium between bicarbonate ions and carbonic acid. At a pH of 6·75 the ratio of bicarbonate to carbonic acid is about 4·5:1. Saliva contains the enzyme carbonic anhydrase which catalyses the reaction:

$$CO_2 + H_2O \rightleftharpoons H_2CO_3$$

Bicarbonate is the main buffering system of saliva (see p. 317).

Factors controlling the composition of saliva

There is a great deal of personal variation in the composition of saliva. Two people with identical diets and who are collecting saliva under identical conditions may produce salivas at different rates and with different compositions. Within reasonable limits the saliva of one individual tends to retain its own 'pattern' of composition over long periods. This personal variation which, of course, applies to other metabolic activities of the body, introduces great difficulty into the quantitative study of saliva.

EFFECT OF RATE OF FLOW ON COMPOSITION
The rate of flow and the duration of the stimulus are important factors influencing the composition of saliva and comparisons between different saliva samples may be quite invalid unless these factors are controlled or allowed for.

The effects of flow-rate on the composition of submandibular and parotid saliva are summarized in Fig. IX.7(a) and (b). The concentrations of most constituents rise with increased flow, phosphate and magnesium fall and potassium is almost independent of it.

The more striking effects of rate of flow are detectable either by studying saliva from the same subject in whom the rates of flow are varied or by comparing the composition from subjects who are fast or slow secretors.

A further complication is that even if the rate of flow of parotid saliva is kept constant, the concentration of some constituents varies over a period of

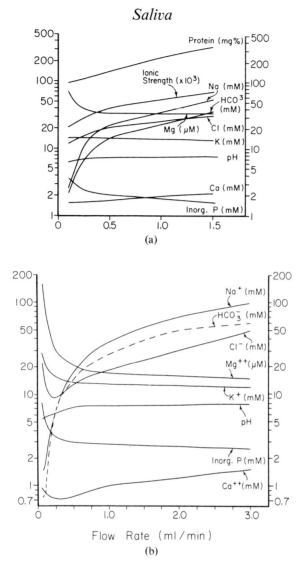

FIG. IX.7. The effect of flow-rate on the concentration of certain constituents of (a) submandibular saliva, and (b) parotid saliva.

10–15 min (Dawes 1967, 1969). For example, 2 or 3 min after the beginning of stimulation with sour lemon drops the protein concentration fell but rose in the following few minutes eventually to reach concentrations higher than the resting figure. The extent of the rise depended on the rate of flow; with a rapid flow (1 ml min⁻¹) from vigorous stimulation, the final concentration was about double that of the resting value but with low rates (0·26 ml min⁻¹) the concentration not only rose more slowly but did not reach such a high

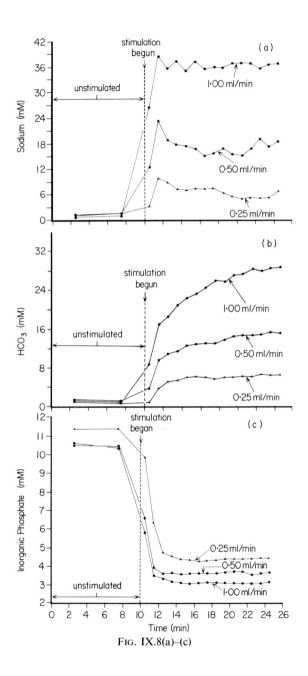

FIG. IX.8(a)–(c)

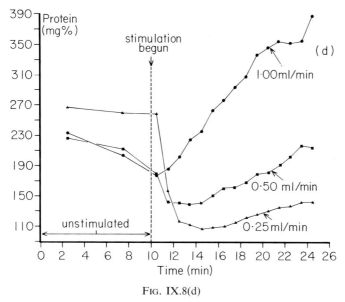

FIG. IX.8(d)

FIG. IX.8. The effect of duration of the stimulus on the concentration of some constituents of parotid saliva.

value (Fig. IX.8(d)). Although all of a group of nine subjects showed a rise with time there was some variation in detail. The behaviour of some other substances in saliva in relation to duration of flow are shown in Fig. IX.8 and may be summarized as follows. Sodium concentration remains approximately constant (Fig. IX.8(a)) especially at higher levels of flow, bicarbonate rises with time (Fig. IX.8(b)) and phosphate (like magnesium and potassium) fall immediately after stimulation and then remain approximately constant (Fig. IX.8(c)). Calcium falls on stimulation then gradually rises at high rates of flow (1 ml min^{-1}) but remains low with lower flow-rates.

The bicarbonate concentration of stimulated saliva may exceed that of the plasma because bicarbonate formed in the gland (from the increased CO_2 produced following intense activity) enters the secretion. Sand (1951) injected into rabbits lactate and bicarbonate labelled with ^{14}C and found that, after lactate injection, the radioactivity of the bicarbonate of saliva was higher than that of the plasma, showing that the lactate was a source of salivary bicarbonate. After the labelled bicarbonate was injected, the radioactivity of the salivary bicarbonate was less than that of the plasma, indicating that some of it must have come from non-radioactive CO_2 formed in the gland. Several other ions have a higher concentration in human saliva than in the plasma, for example phosphate, potassium and iodide.

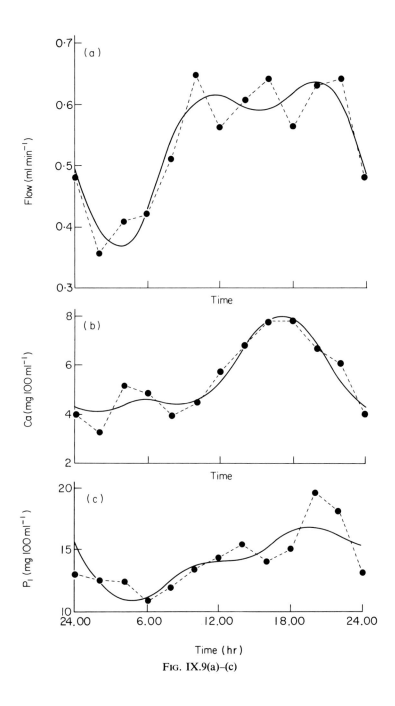

FIG. IX.9(a)–(c)

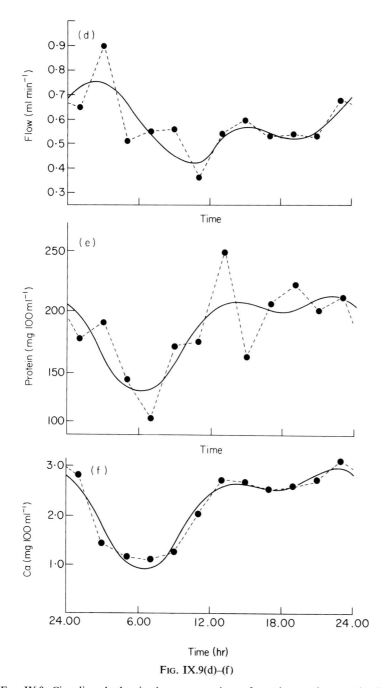

FIG. IX.9(d)–(f)

FIG. IX.9. Circadian rhythm in the concentrations of certain constituents of saliva (submandibular (a)–(c), and parotid (d)–(f)). The dotted line joins experimental observations and the solid line is a plot of the best-fitting sine curve.

CIRCADIAN RHYTHMS

Daily rhythms in the secretion rate and composition of saliva have been studied for many years (the early results are tabulated by Ferguson *et al.* 1973). The earlier workers were unaware of the need of controlling the rate and duration of flow and they rarely collected samples at night or for more than 1 day or analysed their results statistically.

Studies by Dawes (1972); Dawes & Ong (1973) and Ferguson *et al.* (1973, 1974) were planned to meet these problems. The subjects in Dawes's experiments had developed a technique for maintaining the rate of flow of stimulated parotid saliva collected with a cannula. Unstimulated mixed and stimulated parotid saliva were collected over a fixed period (5 and 10 min, respectively), with collections at least 1 hr apart so that one collection did not influence the composition of those following it. The constant flow, although making it impossible to test rhythms in stimulated flow-rate, did ensure that variations were related to changes in the secretory mechanisms and not merely changes secondary to changes in flow rates. Ferguson *et al.* adopted the constant stimulus method so that variation in rates of flow could be measured and they argued that influences resulting from changes in rates might themselves be an important constituent of daily rhythms; in addition, they studied resting submandibular saliva.

There were considerable differences between individuals but any one individual showed fairly constant results. For most constituents, the daily rhythm showed a sine curve with well-marked maxima and minima but some substances in individual salivas (for example calcium and phosphate in stimulated parotid) showed only a peak or a trough on an otherwise fairly constant curve. The amplitude of the rhythm varies considerably but averages about 40–50%.

The results show differences in detail between stimulated and unstimulated and between parotid and submandibular saliva. Some typical results are summarized in Fig. IX.9(a)–(f). The main points observed were that in unstimulated whole saliva the flow rate reached a maximum at about 15.30 hr with rhythmic concentrations in sodium and chloride, the maxima being at 05.00 hr, but the other constituents studied (protein, calcium, potassium, phosphorus, urea) showed no significant rhythm, whereas in the one result on stimulated saliva, the flow-rate was greatest at 03.00 hr. Stimulated parotid salivas showed significant rhythms for the following constituents (with approximate time of maxima): sodium (05.00 hr), chloride (05.00 hr), potassium (17.00 hr) protein, fairly steady but sharp minimum at 06.00 hr and small variation in calcium (significant in only three out of eight subjects) (19.30 hr), but no rhythm for phosphate or urea.

Unstimulated submandibular saliva showed average rhythms of large amplitude in rate of flow (minimum 05.00 hr), potassium (maximum 14.00 hr), chlorine (maximum 05.00 hr with well marked minimum at about 20.00

hr), sodium (maximum 07.00 hr, minimum between 13.00 and 20.00 hr) and changes of lower amplitude for phosphate (minimum 04.00 hr, maximum 22.00 hr). Because the maxima and minima do not always correspond in different individuals, the significance of the rhythms on a group basis was rather low.

The variations in flow rate of mixed saliva correspond with those of ADH output and the two may be related causally. The changes in sodium, potassium and chlorine, which were among the most consistent, could arise from rhythms in aldosterone secretion (related to posture and sleep-wakefulness) acting directly on the salivary gland (these ions do not show a rhythm in the plasma). The rhythm in protein concentration was not affected by doses of dexamethasone, a drug which suppresses the rhythm in plasma cortisol, proving that the rhythm in saliva did not arise from variations in synthesis of protein stimulated by varying levels of this corticosteroid.

It is perhaps unfortunate that many workers on saliva collect their samples early in the working day at the time when the rate of change arising from the daily rhythm is at its maximum; small variations in timing could have large effects on composition and would increase the differences between samples from different individuals. Collection between 14.00 and 16.00 hr would be preferable.

It is somewhat unexpected that, although resting flow virtually ceases during sleep, some stimulated samples taken after the subjects were wakened showed a maximum flow-rate at 03.00 to 04.00 hr.

In those studies in which flow-rate varied, the variation in sodium and chlorine were associated with flow-rate but their magnitude was greater than would be expected from this cause alone.

Curiously enough, circadian rhythms in stimulated whole saliva have been studied very little but the few results that have been obtained (by Shannon & Prigmore 1962) suggest that the differences observed at different times of day were not consistent on different days. Presumably the rhythm in the secretion of the various glands differed and cancelled each other out in the mixture.

THE RELATIVE CONTRIBUTIONS FROM THE DIFFERENT GLANDS

Measurements of the rates of flow from the different glands show that the submandibular produces the greatest flow, especially under 'resting' conditions. When stimulated with acetic acid placed on the tongue, the parotid gave a proportionately higher response than the submandibular (see Fig. IX.10 and Table IX.3).

The great variation between individuals is clearly brought out in the figures for the range; in some subjects, there was no detectable secretion from either the sublingual or parotid, even when acetic acid was used as a stimulus. Owing to the impossibility of chewing food when the segregator was in place, it is still not known how this normal stimulus influences the flow from the

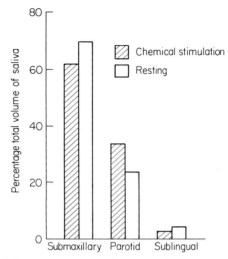

Fig. IX.10. The relative contributions of the three pairs of salivary glands to the total flow of resting and acid-stimulated saliva (based on the data of Schneyer & Levin 1955).

TABLE IX.3

Rates of flow (ml min^{-1}) of resting and acid-stimulated saliva from the main glands

	Resting (23 subjects)		Acid stimulated (16 subjects)	
	Average	*Range*	*Average*	*Range*
Submandibular	0·26	0·05–0·59	0·48	0·14–1·20
Sublingual	0·012	0·00–0·033	0·02	0·00–0·085
Parotid	0·11	0·00–0·48	0·29	0·00–0·54

(Data from Schneyer & Levin 1955.)

various glands. It has been stated by Gore (1938) who worked on one subject only, himself, with a segregator that wax-stimulated saliva came mainly from the parotid and caused only a small increase in the flow from the mixed glands. The stimulus of food, on the other hand, caused approximately equal responses in both sets of glands.

There appears to be no other data on the relative influence of food but it has been shown by Shannon (1962) that when rubber bands are used as an experimental stimulant the proportion of parotid saliva (measured from a cannula) increases as the number of bands increases (comparable with increases in bolus size). This occurred because the rate of parotid flow increased by 46% as the bolus increased (this has also been found with pieces of wax varying in size) but the rate of secretion from the other glands only increased by an average of about 4%. When pilocarpine was used as a stimulus secretion rate from all glands was increased but the rate of the parotid flow was increased more than that from the other glands so that again the percentage contribution from the parotid rose.

EFFECT OF THE NATURE OF THE STIMULUS
Pavlov found in dogs that the composition and properties of the saliva depended on the nature of the stimulus. Dry food or sand evoked a watery secretion, whereas meat (which is swallowed whole and therefore requires lubrication) caused the production of a thick saliva but, curiously enough, this particular much-quoted experiment does not seem to have been repeated nor possible explanations investigated.

Pickerill (1912) found, in the human subject, that when acid is used as a stimulant the saliva is highly alkaline, which he interpreted as a protective response to the acid. There are several possible ways in which such adaptations to the type of stimulus might be brought about but they have not been widely studied in man: (1) if different types of stimulus increased the rate of flow to different extents this would alter the composition since, as already emphasized, composition depends on rate of flow; (2) it is also possible that different stimuli could alter the composition of saliva from a particular gland even if the rates of flow were the same; and (3) different stimuli might influence the proportion of saliva from the various glands, which would alter the composition of the mixed secretion.

Dawes & Jenkins (1964) investigated this question and found that most of the differences in composition produced in response to varied stimuli could be explained on a basis of their different rates of flow. This was clearly the explanation of the effect of acid in producing an alkaline saliva (see Fig. IX.6) as stimulation by either acid or bicarbonate, if given at such concentrations as to produce saliva at the same rates of flow, produced saliva at the same high pH. Strong acid produces an alkaline saliva merely because it is a powerful stimulus and not as a specific protective response. Few examples have been discovered in which the composition of human saliva was affected by the nature of the stimulus independently of the rate of flow: (1) the amylase concentration of parotid and the total protein of submandibular saliva was higher, at high rates of flow, when salt was the stimulus than with other stimuli; and (2) Newbrun (1962) reported that amylase concentration was not greatly affected by flow-rate but that sucrose produced a higher concentration than other stimuli. There is no obvious physiological advantage in either of these responses nor is their mechanism clear but it establishes the possibility that a few stimuli may influence the composition of saliva independently of the rate of flow. Dawes & Jenkins confirmed Gore's observation (pp. 311–12) that mechanical stimuli (wax and sand) increased the proportion of saliva from the parotid (thereby providing a more watery secretion) more than did chemical stimuli but this experiment was possible only on the one subject who was able to retain three cannula in position (to measure simultaneously the flow from the different glands) whilst chewing vigorously.

In the dog submandibular gland, the composition of the glycoproteins secreted depends on the nature of the stimulus. Nerve stimulation and pilocarpine injection result in the production of proteins differing in their carbohydrate content but the significance of this for normal stimuli is unknown (Dische *et al.* 1962).

EFFECTS OF DIET ON THE COMPOSITION OF SALIVA

About 60 years ago, several workers reported that the consumption of diets high in carbohydrates is followed by a rise in the amylase content of saliva and this has been confirmed in a study of three groups of Africans. The first group normally ate a predominantly carbohydrate diet, the second group (consisting of Bushmen from the Kalahari Desert) living on a high protein, low carbohydrate diet, had an average of one tenth of the activity of salivary amylase found in the first group. By a piece of good fortune, it was also possible to study five Bushmen who had for 3 months been held as court witnesses, during which time they had received an unwontedly high carbohydrate diet. Their amylase activity was about four times that of the Bushmen on their normal diet and about half that of the first group (Squires 1953). In Ghana, the salivary amylase activity of villagers on a high carbohydrate diet averaged over three times that of groups of Europeans and of students in a university hall of residence although rates of flow were not significantly different. In the converse experiment by Bates (1958), severe restriction of carbohydrate feeding among a group of students did not consistently lower the amylase concentration of parotid saliva but the results may have been complicated by the loss of weight during the experiment.

There is also evidence that the buffering power of saliva may be altered by diet. The ingestion for 3–4 weeks of diets high in either protein or carbohydrates was reported to raise and lower, respectively, the buffering power of saliva, and a high vegetable intake (especially of spinach) was said to raise it (Forbes & Gurley 1932). More data are required on these points along with closer control of rate of flow of the saliva and time of day of collections which might indirectly produce changes in buffering power. Also, the buffering power, pH and rate of flow of wax stimulated saliva is higher immediately after a meal than it is between meals, which is another complication which was not realized when these studies were carried out.

These results were not confirmed by Bates who compared the salivary buffering powers and rates of flow of the group of students mentioned above before and after their 4-week period of severe restriction of starch intake and concluded that the buffering power of saliva is not significantly altered by the carbohydrate content of the diet.

EFFECTS OF INDIVIDUAL DIETARY CONSTITUENTS ON SALIVARY COMPOSITION

The question as to whether the concentration of a salivary constituent can be raised by increased dietary intake of that constituent has been investigated on only a few substances.

Experiments on animals have suggested that increases in the plasma phosphate may be followed by a rise in the phosphate of saliva but that changes in plasma calcium, unless very large, do not affect the saliva level. Some experiments in man have also suggested that increases in dietary phosphate may raise salivary levels and also that after eating carbohydrate (which lowers plasma phosphate) the phosphate concentration of saliva falls. These are important points since the phosphate of saliva is likely to affect the concentrations in plaque and thus to influence the critical pH at which the tooth dissolves (see p. 299).

The latter experiments were poorly controlled, no account being taken of rates of flow or time of day and in a more thorough investigation of this question Bates (1958) found an increase of only 7% after an infusion of phosphate buffer which more than doubled plasma phosphate. Ericsson (1959) found that feeding 0·3 g of bone meal before meals for 3 days had no significant effect on buffering power, phosphate concentration or rate of flow but did increase slightly the calcium concentration. This result differs from that of most other workers who have found that salivary calcium concentration is unaffected by the diet. Intake of carbohydrates has been found to lower salivary phosphate temporarily, presumably because, during the metabolism of carbohydrate, the need of phosphate by the tissues causes a fall in blood phosphate. The relative independence of the calcium of saliva from that in the diet is probably explained by the steadiness with which blood calcium is maintained.

EFFECT OF FATIGUE

If the salivary glands are stimulated vigorously for an hour or so, the volume of saliva secreted per minute shows little tendency to fall, but some of the solid constituents (for example the immunoglobulins) do decrease in concentration whereas others (for example urea, sodium, potassium and chloride) may maintain their concentration for as long as 3 hr. The fall in organic constituents probably arises from the exhaustion of reserve material in the cells which can be confirmed histologically by the reduction in the number of granules which the cells contain.

EFFECT OF HORMONES

In man the injection of adrenocorticotrophic hormone and cortisone causes a lowering of salivary sodium but little change in salivary potassium. It is of interest that although the potassium concentration of saliva is some four times that of the blood plasma (20 mg%) the sodium concentration varies between one-third and one-fifteenth that of the plasma (Dreizen *et al.* 1952). This is proof that saliva is not a mere filtration from the blood but that the cells exert a selective action which is at least partly affected by ACTH. No other hormone effects on saliva appear to have been fully established in man. A tendency for the sodium concentration of saliva (pre-breakfast samples) to be lower during the second half of the menstrual cycle has been reported, and this is presumably controlled by hormones. The rate of flow of resting saliva shows some relation to the rhythmic secretion of the anti-diuretic hormone (Dawes 1972).

Properties of saliva

In samples of parotid saliva from 384 subjects, the mean specific gravity varied between 1·0024 and 1·0061 at rates of flow of 0·32 and 0·94 ml min^{-1} respectively (Shannon 1974). The osmotic pressure is between half and three-quarters that of blood (Wilsmore 1937), but sublingual saliva has approximately the same osmotic pressure as blood.

VISCOSITY AND SPINNBARKEIT
Saliva is a viscous fluid and also shows the property of 'spinnbarkeit', i.e. the ability to be drawn out into long elastic threads.

The cause of the viscosity of so dilute a solution as saliva is not understood. Gottschalk (1961) suggested that the mutual repulsion of the highly-ionized sialate groups at the end of the side-chains of glycoproteins would tend to keep the polypeptide core treeched and the molecule elongated. Molecules of this shape make their solution viscous by the considerable friction incurred in the movement relative to one another. There is considerable doubt, however, about the validity of this explanation of viscosity because the sialate contents of human parotid and submandibular salivas are similar whereas their viscosities are very different and the viscosity of saliva can change without the release of the sialate from the side-chains. Schrager & Oates (1971) showed that the side-chains end in sulphate groups which might perform the role originally suggested for sialate. Large numbers of water molecules become attached to the glycoproteins and the great bulk of these hydrated molecules may contribute to the viscosity of saliva, an effect not dependent on highly-charged side-chains. The viscosity and spinnbarkeit of wax-stimulated saliva are much lower than those of resting saliva collected by draining from the mouth. It may be speculated that the high viscosity of resting saliva may be due to an effect of rate of flow or to the fact that a higher proportion of the saliva collected in this way comes from the submandibular and sublingual glands. This does not appear to have been adequately studied perhaps because difficulties arise in measuring the saliva from submandibular and sublingual ducts owing to its consisting of an aqueous and semi-gelatinous phase and also the rapidity with which its viscosity changes.

The relative viscosities of the three main secretions after acetic acid stimulation were found by Schneyer (1955) to be: parotid 1·5, submaxillary 3·4, and sublingual 13·4.

THE BUFFERING POWER OF SALIVA

The buffering power (the power to resist changes of pH when acid or alkali are added) of a complex solution like saliva will vary at different pH values because different systems of buffers are effective over different parts of the pH range. Salivary buffers consist of bicarbonates, phosphates and proteins. This has been shown by Lilenthal (1955), who measured the buffering power of saliva before and after the removal of bicarbonate by a current of CO_2-free air at pH 5, and before and after dialysis, which removed both phosphates and bicarbonate but which does not remove the larger proteins.

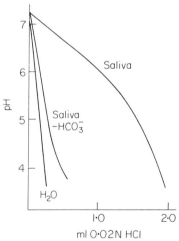

FIG. IX.11. Buffering curve of wax-stimulated saliva (pH plotted against volume of acid added) compared with that of distilled water and saliva from which bicarbonate had been removed. These curves show that bicarbonate is the most important buffer in saliva (after Lilienthal (1955), confirmed in the author's laboratory).

Removal of the bicarbonate greatly reduced the buffering power (Fig. IX.11) and dialysis removed the whole of it. He concluded that bicarbonate is the most important buffer, that phosphate plays some part, but that, contrary to previous views, the proteins can be disregarded as buffers in saliva over the physiological pH range, but are the chief buffers of plaque (see pp. 393–4). Buffers work by converting any highly ionized acid or alkali which is tending to alter the pH of a solution, into a more weakly-ionized substance (that is, one which releases fewer H^+ or OH^- ions). Bicarbonates release the weak carbonic acid when an acid is added and since this acid is rapidly decomposed into water and CO_2, which leaves the solution, the result is not the accumulation of a weaker acid (as with most buffers) but the complete removal of acid. Bicarbonates are therefore very effective buffers against acid and are important in reducing pH changes in plaque after meals. Unstimulated saliva, which has a much lower bicarbonate content, is a less powerful buffer near neutrality.

Ericsson (1959) studied the diurnal variation in buffering power of saliva in five subjects. He found that (1) it was high immediately on rising in the morning, but rapidly fell; (2) it increased about a quarter of an hour after meals but usually fell within half to one hour after meals; and (3) there was an upward trend in the buffering power throughout the day until evening when it usually tended to fall.

THE REDUCING POWER OF SALIVA

In any complex biological system like saliva with its teeming flora, some chemical reactions in progress will be oxidations and others reductions. The algebraic sum of these reactions is such that mixed saliva normally has reducing properties.

In addition to bacterial reductions, saliva contains a complex mixture of substances with reducing properties which have been mistakenly assumed in the past to be glucose. These reducing substances are present in saliva collected from the duct as well as in 'mouth' saliva. They include carbohydrate split off from glycoproteins, nitrites and some unidentified substances of low molecular weight.

The Secretion of Saliva

Factors controlling the rate of flow

Saliva seems to be unique among the digestive juices in that its secretion is controlled exclusively by nerves. No hormone has been discovered which controls specifically its rate of flow, although hormones may alter its composition (see p. 316) and the hormones of the thyroid gland and suprarenal cortex influence the general activity of the gland (Osorio 1960). There is some unconfirmed evidence that the posterior pituitary secretion may increase the rate of flow in the sheep, presumably by stimulating the myoepithelial cells. The hypersecretion sometimes occurring in pregnancy (p. 324) indicates an influence of sex hormones. A polypeptide has been isolated from rat and bovine hypothalamic tissue which is a powerful stimulant of saliva flow in the rat but its physiological significance is not known (Leeman & Hammerschlag 1967).

THE 'RESTING FLOW'
In man, unlike anaesthetized animals, the salivary glands are always secreting under waking conditions, even in the absence of obvious stimuli, although it is difficult to be certain that feeble, undetected stimuli are not present. The 'resting flow' of saliva may be studied by means of a Lashley cannula, in a subject who is accustomed to using it. A simpler method consists of spitting out at intervals for, say, 5 minutes, during which the attention is directed away from thoughts of salivation by reading. Another procedure is to allow saliva to drain directly into a beaker from the open mouth with the head bent forward to a horizontal position. It is difficult to direct attention away from salivation in this method, and mouth breathing must be avoided otherwise the dry mouth reflex (see p. 344) will stimulate the salivary flow. The method used affects the results, draining giving a lower and spitting a higher quantity. The flow-rate is presumably influenced by the amount of disturbance in the mouth, although it is possible that the very viscid, resting saliva is incompletely removed by draining.

Becks (1939) who studied the resting flow of forty individuals on five occasions spread over 2 years, found that there is great variation in the rate of flow between different individuals, but that any one individual is fairly consistent in his rate of output on different days.

In another study on over 600 subjects, the average rate was 19 ml h^{-1} and the range 0·5–111 ml h^{-1} (Becks & Wainwright 1943). When the individual glands are considered, the average resting rate of the submandibular gland is about three times that of the parotid (Fig. IX.10).

The possible causes of this individual variation was studied by Ericson (1971) who measured the correlation between parotid flow-rate stimulated by citric acid and thirty other variables including general health, body weight and sensitivity to taste. The flow-rate was significantly related to the subjective assessment of the acid taste and negatively correlated with age but the only variable with a highly significant correlation with flow-rate was the size of the parotid gland as measured radiographically after the injection of radiopaque material up the duct. These factors did not account for all the variance, implying that some influences on flow-rate have still not been detected.

Two early observations made on human subjects with fistulous openings of their parotid ducts suggested that saliva did not flow without stimuli, although in diseased glands the amount of functioning tissue may be less than usual. Schneyer *et al.* (1956) confirmed this conclusion by studying the flow from the glands separately during sleep. There was no detectable flow from the parotid in three subjects, only a trace (0·2 ml h^{-1}) from the sublingual in the one subject tested, and 1·0 ml h^{-1} from the submandibular gland. The appliance may have acted as a stimulus as it did lead to disturbed sleep. Schneyer concludes that there is probably no true resting secretion and Kerr (1960) found that the resting secretion ceased after an injection of atropine, strongly suggesting that impulses in the parasympathetic nerves are essential for it. Even the onset of drowsiness during prolonged experiments on saliva collection is accompanied by a reduction in the rate of flow.

Experiments on anaesthetized animals show that, in most species, the major glands do not secrete unless a stimulus is applied; in contrast, the parotid of ruminants, the sublingual in dogs, cats and rats secrete even when dissected out and suspended in an oxygenated artificial medium (Emmelin 1953, 1972). The mucous glands of the human palate also secrete spontaneously since biopsy specimens, if kept under suitable conditions, become covered with a film of mucoid (Östland 1953).

Dehydration reduces the resting flow-rate; the results of drinking large volumes of water are uncertain, one experiment showing no difference while in another the resting rate almost trebled after drinking 2 l. of water in 10 min. The average rate of flow of unstimulated parotid saliva in one experiment in Texas, USA decreased in summer from 0·046 to 0·03 ml min^{-1}, possibly related to dehydration arising from high temperatures (Shannon 1966).

Unpractised subjects frequently experience difficulty in collecting resting saliva because the rate is so slow that they more or less subconsciously apply stimuli to increase the secretion. For this reason, and because of the volume which can be readily collected, most work on human saliva in relation to dental conditions has been carried out on saliva secreted in response to the mastication of paraffin wax or rubber bands. Wax is known to take up some organic constituents of saliva, a point which does not appear to have been tested with rubber bands but this product often contains more froth than with wax. Rubber bands are easier to control because by using one, two or more bands the intensity of the stimulation can be readily altered. Becks (1939) and Wainright (1939) studied the rate of flow of wax-stimulated saliva in the forty subjects mentioned above and found that the range of variation was smaller in the stimulated samples (46–249 ml hr^{-1}) which means that stimulation tends to minimize the differences in rates of flow between different people, just as it does for calcium content (p. 297). Although most subjects who were slow producers of resting saliva also had an output lower than average for stimulated saliva and vice versa, there were some exceptions. The response to stimulation was less consistent on different days for any one individual than was the resting flow although the contrary result was obtained by Bates & Adams (1968) on ten subjects studied on ten occasions. In at least one respect, and possibly in two (depending upon whether further work does or does not confirm the greater constancy in flow rate of resting saliva), the output of stimulated saliva is less characteristic of an individual than is the output of resting saliva. Since the aim of most investigations is to find out whether the saliva from people with some dental condition, such as caries, differs from people free from that condition, it would seem desirable to use a salivary sample which emphasizes, rather than minimizes, individual differences, that is, if possible, resting saliva would seem preferable. Also, in most subjects, resting saliva is secreted for a higher proportion of the day and presumably has a greater influence on the oral environment than has stimulated saliva.

PSYCHIC FLOW

The experiments of Pavlov, which proved the existence of conditioned reflexes in the control of the salivary flow in dogs, are so well known that little need be added here. It is sufficient to say that by experience stimuli not primarily connected with food may cause a secretion of saliva in animals. Lashley (1916) found that mention of food, even to a hungry individual, had no effect on parotid flow, but the sight of food gave a positive response. He also noted that his subjects became conditioned to the sight of the bottles containing acids which he used as unconditioned stimuli.

Kerr (1960) pointed out that attempts to measure the conditioned flow of saliva in man had either been inadequately controlled or had shown that the response was negligibly small. In a study of the secretion of saliva in response to conditioned reflexes Kerr found that even in three hungry subjects watching the cooking of bacon and eggs, only a very slight response was produced in two and none in the third. One of the subjects stated that he felt his 'mouth watering' profusely during the experiment although measurements showed that his rate of flow had not increased. Kerr concluded that having one's attention drawn to food leads to a sudden awareness of saliva already present in the mouth which is interpreted as an increase in flow and described as 'mouth watering'. It is possible also that conditioned stimuli cause unconscious movements in the mouth which may squeeze out secretions in the ducts. This was indicated by Kerr's finding that the handling and unwrapping of sweets increased saliva flow very slightly, compared with resting flow, but during the following minute the resting flow fell, suggesting that a dead space emptied during the stimulus was being refilled.

Several workers have shown the existence of naturally acquired conditioned reflexes. In one experiment on over 100 students the average rate of flow was significantly greater (2·34 ml) during 5 min in which they were asked to concentrate their thoughts on food than in a similar period of resting flow (1·51 ml) (Dawes & Jenkins 1966). Holland & Matthews (1970) showed the establishment of an experimental conditioned reflex on four subjects in which a buzzer and light was accompanied by the squirting of 1 ml of orange juice on to the tongue. After ten conditioning stimuli, the buzzer and light alone increased salivation slightly (from an unrecordable rate to 20 μl min^{-1} for 30 s). It is doubtful whether these small increases of flow for such short periods would have any physiological effect but they might be large enough to account for 'mouth watering'.

UNCONDITIONED REFLEXES

The presence of food in the mouth is a powerful stimulus to salivation and experiments show that this effect is made up of three main components. First, taste forms one group of stimuli, different tastes varying in their effectiveness as stimuli. The influence of the smell of foods has not been thoroughly studied but Kerr (1960) found that inhaling air which had been bubbled through orange essence or amyl acetate had a definite but small effect in increasing rate of flow compared with the resting rate. Secondly, mechanical stimulation of the oral mucosa plays some part, but unless the food is very coarse, a small one. Thirdly, masticatory movements which normally follow the taking of food, also provide stimuli to the human parotid gland; the nature of these stimuli has been studied by Lashley and by Kerr (1960) whose main results are described below but further work is needed to establish more definitely their conclusions. The type of device usually used for collecting submandibular saliva separately has precluded an analysis of the effect of mastication on its rate of flow.

Mastication is accompanied by many sensory impulses, such as mechanical irritation of the oral mucosa, pressure on the teeth and kinaesthetic impulses from the masticatory muscles. Somewhat surprisingly, moderate mechanical irritation produces only a small response unless applied to the 'nausea areas' (for example the soft palate and the posterior part of the tongue). Violent irritation in all parts of the mouth is an effective stimulus. Lashley found that kinaesthetic impulses brought about by movement of the mandible or occlusal pressure on the teeth did not cause secretion. Lashley concluded that a 'pattern of stimuli', i.e. several stimuli applied simultaneously, was necessary for the full response to mastication. Kerr, on the other hand, who studied the effect of occlusal pressure in more detail, suggested that the *duration* and *rate of change* of pressure on the teeth were the main stimuli in mastication. He used as stimuli pieces of wax differing in size and in melting points between 39° and 56° C (equivalent to differences in hardness when at mouth temperature) and found that the larger the piece and the higher the melting point the more effective it was as a stimulus. The size would influence the number of nerve endings stimulated and possibly the duration of the stimulus and the hardness would decide whether a slowly-yielding or rapidly-yielding substance was between the teeth. The importance of pressure on the teeth was, in general, confirmed in experiments in which the periodontal membranes on one side were anaesthetized resulting in a reduction in the rate of flow to less than half that before the anaesthetic.

The flow of both resting and stimulated parotid saliva are reduced by blind-folding or darkening the room, the effect being especially marked with unstimulated—in one experiment it fell from 0·056 to 0·026 ml min^{-1} (Shannon & Suddick 1973). It is suggested that light stimuli from the retina may induce sympathetic impulses to the salivary gland so that when these are absent the flow-rate falls.

Unilateral stimuli produce a greater response on the stimulated side but some effect on the opposite side. This is an important point because an individual who for any reason prefers to chew on one side will lose much of the cleansing and protective effect of saliva on the other side of the mouth. Even if the stimuli are equal on both sides, the response may be stronger on one side than the other.

The rate of saliva flow is independent of the number of masticatory strokes when the number is in the normal range of between 40 and 80 strokes per minute; below this number, the rate of flow diminishes and if exceeded, the flow increases.

A reduction in saliva flow during stress is familiar to all; this has been studied quantitatively on students who collected stimulated and unstimulated saliva 30 min before and, at the same time of day, a week after an examination. Their rates under stress were smaller although the difference was marked only with the stimulated samples (Bates & Adams 1968).

Salivation is inhibited during muscular exercise and during the application of sensory stimuli to the skin. Mental work and emotion influence secretion rates but in some subjects it is increased and in others decreased. The acts of swallowing and yawning are followed by a transient increase in rates of flow from the parotid and then usually a compensatory pause. These changes probably arise as a result of mechanical pressure altering the dead space of the gland, rather than the true secretion rate.

Chemical stimuli vary greatly in their effectiveness. Kerr (1960) found, in a group of seventy subjects, that the average increases over the resting flow rates were: tenfold for 4% citric acid, sevenfold for 20% sodium chloride, and about fourfold for 10% sucrose, which was about the same as the maximal effect of chewing wax.

The response to 1 ml of 0·05 M citric acid was not significantly different from that of 5 ml of 0·01 M from which it may be concluded that the response depends on the number of molecules rather than on their concentration. The response increases with increasing amounts of stimulating substance (Kerr found the rate to be directly proportional to the logarithm of the strength of the stimulus).

Distension, or irritation, of the oesophagus has been found in animals to be a powerful stimulus to salivation. This would serve a useful purpose in the event of a blockage of the oesophagus for the following reason. Irritation of the oesophagus does not in itself cause peristalsis but swallowing does. The saliva reflexly produced would lead to swallowing which would initiate peristaltic waves to assist in the removal of the obstruction. In addition, the saliva would have some lubricating action.

Chronic irritation of the oesophagus, resulting from disease (for example carcinoma of the oesophagus) is often accompanied by excessive salivation.

Chemical irritation of the lining of the stomach or any other stimulus leading to nausea, is also a powerful stimulus to salivation. Since nausea is usually a prelude to vomiting, the value of saliva in diluting and washing away the irritant is obvious.

Excessive salivation is often present during pregnancy ('ptyalism' or 'hypersalivation in pregnancy').

The response of the salivary glands to drying of the mouth is described on pp. 344–5.

The fluid arising from the gingival pocket

When small strips of filter paper were placed either over the gingival crevice or pushed gently into the crevice of human subjects or anaesthetized dogs and left for 3 min, fluid was taken up by the paper, 0·1 mg being a typical amount. When a similar experiment was carried out after fluorescein had been taken by mouth, the fluorescein was detected on the paper strips, especially from those areas with inflammation in the gingival region (Fig. IX.13). Strips placed on other parts of the oral mucosa gave negative results except for the stretched mucosa over a tooth about to erupt. Experiments on subjects who had received fluorescein by mouth suggested a circadian rhythm with a maximum flow at 22.00 hr, although this point needs re-investigation with other methods of measurement. These experiments show that a fluid passes into the mouth from the epithelium of the gingival pocket; the fluid absorbed by the filter paper stained for protein by ninhydrin (Brill 1962).

Although subsequent histological study showed that the paper strips placed in the gingival pocket usually led to damage to the epithelium, which might cause a fluid exudate, this would not be expected to apply to the strips placed over the gingival crevice. It is still uncertain whether completely healthy gingivae give rise to fluid—it is certainly present in most people but this may merely be the result of the almost universal presence of some inflammation in this area.

Mechanical stimulation of the gingivae by tooth brushing, chewing a hard wax or stimulating the flow of tissue fluid by histamine injections increased the rate of flow as judged by the amount of ninhydrin stain on the filter paper strips. A dog on a hard diet with healthy gingivae produced less than a similar dog on a soft diet which led to marked inflammatory changes. There is evidence that an increased permeability of the capillaries, and especially of the venules, of the gingivae is an important factor determining the flow. If

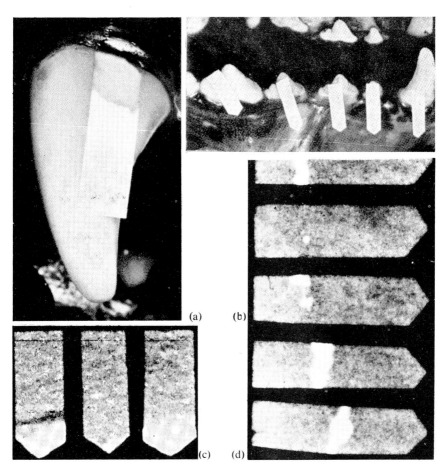

FIG. IX.12. Methods of collecting gingival fluid: (a) by placing filter paper on the crevice (intracrevicular); (b) filter paper placed over the crevice (extracrevicular); (c) the white areas represent fluorescent material recovered from the gingival crevice after it has been injected into the dog; (d) same as (c) but collected by the extracrevicular method.

Evans blue (a dye which binds to plasma proteins) is injected into dogs with healthy gingivae, no gingival fluid can be detected but as soon as mechanical stimuli are applied or histamine injected, a flow can be detected and it contains Evans blue, indicating that vascular permeability had increased sufficiently to allow the stained protein to escape.

THE COMPOSITION OF GINGIVAL FLUID
Some analyses of gingival fluid have been published (Table IX.4) and the

TABLE IX.4

Composition of gingival fluid (mg/100 ml)

Sodium	204
Potassium	70
Calcium	20
Magnesium	1
Inorganic phosphate	4
Protein (g/100 ml)	6·83

general trends of its composition are reasonablly well established. The calcium, sodium and potassium concentrations are all higher than in serum and become higher still with increased inflammation of the gingivae (Kaslick *et al.* 1970; Biswas *et al.* 1977b). They show a circadian rhythm, which is somewhat surprising if gingival fluid is an exudate since plasma levels of sodium and potassium have been stated not to be rhythmic. The sodium: potassium ratio is much lower than in plasma, probably because the fluid is passing damaged cells and taking up some of the intracellular potassium released from them.

The protein concentration is uncertain—samples collected on paper contained only about one-tenth that of plasma, whereas when collected in capillary tubes the concentrations were similar to those in plasma and from inflamed gingivae, higher than in plasma. The individual proteins detected are albumin, fibrinogen, transferrin, IgA and IgG (in the ratio of 1:8) and IgM. The IgA of gingival fluid does not contain a secretory piece (p. 293) which is not surprising since it is derived by exudation and is not secreted by specialized cells (Cimasoni 1974).

The globulins exert an antibacterial effect in the crevice supplemented by mechanical removal as the gingival fluid moves beyond the gingivae. This effect has been studied in rabbits by placing bacteria in the crevice and taking samples at intervals. Even 10 min later only 25% of the bacteria were viable and none were detectable an hour later. Leucocytes (mostly polymorphs) are present even in the absence of fluid. They have been reported also in germ-free rats.

The following enzymes have been identified in gingival fluid: acid and alkaline phosphatases, glucuronidase, various proteases, lysozyme and lactic dehydrogenase. They are usually in concentrations considerably higher than in plasma, and originate from either bacteria or lysosomes of degenerating cells. Among other organic substances are lactic acid, urea (in higher concentrations than plasma), hydroxyproline (from bacterial decomposition of collagen) and bacterial endotoxins. The high urea concentration is surprising and the following explanations have been suggested: possibly the passage of water is slower than that of the very diffusible urea or that water is reabsorbed during passage through the gingival tissue. Active transport of urea is another possibility, but most unlikely (Golub *et al.* 1971). The composition of gingival fluid collected from inflamed gingivae differs from that exuding from healthy gingivae (Biswas *et al.* 1977a). The concentrations of urea is lower and of protein, sodium and calcium are higher in fluid from inflamed tissue.

The total volume of saliva secreted

It is often stated that the total volume of saliva amounts to between 1·0 and 1·5 l. a day although the basis for this figure is obscure. It is much higher than would be expected from published data on the rates of flow under varied conditions. If we assume an average resting flow-rate of 20 ml hr^{-1} (approximating to that found by Becks and Wainwright) for 15 hours a day, the volume is 300 ml. If a generous estimate of 2 hr is taken for the time spent eating, this would amount to about another 300 ml and the secretion during sleep (say, 20 ml) gives a total of 620 ml per day. This agrees reasonably well with the measured volume of about 500 ml obtained by McKeown & Dunstone (1959) on two patients with oesophageal fistulae.

The nervous control of secretion

THE DOUBLE NERVE SUPPLY
The salivary glands receive a double nerve supply (1) from the parasympathetic (a branch of the facial nerve to the sublingual and submandibular and a branch of the glossopharyngeal to the parotid), and (2) from the sympathetic (fibres arising between the first and fourth thoracic segments and relaying in the superior sympathetic ganglion). There is still uncertainty about the detailed distribution of nerves to the salivary glands. In animals, nerve sections which would be expected to stop secretion frequently only reduce it, indicating the existence in some animals of subsidiary nerve pathways (Holmberg 1972).

The significance of the double nerve supply to the salivary glands has been the subject of much discussion and experiment. The cells of the various types of ducts are also innervated, in some species, more densely than the cells of the acini. This topic is complicated by species differences and as it is not known how much of the large mass of recorded data on animals refers to man, it will be dealt with briefly here. A full account of earlier work on nerve stimulation will be found in Burgen & Emmelin (1961). The main possible interpretations of the double nerve supply are as follows.

(1) Secretory cells are supplied by both types of fibre. In Heidenhain's (1878) view, the parasympathetic fibres are 'secretory', since electrical stimulation in dogs led to a profuse flow of saliva containing little organic matter, and the sympathetic fibres are 'trophic', that is, stimulation causes an increased concentration of the organic constituents. In the dog parotid, for example, sympathetic stimulation produces no saliva but does increase the concentra-

tion of organic matter in saliva secreted in response to parasympathetic stimulation. Langenskiold (1942) and Emmelin (1955) found that if the parasympathetic nerves are stimulated maximally and, while the potential changes in the gland are recorded, a sympathetic stimulus is also applied simultaneously, the record does not change. This result indicates that both stimuli reached the same cells and, since the parasympathetic stimuli were maximal, additional stimuli from the sympathetic had no effect. If the two stimuli reach different cells the effect of the sympathetic stimulus would have been expected to be superimposed on that of the parasympathetic when the second stimulus was applied.

(2) Serous cells receive one type of nerve fibre and mucous cells the other. Histological work has given some support to this view but unexpected species differences have been reported on which type of cell receives the sympathetic or parasympathetic nerves. For example, in the cat, stimulation of the parasympathetic nerves to the submandibular gland produces a flow of thick mucous saliva and stimulation of sympathetic causes a thin watery flow, whilst the opposite result is obtained in the dog.

(3) Some of the nerves may be wholly or partly concerned with control of the blood vessels, which do receive both sympathetic constrictor fibres and parasympathetic dilator fibres. The constrictors are more likely to be concerned with general blood pressure control than with salivary gland function. It is possible that chemical transmitters released from vasomotor fibres may diffuse to the secreting cells of the gland in sufficient concentration to stimulate them.

(4) Some of the nerve fibres may contract the myoepithelial cells present in the gland and expel the saliva already formed. Bradykinin and kallikrein produced contraction of myoepithelial cells and the very high pressures recorded in the salivary ducts in the classical experiments of Ludwig (1851) may have been partly caused by myoepithelial cells (Emmelin *et al.* 1970).

The evidence may be summarized in general as follows (although species differences exist). The parasympathetic nerves are probably secretory and vasodilator and the sympathetic contain vasoconstrictor fibres, increase the concentration of protein in the secretion and in some glands in some species stimulation may produce a small volume of concentrated secretion.

Direct information on the functions of the nerves to the salivary glands in man is not available but can be deduced indirectly by observations on the effects of drugs. Drugs which produce effects similar to those of stimulation of parasympathetic nerves produce a copious watery secretion, which implies that the parasympathetic nerves control the serous glands. The composition of saliva produced by pilocarpine differs from that at the same rate of flow responding to taste stimuli. The chorda nerve appears to have been stimulated experimentally only once in man, by Diamont *et al.* (1959) but they did not comment on the type of saliva which was secreted.

In one experiment on human subjects, adrenaline injections in sufficient dosage to have marked circulatory effects did not have detectable effects on saliva flow. In another experiment, an increased flow occurred from the submandibular gland but not from the parotid and in yet another, the parotid flow was reduced by adrenaline. The influence of the sympathetic has also been studied in human subjects by sudden body cooling (immersing up to the waist in water at 4–5° C) while subjects were secreting parotid saliva in response to acid stimulation. The effect on flow rate varied but the amylase concentration increased following the sympathetic stimulation and decreased when the β-adrenergic blocker, propranolol, was administered (Speirs *et al.* 1974).

THE MOTIVE FORCE FOR SECRETION

Ludwig (1851), in a famous experiment, found that if the submandibular duct of a dog was clamped during secretion, the pressure could reach values higher than that in the femoral artery (he did not measure the blood pressure in the salivary gland). He concluded, and most workers have accepted, that hydrostatic pressure of the blood to the salivary gland was not the motive force of secretion because it could be exceeded by the gland cells.

However, if the artery to the rat submandibular is ligated, the saliva flow falls to about one-third within 0·5 min and ceases altogether within 3 min. Lack of oxygen would not be expected to have such rapid effects suggesting that hydrostatic pressure or the immediate supply of fluid does play a part. Also, if the saliva and venous blood from the salivary gland are made to flow into open tubes raised step by step so that a head of pressure develops, the flow of both gradually falls and eventually ceases, when the pressure of the saliva is slightly below, or the same as, that of the venous blood (Shannon 1974). This suggests that the hydrostatic pressure of the blood is an important motive force for salivary secretion and that Ludwig's experiment was wrongly interpreted. This may have arisen because (1) systemic blood pressure and that in the salivary gland may not be the same (2) the build-up of pressure in a clamped duct may not be a satisfactory model for the transfer of secretion into open ducts or (3) contraction of myoepithelial cells, known to be stimulated by kallikrein, or the secretion of zymogen granules could conceivably have contributed to the pressure in the closed system of Ludwig's experiment (Shannon *et al.* 1974).

Stimulation of the chorda tympani produces a marked vasodilation in the gland the nature of which has been widely discussed. Some have thought that the chorda contains dilator fibres but the dilation, unlike the secretion, is not inhibited by atropine, suggesting that the vasodilation results from the accumulation of metabolites. Hilton & Lewis (1955) showed that chorda stimulation in the cat releases an enzyme or activator (kallikrein) which reacts with globulins in the plasma which have escaped into the tissue fluid of the gland to release a vasodilator polypeptide called bradykinin (also known as kallidin) and this substance could explain the vasodilation. Calcium is necessary for the secretion of the enzyme and is also believed to have a role in stabilizing the intracellular granules containing kallikrein (Gautvik *et al.* 1972). The role of kallikrein has been questioned, however, because the parasympathetic nerves still cause vasodilation after the glands have been desensitized to kallikrein or after the depletion of the gland of this substance which occurs if the duct is ligated. The view that the parasympathetic nerve contains active vasodilator fibres has been revived and its insensitivity to atropine has been explained either from the known variability of the receptors to this drug or possibly by the existence of adrenergic fibres in the chorda nerve. A complication, which makes the reasoning uncertain, is that duct ligation increases the sensitivity of the blood vessels to the dilating action of bradykinin; thus the increased sensitivity might nullify the effect of the reduced concentration (Hilton & Torres 1970).

EFFECTS OF DENERVATION

Denervation of the glands in animals does not necessarily lead to their permanent inactivity. As already mentioned, some of the glands can secrete spontaneously without nerve impulses and a day or two after nerve section, secretion may continue probably from the release of acetyl choline and noradrenaline from the degenerating nerve endings. Claude Bernard, in 1862, described a 'paralytic secretion'—in some circumstances, a denervated gland becomes hypersensitive to adrenaline and noradrenaline released into the circulation from other organs.

ELECTRICAL CHANGES IN THE SALIVARY GLANDS DURING STIMULATION

Records were made by Langenskiold (1942) and Lundberg (1958) of the electrical changes occurring during stimulation of the cat submandibular gland with one electrode on the surface and the other in the hilus of the gland. The parasympathetic produces a somewhat variable result but in general the hilus becomes positive at first, and then may be either slightly positive or negative, followed by a positive wave at the end of stimulation ('off-effect'). Sympathetic stimulation produces a rapid then a slower positive wave with a gradual return to the baseline, without an off-effect. In dogs the wave is of similar shape but of opposite sign.

When micro-electrodes are introduced into the cells of the salivary glands of the cat, the resting potential of the acinar cell is about -30 mV. After stimulation, this changes to between -50 and -60 mV, possibly as a result of the loss of potassium from the cell as the stimulation makes the membrane more permeable. In a perfused gland, changes in the potassium concentration of the perfusing fluid had more effect on the potential of the cells than that of any other ion.

Two separate types of experiment have shown that sympathetic stimuli cause
an increased size of the submandibular gland in rats but their significance in
man is quite unknown. Repeated cutting of the incisor teeth leads to enlarged
glands but the effect is prevented by removal of the sympathetic supply. The
effect is more complicated than a mere stimulation of saliva flow by pain or
irritation. A somewhat similar enlargement of the glands occurs after injection
of large doses of isoproterenol—an analogue of adrenaline.

The number of mitoses and size of the rat parotid gland are greatly influenced by the number of stimuli it receives. On a hard or bulky diet, requiring
vigorous mastication, mitoses increased whereas on a milk diet even for only
4 days, they decreased and the parotid weight may fall by 35% and be
restored to normal if the hard diet is resumed. Section of the nerve supply
also reduces parotid weight, removal of the parasympathetic having a
greater effect than the sympathetic. It is possible that the nerve stimulation
leads to depletion of amylase stores which are in some way linked to mitosis;
a correlation has been observed between effects of drugs on amylase depletion
in the parotid and on mitosis (Schneyer 1974).

THE NATURE OF THE SECRETORY PROCESS
Electron micrographs have made it possible to picture the main sequence of
events during the process of secretion although the great species differences
make it impossible to generalize.

The basal side of the glandular and duct cells are elaborately infolded thus
giving the appearance of presenting an increased surface area—even up to
sixty-fold—which presumably facilitates the uptake of water and dissolved
substances from the tissue fluid. Mitochondria are sometimes, but not always,
closely associated with the infoldings. Absorption may also occur by 'pino-
cytosis' or 'cell drinking' which is the formation of small vesicles on the cell
wall that contain dissolved substances and are transferred across the wall.

The endoplasmic reticulum is concerned with the synthesis of proteins
including the enzymes and mucoids of the saliva which are released as microsomes. When ^{14}C-labelled amino acids are injected, the microsomes contain
labelled amylase within 5–10 min. It is probable that the newly-synthesized
protein molecules are transported to the Golgi apparatus which converts them
into the secretion granules so well shown by the light microscope. This is supported by the finding that 2 hr after the injection of labelled amino acids, the
secretion granules contain the greater part of the labelled amylase. The energy
for the synthesis is provided by oxidative phosphorylation occurring in the
mitochondria.

The number of granules increases after various procedures such as injection
of pilocarpine or adrenaline which increase secretion.

In the parotid gland (as in the pancreas) synthesis of amylase appears to be independent of nerve control and is regulated by a chemical equilibrium so that when stores are depleted after secretion, more synthesis occurs. In the submandibular and sublingual glands, however, synthesis is increased by pilocarpine, or by eating (which causes nerve stimulation) and is prevented by atropine (Schneyer & Schneyer 1961). These observations strongly suggest that in these glands synthesis is under nervous control. Amylase can be detected

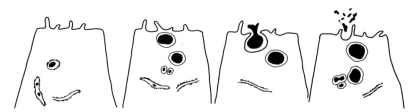

FIG. IX.13. Successive stages (from left to right) in one method of extrusion of secretion granules observed in the salivary glands.

Saliva

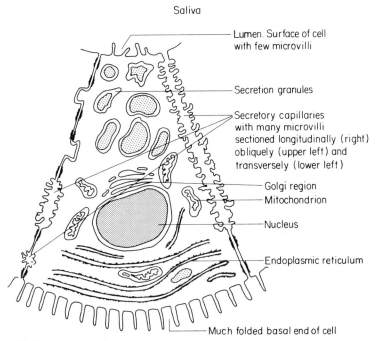

Lumen. Surface of cell with few microvilli

Secretion granules

Secretory capillaries with many microvilli sectioned longitudinally (right) obliquely (upper left) and transversely (lower left)

Golgi region

Mitochondrion

Nucleus

Endoplasmic reticulum

Much folded basal end of cell

FIG. IX.14. Diagram of the main features common to most secretory cells of the salivary glands based upon electron microscope studies. These cells show considerable species differences and in some species (for example mice) differ in the two sexes.

histochemically in the acini of the human parotid and the serous cells of the submandibular glands but some regions show more activity than others; the gland does not appear to act as a whole but some regions secrete while others are at rest presumably synthesizing enzyme for future use. No amylase activity is detectable in the minor human glands nor in any glands of the dog.

Several types of extrusion mechanisms have been described from electron micrographs of various secreting cells; the one most frequently seen in the salivary glands is as follows. In the cytoplasm a secretion granule forms, the outer membrane of which approaches and fuses with the microvilli of the inner secreting surface of the cell. The membrane then ruptures allowing the contents of the granule to escape. What was the wall of the secretion granule then straightens out and becomes a new part of the cell wall (Fig. IX.13).

The 'secretory capillaries' between the serous cells (Fig. IX.14) have many microvilli projecting into them (unlike the inner surface of the cells on which microvilli were found to be rather sparse) and this is presumably the route by which some of the products reach the lumen.

MYOEPITHELIAL CELLS

The flow of saliva is affected, not only by nerves which alter the rate of secretion by the gland cells, but also by the contraction of the myoepithelial cells which surround the cells of the acini and the ducts. This would probably lead to a more rapid entry of saliva into the mouth than would occur if it depended only on secretion from the glands. They may also facilitate secretion, particularly of very viscid saliva, by keeping the walls of the ducts more rigid and thus maintain a secretory pressure. They contain myosin which is presumably responsible for their contraction. Single parasympathetic stimuli to all three salivary glands in cats cause a rise in pressure in the duct, which is abolished by atropine. However, such stimuli were stated by Emmelin *et al.* (1968) to produce secretion only exceptionally and they concluded that the rise in pressure was caused by the contraction of the myoepithelial cells. Single sympathetic stimuli had no effect in cats, although other evidence does suggest that myoepithelial cells receive a sympathetic supply (and this is certainly true in dogs). Others have denied that single shocks do not stimulate secretion and consider that the secretion explains the rise in pressure (Darke & Smaje 1971).

THE INITIATION OF THE SECRETION

Acetyl choline is thought to initiate the secretion by greatly increasing the blood flow and by increasing the permeability of the cell membrane, perhaps by some conformational change in its proteins. Some experiments suggest that calcium ions are also concerned with the control of secretion, as they are in the pancreas, although perfusion with a calcium-free fluid did not inhibit secretion. However, acetyl choline enhanced the release of ^{45}Ca from a gland previously exposed to it, suggesting that this stimulus releases calcium from stores in their microsomes, known to be capable of binding calcium. The calcium thus released may then trigger the secretion or may be concerned with maintaining normal permeability. There is evidence that adenyl cyclase is activated by sympathetic (but not parasympathetic) stimuli producing an increased concentration of cyclic AMP which in turn stimulates secretion of amylase. The action of cAMP on secretion from parotid slices, but not the action of adenyl cyclase, is dependent on the presence of calcium in the medium to maintain the calcium concentration of the cell (salivary cells contain higher concentrations than most cells, probably attached to secretion granules). A suggested role for calcium is that it either alters the permeability of the cell membrane or affects the surface of the granules of the amylase precursor so

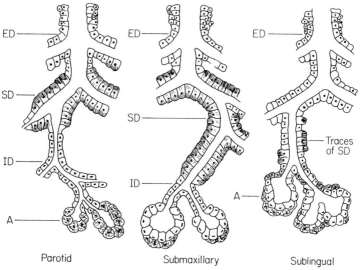

Parotid   Submaxillary   Sublingual

Fig. IX.15. The distribution of the salivary ducts in the various salivary glands. ED—Excretory duct, SD—striated duct, ID—intercalated duct (absent in some species from sublingual), A—acinus containing serous cells (in the parotid) or serous and mucous cells (submandibular).

that they interact with the cell membrane leading to exocytosis (Fig. IX.13). That calcium has more than one action is shown by the effect of diffusing the submandibular ducts with a solution containing complexing agents which remove calcium ions—after which the absorption of sodium and secretion of potassium by the ducts are both increased (Thorn 1974).

THE SALIVARY DUCTS AND THEIR ROLE IN MODIFYING SECRETION
The salivary glands contain three types of duct differing in their distribution in the various salivary glands and in their histological structure (Fig. IX.15).

Leading directly from the acini are the narrow 'intercalated' ducts lined by cubical epithelium; these lead into the 'striated' or 'secretory ducts' which are wider and are lined by cells containing 'rods', which electron micrographs have shown to consist of mitochondria aligned in a much folded basal wall, and finally there are the excretory ducts lined by clear cubical epithelium.

There is good evidence that, at least in some glands of some species, the ducts play as important a part in forming the secretion as do the acini. This concept, of a secretion formed by the acini but modified as it passes through the ducts, is referred to as the two-stage hypothesis. Several methods have been used to study the effects of the ducts. (1) The first is the 'stop-flow' technique, in which the mouth of the duct is closed and the secretion is not allowed to escape from the duct for several minutes (thus allowing the duct cells to exert their absorbing or secreting effects for much longer than usual). The flow is released and the secretion is then collected in serial fractions so that the fluid in distal, middle and proximal parts can be analysed separately and the effect of each part of the duct can be worked out. This method has now been replaced by (2) micropuncture of various parts of the duct system and analysis of the minute quantities of fluid which collect over, say, 5 min (Martinez *et al.* 1966). This technique has been applied to the acini of all three glands in the rat, and to the submandibular and sublingual in the cat and the parotid in man (Knauf & Fromter 1970). The results show that the fluid secreted by the acini is isotonic or slightly hypotonic, sodium and chloride being the ions in highest concentration. Its composition is independent of rate of flow or whether stimulated by the sympathetic or parasympathetic nerves. From what is known or speculated about the composition of extracellular fluid and of the cell contents it can be deduced that sodium and chloride diffuse into the cell at the serosal side but are actively secreted into the lumen, the reverse being true of chloride and potassium (Fig. IX.16). These are the net changes— even when sodium is actively secreted there may be some uptake in the reverse direction. The striated ducts of the submaxillary gland show histological changes after stimulation of both sympathetic and parasympathetic nerves suggestive of the secretion of material stored in the cells. (3) Perfusion of the ducts. Owing to their position deep in the glands the striated ducts cannot be located in the intact gland so that micropuncture has not been possible. However, microcannulae can be passed up the ducts almost to the level of the striated region so that their contents can be collected. The accessible excretory ducts can be perfused with various solutions both *in situ* and *in vitro* and the changes they undergo during passage through the ducts can be studied.

There is no evidence that water is added to the secretion by the ducts. Although there are species differences and variation in different glands, typical findings are that when unstimulated glands are perfused, the concentrations of sodium and chloride fall in the excretory duct fluid whereas those of

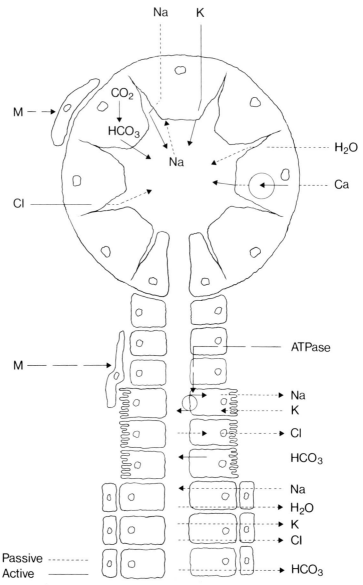

Fɪɢ. IX.16. Diagram of some of the postulated active and passive movements of ions into the acini of the salivary glands and across various parts of the walls of the ducts (m = myoepithelial cells).

potassium and bicarbonate rise but to a smaller extent so that the osmotic pressure falls. After stimulation, only the striated ducts modify the composition and their effect is smaller than those of the excretory ducts on unstimulated secretion.

These changes in composition might be brought about in several ways but the combined evidence of all the above methods suggest that the ducts absorb sodium (actively) and chloride (passively), are highly impermeable to water and secrete potassium and bicarbonate actively so that concentrations in saliva of the two latter frequently exceed those of plasma. These are net changes, some sodium may be secreted but in smaller amounts than that absorbed. Active transport may be carried out by an enzyme, Na^+K^+ATPase, known to be in the membranes of many cells including those of the salivary glands. This magnesium-dependent enzyme provides energy, by the breakdown of ATP, with which it transports Na^+ out of, and K^+ into, the cells against concentration gradients: Na^+ is affected more than K^+. The absorption is proportional to the rate of flow and is believed to be under nervous control so that flow-rate and the secretion of these ions both increase in response to nerve stimuli. At very low flow-rates the sodium concentration tends to rise, possibly because at the distal end of the excretory duct the absorptive mechanism is lacking and the contents of the ducts tend to equilibrate with plasma. For the same reason the concentration of constituents which are higher on the saliva tend to fall.

Carbonic anhydrase is present in salivary glands and may be presumed to play a part in the production of bicarbonate from carbon dioxide. Nevertheless, an inhibitor of this enzyme has not, in most experiments, blocked bicarbonate transport in the ducts. It is possible that the enzyme is not accessible to the inhibitor in the intact gland.

As mentioned above (p. 328) stimulation of the sympathetic β-receptors also causes secretion, at least in some species (for example rat submandibular but not human parotid). The composition of the secretion is quite different from that produced by parasympathetic stimuli and is affected much more by the rate of flow. It is virtually an isotonic solution of potassium bicarbonate with about one-tenth the concentration of sodium and chloride along with higher concentrations of the organic constituents than in the parasympathetic secretion.

The composition of saliva produced by sympathetic or parasympathetic stimulation in the rat differ although, as mentioned above, micropuncture studies show that the primary secretion has the same composition whichever type of stimulus is used. The differences in the final composition can be explained on the two-stage hypothesis by assuming that the volume of primary secretion from sympathetic stimulation is much lower (one-eighth) than from parasympathetic stimulation but that both stimuli increase the secretion of potassium and bicarbonate from the ducts to about the same extent. This would mean that with sympathetic stimulation, potassium and bicarbonate would be added to a small volume of primary fluid and therefore have a large effect on its composition. Parasympathetic stimulation would be adding the same absolute amounts to eight times the volume of primary fluid with correspondingly smaller effects on its composition. Perfusion experiments on the ducts with drugs which mimic the effects of autonomic stimulation have supported these concepts (Young & Martin 1972; Martin *et al.* 1972). Sympathetic stimulation increases both the protein synthesis within the gland and the transfer of organic substances. The ducts are affected by hormones concerned with ion transport. Aldosterone increases the ability of the duct cells to absorb sodium and secrete potassium and antidiuretic hormone stimulates sodium absorption.

AN ALTERNATIVE TO THE TWO-STAGE HYPOTHESIS

The data of Shannon *et al.* (1974) on the composition of human parotid saliva at different flow-rates are not in good agreement with the two-stage hypothesis based largely on animal experiments. They believe that the secretory cells of the parotid acini produce a hypotonic secretion without the intervention of the ducts by the following sequence of events. Stimulation results in (1) a rise in hydrostatic pressure of vascular origin, and (2) increased permeability of the interstitial (i.e. the non-secreting) surfaces of the cell leading to an influx of fluid containing Na^+ into the cell. This leads to (3) an increased activity of the $Na^+K^+ATPase$ pump which expels Na^+ into the interstitial fluid and absorbs K^+ from it, thus preventing an excess of Na^+ in the cell. The influx of fluid then leads to the secretion of hypotonic fluid low in Na^+ into the lumen.

Functions of Saliva

Saliva has many functions and, although not essential for the maintenance of life, it makes important and varied contributions to the efficient working and protection of the body.

Digestive functions

The only important digestive enzyme present in saliva is ptyalin or salivary amylase. This enzyme digests starch provided it has been previously cooked; heat breaks up the outer envelope of starch granules, after which their contents form a colloidal suspension which the enzyme can attack. The envelope does not consist of cellulose, as frequently stated, but of a specially insoluble type of starch which is made soluble by heat.

Starch consists of two polysaccharides: amylose, an unbranched chain made up of glucose molecules linked in the 1:4 position and amylopectin, a molecule in which at approximately every twenty-five of the glucose units a branch occurs at the 1:6 link.

Amylases are of two types originally known as α- and β-amylases, now designated more exactly as α-1:4 glucan-4-glucanohydrolase and α-1:4 glucan-maltohydrolase.

α-Amylase attacks randomly the 1:4 bonds between the glucose molecules in amylose and amylopectin. The end-products are maltose, some glucose from amylopectin and some 'limit dextrins' which contain bonds at the 1:6 position and are therefore not broken down by this enzyme. An α-dextrinase (also known as isomaltase) in the intestinal mucosal cells breaks down the limit dextrins to glucose. Salivary amylase is entirely of this type, like other animal amylases. β-Amylases are found in plants and may be present in the mouth from bacteria. They attack the starch by breaking off maltose units one at a time, thus gradually reducing the size of the molecule.

The course of the reaction may be followed from the changes in the reaction of the products with iodine and the gradual build-up of reducing sugars. It is doubtful whether the action of amylase is sufficiently prolonged in the mouth or stomach for the final stage to be reached, but this is unimportant as the digestion of carbohydrate is completed by means of the enzymes in the pancreatic and intestinal juices.

There are up to six (one report suggests up to eight) isoenzymes of salivary amylase; submandibular amylases consists of two groups, one with and another without 6 moles of carbohydrate in the molecules (mol. wt 67 000 and 62 000 respectively).

While the major isoenzymes are probably genetic variations some may be artefacts formed during experimental procedures or result from ageing changes analogous to those known to occur in some other enzymes.

Wheat endosperm (i.e. the inner, starch-containing part of the grain) contains an amylase inhibitor. If saliva is incubated with bread or wheat flour, somewhat less digestion can be detected than with purified wheat starch, although its effect is probably too small to be of practical importance. The amylase inhibitor is a basic protein (mol. wt 26 300) which combines with the enzyme and prevents its access to starch, and is digested by the gastric juice so that it will have no effect in the intestine but presumably is active in the mouth; this does not seem to have been investigated.

The optimum pH of salivary amylase under conditions in the mouth is 6·8 but this enzyme is unusual in that the optimum pH depends on the anions present. If saliva is dialysed to remove the ions, the amylase activity is greatly reduced and the optimum pH is lowered to about 6·0. The activity is almost fully restored, and the optimum pH raised to 6·8, by the addition of chloride ions to the dialysed saliva. The optimum pH can be altered by the addition of ions other than chloride to dialysed saliva but none of the ions studied restores as much activity as do chloride ions. Calcium is also a cofactor but is probably bound too tightly to the amylase for dialysis to remove it.

The amylase activity of saliva from different individuals shows great variation. Low amylase activity will no more than delay the digestion of starch since pancreatic juice contains powerful amylase activity. Activity has been found to be low before breakfast and to rise during the morning with a less consistent tendency to fall during the rest of the day. Parotid saliva has a concentration at least four times that of submandibular saliva and extracts of human sublingual glands (post-mortem material) contain no activity at all (Jacobsen 1970). The effect of flow-rate on amylase concentration is uncertain: some workers have found that it is not affected but more recent results suggest a rise in concentration as the flow rate increases. With mixed saliva, however, the activity rises with increased rates of flow; this occurs because the proportion of the more active parotid saliva increases with increased stimuli. Sucrose and salt produce a higher amylase activity than other taste stimuli in the parotid (Newbrun 1962). Crystalline salivary amylase has been prepared and it is similar to pancreatic amylase but electrophoretic studies show that the two enzymes are not identical. Amylase is stated to be absent from the salivas of the cat and dog and this is probably true of other carnivorous animals, though few have been tested.

It is clear that food remains in the mouth for too short a time to allow much digestion of starch to occur. However, after a large meal, the pH of the food which enters the stomach last remains nearly neutral for up to 30 min or more, during which amylase activity may continue. Once the gastric hydrochloric acid soaks into the food and lowers the pH, amylase is inactivated and is eventually digested by pepsin, like any other protein.

It is possible that the main action of salivary amylase is to digest starch from food residues which remain in the mouth after meals, rather than to contribute to digestion as a whole.

The antibacterial function of saliva

Although bacteria are always present, wounds in the mouth rarely become infected (Radden 1962). This fact suggests that saliva contains some means of keeping in check harmful bacteria and that the organisms normally present in the mouth are those which have become resistant to salivary inhibition.

Many antibacterial actions of saliva have been observed but opinions differ as to their relative importance. Dog saliva inhibits many bacteria more powerfully than does human, and this is believed to account at least partly for the freedom of the dog from dental caries.

Saliva has some mechanical action in removing bacteria from the mouth and conveying them to the stomach where most of them are killed and digested by the gastric juice. Although bacterial growth on some surfaces of the mouth is greatly restricted by this means, it probably has little effect on the bacteria in sheltered places such as the crevices between the teeth.

Microscopical examination of smears of saliva shows the presence of phagocytic leucotyes, and although the majority are disintegrating, ingested bacteria can be demonstrated within those cells which remain alive.

LEUCOTAXIN AND OPSONINS

Two properties of saliva have been described which may be related to its antibacterial power: (1) saliva increases capillary permeability, and (2) mixed saliva possesses leucotactic activity, i.e. the power of attracting polymorpho-nuclear leucocytes (Dietz 1939), but this is absent from saliva collected from the ducts and is greatly reduced after thorough brushing of the teeth and the dorsum of the tongue. The activity returns within 1–3 hr in different indivi-duals (Wright & Tempel 1974). Evidently, the 'leucotaxin' (a polypeptide with the above properties) is produced by proteolytic enzymes of bacteria acting on the proteins of saliva. Whether the leucotaxin in saliva plays any part in the normal supply of leucocytes in the mouth is not known, but if the tissues are injured it would gain access to the damaged area and by its dual action may promote the accumulation of leucocytes. Plaque also contains a leucotaxin which can be demonstrated in extracts and is much more active than in saliva. Its presence may account for the increased number of leucocytes passing through the gingival tissue when inflamed and with much plaque present (Helldén & Lindhe 1972).

Leucocytes thoroughly washed free of plasma and suspended in saline do not phagocytose bacteria, but if a trace of plasma is added phagocytosis readily occurs. The substances in plasma which make bacteria more 'palatable' to leucocytes are called 'opsonins' now thought to be IgG, IgM and certain constituents of complement. Saliva contains opsonins, but being immunoglobu-lins, they are much less active than in plasma. Saliva from caries-free individuals has been stated to show more opsonic activity than 'caries-active' saliva (Hammond & Weinmann 1942).

In addition to the above mechanisms, saliva contains chemical substances which exert a direct bacteriocidal action. Even bacteria normally found in saliva are weakly inhibited *in vitro* but it is obvious that these organisms have at least some degree of resistance to the oral antibacterial factors, otherwise they would not survive in the mouth. There is an erratic variation in the antibacterial potency of saliva from different individuals and from the same individual at different times (Bibby *et al.* 1938).

THE NATURE OF THE ANTIBACTERIAL SUBSTANCES IN SALIVA

In 1922 Fleming discovered in tears, nasal secretion, saliva, egg white and in most tissues and body fluids a substance which dramatically kills and dissolves the organism *Micrococcus lysodeikticus* and, more slowly, many other species of bacteria. This substance is called 'lysozyme' or 'muramidase', an enzyme which splits the 1:4 links between N-acetylmuramic acid and N-acetylglucosamine, these links being present in the walls of certain bacteria the splitting of which causes their death and disintegration. If these polysaccharides are absent from a species of bacteria, then it is not destroyed by lysozyme. Saliva and gingival fluid have higher concentrations than plasma but its concentration decreases with stimulation (Helderman 1976). The effectiveness of lysozyme in saliva is probably reduced by the presence of mucin which inhibits its action (Simmons 1952). There is contradictory evidence on the effectiveness of lysozyme against the indigenous flora of the mouth; one group of workers (Gibbons *et al.* 1966) were unable to detect any effect on over 100 strains of oral bacteria but another group (Coleman *et al.* 1971) stated that the viability of most cariogenic and noncariogenic streptococci was reduced by lysozyme, although the bacteria were not fully lysed.

In addition to lysozyme, at least one other antibacterial factor exists as a normal constituent of parotid and submandibular saliva in concentrations varying sixteen-fold in different subjects. Most of the experiments have been carried out on lactobacilli but it is active on many organisms. Its activity was shown by dialysis to consist of two fractions, a small ion which dialysed and a large molecule which remained inside the dialysing membrane. The small ion was identified as thiocyanate and the non-dialysable constituent as the enzyme peroxidase (Dogon *et al.* 1962; Dogon & Amdur 1970). With hydrogen peroxide (present in saliva as a product of bacterial metabolism) these substances react to form an unstable antibacterial factor, possibly cyanosulphurous acid (HO_2SCN), cyanosulphuric acid (HO_3SCN) or sulphur dicyanoxide.

If this were the only reaction the addition of catalase (which decomposes hydrogen peroxide) would be expected to abolish the effect whereas it only reduced it, thus showing the existence of a second factor not dependent on hydrogen peroxide but also inactive without thiocyanate. Experiments with ^{14}C thiocyanate show that the product in the presence of hydrogen peroxide is volatile whereas that formed without hydrogen peroxide is not. The activity of this factor does not seem to have been compared in saliva from caries-active and caries-free subjects.

The concentration of immunoglobulins (mainly IgA) in saliva is about 1–3% that of plasma and it does not contain complement (p. 293). Gingival fluid contains IgG, IgA, IgM and complement in a ratio similar to that of plasma but only one-third the concentration (Shillitoe & Lehner 1972); they may have an action localized to the gingivae but owing to dilution by the saliva are unlikely to have much effect in the mouth generally. The concentration of IgA in both parotid and submandibular saliva falls with increased rate of flow from an average of 33 mg 100 ml^{-1} (resting flow) to 6–

7 mg 100 ml^{-1} with vigorous stimulation with acid (Mandel & Khurana 1969).

Another factor is a globulin which Green (1959) isolated from 'caries-free' saliva (but was occasionally found in low concentration in 'caries-active' saliva) which attaches itself to lactobacilli and is stated to inhibit their growth and bring about their lysis. It also has some effect on streptococci. This work contained some discrepancies and Geddes (1972) was unable to confirm it.

BACTERIAL ANTAGONISMS

Some organisms are unable to survive in the mouth because they are killed in the presence of other salivary organisms. This topic has been reviewed and new results published by Donohue & Tyler (1975). The effect has been demonstrated by pouring a suspension in agar of one species of organisms over previously grown colonies of other organisms killed by UV light. On further incubations the organisms may fail to grow in the vicinity of the dead colonies.

As well as unidentified factors, hydrogen peroxide and lactic acid (which is said to have antibacterial properties greater than can be accounted for by its pH) are products of salivary bacteria which antagonize other species in the oral flora. There is uncertainty about the extent of this antagonism *in vivo*, particularly by hydrogen peroxide which might be broken down by catalase in the plaque. However, it seems likely that, at least in some parts of the plaque, bacterial activity is kept in check by these antagonisms.

Certain oral streptococci synthesize bacteriocins—bactericidal substances which are active against some strains of the same or closely-related species as those that produce them, but not against unrelated species. Bacteriocins are produced in the mouth and they could influence the particular strains which flourish in this environment.

In germ-free rats, a mixture of three species of organisms produced less caries than any of these species alone because one of the organisms removed lactic acid which, as the main metabolic product dissolving enamel, thereby reduced the intensity of the acid attack.

There is evidence that saliva acts as a barrier to the penetration of substances into the oral mucosa. Various dyes were placed on the oral mucosa of rats and their penetration was measured in histological sections from animals killed at intervals. The penetration was much greater if saliva flow had been previously inhibited by the injection of hyoscine (Adams 1974). This work followed a previous finding that carcinogens diffused through the skin much more readily than through the oral mucosa—skin transplanted into the mouth also became more resistant to diffusion. The oral mucosa allows between ten and one hundred times as much water to pass through as the skin.

SALIVA AND BLOOD COAGULATION

When freshly-shed blood is diluted with saliva, its clotting time is reduced

(Nour-Eldin & Wilkinson 1957), an activity destroyed by trypsin but enhanced by chymotrypsin (Lundblad & Puryear 1971).

This property of saliva has been studied quantitatively by Doku (1960) whose main findings were as follows. (1) If blood is diluted with saline, the clotting time is reduced to about 40% of normal but when diluted with saliva it is reduced to 10% of normal the effect being similar whether the blood:saliva ratio was 4:1 or 1:1. (2) Saliva from all three glands as well as both sediment and supernatant from whole saliva all contained the coagulation factors normally present in serum. (3) Whole saliva contains factors which act like tissue thromboplastins. (4) Whole saliva could replace the platelet factor in experimental clotting but parotid or submandibular saliva could only do so partially. (5) Saliva as secreted from the ducts does not contain factor V but whole saliva and its sediment did contain some of the factor.

Buffering power of saliva

The buffering power of saliva is discussed on p. 317.

Saliva as a lubricant

The glycoproteins which are the main protein of saliva, have the important property of giving saliva its slimy character. The moistening of the food is important for bolus formation and its lubrication facilitates swallowing. Claude Bernard found that a horse with a parotid fistula had great difficulty in swallowing dry food. In man the lubrication of the mouth is necessary for clear speech. The accurate positioning of the tongue in relation to the teeth becomes difficult when the mouth is dry. The lubricating function of saliva is perhaps best appreciated when salivary flow is inhibited during nervousness or embarrassment. Under these circumstances, the swallowing of dry food or clear speaking in public becomes very difficult.

Saliva and water balance

Cannon (1937) first observed that the drying of the mouth due to excessive evaporation of saliva, as during prolonged talking, acted as a stimulus to salivary flow, the 'dry mouth reflex', and its existence has been thoroughly confirmed. One of the theories of the nature of thirst is that it results from drying of the mucous membrane in the pharynx. If the mouth becomes dry, and the dry mouth reflex operates, salivary flow is stimulated which prevents drying of the pharynx and, according to this theory, thirst is avoided. If the body tissues are short of water, the reflex does not occur and in these circumstances thirst follows any drying of the mouth, thus encouraging the individual to put the situation right by taking a drink. This suppression of the dry mouth reflex does not require an actual loss of fluid by the body, but occurs after meals, when several litres of fluid are transferred from the blood and tissues into the gut as digestive juices. This could explain the thirst which frequently follows a meal. It is now thought that thirst follows from some stimulus, probably a rise in osmotic pressure of the blood, acting on the thirst centre in the hypothalamus but as thirst is quenched immediately after drinking—long before blood osmotic pressure could be changed—there is probably some additional effect in the mouth or pharynx which could be influenced by the dry mouth reflex.

Saliva and taste

The sensation of taste is produced only by substances in solution. Some foods, such as fruits, contain such a high proportion of water that probably all the substances which have a taste are already in solution and their taste may be perceived as soon as they are released by mastication. Other foods, biscuits for example, contain relatively little water and before their taste becomes apparent saliva must dissolve out the flavoured constituents. By this means saliva not only makes eating more pleasurable but may assist in the detection of unwholesome contaminants of food.

Desalivated rats show increased water intake and impaired taste discrimination, for example when presented with either water or sodium chloride solution on different days, between 53 and 65% of the fluid drunk by the control rats was saline whereas the desalivated drank up to 93% saline. When solutions of acid or bitter substances were given, control rats drank very little of the sapid solution (i.e. with a taste) whereas, with certain concentrations, the desalivated rats preferred them (Catalanotto & Seeney 1972).

Saliva as a route of excretion

It is frequently stated that the saliva is a route by which certain substances are excreted. It seems doubtful whether this can apply to any of the normal constituents of saliva since they would be absorbed from the intestine after the saliva was swallowed. Saliva can only be an effective route of excretion for substances that are either destroyed or rendered insoluble during their passing through the gut after swallowing.

It is undoubtedly true that mercury and lead are present in traces in the saliva of people suffering from poisoning by these metals but both are known to be absorbed from the intestine. Among the symptoms of severe mercury poisoning are an unpleasant metallic taste and an increased flow of saliva. The amount of excretion through saliva would seem to be insignificant compared with that via the kidney.

The viruses responsible for such diseases as rabies, poliomyelitis and mumps are present in the saliva of infected individuals and would therefore be swallowed. Since the viruses are proteins they would, at least in some cases, be destroyed by the digestive mechanisms of the gut. In virus disease, however, the tissues are so thoroughly invaded by the rapidly dividing virus molecules that the proportion lost through the saliva is unlikely to be significant. Incidentally, the saliva of sufferers from these virus diseases is a potential source of infection for others.

Reported functions of uncertain status

THE NERVE GROWTH FACTOR (NGF)

Extracts of mouse submandibular gland increase greatly the growth of sympathetic ganglia and of sensory nerves. The rate at which sympathetic neurones are produced from undifferentiated cells is increased so that the number of neurones eventually exceeds the normal, as well as the rate at which they reach maturity.

The active substance is a protein (mol. wt. 29000) composed of two identical peptide chains. NGF is present in many organs and the serum of all the species so far studied but the richest source is the submandibular gland of adult male mice. Removal of the salivary glands from mice did not reduce the growth of these nerve tissues, suggesting that the glands were not the only source. Injection of an anti-serum to the growth factor into new-born mice, rats and rabbits, which would inhibit the factor wherever it was formed, specifically reduced the growth of sympathetic ganglia so that they eventually contained only 1% of the normal number of cells which, remarkably, had no detectable effect on the development of the animals (Levi-Montalcini & Angeletti 1968).

EPIDERMAL GROWTH FACTOR

A peptide has been isolated from the submandibular gland of male but not female mice (other species tested are not good sources) which stimulates epithelial growth (the epidermal growth factor, EGF), has a similar amino acid constitution and may be identical to urogastrone, the substance in urine which inhibits gastric acid secretion. A similar substance is present in human pregnancy urine but its source is unknown. The physiological importance of EGF is not known (for references see Gregory 1975).

PAROTIN, A HORMONE-LIKE SUBSTANCE ISOLATED FROM THE PAROTID GLAND

Japanese workers have reported very detailed experiments (reviewed by Ito 1960) which showed that extracts of the parotid gland contain a protein substance which when injected into rabbits has the following effects: (1) blood calcium was lowered, (2) the leucocyte count was at first lowered then greatly increased, and (3) the mineralization of the incisor dentine was enhanced. A highly purified, crystalline substance with these properties was isolated and similar activity was found in the submandibular gland and in human saliva and urine. These results have not been fully established although Fleming (1960) has described effects on enamel, developing bone, the ovary and testis after parotin injections in mice. The status of parotin as a 'true' hormone has not been clarified.

IODINE METABOLISM

Saliva contains iodide in concentrations between twenty and one hundred times that of the plasma. The mechanism for concentrating the iodide shows similar properties to that of the thyroid gland except that it is not enhanced by the thyroid stimulating hormone of the anterior pituitary and the iodide is passed into the saliva and not retained by the cell as in the thyroid. Auto-radiographs after ingestion of ^{131}I have shown that the striated ducts carry out this concentration.

The effects of removal or inactivity of salivary glands

The salivary glands have been removed from rats and the results which followed confirm the views already stated on the important function which saliva plays in the welfare of the mouth. The most striking effect was an increase in the number of bacteria in the mouth and in the incidence of dental caries. In one experiment, when all three pairs of salivary glands were removed, dental caries increased almost ten times in rats given a caries-producing diet and in another group, some caries developed when they were fed on a diet which does not normally cause caries in this species (Weisberger *et al.* 1940). Similar results have been repeatedly found by others.

Other effects which have been observed are a severe recession of the gingivae round the anterior teeth resulting in the exposure of the cementum, which occurred in 14–18 days from the removal of the glands. The exposed cementum became carious and debris accumulated, which caused ulceration of the soft tissues and resorption of the alveolar bone.

In man, salivary glands sometimes fail to produce saliva for various reasons, a condition known as 'aptyalism' or 'xerostomia'. The chief symptoms are difficulty of swallowing or talking without frequently sipping water, and if the condition is prolonged, rampant caries may develop even in elderly people whose teeth had been previously fairly free from decay.

The effect of desalivation on other organs

A fall in body weight and especially in the weights of the adrenals, testis, ovary and uterus has been reported by Bixler *et al.* (1957) following the removal of the salivary glands in the rat probably caused by the reduced food consumption which occurs in the absence of saliva. This conclusion followed from the use of the 'paired feeding' technique, in which a control group has its food intake reduced to the same level as the animals from which the salivary glands have been removed.

Saliva and Dental Caries

The composition of saliva and dental caries

Many attempts have been made to relate the composition of saliva to the presence or absence of caries. There are several fundamental difficulties in this approach to the caries problem. In addition to the difficulties already mentioned in establishing normal standards for the composition of saliva, it is equally difficult to assess quantitatively the degree of dental caries. A common method of assessing caries is to enumerate the number of decayed, missing or filled teeth (DMFT, or simply DMF) either present on a particular examination or developing over a period. The DMF figure assumes that all missing teeth were extracted because they were carious (which is approximately true for young subjects) but makes no distinction between a small and a large filling. A more refined method of scoring caries is to record the numbers of decayed, missing or filled *surfaces* (DMFS)—this takes into account the severity of the attack on each tooth. The age of the subject is important in considering the annual change in DMF because the incidence of new cavities falls off with advancing age; it is undecided whether this is caused by a change in the resistance of the tooth or whether it is merely because the most vulnerable parts of the teeth become carious in youth. When comparing the salivas of caries-active and caries-free individuals, it is difficult to get two equally large groups because caries-free individuals of a mature age are rare and difficult to find in westernized countries. This inequality in the size of the groups tends to lower the statistical significance of the results.

It has been suggested that saliva from caries-free individuals has higher values than the average for the following (but none of them are fully confirmed or apply to all caries-free subjects): rate of flow (and therefore higher pH and buffering power), calcium and phosphorus concentrations, ammonia concentration or ammonia production during incubation, the concentrations of adenosine triphosphate and fructose diphosphate, the aldolase activity and the oxygen uptake of the bacteria (suggesting a more rapid destruction of sugar and the oxidation of the end-products by caries-free saliva), opsonin activity, general antibacterial activity and an antibacterial substance specific to lactobacilli and streptococci, the number of leucocytes in intact condition and differences in the proportion of epithelial cells to leucocytes. Some workers have found a higher, others a lower, amylase activity in caries-free people. Some of these claims are unconfirmed, others are either disproved or disputed. The two differences which have gained the widest acceptance, but even these are not unanimously agreed, are in the smaller number of acid-producing organisms, especially *Lactobacillus acidophilus* or *Streptococcus mutans* (but see p. 432), in the saliva of caries-free individuals, and a higher rate of flow and therefore of buffering power. It seems likely that there is no single factor common to all caries-free subjects.

Changes occurring during the incubation of saliva

If saliva is incubated for 24 hr, its pH rises to over 8·0 owing to ammonia production (see p. 395). A powerful putrid odour develops. These changes are presumably similar to those occurring some hours after a meal, or during sleep, which lead to halitosis.

A very different series of changes take place if saliva is incubated with carbohydrate and these have been studied extensively in the hope that they may throw some light on this role of carbohydrate in caries. The pH begins to fall after about an hour and reaches 5·0 within 3 hr in most salivas but these changes are usually much slower in saliva from caries-free subjects. The acid arises from bacterial breakdown of the carbohydrate to lactic and other acids. Ammonia production and putrefactive changes are suppressed. These changes resemble those occurring in the plaque after a carbohydrate meal except that in saliva they are much slower because the bacteria are less concentrated. After 6–8 hr incubation, the pH reaches about 4·0 after which acid production ceases; unlike plaque, saliva incubated with carbohydrates shows no tendency for a final rise in pH unless the carbohydrate concentration is very low (less than 0·5%).

These changes are of interest in showing that saliva contains both acid-producing and alkali-producing bacteria and that the group which becomes dominant depends on whether carbohydrate is present or not.

During the first hour or so of the incubation of saliva without added carbohydrate the pH may fall slightly before it begins to rise. This occurs because the carbohydrate fraction of the salivary glycoproteins may be metabolized and converted into acids but their amounts are too small to produce a marked fall in pH. This effect is not always detected because the pH of fresh saliva is unstable owing to loss of CO_2 and the slight fall in pH may therefore be obscured. Oxygen uptake also occurs without added carbohydrates and the amino acids released from salivary protein by bacterial enzymes are the main substrates (Molan & Hartles 1971).

When saliva is centrifuged, a slimy, semi-solid mixture of bacteria and protein separates out which is often referred to as 'salivary sediment'. This material is sometimes used in experiments as a substitute for plaque (the salivary sediment system or SSS) although many chemical and bacteriological differences have been shown between plaque and sediment. The bacteria resemble those from the tongue rather than those of plaque and the water content is higher, 90% compared with 80–85% for plaque and it does not concentrate calcium or phosphate to the same degree as plaque. In spite of these differences it resembles plaque more than saliva (Kleinberg *et al.* 1973) in that acid production during incubation with sugar begins immediately after the sugar is added and reaches its lowest pH value within about half an hour or less (saliva takes over 4 hr).

If salivary sediment is washed with water or saline, its capacity for producing acid from carbohydrate falls greatly but can be restored if the sediment is suspended in the supernatant fraction of centrifuged saliva. Evidently saliva contains co-factors necessary for bacterial metabolism. They have not been fully identified but one factor appears to be a polypeptide or small protein which probably stimulates growth and this energy requiring process in turn stimulates glycolysis (Molan & Hartles 1972). Another factor is of low molecular weight and is possibly urea.

A fraction of saliva called the 'pH rise factor' or 'sialin' which stimulates glucose uptake by bacteria has also been detected. If the glucose concentration is above 0·5% this factor increases acid production but if the concentration is very low (0·05%) the increased uptake of glucose caused by the factor leads to its more rapid exhaustion so that the system reaches sooner the conditions of absence of carbohydrates which, as mentioned above, favour base production (Kleinberg *et al.* 1973). It is likely that the salivary factor which stimulates glycolysis is similar or identical to the pH rise factor.

Halitosis

Halitosis (foetor oris, bad breath) is a condition which is almost universal if the odour of breath on waking is included and it increases in the intervals between meals and is reduced by eating. Halitosis tends to increase with advancing age.

Halitosis has been measured by trapping the odoriferous substances of breath by expiring into a column surrounded by liquid nitrogen which froze them. They were then warmed up and their odour measured in an osmoscope in which air containing the odour is quantitatively diluted until the odour disappears. The strength of the odour is estimated by the amount of dilution needed.

Unpleasant odours in the mouth could arise from the alimentary canal, from the lungs or from bacterial activity in the mouth itself. Most of the evidence suggests that, if subjects with gross disease are excluded, breath odours arise almost entirely from the mouth. For example, when measurements were made (on 200 normal subjects) of the odour of the breath collected from expired air the value was almost identical to that obtained by circulating atmospheric air through the mouth so that it picked up odours from the mouth only. The main factors producing mouth odour are: (1) stagnation of food debris or epithelial cells which may arise from reduced saliva flow or reduced friction in the mouth. The accumulated material is then broken down by the oral bacteria. (2) Tissue destruction as in periodontal disease or caries also leads to substrates which can give rise to odours. (3) The smell of certain foods such as garlic cling to the mouth, presumably the odoriferous constituents tend to become adsorbed on to the oral mucosa. Saliva itself readily gives rise to bad odours especially during mouth-breathing, prolonged talking or hunger. Eating reduces halitosis partly because it increases saliva flow and friction in the mouth, with the effect of removing the sources of odour, and possibly because if the food contains carbohydrate the growth of acid-producing bacteria is encouraged and bacteria which metabolize proteins and protein derivatives are suppressed because they cannot compete for the limited growth factors in saliva.

Analysis of mouth air by gas chromatography showed that H_2S and methyl mercaptan were the constituents responsible for approximately 90% of the odour, a third minor constituent being dimethyl sulphide. Surprisingly, the usual products of putrefaction—the tryptophane derivatives (skatole, indole, other amines and ammonia) were found to be unimportant—although present in saliva they were insufficiently volatile at the pH of saliva to be detected as smells (Tonzetich *et al.* 1967). The unpleasant odour seems to depend on the presence of —SH groups and was therefore favoured by H transfer (reduction, which converts —S—S— groups into —SH) and inhibited if H transfer was prevented, i.e. if oxidation is favoured (Tonzetich & Richter 1964).

Saliva incubated for 60–90 min produced similar odoriferous substances. Plaque suspended in saliva supernatant required much longer periods of incubation to produce comparable amounts of odoriferous material. Addition of the sulphur-containing amino acids showed that they were the substrates from which the odour were produced, the mercaptan being the dominating product from methionine and H_2S from cysteine and cystine. The epithelial cells are the main source of these amino acids in the mouth.

Methods of preventing halitosis are still inadequate but temporary improvement follows mouth rinsing, tooth brushing and especially rubbing epithelial cells from the tongue. In one experiment, rinsing the mouth with water reduced the concentration of volatile sulphur compounds in the mouth air immediately on waking but they returned to about 80% of their initial value within 1 hr. If the teeth are thoroughly brushed with various dentifrices, however, their concentrations returned 1 hr later to only between 15 and 30%

of the initial value. This is further evidence that the odour originated in the mouth (Tonzetich 1971). Other methods of dealing with halitosis are: (1) antiseptic mouthwashes which inhibit the bacterial activity, (2) in view of the above biochemical findings, oxidizing agents (by preventing H transfer) would be expected to reduce halitosis, and (3) frequent drinks and means of stimulating saliva flow would also be expected to be beneficial but do not appear to have been tested in controlled experiments.

References

The following are general reviews on the subject:

AFONSKY D. (1961) *Saliva and its Relation to Oral Health*. University of Alabama Press, Birmingham

BURGEN A.S.V. & EMMELIN N.G. (1961) *Physiology of the Salivary Glands*. Arnold, London

KERR A.C. (1960) The physiological regulation of salivary secretion in man. *Int. Ser. of Monographs on Oral Biology*. Pergamon Press, Oxford

SCHNEYER L.H., YOUNG J.A. & SCHNEYER C.A. (1972) Salivary secretion of electrolytes. *Physiol. Rev.* **52**, 720

SHANNON I.L. *et al.* (1974) *Monographs in Oral Science*, Vol. 2. Saliva: composition and secretion. S. Karger, Basel

SREENBY L.M. & MEYER J. (1964) Salivary glands and their secretions. *Int. Ser. of Monographs on Oral Biology*. Pergamon Press, Oxford

THORN N.A. & PETERSEN O.H. (Eds) (1974) *Secretory Mechanisms of Exocrine Glands*. Munksgaard, Copenhagen

UNITED STATES OFFICE OF NAVAL RESEARCH (1960) *Bibliography on Saliva*. Dept. of Navy, Washington

The following refer to special aspects of the subject:

ADAMS D. (1974) Penetration of water through human and rabbit oral mucosa *in vitro*. *Archs oral Biol.* **19**, 865

ATTSTROM R. (1970) Presence of leukocytes in crevices of healthy and chronically inflamed gingivae. *J. periodont. Res.* **5**, 42

BABOOLAL R. & POWELL R.N. (1971) The effect of oral microbial endotoxins on rabbit leukocyte migration and phagocytosis. In *The Prevention of Periodontal Disease*. Eds EASTOE J.A., PICTON D.C.A. & ALEXANDER A.G. Kimpton, London

BALEKJIAN A.Y. *et al.* (1972) Isolation of a protamine from human parotid fluid. *J. dent. Res.* **51**, Abstracts, 50th General session, I.A.D.R. Abs. no. 946

BATES J.F. (1958) Effect of ingested carbohydrates on the concentrations of amylase, orthophosphate and carbon dioxide in human parotid saliva. *J. dent. Res.* **37**, 755

BATES J.F. & ADAMS D. (1968) The influence of mental stress on the flow of saliva in man. *Archs oral Biol.* **13**, 593

BATTISTONE G.C. & BURNETT G.W. (1961) The free amino-acid composition of human saliva. *Archs oral. Biol.* **3**, 161

BECKS H. (1950) Carbohydrate restriction in the prevention of dental caries using the *Lactobacillus acidophilus* count as one index. *J. Calif. State dent. Ass.* **26**, 53

BECKS H. See also separate list at the end of these references

BIBBY B.G. *et al.* (1938) The antibacterial action of human saliva. *J. Amer. dent. Ass.* **25**, 1290

BISSET K.A. & DAVIS G.H.G. (1960) *The Microbial Flora of the Mouth*. Heywood & Co. Ltd., London

BISWAS S.D. *et al.* (1977a) Study of periodontal disease in children and young adolescents. Part I. Effect of age, sex and gingival influence on crevice fluid volume, pocket depth, pH of supra gingival plaque and crevice collagenase activity and urea. *J. Periodont. Res.* **12**, 250

BISWAS S.D. *et al.* (1977b) Study of periodontal disease in children and young adolescents. Part II. Effect of age, sex and gingival influence on crevice fluid protein, carbohydrate, total calcium, phosphate and nitrogen. *J. Periodont. Res.* **12**, 265

BIXLER D. *et al.* (1957) The effects of salivariadenectomy on the reproductive organs of the female rat. *J. dent. Res.* **36**, 559

BRANDTZAEG P. (1971) Human secretory immunoglobulins—VII. Concentrations of parotid IgA and other secretory proteins in relation to the rate of flow and duration of secretory stimulus. *Archs oral Biol.* **16**, 1295

BRILL N. (1962) The gingival pocket fluid: studies of its occurrence, composition and effect. *Acta odont. Scand.* Supp. 32 (also in *Acta odont. Scand.* (1958) **16**, 233; (1959) **17**, 11; (1960) **18**, 95; (1965) **23**, 115)

BURGEN A.S.V. (1956) The secretion of potassium in saliva. *J. Physiol.* **132**, 20

CANNON W.B. (1937) *Digestion and Health.* Secker & Warburg, London

CATALANOTTO F.A. & SWEENEY E.A. (1972) The effects of surgical desalivation of the rat upon taste acuity. *Archs oral Biol.* **17**, 1455

CHAUNCEY H.H. (1961) Salivary enzymes. *J. Amer. dent. Ass.* **63**, 361

CIMASONI G. (1974) *The Crevicular Fluid.* Karger, Basel

COLEMAN S.E. *et al.* (1971) Lysis of cariogenic and non-cariogenic oral streptococci with lysozyme. *J. dent. Res.* **50**, 939

CURBY W.A. (1953) Device for collection of human parotid saliva. *J. Lab. Clin. Med.* **41**, 493

DARKE A.C. & SMAJE L.H. (1971) Myoepithelial cell activation in the submaxillary salivary gland. *J. Physiol. (Lond.)* **219**, 89

DAWES C. (1967) The effect of flow rate and length of stimulation on the protein concentration in human parotid saliva. *Archs oral Biol.* **12**, 783

DAWES C. (1969) The effects of flow rate and duration of stimulation on the concentrations of protein and the main electrolytes in human parotid saliva. *Archs oral Biol.* **14**, 277

DAWES C. (1972) Circadian rhythms in human salivary flow rate and composition. *J. Physiol.* **220**, 525

DAWES C. & CHEBIB F.S. (1972) The influence of previous stimulation and the day of the week on the concentrations of protein and the main electrolytes in human parotid saliva. *Archs oral Biol.* **17**, 1289

DAWES C. & JENKINS G.N. (1964) The effect of type of stimulus on the composition of saliva. *J. Physiol.* **170**, 86 (see also: *Archs oral Biol.* (1966) **11**, 1203)

DAWES C. & WOOD C.M. (1973a,b) The contribution of oral minor mucous gland secretions to the volume of whole saliva in man. *Archs oral Biol.* **18**, 337, 343

DAWES C. & ONG B.Y. (1973) Circadian rhythms in the flow rate and proportional contribution of parotid to whole saliva volume in man. *Archs oral Biol.* **18**, 1145

DIAMONT H. *et al.* (1959) Salivary secretion in man elicited by means of stimulation of the chorda tympani. *Acta physiol. Scand.* **45**, 293

DIETZ A.K. (1939) The chemotactic influence of human saliva upon leukocytes. *J. dent. Res.* **18**, 361

DIRKSEN T.R. (1963) Lipid constituents of whole and parotid saliva. *J. dent. Res.* **42**, 920

DISCHE Z. *et al.* (1962) Influence of the nature of the secretory stimulus on the composition of the carbohydrate moiety of glycoproteins of the submaxillary saliva. *Arch. Biochem. Biophys.* **97** 459

DISRAELY M.N. *et al.* (1959) The occurrence and origin of certain vitamins in human saliva. *Archs oral Biol.* **1**, 233

DOGON I.L. & AMDUR B.H. (1970) Evidence of the presence of two thiocyanate-dependent antibacterial systems in human saliva. *Archs oral Biol.* **15**, 987

DOGON I.L. *et al.* (1962) Characterization of an antibacterial factor in human parotid secretions, active against *Lactobacillus casei. Archs oral Biol.* **7**, 81

DONOHUE H.D. & TYLER J.E. (1975)

Antagonisms amongst streptococci isolated from the human oral cavity. *Archs oral Biol.* **20**, 381

DOKU H.C. (1960) The thromboplastic activity of human saliva. *J. dent. Res.* **39**, 1210

DREISBACH R.H. (1960) Calcium binding by normal human saliva. *J. dent. Res.* **39**, 1133

DREIZEN S. *et al.* (1952) The effect of ACTH and cortisone on the sodium and potassium levels of human saliva. *J. dent. Res.* **31**, 271

DREIZEN S. *et al.* (1970) Comparative concentrations of selected trace metals in human and marmoset saliva. *Archs oral Biol.* **15**, 179

EDGAR W.M. & JENKINS G.N. (1972) Inorganic pyrophosphate in human parotid saliva and dental plaque. *Archs oral Biol.* **17**, 219

EMMELIN N. (1952) On the mechanism of paralytic secretion. *Acta physiol. Scand.* **26**, 232 (also *Physiol. Rev.* (1952) **32**, 21)

EMMELIN N. (1953) On spontaneous secretion of saliva. *Acta physiol. Scand.* **30**, Suppl. 111, 34

EMMELIN N. (1955) On the innervation of the submaxillary gland cells in cats. *Acta physiol. Scand.* **34**, 11

EMMELIN N. *et al.* (1970) Actions of kinins on salivary myoepithelial cells. *J. Physiol.* **207**, 539

ERICSON S. (1971) The variability of the human parotid flow rate on stimulation with citric acid, with special reference to taste. *Archs oral Biol.* **16**, 9

ERICSSON Y. (1949) Investigations into the calcium phosphate equilibrium between enamel and saliva and its relation to dental caries. *Acta odont. Scand.* **8**, Supp. 3

ERICSSON Y. (1959) Clinical investigations of the salivary buffering action. *Acta odont. Scand.* **17**, 131

EVERSOLE L.R. (1972) The mucoprotein histochemistry of human mucous acinar cell containing salivary glands. *Archs oral Biol.* **17**, 43

FERGUSON D.B. *et al.* (1973) Circadian rhythms in human parotid saliva flow rate and composition. *Archs oral Biol.* **18**, 1155. Also (1974) **19**, 47

FLEMING H.S. (1960) The effect of parotin in mice. *Ann. N.Y. Acad. Sci.* **85**, 313

FORBES J.C. & GURLEY W.B. (1932) Effect of diet on acid-neutralizing power of saliva. *J. dent. Res.* **12**, 637, 749 (see also *J. dent. Res.* (1938) **18**, 409)

FOSDICK L.S. & STARKE A.C. (1939) Solubility of tooth enamel in saliva at various pH levels. *J. dent. Res.* **18**, 260, 417

GAUTVIK K.M. *et al.* (1970) Studies on kinin formation in functional vasodilatation of the submandibular salivary gland in cats. *Acta physiol. Scand.* **79**, 174

GEDDES D.A.M. (1972) Failure to demonstrate the antibacterial factor of Green in caries-free parotid saliva. In *Host Resistance to Commensal Bacteria.* Ed. MCPHEE T. Churchill Livingstone, Edinburgh

GEDDES D.A.M. & JENKINS G.N. (1974) Intrinsic and extrinsic factors influencing the flora of the mouth. In *The Normal Microbial Flora of Man*, p. 85, eds SKINNER F.A. & CARR J.G. Academic Press, London

GIBBONS R.J. *et al.* (1966) Lysozyme insensitivity of bacteria indigenous to the oral cavity of man. *J. dent. Res.* **45**, 877

GLAVIND J. *et al.* (1948) The presence of vitamins in the saliva. *Internat. Ztshr. Vitamin forsch.* **20**, 234

GOLUB L.M. *et al.* (1971) Urea content of gingival crevicular fluid and its relation to periodontal disease in humans. *J. periodont. Res.* **6**, 243

GORE J.T. (1938) Saliva and enamel decalcification. II. Saliva separator. *J. dent. Res.* **17**, 69

GOTTSCHALK A. (1961) Studies on mucoproteins. *Biochim. et Biophys. Acta.* **43**, 81, 91, 98

GREEN G.E. (1959) A bacteriolytic agent in salivary globulin of caries-immune human beings. *J. dent. Res.* **38**, 262 (see also *J. dent. Res.* (1961) **40**, 717; (1962) **42**, 1380)

GREGORY H. (1975) Isolation and structure of urogastrone and its relationship to epidermal growth factor. *Nature (Lond.)* **257,** 325

GRØN P. (1973) The state of calcium and inorganic orthophosphate in human saliva. *Archs oral Biol.* **18,** 1365 (see also 1379, 1385)

GRØN P. & HAY D.I. (1976) Inhibition of calcium phosphate precipitation by human salivary secretions. *Archs oral Biol.* **21,** 201

HAMMOND C.W. & WEINMAN J.P. (1942) Opsonin in saliva. *J. dent. Res.* **21,** 279

HANDLEMAN S.L. & HESS C. (1970) Effect of dental prophylaxis on tooth surface flora. *J. dent. Res.* **49,** 340

HARDIE J.M. & BOWDEN G.H. (1974) The normal microbial flora of the mouth. In *The Normal Microbial Flora of Man,* p. 47, eds SKINNER F.A. & CARR J.G., Academic Press, London

HELDERMAN W.H. VAN PALENSTEIN (1976) Lysozyme concentrations in the gingival crevice and at other oral sites in human subjects with and without gingivitis. *Archs oral Biol.* **21,** 251

HARDWICK J.L. & MANLEY E.B. (1952) Caries of the enamel. *Brit. dent. J.* **92,** 225

HARTLES R.L. & WASDELL M. (1955) The metabolism of the oral flora. *Brit. dent. J.* **99,** 334

HAY D.I. *et al.* (1971) Characteristics of some high molecular weight constituents with bacterial aggregating activity from whole saliva and dental plaque. *Caries Res.* **5,** 111

HAY D.I. (1973) The interaction of human parotid salivary proteins with hydroxy-apatite. *Archs oral Biol.* **18,** 1517, 1531. Also (1975) **20,** 553

HAY D.I. (1975) Fractionation of human parotid salivary proteins and the isolation of an histidine-rich acidic peptide which shows high affinity for hydroxyapatite surfaces. *Archs oral Biol.* **20,** 553

HAY D.I. & OPPENHEIM F.G. (1974) The isolation from human parotid saliva of a further group of proline-rich proteins. *Archs oral Biol.* **19,** 627

HELLDÉN L. & LINDHE J. (1972) Enhanced emigration of crevicular leukocytes mediated by factors in human dental plaque. *Scand. J. dent. Res.* **81,** 123

HENRIQUES B.L. & CHAUNCEY H.C. (1961) A modified method for the collection of human and submaxillary and sublingual saliva. *Oral Surg. Med. Path.* **14,** 1124

HILDES J.A. & FERGUSON M.H. (1955) The concentration of electrolytes in normal human saliva. *Canad. J. Biochem. Phys.* **23,** 217

HILTON S.M. & LEWIS G.P. (1955) The mechanism of the functional hyperaemia in the submandibular salivary gland. *J. Physiol.* **129,** 253; **134,** 471

HILTON S.M. & TORRES S.H. (1970) Selective hypersensitivity to bradykinin in salivary glands with ligated ducts. *J. Physiol.* **211,** 37

HOLLAND R. & MATTHEWS B. (1970) Conditioned reflex salivary secretion in man. *Archs oral Biol.* **15,** 761

HOLMBERG J. (1972) On the nerves to the parotid gland. In *Oral Physiology* pp. 17–19. Eds EMMELIN N. & ZOTTERMAN Y. Pergamon Press, Oxford

ITO Y. (1960) Parotin: a salivary gland hormone. *Ann. N.Y. Acad. Sci.* **85,** 228

JACOBSEN N. (1970) Salivary amylase. II. Alpha-amylase in salivary glands of the *Macaca irus* monkey, the *Cercopithecus aethiops* monkey, and man. *Caries Res.* **4,** 200

JOHNSON D.A. & SREEBNY L.M. (1973) Effect of increased mastication on the secretory process of the rat parotid gland. *Archs oral Biol.* **18,** 1555

KASLICK R.S. *et al.* (1970) Concentrations of inorganic ions in gingival fluid. *J. dent. Res.* **49,** 887

KATZ F.H. & SHANNON T.L. (1969) Adrenal corticosteroids in submaxillary fluid. *J. dent. Res.* **48,** 448

KELSTRUP J. & GIBBONS R.J. (1969) Bacteriocins from human and rodent streptococci. *Archs oral Biol.* **14,** 251

KERR A.C. (1960) The physiological regulation of salivary secretion in man. *Int. Ser. of Monographs on Oral Biology.* Pergamon Press, Oxford

KESEL R.G. (1943) Dental caries: etiology,

control and activity tests. *J. Amer. dent. Ass.* **30**, 25

KESEL R.G. *et al.* (1946) The biological production and therapeutic use of ammonia in the oral cavity in relation to dental caries prevention. *J. Amer. dent. Ass.* **33**, 695. (1949) *Oral Surg., Med., Path.* **2**, 459

KESEL R.G. *et al.* (1958) Further studies on *Lactobacilli* counts after elimination of carious lesions. *J. dent. Res.* **37**, 50

KLEINBERG I. *et al.* (1973) Effect of salivary supernatant on the glycolytic activity of the bacteria in salivary sediment. *Archs oral Biol.* **18**, 787

KNAUF H. & FROMTER E. (1970) Die Kationenausscheidung der grossen Speicheldrüsen des Menchen. *Pflügers Arch ges. Physiol.* **291**, 184

KRAUS F.W. & MESTECKY J. (1971) Immunohistochemical localization of amylase lysozyme and immunoglobulins in the human parotid gland. *Archs oral Biol.* **16**, 781

KRÖNCKE A. *et al.* (1958) Biochemical experiments in saliva: peptides in human saliva. *J. dent. Belge.* **49**, 391

LANGENSKIOLD A. (1942) Component potentials of the submaxillary gland electrogram. *Acta physiol. Scand.* **2**, Supp. 6

LANGSTROTH G.O. *et al.* (1938) The secretion of protein material in the parasympathetic submaxillary saliva. *Proc. Roy. Soc. B.* **125**, 335

LANKE L.S. (1957) Influence on salivary sugar of certain properties of foodstuffs and individual oral conditions. *Acta odont. Scand.* **15**, Supp. 23

LASHLEY K.S. (1916) Reflex secretion of the human parotid gland. *J. exp. psychol.* **1**, 461

LEEMAN S.E. & HAMMERSCHLAG R. (1967) Stimulation of salivary secretion by a factor extracted from hypothalamic tissue. *Endocrinology* **81**, 803

LEUNG W.S. (1961) A demonstration of the importance of bicarbonate as a salivary buffer. *J. dent. Res.* **30**, 403 (see also (1961) *Archs oral Biol.* **5**, 236)

LEVI-MONTALCINI M.R. & COHEN S. (1960) Effects of the extract of mouse sub-maxillary salivary glands on the sympathetic system of mammals. *Ann. N. Y. Acad. Sci.* **85**, 324

LEVI-MONTALCINI R. & ANGELETTI P.V. (1968) Nerve growth factor. *Physiol. Rev.* **48**, 534

LEVINE M. *et al.* (1973) The isolation from human parotid saliva and partial characterization of the protein core of a major parotid glycoprotein. *Archs oral Biol.* **18**, 827

LEVINE M.J. & ELLISON S.A. (1973) Immuno-electrophoretic and chemical analysis of human parotid saliva. *Archs oral Biol.* **18**, 839

LILIENTHAL B. (1955) An analysis of the buffer system in saliva. *J. dent. Res.* **34**, 516

LUNDBERG A. (1958) Electrophysiology of salivary glands. *Physiol. Rev.* **38**, 21

LUNDBLAD R.K. & PURYEAR G.M. (1971) Human salivary coagulant activity: the stimulation by chymotrypsin. *Archs oral Biol.* **16**, 985

LUNDQVIST C. (1952) Oral sugar clearance. *Odont. Revy.* **3**, Supp. 1

LURA H. EGGERS (1947) Investigations on the salivary phosphate and phosphatases. *J. dent. Res.* **26**, 203 (see also (1948) *J. dent. Res.* **27**, 167, 169)

McCOOMBE G. *et al.* (1961) The carbohydrate constituents of human saliva. *Archs oral Biol.* **3** 171

McKEOWN K.C. & DUNSTONE G.H. (1959) Some observations on salivary secretion and fluid absorption by mouth. *Brit. med. J.* **ii**, 670

MANDEL I.D. (1974) Relation of saliva and plaque to caries. *J. dent. Res.* **53**, 246

MANDEL I.D. & EISENSTEIN A. (1969) Lipids in human salivary secretions and salivary calculus. *Archs oral Biol.* **14**, 231

MANDEL I.D. & KHURANA H.S. (1969) The relation of human salivary gamma-A globulin and albumin to flow rate. *Archs oral biol.* **14**, 1433

MANDEL I.D. *et al.* (1964) The carbohydrate components of human submaxillary saliva. *Archs oral. Biol.* **9**. 601

MARTIN C.J. *et al.* (1972) Electrolyte transport in the excurrent duct system of the submandibular gland. In *Oral Physiology* pp. 115–25. Eds EMMELIN N. & ZOTTERMAN Y. Pergamon Press, Oxford

MARTINEZ J.R. *et al.* (1966) Micropuncture study of submaxillary glands of adult rats. *Pflügers Arch ges. Physiol.* **290**, 124

MASON D.K. & CHISHOLM D.M. (1975) *Salivary Glands in Health and Disease.* Saunders, London

MOLAN P.C. & HARTLES R.L. (1971) The nature of the intrinsic salivary substrates used by the human oral flora. *Archs oral Biol.* **16**, 1449

MOLAN P.C. & HARTLES R.L. (1972) A study of the enhancement of glycolysis in human saliva. *Archs oral Biol.* **17**, 1671

MORRIS E.O. (1953) The bacteriology of the oral cavity. *Brit. dent. J.* **95**, 77, 259; **96**, 95, 259; **97**, 29

NEWBRUN E. (1962) Observations on the amylase content and flow rate of human saliva following gustatory stimulation. *J. dent. Res.* **41**, 459

NISTRUP MADSEN S. & BADAWI I. (1976) Variations in the content of cyclic adenosine monophosphate in human mixed saliva during physiological stimulation. *Archs oral Biol.* **21**, 481

NOLTE W.A. (1973) *Oral Microbiology*, 2nd Ed. Henry Kimpton, London

NOUR-ELDIN F. & WILKINSON J.H. (1957) The blood clotting factors in human saliva. *J. Physiol.* **136**, 324

OSARIO J.A. (1960) Relation of the adrenal cortex to the salivary secretion mechanism of the dog. *J. dent. Res.* **39**, 947

OSTER R.H. *et al.* (1953) Human salivary buffering rate measured *in situ* in response to an acid stimulus found in some common beverages. *J. app. Physiol.* **6**, 348

ÖSTLAND S. (1953) Palatine glands and mucin. *Odontol. Tids.* **62**, 1

PICKERILL H.P. (1912) *The Prevention of Dental Caries and Oral Sepsis.* Baillière, Tindall & Cox, London

PIGMAN W. & REID A.J. (1952) The organic compounds and enzymes of human saliva. *J. Amer. dent. Ass.* **45**, 325

PRITCHARD E.T. *et al.* (1967) Investigation of lipids and lipid metabolism in sub-

mandibular salivary gland of the rat. *Archs oral Biol.* **12**, 1445

RADDEN H.G. (1962) Mouth wounds. *Brit. dent. J.* **113**, 112

RÖLLA G. & JONSEN J. (1967) The calcium-binding effect of a human salivary glycoprotein. *Caries Res.* **1**, 343

SAND H.F. (1951) Source of the bicarbonate of saliva. *J. app. Physiol.* **4**, 66

SAWINSKI V.J. & COLE D.F. (1965) Phosphate concentrations of sterile human parotid saliva and its relationship to dental disorders. *J. dent. Res.* **44**, 827

SCHIOTT L.R. & LÖE H. (1970) The origin and variation in number of leucocytes in the human saliva. *J. periodont. Res.* **5**, 36

SCHMIDT-NIELSEN B. (1946) The pH in parotid and mandibular saliva. *Acta physiol. Scand.* **11**, 104

SCHNEYER L.H. (1955) Method for the collection of separate submaxillary and sublingual salivas in man. *J. dent. Res.* **34**, 257

SCHNEYER L.H. & LEVIN L.E. (1955) Rate of salivary secretion. *J. app. Physiol.* **7**, 508, 609

SCHNEYER L.H. *et al.* (1956) Rate of flow of human parotid, sublingual, and submaxillary secretions during sleep. *J. dent. Res.* **35**, 109

SCHNEYER C.A. & SCHNEYER L.R. (1961) Secretion by salivary glands deficient in acini. *Amer. J. Physiol.* **201**, 939

SCHNEYER L.H. & TURNER F. (1954) The sodium and potassium concentration of 'resting' saliva from individual gland pairs in man. *J. dent. Res.* **33**, 716

SCHNEYER C.A. (1974) Autonomic regulation of secretory activity and growth responses of rat parotid gland. In *Secretory Mechanism of Exocrine Glands.* Eds THORN N.A. & PETERSEN O.H. Munksgaard, Copenhagen

SCHRAGER J. & OATES M.D.G. (1974) The chemical composition and some structural features of the principal salivary glycoprotein isolated from human mixed saliva. *Archs oral Biol.* **19**, 1215 (see also (1971) **16**, 287, 1269)

SHANNON I.R. (1958) Na and K levels of human saliva. *J. dent. Res.* **37**, 391

SHANNON I.R. (1962) Parotid fluid flow as related to whole saliva volume. *Archs oral Biol.* **7**, 391

SHANNON I.R. (1966) Climatological effects on human parotid gland function. *Archs oral Biol.* **11**, 451

SHANNON I.R. *et al.* (1974) *Saliva Composition and Secretion.* Karger, Basel

SHANNON I.R. & EDMONDS E.J. (1972) Effect of fluoride dosage on human parotid saliva fluoride levels. *Archs oral Biol.* **17**, 1303

SHANNON I.R. & PRIGMORE J.R. (1962) Parotid fluid as a medium for the determination of human adrenocorticoid status. *Oral Surg., Med., Path.* **13**, 878

SHANNON I.L. & SUDDICK R.P. (1973) Effects of light and darkness on human parotid salivary flow rate and chemical composition. *Archs oral Biol.* **18**, 601

SHEAR M. (1966) The structure and function of myoepithelial cells in salivary glands. *Archs oral Biol.* **11**, 601

SHILLITOE E.J. & LEHNER T. (1972) Immunoglobulins and complement in crevicular fluid, serum and saliva in man. *Archs oral Biol.* **17**, 241

SHROFF F.R. (1955) An observation on the attachment of calculus. *Oral Surg., Med., Path.* **8**, 154

SIMMONS N.S. (1952) Studies on the defence mechanism of the mucous membranes with particular reference to the oral cavity. *Oral Surg., Med., Path.* **5**, 613

SMITH Q.T. *et al.* (1975) Polyacrylamide gel patterns of parotid saliva proteins in Caucasoids and Amerindians. *Archs oral Biol.* **20**, 369

SÖNJU T. & RÖLLA G. (1974) Distribution of sulphated macromolecules in the salivary secretions of *Macaca irus. Archs oral Biol.* **19**, 897

SOUTH M.A. *et al.* (1966) The IgA system. I. Studies of the transport and immunochemistry of IgA in the saliva. *J. exp. Med.* **123**, 615

SPEIRS R.L. (1971) The effects of interactions between gustatory stimuli on the reflex flow-rate of human parotid saliva. *Archs oral Biol.* **16**, 351

SPEIRS R.L. *et al.* (1974) The influence of

sympathetic activity and isoprenaline on the secretion of amylase from the human parotid gland. *J. dent. Res.,* **53**, 1060, *Abstract 67*

SQUIRES B.T. (1953) Human salivary amylase secretion in relation to diet. *J. Physiol.* **119**, 153

THORN N.A. (1974) Role of calcium in secretory processes. In *Secretory Mechanisms of Exocrine Glands,* p. 305. Eds THORN N.A. & PETERSEN O.H. Munksgaard, Copenhagen.

TOMASI T.B. (1964) Characteristics of an immune system common to certain external secretions. *J. clin. Invest.* **43**, 1290 (see also (1965) *J. exp. Med.* **121**, 101)

TONZETICH J. (1971) Direct gas chromatographic analysis of sulphur compounds in mouth air in man. *Archs oral. Biol.* **16**, 587

TONZETICH J. & RICHTER V.J. (1964) Evaluation of volatile odoriferous components of saliva. *Arch. oral Biol.* **9**, 39, 47; (1969) **14**, 815

TONZETICH J. *et al.* (1967) Volatility as a factor in the inability of certain amines and indoles to increase the odour of saliva. *Archs oral Biol.* **12**, 1167

TRUELOVE E.L. *et al.* (1967) Simplified method for collection of pure submandibular saliva in large volumes. *J. dent. Res.* **46**, 1400

VOGEL J.J. & AMDUR B.H. (1967) Inorganic pyrophosphate in parotid saliva and its relation to calculus formation. *Archs oral Biol.* **12**, 159

WAINWRIGHT W.W. See separate list at the end of these references

WEISBERGER D. *et al.* (1940) Development of caries on the teeth of albino rats following extirpation of the salivary glands. *Amer. J. Orthodont.* **26**, 88

WILLS J.H. & FORBES J.C. (1939) Dietary effects upon the acid neutralizing power of the saliva. *J. dent. Res.* **18**, 409

WILSMORE N.M. (1937) A consideration of the osmotic pressure and viscosity of saliva. *Aust. J. Dent.* **41**, 161

WRIGHT D.E. (1964) The source and rate of entry of leucocytes in the human mouth. *Archs oral Biol.* **9**, 321

WRIGHT D.E. & JENKINS G.N. (1953) Leucocytes in the saliva of caries-free and caries-active subjects. *J. dent. Res.* **32,** 511

WRIGHT W.E. & TEMPEL T.R. (1974) Effect of oral hygiene on the clearance of soluble chemotactic bacterial products from human saliva. *J. Periodont.* **45,** 134

WOLDRING M.G. (1955) Free amino acids of human saliva. *J. dent. Res.* **34,** 248 (see also (1957) *J. dent. Res.* **36,** 297)

WOLF R.O. & TAYLOR L.L. (1964) The concentration of blood-group substance in the parotid, sublingual, and submaxillary salivas. *J. dent. Res.* **43,** 272

YAO K. & GRØN P. (1970) Fluoride concentrations in duct saliva and in whole saliva. *Caries Res.* **4,** 321

YOUNG J.A. & MARTIN C.J. (1972) Electrolyte transport in the excurrent duct system of the submandibular gland. In *Oral Physiology*, pp. 99–112. Eds EMMELIN N. & ZOTTERMAN Y. Pergamon Press, Oxford

Since many of the papers published by Becks and Wainwright either individually or jointly refer to closely related aspects of the earlier work on the calcium and phosphorus of saliva, their papers are brought together in a separate list for greater convenience.

BECKS H. & WAINWRIGHT W.W. (1934) A critical discussion of former salivary calcium studies and their value in the establishment of normal standards. *J. dent. Res.* **14,** 387

BECKS H. & WAINWRIGHT W.W. (1937) Critical discussion of former salivary phosphorus studies and their value in the establishment of normal standards. *J. dent. Res.* **17,** 197, 207

BECKS H. (1939) Human saliva. VII. A study of the rate of flow of resting saliva. *J. dent. Res.* **18,** 431

BECKS H. (1943) Total calcium content of resting saliva of 650 healthy individuals. *J. dent. Res.* **22,** 397

The above papers give a detailed account of the difficulties inherent in salivary analysis. Other aspects of salivary calcium and phosphate are discussed in *J. dent. Res.* (1941) **20,** 171, 627, 637; (1942) **21,** 87

WAINWRIGHT W.W. (1939) A study of rate of flow of activated saliva. *J. dent. Res.* **18,** 441

WAINWRIGHT W.W. (1943) Inorganic phosphorus content of resting saliva of 650 healthy individuals. *J. dent. Res.* **22,** 403

BECKS H. & WAINWRIGHT W.W. (1943) Rate of flow of resting saliva of healthy individuals. *J. dent. Res.* **22,** 391

CHAPTER X

PELLICLE, PLAQUE AND CALCULUS

Dental Plaque and Pellicle

The deposit which forms on the enamel surface if the teeth are not cleaned is now known as the dental plaque or simply 'plaque'. It is removed from the smooth surfaces (but not necessarily from around the contact points or fissures) by tooth brushing. It is of great clinical importance as the source of both the acids which dissolve the tooth in caries and of the still unidentified substances which inflame the gingivae and set in motion the changes leading to periodontal disease. Several other layers may exist on the enamel surface at various stages of its life-cycle, some of embryonic origin, others being deposits from saliva.

There has been much confusion in the past over the terminology of these various layers present on the enamel surface. Dawes *et al.* (1963) collected some of the many names which had been used to refer to these layers and suggested a standardized usage. Some of these names are mentioned in Table X.1.

Acquired pellicle

Under most plaques, separating them from the enamel, is a layer of material usually 1–3 μm thick but occasionally reaching 10 μm, free from bacteria and usually differing in staining reaction and electron density from the plaque matrix (Fig. X.1(a) and b). This is called (among other names) the acquired pellicle, or simply, pellicle. Some workers have subdivided this into a 'surface cuticle', 0·2 μm thick differing in staining from the pellicle, which is 1–10 μm thick and lies outside it (Meckel 1965) but these layers cannot always be distinguished and the existence of the cuticle as a separate entity has not been fully established. If the tooth is thoroughly cleaned by a tooth brush, plaque is removed, but the pellicle remains and can only be removed by the more vigorous treatment of a 'prophylaxis', or scale and polish, with an abrasive paste. Pellicle can sometimes become impregnated with calcium and phosphate. On some surfaces of the teeth, pellicle is present without any overlying plaque and, in some places, the bacteria of the plaque are in direct contact with the apatite

TABLE X.1

A summary of the nomenclature used for the integuments of the enamel surface

	Integument	*Some previous names*	*Proposed names*
Structures of developmental origin	(*a*) The accellular layer	(1) Inner structureless layer of Nasmyth's membrane	Primary enamel cuticle
		(2) Primary enamel cuticle	
		(3) Nasmyth's membrane	
	(*b*) The cellular layer	(1) Outer cellular layer of Nasmyth's membrane	Reduced enamel epithelium
		(2) Dental cuticle	
		(3) Reduced dental epithelium	
Structures acquired after eruption	(*a*) A cuticle acquired after eruption	(1) Mucin plaque	Acquired pellicle
		(2) Plaque and film	
		(3) Brown pellicle	
		(4) Pigmented pellicle	
		(5) Stained pellicle	
	(*b*) Part of the cuticle permeating the outer enamel	(1) Sub-surface cuticle	Sub-surface cuticle
		(2) Dendritic layer	
	(*c*) Food debris	(1) Materia alba	Food debris
	(*d*) A dense bacterial layer	(1) Gelatinous plaque	Dental plaque (or, in a dental context, simply 'plaque')
		(2) Mucinous plaque	
		(3) Plaque	
		(4) Materia alba	
	(*e*) Outer less consolidated layer of plaque	None	Materia alba
	(*f*) Mineralized deposits	(1) Calculus	Calculus
		(2) Tartar	

crystals of enamel without an intervening layer of pellicle (Fig. X.2). The absence of pellicle in some old-established plaques may occur because the bacteria have broken it down.

NATURE AND COMPOSITION OF PELLICLE

The pellicle has usually been collected by dipping an extracted tooth in 2 or 5% HCl which, by dissolving away the underlying enamel, releases it as a membrane which can easily be seen and handled. It is obvious that if pellicle contains any acid-soluble constituents they would be removed by this treat-

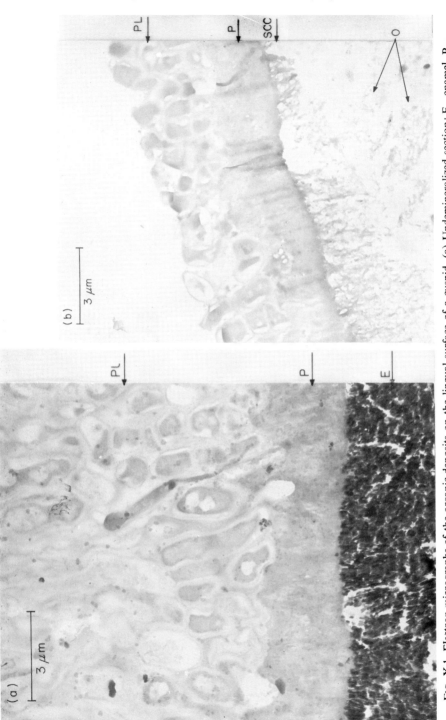

Fig. X.1. Electron micrographs of the organic deposits on the lingual surface of a cuspid. (a) Undemineralized section; E—enamel, P—pellicle. (b) Demineralized cross-section. PL—plaque, P—pellicle, SSC—subsurface cuticle, O—organic residue of enamel.

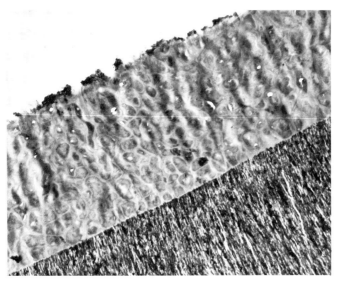

FIG. X.2. Electronmicrograph of fully-developed plaque on undemineralized enamel (bottom) with approximately 12 layers of bacteria in a matrix. In this specimen the pellicle is absent. × 10 000.

ment. This was first pointed out by Mayhall (1970) who analysed both the insoluble membrane and the acid-soluble fraction. Unfortunately, on the assumption (now questioned) that all the constituents of pellicle would have a high molecular weight, the combined material was dialysed so that if low molecular weight proteins were present they would be lost. These difficulties have been overcome by some workers who have collected pellicle by scraping it off the enamel with a scaler shortly after a prophylaxis (Sönju & Rölla 1973) but this can only be done with 'young' pellicle (a few hours old) as later it becomes too difficult to separate from plaque. The workers who first noticed that an organic membrane could be floated off the teeth with acid thought that it was the remains of 'Nasmyth's membrane'—the layers of developmental origin detectable on unerupted teeth (p. 154). Microscopical examination by Turner (1958) of pellicles removed by acid from young and old teeth showed differences similar to those of celloidin replicas of enamel of different ages (Fig. X.3(a) and (b)). In young enamel, the rod ends are visible but they have largely disappeared from old enamel (Scott *et al.* 1949) indicating that some of the mineralized tissues is worn off in older teeth and this could not occur without removing the developmental layers. Pellicle must also be removed in the course of attrition sufficiently marked to remove enamel but is constantly reforming. The finding that this membrane rapidly reformed after removal and

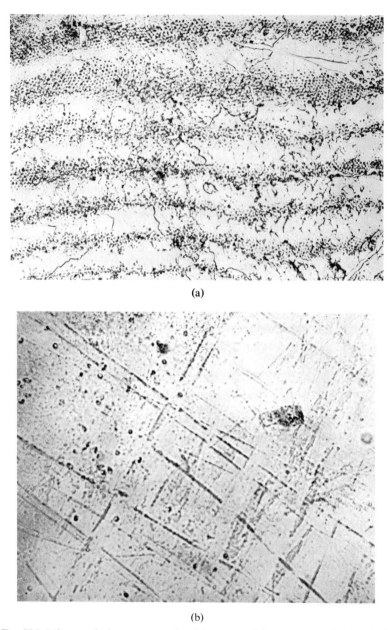

(a)

(b)

Fig. X.3. Microscopical appearance of cuticles removed from young teeth (a) and old teeth (b). In (a), the impressions of the prism ends can be seen but these have been removed in (b), presumably by gradual wear of the outer surface of the enamel; (b) also shows the presence of numerous scratches which are absent from (a) but are, however, sometimes found in other specimens from young subjects. These naturally-formed replicas in pellicle resemble closely replicas made artificially by Scott *et al.* (1949) to study the effect of age on the surface of enamel.

study of its chemical composition eventually proved that it was a deposit from oral fluids.

If enamel of an extracted tooth with its pellicle intact is demineralized, fixed and sectioned, organic material continuous with the pellicle and differing from the finer, less electron-dense enamel matrix can be seen in many sections, penetrating the space originally occupied by the enamel (Fig. X.1(b) from Meckel 1965). It is assumed that some of the deposit enters the spaces between the enamel crystals and the enamel organic matter to form the 'subsurface cuticle', also known as the 'dendritic layer'. This corresponds with the observed rise in organic matter of outer enamel with increasing age (p. 178) but Meckel states that it forms only on enamel which has, for any reason, become slightly porous and not on completely sound enamel.

The formation of pellicle has been studied *in vivo* by the following methods: (*a*) by wearing pieces of polished enamel attached to dentures, (*b*) by scraping it off normal enamel surfaces some hours after a prophylaxis, and (*c*) by demineralizing sections of teeth extracted at intervals after a prophylaxis (McDougall 1963). Pellicles floated off extracted teeth with acid consist of protein high in glutamic acid and alanine (some analyses suggest high also in glycine) and low in S-containing amino acids and resembling protein precipitated from submandibular saliva by acetic acid. Pellicle also contains carbohydrates and muramic acid—a constituent of bacterial cell walls. Histological study of old pellicles shows them to have a scalloped edge from the spaces once occupied by bacteria. Carbohydrates are not present in the same proportion as in salivary proteins, suggesting that pellicle contains only selected salivary proteins. Samples of 'young' pellicle formed within 1 hr of a prophylaxis and scraped off the enamel were free from bacterial wall constituents and the amino acids of its protein differed from those of pellicles floated off extracted teeth because this material, unlike that of old-established pellicles, had not been exposed to the acids or enzymes released from bacteria. The amount obtainable did not increase after 1 hr. Its composition was similar when collected from teeth in different parts of the mouth. The proportions of its amino acids resembled those of a crude acid precipitate of submandibular–sublingual saliva but had no resemblance to that of acid precipitates of parotid saliva. It might seem surprising that the submandibular saliva could be considered as a source of pellicle on enamel in all parts of the mouth. However, a simple experiment shows that submandibular saliva spreads over the whole mouth; if some clearly visible, insoluble material, such as powdered charcoal, is placed under the tongue it will be seen to be spread over the whole mouth within a few minutes. It is presumably transported by the steady flow of unstimulated saliva.

Schlatter *et al.* (1961) engraved marks on teeth *in vivo* with a diamond point and made replicas immediately and some weeks after—1 week later the marks appeared to be of smoother outline and after 6 weeks the average depth

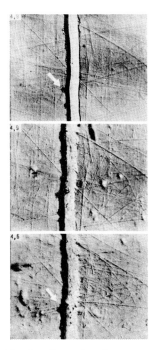

FIG. X.4. Photographs (× 32) of replicas taken from enamel with a fresh mark, 4·9 *μ* deep, made on the enamel (top); same 1 week later (middle); same 6 weeks later (bottom), showing that the mark has become partly filled in with deposits from the saliva. Tooth brush scratches are also visible, some of which appear to have remained unchanged during the 6 weeks.

had decreased. Evidently pellicle material had been deposited in the mark (Fig. X.4). The rate of deposition varied from subject to subject. In further experiments, the teeth were etched with 0·3N HCl for 10 s, and replicas taken immediately after and at intervals up to 48 days. The ends of the prisms become visible after etching, but they were largely obliterated by a deposit within a few days of exposure to the normal mouth environment.

POSSIBLE PROTECTIVE EFFECTS OF PELLICLE

It has been suggested, especially as a result of experiments by Darling (1943) and Meckel (1965), that the pellicle protects the tooth against acid attacks including caries. It is well established that if extracted teeth are exposed to acid, visible signs of demineralization (such as a chalky appearance) occur most rapidly on parts of enamel from which the outer layers have been removed, for example attrition areas or places damaged during extraction.

It is also well known that the outer layers of enamel are less soluble than the inner enamel and again the pellicle (and also the high fluoride concentration on the surface) have been suggested as the cause. The pellicle cannot be the only cause, as the outer layers remain less soluble after removal of the organic layers with ethylene diamine. This experiment does not prove that the organic layers have *no* effect whatever on the tooth solubility and Mannerberg (see below) suggests that it has. Schüle (1961, 1962), on the other hand, has shown that the various organic layers on enamel are freely permeable to acid and to calcium and phosphate ions, which would suggest that they would not affect the rate at which enamel dissolved.

Mannerberg (1960) classified tooth surfaces according to the microscopical appearances of replicas into those with an organic cuticle present, those with an acquired calcified layer and those with neither—in which the prism ends could be seen. In a group of subjects he made three replicas of enamel *in vivo*, one before, and the second immediately after, placing drops of lemon juice on the teeth and a third some time (up to 14 days) after. He found the presence of an organic layer seemed to reduce or prevent erosion by the lemon juice. Those with inorganic deposits were affected but, after 14 days, a deposition of inorganic material had occurred and the effect of the erosion had largely disappeared. With neither type of layer present, the effect of the lemon juice was to make the prism ends very distinct (presumably some enamel had dissolved) and 14 days later there was little change. When enamel with its pellicle ground off is exposed to saliva so that a pellicle reforms, the penetration of acid was reduced compared with controls; less protection occurred if dialysed saliva was used—possibly the absence of calcium from the dialysed saliva prevented or reduced pellicle formation (Moreno *et al.* 1974). Most workers, therefore, think that the protein deposits on enamel do exert some protective effect and may be an important factor in making caries a penetrating lesion instead of a complete dissolution of the outer enamel (pp. 415–6).

MODE OF FORMATION

Many proteins, including those in saliva, are readily adsorbed by hydroxyapatite (HA) and it is believed that this process accounts for pellicle formation. Electrophoresis of saliva before and after shaking with HA have shown the selective nature of this adsorption. It is well known that proteins can be desorbed from apatite by inorganic phosphate. The adsorption of some substances to apatite is also affected by concentrations of phosphate over the range of physiological variation of saliva; it is suggested that differences between the salivary phosphate of different individuals might affect the amount of pellicle formed or remaining on the enamel. When whole or parotid saliva is treated with HA the proteins which adsorb most strongly are those (p. 292) from the parotid of low molecular weight which are high in proline, including one with an isoelectric point of about 9·0 (Armstrong 1971, Hay 1973). Most analyses of pellicle have not suggested that the proline is high but, as mentioned above, many samples have been exposed to acid or (as with the preparations of Mayhall (1970)) were dialysed, two processes which would remove protein of low molecular weight. Nevertheless, proline was low in the very early pellicle scraped off enamel by Sönju & Rölla (1973) and it was not especially high in tyrosine or histidine—two of the amino acids in the proteins adsorbed by the apatite. Either the proteins which deposit on to thoroughly-cleaned enamel within a few hours are not typical of the more mature pellicle, or adsorption by apatite *in vitro* is not a true indication of the proteins entering pellicle.

It may be concluded that pellicle is formed by the selective adsorption of certain salivary proteins by the apatite of enamel. The young pellicle scraped off the teeth and analysed by Sonju & Rölla possessed blood group activity and inhibited virus haemagglutination (a protein with these properties is present in saliva) but contained no amylase, again showing the selectivity of the protein adsorption. Whereas analysis suggests that those adsorbed first are from the submandibular or sublingual glands the proteins most readily adsorbed are from the parotid; the source of pellicle is therefore still not clear. The process occurs without bacteria (for example it may be demonstrated *in vitro* with sterilized saliva) and affects especially acidic proteins (i.e. with an excess of dicarboxylic acids). The free carboxylic group presumably plays a part in binding to the apatite surface. It is possible the other acid groups present in some salivary proteins (for example sialate and sulphate) might have a similar effect. Although sialate is absent from plaque (p. 376) it is certainly present in some of the salivary proteins which readily adsorb on to apatite. Sulphated proteins are present in human saliva and have been studied in the secretions from the sublingual and minor glands of the monkey. After injecting $^{35}SO_4$ into monkeys, the labelled SO_4 was present in plaque, and in a similar experiment in rabbits was detected in pellicle (Rölla *et al.* 1975a, b).

It is obvious that once apatite is coated with protein its opportunities for further adsorption will cease. Any later deposition depends therefore either on adsorption by the protein already on the apatite or some entirely different process. In the normal mouth, the apatite of the enamel is likely to be fully covered so adsorption by apatite is unlikely to be important in the thickening of the pellicle or the deposition of plaque. Apatite coated with salivary protein does adsorb dextrans (p. 385) and bacteria, however; its ability to adsorb more protein does not seem to have been investigated. (See Rölla 1977.)

Plaque

Chemical and histological structure of plaque

METHODS OF COLLECTION
The histological structure of plaque can be studied by fixing and embedding

extracted teeth and sectioning them with or without previous demineralization. A method of collecting plaque and retaining its morphology without

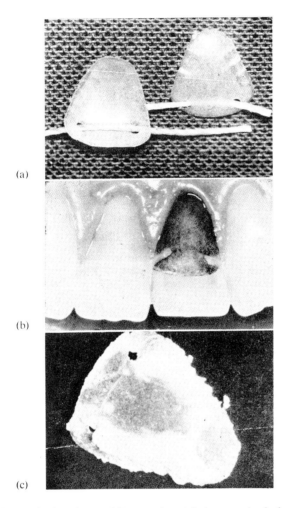

(a)

(b)

(c)

Fig. X.5. (a) The plastic strips used for experimental plaque and calculus formation.
(b) The strips attached to the lingual incisor (the strip on the left is dyed to make it
more clearly visible. (c) The deposit on the strip after 7 days' exposure in the mouth
(Mühlemann & Schneider 1959).

extracting the tooth (Mandel *et al.* 1957) is to place strips of Mylar or other
plastic (preferably with a roughened surface) to the teeth and removing them
after varying intervals for examination by histological, bacteriological or

chemical methods (Fig. X.5). An artificial fissure made of Mylar, inserted in a gold receptacle placed in large occlusal amalgam fillings has been used to study fissure plaque (Löe *et al.* 1973).

For chemical analysis, the plaque is usually scraped off the enamel, and since it is virtually impossible to preserve its morphology or to differentiate between inner and outer layers, there is consequently very little information about variation in chemical composition at different depths. The composition varies in different sites but only recently with the development of sensitive methods of analysis has it been possible to analyse plaque from single teeth, and even now this can be done only for some constituents.

METHODS OF ESTIMATING THE AMOUNT OF PLAQUE

The amount of plaque formed on Mylar may be estimated by weighing the strip before and after exposure in the mouth. Plaque on the natural enamel surface may be collected with a scaler (preferably of plastic to minimize the possibility of including any enamel) either from the whole dentition or from selected teeth and weighed either wet or after drying. As it is impossible to collect all the plaque the method is imprecise, but comparisons can be made fairly satisfactorily because the amount left behind is presumably similar in different subjects. The amount formed is very variable but 10–20 mg in 1 day is typical. The proportion of the enamel surface covered by plaque can be recorded, usually on some arbitrary scale ('less than one-third', 'more than one-half', etc.) with or without staining with disclosing solution. The plaque score without staining correlates well with plaque weight but, when stained, thin layers of plaque low in weight become clearly visible and the correlation with weight falls (Loesche & Green 1972). Electron micrographs of extracted teeth with a mature plaque on their surface show that it is made up of a matrix and up to a dozen layers (the numbers depending on the age and location of the plaque) of tightly-packed bacteria of several types, some in contact with each other, some separated by matrix (Fig. X.1(a), (b) and X.2).

The nature of plaque matrix

It was originally assumed that plaque matrix consisted simply of precipitated salivary proteins but McDougall (1963) showed by staining reactions, which have since been confirmed by others, that it cannot be unchanged salivary glycoproteins but leave open the possibility that it may be derived from them. Other possibilities are that plaque matrix originates as pellicle but is modified by bacterial action or that it is entirely a bacterial product. The usual view now is that it consists of certain selected salivary proteins perhaps modified by bacterial enzymes, with varying quantities of polysaccharide of bacterial origin.

Composition of plaque

Both the chemical and bacteriological composition of plaque vary from one area of the mouth to another although the details have not been fully established. Ideally, plaque from different areas should be collected and studied separately but in order to obtain enough material plaque from the mouth as a whole often has to be pooled.

The water content of plaque is remarkably constant, considering the variation in its contact with drinks and saliva, but the values depend on the method of estimation used. The most accurate values based upon weight loss at 105° C range between 80 and 85% (mean 82%) of which about 50% is in the cells and 32% in the matrix.

To obtain meaningful results on the composition of plaque it is necessary to separate the cells (about 70% by volume of the whole) from the matrix. This cannot be achieved fully but two methods have been used. (1) Plaque (10 μg ml^{-1}) is dispersed by mechanical stirring in water at pH 6·4, the bacteria are removed by centrifuging and by filtering the supernatant through a millipore filter (Krembel *et al.* 1969). Unfortunately, the separation is not complete because the procedure is unlikely to dissolve the whole of the matrix, and some polysaccharides, even if soluble, do not pass through the filter. (2) Plaque is extracted with alkali (pH 12) and centrifuged. The alkaline supernatant contains virtually all the matrix but is contaminated with some bacterial contents (Silvermann & Kleinberg 1967; Fox & Dawes 1970a, b). Plaque contains many enzymes and, unless precautions are taken, many of the constituents will break down during the separation.

Owing to differences between the methods of fractionation of plaque, the results of different workers cannot be pooled and no agreed chemical analysis can be given. However, approximately one-third of the dry weight is water-soluble and much of this fraction is dialysable, consisting of proteins, peptides and free amino acids. Sugars and polysaccharides, mostly derivatives of glucose, have been estimated as 6% of the dry weight (Critchley 1969). The fraction insoluble in water (about 70% of dry weight), consisting of the insoluble matrix and most of the bacterial contents, has been reported to contain about 11% of carbohydrate and 7% nitrogen, equivalent to about 40% protein, much of it of high molecular weight (Hotz *et al.* 1972) but, if it contains carbohydrate, the percentage of glycoprotein will be even higher. The total carbohydrate has been reported as 13–17% of the dry weight but depends on the time between eating and collecting the plaque. The lipid is reported as 10–14% dry weight of the plaque mostly in the matrix (Krembel *et al.* 1969).

The mineral matter has been reported as 10% (dry weight) of the total plaque, more than half of it being in the acellular fraction. The concentration of calcium and phosphate, the minerals of greatest physiological importance

TABLE X.2

Some published data on plaque composition

	Mixed	Lower incisor	Upper incisor	Soluble in alkali (matrix)	Insoluble (cells)
Percentage water (range 80–85)	82				
Percentage dry wt					
Protein	40–50			4	40
Nitrogen				1·2	7
Carbohydrate	13–17			6	11
Lipid	10–14			26–30	1·3–5
Ash	10			11	15
μg mg^{-1} dry wt					
Calcium	8	15	5		
Total phosphorus	16	—	—		
Inorganic phosphate (P$_i$)		9	4		
F ppm dry wt	20–100				

because they maintain the saturation of the environment of the tooth, are very variable but typical figures are calcium 8 μg mg^{-1} and inorganic phosphate (as P) 16 μg mg^{-1}.

The calcium and phosphate concentrations of plaque in the lower incisor region are higher than elsewhere (Dawes & Jenkins 1962; Ashley 1975a, b). Although much of this mineral is bound, some of the calcium is released when the plaque pH falls and will tend to lower the critical pH and may explain why these teeth are so resistant to caries. Studies with X-ray diffraction have detected crystals of brushite and apatite in 40% of samples formed even as early as 12 hr after tooth brushing and 75% of plaque samples 3 days old contain crystals. However, these figures refer to dried plaque and crystals cannot be detected in plaque in its normal state.

As plaque develops during 4 days, its chemical composition changes; the concentration of calcium and phosphate have been reported to fall between the first and second day then gradually increase up to the fourth day. The changes in carbohydrate follow the reverse pattern—increasing between days 1 and 2 then falling. Presumably a precipitate high in calcium and phosphate forms first and as more bacteria enter the matrix, more carbohydrate is synthesized and stored thus diluting the minerals laid down initially and possibly leading to acid production which, in turn, dissolves some calcium and phosphate which is lost by diffusion.

Early plaque, especially in the gingival area, contains some epithelial cells which appear to autolyse providing another possible source of protein for plaque matrix as well as nutrients for bacteria. Leucocytes are also present in gingival plaque and they disintegrate, releasing lysosomal enzymes which may modify plaque constituents, for example digest pellicle or plaque matrix, but are rarely present in mature plaque. Food debris is not usually present in plaque although some large indigestible particles (for example meat fibres or fruit pips) may become impacted between the teeth or in fissures.

The composition of plaque fluid

The values for the gross composition of a heterogeneous material like plaque have little relevance in considering the effect of plaque on the tooth. The relevant information is the composition of the aqueous phase of the innermost layers of plaque which are in contact with the enamel or its pellicle. Although this information is not available, the fluid phase of plaque as a whole has been collected by centrifuging and some of its constituents estimated (Edgar & Tatevossian 1971). It has an osmotic pressure higher than plasma and saliva

TABLE X.3

Composition of mixed saliva, plaque and gingival fluids (mM)

	Saliva	Plaque fluid	Gingival fluid
Sodium	13	$35 \pm 9 \cdot 0$	89 ± 31
Potassium	20·5	$61 \pm 13 \cdot 5$	17 ± 9
Calcium	1·45	$6 \cdot 5 \pm 2 \cdot 1$	$5 \pm 1 \cdot 8$
Magnesium	0·41	$3 \cdot 7 \pm 1 \cdot 1$	$0 \cdot 4 \pm 0 \cdot 3$
Inorganic phosphate	5·4	$14 \cdot 2 \pm 3 \cdot 1$	$1 \cdot 3 \pm 0 \cdot 9$
Protein (g/100 ml)	0·28	$1 \cdot 49 \pm 0 \cdot 06$	$6 \cdot 83 \pm 1 \cdot 26$

Data from Tatevossian & Gould (1976)

and concentrations of most ions are greatly in excess of the values in saliva or gingival fluid (Table X.3). Its very high calcium and phosphate concentrations, indicating a high degree of supersaturation, could exist in solution only in the presence of complexing agents or substances which inhibit crystallization. One of the acidic peptides of saliva (p. 292) has been identified as the factor which prevents the precipitation of calcium in both saliva and plaque (Hay & Grøn 1975). This substance may play an important part in maintaining the environment of the tooth saturated with calcium phosphate.

Plaque formation

The chemical processes involved in the formation of plaque are still controversial. Most attention has been given to plaque on the smooth surfaces, in the gingival region—the factors involved in the very different environment of the occlusal fissures have been neglected. Most of the early work on plaque formation attempted to answer the question: What is the nature of plaque matrix and how is it formed? It was assumed that the matrix came first followed by a more or less random colonization with bacteria. It is now well established that certain salivary constituents agglutinate bacteria and this finding has focused interest on the entry of bacteria into plaque which some workers believe is primary, the matrix being mainly or entirely a bacterial product (Gibbons 1966). A summary of the evidence for and against the various theories is given below.

Hypotheses on the formation of plaque matrix

(A) SPONTANEOUS PRECIPITATION
When plaque is well established after colonization by bacteria, it is likely that metabolic changes by the bacteria play the main part in extending it. Surface action by existing plaque matrix might cause any proteins coming into contact with it to alter their internal bonds and become denatured and insoluble. This is particularly true of some of the proteins from the submandibular and sublingual glands which are readily precipitated by shaking, contact with the walls of the collecting vessel or, in some individuals, quite spontaneously. It would be expected that such a deposition would be favoured if the tooth surface were alternately wetted and dried, as each time a film of saliva dries, a layer of protein will be deposited and this has been suggested as one factor operating in the mouth. However, plaque forms as readily on the posterior teeth (where drying seems unlikely) as on the anterior teeth (which probably do become dry fairly often). It must be concluded that drying does not play an essential part in the deposition of plaque and it is doubtful if it plays any part. Drying would be expected to result in a deposit of all the proteins of saliva which may occur in habitual mouth-breathers or during sleep (with its occasional or even frequent periods of mouth-breathing) or prolonged speaking although this deposit does not appear to have been studied.

(B) ISO-ELECTRIC PRECIPITATION OF SALIVARY PROTEIN
This is the oldest hypothesis, based on the observation that slight acidification of saliva leads to the precipitation of some of its proteins, and it was assumed that acid production by bacteria would lower the pH levels at which precipitation occurred. It was criticized by Dawes (1964) who concluded that the precipitation of salivary protein at slightly acid pH values still within the physiological range (say 4·9–7·0) was an artefact. He showed that if saliva is acidified by the addition of buffers over the range 2–6, no precipitation was detectable visually in parotid saliva and none in submandibular until the pH was lowered to 3·5. He concluded that the iso-electric points of the major pro-

teins of saliva are below the pH which would be reached by bacterial acid production. If, however, HCl or unbuffered organic acid is added precipitation appears to occur even at pH values of about 6. Dawes interprets these findings as follows. When HCl is added, the buffering power of the saliva is overcome in the immediate vicinity of the drops of acid, the pH falls to the iso-electric point of the protein which then precipitates. The saliva is usually shaken before the pH is measured which disperses and dilutes the HCl so that the pH of the saliva as a whole may then be quite high, say 5·5, but the protein precipitate formed locally where the pH was about 2 does not redissolve. When buffers over the range 3–6 are added, the pH never falls below that of the buffer and therefore never reaches the iso-electric point.

These observations have been confirmed but interpreted differently (Jenkins & Hillam 1971, unpublished). Buffers have a high ionic strength compared with HCl and if HCl is added accompanied by high concentrations of KCl, to give an ionic strength comparable with those of buffers, no precipitation occurs, presumably because the high concentration of metallic ions still maintains the proteins as soluble salts, rather than in the less soluble acid form.

Conversely, if dilute buffers were added which would prevent a local pH drop but would not produce much change in ionic strength, precipitation regularly occurred at about pH 5·0. Precipitation by acid within the physiological range may therefore occur and could be a factor in plaque formation. The technique of iso-electric focusing (which separates mixtures of substances in the order of their iso-electric point) shows that the iso-electric point of some salivary proteins covers a very wide range from about 3 to 9. Alkaline extracts of plaque have a similar range of iso-electric points, but as they have been denatured already when entering plaque and may have undergone further modification from bacterial attack while in plaque, this may not be relevant to the acid hypothesis of plaque formation.

Although proteins have their minimum solubility at their iso-electric point proteins present in low concentrations may not be sufficiently insoluble at this pH to precipitate. The amount of plaque formed is usually between 10 and 20 mg per day of which not more than 1 or 2 mg is matrix protein. Any process leading to the precipitation of this minute proportion of the total salivary protein secreted daily (say 1·8 g or 0·3% of 600 ml) would be adequate to explain the formation of plaque matrix, i.e. if only one minor protein was precipitated by acid, it could provide enough to form plaque but would certainly not be detectable as a visual precipitate and might not even be readily detectable by optical measurement.

The main objection to the acid hypothesis is that acid is presumably formed only in the presence of bacteria and unless organisms were already on the tooth there is no means by which the pH would be lowered. Plaque may form during the intervals between meals, or even during fasting, whereas the major acid production is immediately after meals. Nevertheless, plaque does form some acid slowly between meals either from the carbohydrate split off from salivary glycoproteins or from polysaccharides stored within the bacteria. Also, the pH of resting saliva is about 6·0, or even lower in very slow secretors, and iso-electric precipitation of some constituents of sublingual or submandibular saliva may occur spontaneously in slow secretors. Acid is also produced from accumulation of bacteria on the gingiva or tongue which may remain even after the teeth are brushed. Once plaque is well established and contains bacteria, acid formation from sugars may lower the pH in the vicinity still further so that more protein is precipitated which could be a means of increasing the bulk of plaque already formed. Changes in the pH of plaque may also influence other factors which favour plaque formation (see below) besides the precipitation of protein.

(c) CHEMICAL CHANGES IN SALIVARY PROTEIN

Plaque, unlike salivary glycoproteins, contains no sialic acid (Jenkins & Dawes 1964, Leach 1964) and plaque rapidly metabolizes sialic acid when incubated with it (whether it is broken down or incorporated into larger molecules is not known). This suggested that neuraminidase present in most species of salivary bacteria might remove the sialate, and this would be expected to raise the iso-electric point and thus reduce the solubility of the glycoprotein and other enzymes would remove other sugars.

This concept was supported by experiments which suggested that incubating duct saliva with neuraminidase led to the precipitation of some of its proteins. These experiments have not, in general, been confirmed and this hypothesis, although it has been widely quoted, is no longer well supported. Although neuraminidase action on glycoproteins does not in itself lead to their precipitation, it does make them slightly more readily precipitated by calcium (see below).

Sialic acid is not absent from pellicle proteins nor from the proteins which are adsorbed by apatite. Its absence from plaque could be explained either by its removal and metabolic breakdown after a sialoprotein had entered plaque or because only certain salivary proteins enter plaque selectively and they happen not to include those containing sialic acid.

(d) EFFECT OF CALCIUM IONS

Addition of calcium salts to submandibular saliva to double the normal calcium concentration causes a precipitate of protein and calcium which on standing tends to take up phosphate and more calcium; this also occurs with some parotid samples. Several other observations support the hypothesis that calcium precipitation might explain the formation of plaque matrix:

(1) Early plaque contains high concentrations of calcium.
(2) If drops of saliva are evaporated to dryness on a glass slide the resulting

deposit is not washed off by a stream of water; if saliva to which EDTA (which chelates the cations including calcium) has been added is treated in this way, a stream of water removes most of the deposit—evidently the cations normally present, and especially calcium, anchor the protein to the glass and could presumably do so to the enamel surface.

(3) The agglutination of bacteria (see later) is favoured by calcium ions.

There are two possible sources of calcium which might raise the concentration of saliva sufficiently to precipitate the protein: the first is the crevicular fluid which is reported to contain 20 mg calcium 100 ml^{-1} although the origin of the calcium which increases its concentration above that of plasma is unknown. It might be speculated that the slow trickle of unstimulated submandibular or sublingual saliva, as it spreads over the mucosa and gingivae, would meet the crevicular fluid and raise locally its calcium concentration possibly sufficiently to precipitate some protein. If that occurred, it could explain precipitation in the cervical region of a clean tooth reasonably free from bacteria. The second source of calcium ions is plaque itself. Once established, when the pH is reduced after eating carbohydrate and the plaque calcium becomes more soluble, some will tend to diffuse out and, as with crevicular fluid, might precipitate protein in its vicinity. A diffusion of calcium can be detected from plaque incubated *in vitro* with sugar.

The concentration of calcium in saliva might be adequate to promote adsorption of protein and agglutination of bacteria.

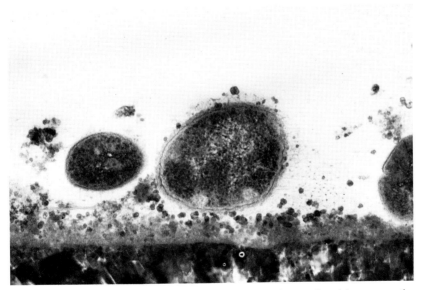

FIG. X.6. Electronmicrograph of bacteria in plaque showing small vesicles apparently leaving the bacteria and entering the plaque matrix. × 52 000.

(E) POSSIBLE BACTERIAL CONTRIBUTIONS TO PLAQUE MATRIX

Electron micrographs of plaque of different ages have demonstrated the presence of dense vesicles in the matrix and on the walls of bacteria (Fig. X.6) in positions suggesting that they are secreted by the organisms (Frank & Houver 1970). In older plaques they were present only in the outer, more recently entrapped, layer of bacteria. This observation suggests that at least one constituent of plaque matrix may arise from the bacteria but this idea does not appear to have been developed or followed up by others. The vesicles could conceivably be precipitates of salivary proteins adsorbed onto the bacterial surface.

The entry of bacteria into plaque

McDougall (1963), from histological studies on sections of teeth extracted after a prophylaxis, concluded that the bacteria of plaque invaded from within, arising from bacteria which had not been removed by the prophylaxis from small crevices in the enamel. The scanning electron microscope studies of Saxton (1973) confirm that some plaque organisms enter this way (Fig. X.7(a), (b)) but show that most of them approach it from the outside (Fig. 7(a) and (d)).

Several factors tend to cause the clumping or agglutination of many species of oral organisms such as: a reduction of pH to below 5·5, the addition of divalent ions such as calcium or magnesium, and of certain protein constituents of plaque and saliva (Fig. 8). These substances would tend to reduce the negative charge (and therefore the mutual repulsion) of the bacteria (Silverman & Kleinberg 1967; Gibbons & Spinell 1970).

A glycoprotein of high molecular weight, containing sialic acid, has been isolated from saliva which has agglutinating properties and readily adsorbs on to apatite. It is in higher concentrations in mixed saliva than in secretions collected from the ducts and may, therefore, arise partly from the minor glands. It may possibly be a constituent of pellicle and, as such, would favour the adhesion of bacteria to the tooth surface. Some oral bacteria which are agglutinated are more readily adsorbed by apatite previously exposed to saliva, and therefore coated with adsorbed protein, than to untreated apatite (Hillman *et al.* 1970).

The salivary agglutinating factors bind to the cell surface and act as bridges between the organisms and their effect is enhanced by calcium ions. It is believed that clumping not only favours the entry of many species of bacteria into plaque but also controls their adhesion to the plaque. Some plaque organisms aggregate with each other under the influence of agglutinating factors, presumably by interactions between constituents of their cell walls, and small groups of one species attached to larger clumps of another species have been described in plaque (the 'corn-cob' formation, Jones 1972). The

(a) (b)

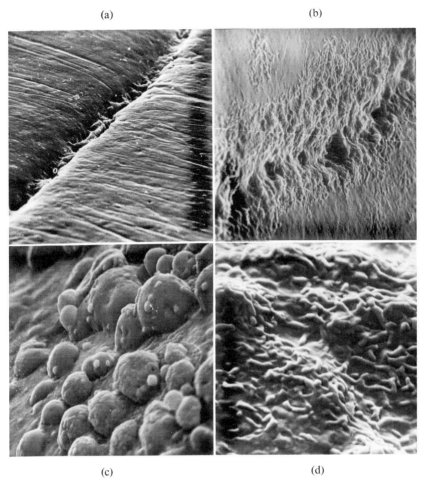

(c) (d)

FIG. X.7. Scanning electronmicrographs of replicas of enamel (a) immediately after a scale and polish, showing scratch marks and an absence of pellicle over the surface and some bacteria remaining in a long crevice, × 1100; (b) same area 24 hr later, the scratch marks are invisible as the enamel surface is covered by pellicle and some bacterial colonization has occurred from the crevice, × 1000; (c) later many clumps of bacteria are attached to pellicle their first appearance near the gingival crevice varying from 5 min to 3 hr, × 5750; (d) fully-established plaque, × 4500.

presence or absence of these interacting sites on the cell walls may be one of the factors which determine whether an organism does or does not flourish in the plaque. Until this idea was developed, the well-known differences between the species of organisms in plaque and saliva were assumed to result because some species could, and others could not, obtain their nutritional requirements in the plaque environment.

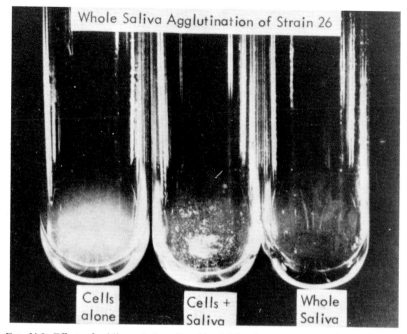

Fɪɢ. X.8. Effect of adding whole saliva (the fairly clear solution on the right) to a suspension of bacteria (left): the mixture (middle) shows the agglutination of the bacteria.

The clumps of bacteria are presumably moved round the mouth by saliva and by chance some of them come into contact with the pellicle-covered tooth surface to which they then adhere. The agglutinating factors would also favour the adhesion of the clumps to bacterial masses already in the plaque. The entry of these bacteria, covered with salivary proteins, also offers an additional possible mechanism for the presence of salivary protein in plaque matrix.

The course of events in the development of plaque has been studied by Frank & Brendel (1966) on electron micrographs of sections of extracted teeth with plaques of unknown age, and by Saxton (1973) with the scanning electron microscope (SEM) on replicas of tooth surfaces (central incisors) *in vivo*.

Contrary to most workers, Frank & Brendel (1966) concluded that the first stage in plaque formation was the apposition of a single layer of bacteria on the surface of enamel or pellicle, later joined by other bacteria which were sometimes separated from each other by matrix, but sometimes the bacterial walls were in contact. From later work, they suggest that the matrix arises, at least partly, from the fusion of vesicles which bud off the bacteria (Fig. X.6).

The teeth studied by Saxton (1973) were given a thorough 'prophylaxis' and replicas taken periodically over the next 24 hr. Immediately after the prophylaxis, scratches on the enamel were visible with occasional cracks or pits containing bacteria not removed by the prophylaxis in agreement with McDougall (1963). Within 20 min, the scratches were obliterated by the deposition of an amorphous pellicle (Fig. X.9(a) and (b)) and in the crevicular region, globular deposits of bacteria ranging from 5 to 20 μm in size were present (Fig. X.7(c) and (d)). After 24 hr, the whole tooth surface became covered with pellicle and in the cervical area was almost completely covered by clumps of bacteria of various sizes becoming enmeshed in newly-deposited amorphous material, presumably matrix. The bacterial clumps enlarged, probably by cell division, and eventually coalesced, presenting an undulating continuous deposit (Fig. X.7(d)). The bacterial clumps first appeared most rapidly (within 5 min) in those subjects with the highest scores for gingival irritation.

Bacteria remaining in the cracks did proliferate and after 24 h had spread over the adjacent enamel; however, the majority of bacteria entered the plaque as clumps from the saliva. Saxton emphasized that the prophylaxis which preceded the taking of the replicas would tend to irritate the gingivae, increase the flow of crevicular fluid and probably accelerate plaque formation in the cervical area. On the other hand, clinical experience shows that plaque formation on the tooth as a whole is much slower than normal for several days after a prophylaxis.

SUMMARY

It seems likely that a combination of factors may promote plaque formation. For example, a low pH may precipitate some proteins directly, and in addition favour the release of calcium from plaque. Similarly, although it is now doubtful whether neuraminidase action favours protein precipitation, there is evidence that after treatment with this enzyme, calcium precipitation occurs more readily. Precipitation is probably not the only mechanism by which salivary glycoproteins may become incorporated in plaque. Proteins adsorbed to enamel, and those involved in bacterial aggregation, presumably constitute a proportion of the plaque matrix, and their incorporation may also be favoured by calcium ions.

The bacteria of plaque

Strålfors (1950) estimated that plaque contained 400 million organisms mg^{-1}, as counted on smears. The proportion of different types differ markedly from those of saliva; for example, *Streptococcus salivarius*, numerous in saliva, are less than 1% of plaque bacteria and lactobacilli about 0·1% of salivary organisms are less than 0·001% of the plaque flora. Anaerobic cultivation of plaque bacteria gives better growth than aerobic conditions, which fits in with the probability that inner plaque has a low oxygen tension.

Gibbons *et al.* (1964) have obtained similar results by culture methods. They classify the main cultivable bacteria in plaque as: facultative streptocci 27%; facultative diphtheroids, 23%; anaerobic diphtheroids, 18%; peptostrepto-cocci, 13%; Veillonella, 6%; Bacteroides, 4%; fusobacteria, 4%; Neisseria, 3%; and vibrios, 2%. Organisms such as lactobacilli, which comprise less than 1% of the total, were not included in this survey.

When plaque bacteria are cultured, many species do not grow on conven-tional media, consequently the proportions of each species of bacteria judged by culture methods may be in serious error. About 90% of the cultivated bacteria which enter the plaque during the first day or two of its formation are Gram-positive cocci (70%) with a minority of rods and these proportion predominate in the 'young' plaque on smooth surfaces of people who clean their teeth daily. If plaque is allowed to remain for 2–4 days, the proportion of cocci and rods diminishes and by 7 days is only about 50% of the total, the the rest being filamentous organisms arranged largely at right angles to the enamel surface. These will be the proportions of bacteria in plaque of subjects who do not clean their teeth and possibly of the inaccessible parts of the plaque of those who do not clean really thoroughly.

As plaque becomes thicker the inner parts of it become anaerobic which probably explains the change in the proportion of organisms as the plaque ages (Ritz 1967, 1970).

Electron micrographs show that cell division occurs in the deeper layers forming dense microcolonies although this cell division is probably slow owing to limited access of nutrients. Many organisms exhibit the thickened walls associated with poor bacterial nutrition.

Many of the species of bacteria in plaque produce acid although there is great variation in the rate at which they do so. The acids produced include lactic, acetic, propionic and traces of other fatty acids. Many of these anions are present in neutral plaques but, following the ingestion of sugar, the pre-dominant acid formed is lactic although it is not usually more than about 50% of the total acid present (Geddes 1972). Some plaque bacteria break down lactic acid and therefore tend to raise the pH. Proteolytic bacteria are present but, except in plaque over large dentinal cavities, their numbers are small and their activity weak compared with acid producers.

FISSURE PLAQUE

There are few data on fissure plaque owing to the difficulty of collecting quantities sufficient for analysis from this source. Some microscopical data suggest that a lower proportion of the organisms in fissures are viable and the microbial composition differs from plaque on smooth surfaces (Schroeder and de Boever 1970). One technique for collecting fissure plaque is to implant

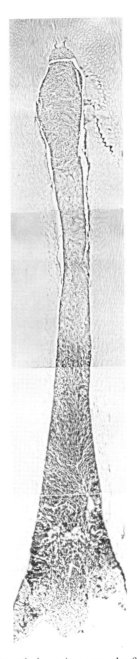

FIG. X.9. Dental plaque in a premolar fissure. × 50.

an 'artificial fissure' made of Mylar plastic into a molar which already has a large amalgam filling. After intervals up to 60 days the Mylar is removed and the fissure plaque studied. Electron micrographs of fissure plaque show many 'ghosts' and dead cells and the surviving cells, mostly Gram-positive cocci, show little sign of division (Fig. X.9). Only in the outer layers, close to the mouth of the fissure, did the plaque resemble that on the smooth surfaces. The organisms did not show the gradual change with age of plaque that occurs on the smooth surfaces. *Streptococcus mutans* represents a smaller proportion of the total flora than in plaque elsewhere (Theilade *et al.* 1973; Karring *et al.* 1974). Food debris, both of plant and animal origin, accompanied by yeasts (probably introduced with the food)

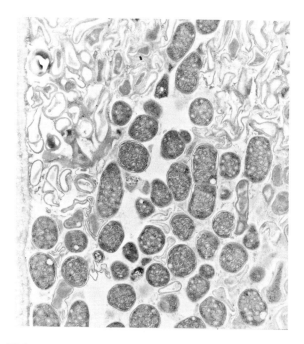

Fig. X.10. Higher magnification of plaque from the depths of a fissure showing the remains of dead cells (left) and the surviving cells (right) seem to be of a uniform type. × 900.

are prominent constituents of early fissure plaque (Fig. X.10), although not usually present in plaque elsewhere, but they became invaded by organisms and after 3–4 weeks had disintegrated and were replaced by bacteria.

MATERIA ALBA

In the outer surface of an old plaque the organisms, usually a mixture of cocci and filamentous types, are less tightly packed and the matrix contains a higher proportion of extracellular polysaccharide (see below). This less compact layer can often be removed by a stream of water unlike the plaque proper; the term 'materia alba', originally applied to the whole of the plaque, has been suggested as a name for this diffuse, loosely attached outer layer.

Polysaccharide synthesis by plaque bacteria

When certain bacteria, including several species from plaque, receive sucrose they may synthesize several types of polysaccharides from it or convert it to acid. During the 1960s evidence accumulated that these polysaccharides were important constituents of plaque and it was thought that they played a leading part in the carious process (see McHugh 1970). This in turn led to great research activity aimed at methods of preventing their accumulation in the expectation that this would reduce caries.

Three main groups of polysaccharides may be formed:

(1) Polymers of glucose (with the general name of glucans) formed as a bulky gelatinous mass outside the bacterial cells, mainly from sucrose, by an enzyme known as dextran sucrase (or glucosyl transferase) on the surface of the bacteria. The enzyme utilizes the energy of the bond between glucose and fructose to synthesize a mixture of polymers, (glucans with most of the links in the 1:6 position), of molecular weight ranging up to several millions, and simultaneously releasing fructose:

$$\text{sucrose} \xrightarrow[\text{sucrase}]{\text{dextran}} \text{dextran} + \text{fructose}.$$

The formation of dextran may be readily seen by comparing the chemical composition of plaque and its appearance in electron micrographs in the fasting condition and after rinsing for 6 to 9 min with a 10% sucrose solution (Saxton 1969, Figs X.11(a) (b)). The formation of dextrans undoubtedly increases the bulk of plaque and analyses showed that the insoluble, high molecular weight fraction could occupy up to 10% of the dry weight of plaque (the total carbohydrate is about 15%). But since about half of it may be metabolized during incubation for a few hours, plaque evidently contains some 'dextranase'. It was speculated that the dextrans would act as a sponge reducing the permeability of plaque and thus preventing acid from leaving and salivary bicarbonate from entering, both of possible importance in caries. It must be emphasized that this widely-quoted speculation on the permeability of dextrans has not been adequately tested and there appears to be little experimental evidence for it. In one of the few attempts to study the permeability of a layer of dextran, fluoride passed through it quite readily (Kirkegaard *et al.* 1975).

(a)   (b)

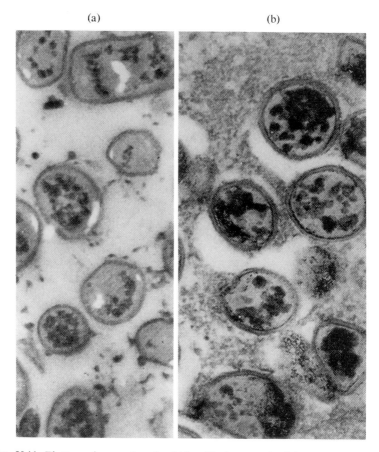

FIG. X.11. Electronmicrographs of a 24-hr-old plaque stained for carbohydrate (a) collected 2 hr after eating, (b) after 10-min rinse with a 10% sucrose solution. Note that the dark staining for carbohydrate is increased both in the matrix between the cells and within the cells. × 12 000.

It was originally though that the linkage in the dextrans was 1:6 and that they would be broken down by dextranase (or α-1:6 glucan-6-glucano hydrolase) which could be isolated from moulds. Later the links were shown to be in the 1:6 and 1:3 position in approximately equal numbers. The main glucan was eventually identified as a 1:3 polymer of glucose (Guggenheim 1970), now called a 'mutan' and broken down by a 'mutanase' (or 1:3 glucan-3-glucanohydrolase).

Dextrans have also been suggested as agglutinating factors for certain bacteria including *Streptococcus mutans*. They also adsorb readily to hydroxy-apatite which gave rise to the suggestion that they might be important in attaching the plaque to the enamel surface. This is a possibility, but when apatite is coated with salivary proteins (to resemble pellicle) its adsorptive power for dextrans is reduced. Phosphate, at concentrations present in saliva and plaque, reduces dextran adsorption and is suggested as a factor influencing the amount of adsorption *in vivo*: with high concentrations (0·1 M) of phosphate, apatite coated with salivary protein adsorbs still less dextran than uncoated (Rölla & Mathiesen 1970).

(2) Another enzyme (levan sucrase) converts sucrose into levans—fairly soluble extracellular polymers of fructose, linked in the 2:6 position but these are formed to a much smaller extent than are dextrans. When the supply of sucrose is exhausted, levans are rapidly metabolized to acid by plaque enzymes, which have not been fully characterized but are variously known as levanase, levan hydrolase or fructan hydrolase.

(3) Many oral bacteria store carbohydrate as intracellular glycogen-like polysaccharides (1:4 glucans) which stain with iodine and may be visualized as granules in electron micrographs (Gibbons & Socransky 1962; Houte van & Jansen 1968). Unlike the extracellular polysaccharides, which are formed mostly from sucrose, the intracellular polysaccharide may be formed from a variety of sugars (including glucose, maltose and sucrose) and are broken down to acid when other sources of carbohydrates are absent, such as between meals. With low concentrations of sugar, only the filamentous organisms store intracellular polysaccharides (Saxton 1975).

Plaque from caries-active subjects has been reported to contain a higher proportion (54%) of the organisms giving an iodine reaction for intracellular polysaccharide than caries-free (29·8%). Low concentrations (2·2 and 4·4 ppm) of fluoride reduce the synthesis of intracellular polysaccharide by oral bacteria (Kleinberg & Sandham 1964) which could be of significance in the action of fluoride in caries.

A reduction in the carbohydrate of the diet for 2 weeks has been stated to reduce the proportion of plaque organisms capable of storing carbohydrate.

Properties of Plaque

The plaque is firmly held on to the tooth surface and is not removed by a stream of water, but is by brushing. It is insoluble in most reagents and its permeability is relatively low, although highly-diffusible molecules like urea can pass through it.

ACID PRODUCTION BY PLAQUE

Experiments were carried out by Stephan (1940) and confirmed by many others who measured, by means of fine antimony electrodes, the pH of the intact plaque undisturbed on the smooth surface of the anterior teeth.

Most of the experiments were carried out on subjects who had allowed a thick plaque to accumulate by abstaining from cleaning their teeth for 4 days. Within 2 or 3 min of rinsing the mouth with sugar solution (between 10% and 50% of glucose or sucrose were used), the pH of the plaque fell from an average of about 6·5 to about 5 and took up to 40 min to return

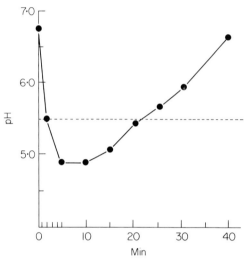

FIG. X.12. The pH of the plaque after rinsing the mouth with 10% glucose solution (a 'Stephan curve'). The dotted line represents a typical value for the pH below which decalcification of enamel begins (the 'critical pH').

to the original figure (a 'Stephan curve', Fig. X.12). When the teeth were thoroughly brushed after the completion of such an experiment, a second sugar rinse produced a much smaller fall in pH since the plaque containing the acid-producing bacteria had been largely removed.

The main results have been confirmed in plaque near the contact points (i.e. potential sites of caries) in preference to the smooth surfaces originally tested, and with normal carbohydrate foods as opposed to the sugar rinses originally used (Jenkins & Kleinberg 1956; Ludwig & Bibby 1957).

Even the addition of very low concentrations of sugar (0·5%) has some effect in lowering plaque pH and if the additions are made at, say, 2-min intervals over a period the reduction in pH continues over that period (Fig. X.13). In this experiment, drops of sugar solution were put on to the plaque direct, contact with the tongue being avoided, so that no stimulation of saliva flow occurred. During normal eating, rapidly flowing saliva with a high pH bathes the plaque and it is likely that the pH may remain high until after

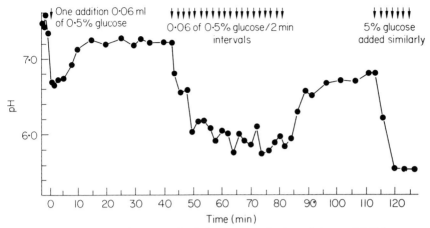

FIG. X.13. The effect of plaque pH of the local application of drops of 0·5% sugar solutions at 2-min intervals—note the marked response to low concentrations of sugar and the prolonged fall. The sugar did not reach the tongue so that saliva flow was not stimulated—this result may, therefore, differ from the changes during normal eating when saliva flow is stimulated and the saliva probably reaches the plaque, but may resemble the changes in plaque when saliva cannot easily reach it as in fissures and inaccessible contact points.

eating has finished and the saliva flow has ceased (see Figs X.16 & 17). The plaque pH during eating has not been adequately studied, however. With foods like white bread, which tend to remain on the plaque (but, contrary to wide belief, do not become fully incorporated into it) the pH may fall and remain at the minimum for a longer time than with sugar. This suggests that the time taken for the carbohydrate to be removed from plaques after meals might be important in controlling the intensity and duration of pH changes after meals and hence of caries activity. Lanke (1957) has studied the rate of sugar clearance of the mouth by measuring the sugar content of saliva after eating various foods. Clearance times differed greatly among different people but each individual treated different foods in a similar way—if clearance time was long for one food it was also long for all foods. Movements of the tongue and lips after food increased the clearance rate which was longer for starchy foods than for sweets or sugars.

Two other methods have been used to study plaque pH changes. In one, small samples (fractions of a milligram) of plaque are taken from most of the smooth surfaces, pooled and its pH measured outside the mouth with an electrode designed for use with small volumes (a 'one drop electrode'). This method has the advantage that the plaque metabolizes the carbohydrate *in vivo* but its pH is measured *in vitro* and the mean change on the teeth as a whole are recorded; on the other hand, since the pH of plaque in different

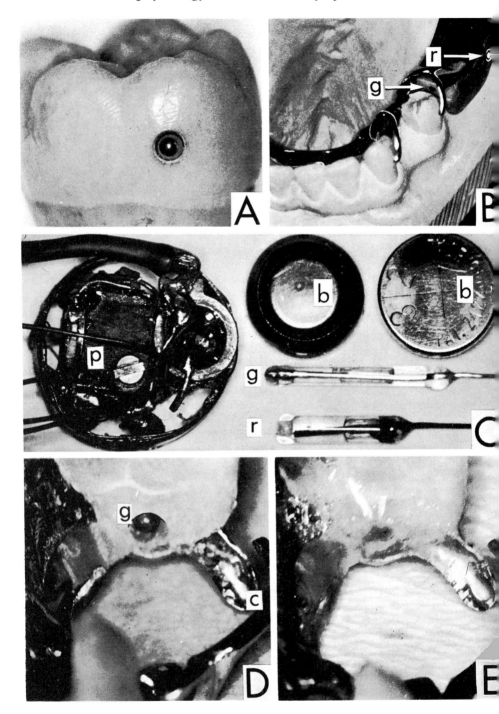

enamel surfaces differ (for example, lower incisors are usually higher than elsewhere) it is important that the contribution from each area is of similar size. The results compare very well with those of Stephan's method.

The third method attempts to measure telemetrically the pH of the inner surfaces of plaque in contact with the enamel, since this is of the greatest importance in caries. Small glass electrodes are built into a hollowed out, extracted tooth mounted on a denture which is worn in the mouth for some days to accumulate plaque. The electrode is connected either to a pH meter by leads from the denture or to a tiny intraoral radio transmitter from which the signals may be detected and recorded outside the mouth (Fig. X.14, from Graf & Mühlemann 1966). By incorporating a fluoride electrode into the device it has been possible to monitor also the fluoride changes in the plaque after various procedures (Clarke & Fanning 1973).

The results show, in general, slower drops in pH often reaching lower

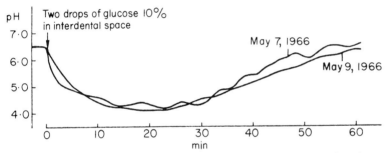

Fig. X.15. Duplicate curves of pH changes in plaque as measured by a microelectrode built into an extracted tooth on 2 days showing that the curves are reasonably reproducible.

figures than with other methods (Figs X.14, 15, 16) and much longer periods of low pH. This may indicate that the inner plaque does change more slowly than the plaque as a whole as measured by the other methods, but the difference may arise because thicker plaques have usually been studied, and these

Fig. X.14. (a) Tip of pH glass electrode incorporated in proximal surface of extracted molar; (b) vitallium partial denture as frame for glass electrode (g) and reference electrode (r) (subject's left side). Not visible: radio transmitter in molar area of right side; (c) package of assembled transmitter components. Miniature potentiometer (p) for frequency adjustment. The coils are wrapped around the component package. Two mercury cells (b) as power source, glass (g) and reference (r) electrodes. Scale in mm; (d) mesial aspect of extracted and mounted molar before insertion of removable partial denture (g = glass electrode, c = clasp); (e) mesial aspect of extracted and mounted molar 5 days after insertion of partial denture. The glass electrode is covered by plaque.

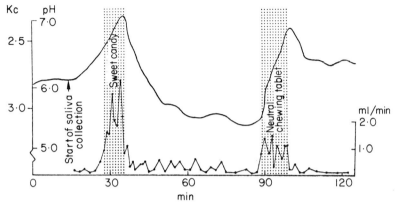

FIG. X.16. Effect of saliva collection, sucking of sweet candy and neutral chewing tablet on telemetered pH of thin 2-day-old proximal plaque and on salivary flow.

may poison the electrode. Also, the plaque may not be quite normal since it is formed on glass and not on the enamel surface.

With this method, the pH may be studied while food is in the mouth. The results confirm that the pH does not necessarily fall during eating provided the plaque is only 1 or 2 days old. With older plaques, the fall begins almost

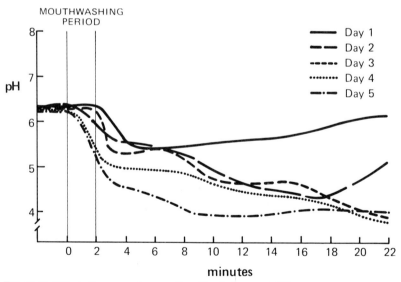

FIG. X.17. Effect of a sugar rinse on the pH of plaque of different ages measured by microelectrodes built into an extracted tooth. With the older plaques the pH fall begins during the sugar rinse, reaches lower values and returns more slowly than with the 1-day-old plaque.

immediately after a sugar rinse enters the mouth (Fig. X.17). This may apply to the less accessible sites of plaque (which are the more usual sites of caries) even in subjects who clean their teeth. The telemetric method has not yet been used extensively to study pH changes during the consumption of a wide variety of foods and drinks.

The importance of the experiments on plaque pH lies in showing, first, that the pH on the tooth surface can fall below the critical level at which demineralization occurs in saliva (and the critical pH for plaque appears to be similar, see p. 397), although, now that these methods have been quite widely used, it is clear that the pH does not always fall below or even approach the critical figure (Fig. X.13). The rapidity of the pH drop is surprising in view of the high buffering power of plaque (Strålfors 1948). A logical conclusion from these results would seem to be that it is desirable to remove plaque before, rather than after, a meal because if the removal is delayed by even 10–15 min it would be too late to avoid the risk of some demineralization of the enamel.

FACTORS INVOLVED IN THE RISE OF pH

When sucrose reaches the plaque some is converted into extracellular polysaccharides and some, after hydrolysis into glucose and fructose, polymerizes into intracellular polysaccharides and the remainder undergoes glycolysis to lactic acid. The pH rises, partly by loss of acid by outward diffusion and partly by conversion of lactic acid into the less highly ionized acetic and propionic acids. After eating, the concentration of sugar in saliva and plaque falls quite rapidly so that further acid production from free sugar ceases but continues from the levans and intracellular polysaccharides (and, to a smaller extent, from the dextrans also). The sugar that induces the acid production will also stimulate a flow of alkaline, heavily-buffered saliva which enters the plaque and moderates the effect of the acid in lowering pH and may play a part in raising it but the secretion is unlikely to be sufficiently prolonged to promote the return to the original value. The saliva will also provide the pH rise factor (see below).

When Lilienthal (1955) carried out tests on the buffering power of plaque removed from the teeth of people who had abstained from tooth-brushing for some days, bicarbonate was absent and he concluded that bicarbonate was unimportant in buffering plaque but this conclusion is clearly wrong. The evidence that saliva (whose chief buffer is bicarbonate) plays an important part in reducing the drop in pH which occurs after carbohydrate and in accelerating the rise in pH is as follows. (1) Englander *et al.* (1959) compared the drop in plaque pH after sugar rinses in subjects when normal access of saliva to the plaque and when saliva was prevented from reaching the plaque. The pH drop was much greater when saliva was restricted (Fig. X.18). (2) In some subjects who are very caries-prone, the pH of the plaque

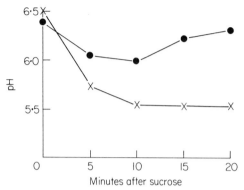

FIG. X.18. pH changes in plaque after a sucrose rinse with and without a restriction of saliva flow. ●, Without salivary restriction; ×, with salivary restriction.

may remain between 5 and 6 for some hours after meals (whether this is caused by the excessive retention of food in plaque or by the synthesis of unusually large amounts of polysaccharide by plaque bacteria is not known). If such subjects suck a sweet, thus increasing saliva flow as well as its pH and buffering power, the pH of the plaque *rises* (Jenkins & Kleinberg 1956, also shown in Fig. X.16). The reason for Lilienthal's finding no bicarbonate in plaque is probably that, in buffering acid, bicarbonate is converted into carbonic acid which volatilizes as carbon dioxide (see p. 318). (3) The incidence of

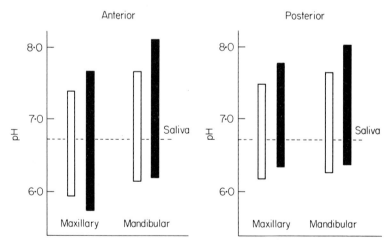

FIG. X.19. The pH range of plaques in different regions. The top of each bar is the fasting pH, note that it is higher than the saliva bathing it (dotted line). Solid bars refer to interproximal regions, open bars labial-buccal. Note that the mandibular pH values are higher than the maxillary.

caries greatly increases in animals after removal of the salivary glands. Evidently saliva has an important influence in reducing caries mainly by its buffering power and partly by its antibacterial actions (p. 340).

Although plaque is greatly affected by the pH of the saliva in its environment it frequently has a pH value higher than that of the saliva bathing it (Fig X.15). This suggests that plaque alkali production, mostly ammonia formation from urea but also some conversion of amino acids to amines by decarboxylation, are important factors governing the pH of plaque. Plaque pH depends therefore on the net effect of acid production, base production and its buffering power. Base production has, however, been studied very little compared to acid production in spite of its potential importance, although a few facts have been established. Until recently, it had been assumed that ammonia was released by a urease but metabolic studies with $[^{14}C]$ urea show that the ratio of NH_3 to CO_2 formed is $1:10$ and not $2:1$ as would be expected with urease action (Biswas & Kleinberg 1971). The NH_2 group of urea is apparently used to synthesize certain amino acids, especially alanine, from which ammonia is released by deamination. Applications of strong concentrations of urea to the plaque were found to make it alkaline and to reduce greatly the fall of pH occurring after subsequent glucose rinses, an effect which was stated to be detectable for up to 24 hr. This fact has been applied in an attempt at caries control by including urea in dentifrices but no satisfactory clinical evidence of their effectiveness has been produced. The optimum pH for amine production by decarboxylation is about 5 so that if plaque becomes acid an automatic increase in base production would be expected as well as the release of CO_2 which would build up the bicarbonate buffering power (Hayes & Hyatt 1974). Although this study was based on plaque bacteria in pure culture and it is not definitely known whether the concentration of amino acids in plaque is sufficiently high for this reaction to be important, it is reasonable to suppose that this change does occur.

A fraction of saliva has been isolated by Kleinberg *et al.* (1973) known as the 'pH rise factor' (sialin) and identified as a basic peptide containing arginine. Its effect is to accelerate the uptake of glucose by salivary organisms, increase acid production and the formation of carbon dioxide and base. Although most of the experiments have been carried out on salivary sediment, similar effects have been reported on plaque (Kleinberg 1977). Its effect on pH depends on the concentration of sugar; with concentrations lower than 0·05%, the increased rate of utilization results in more rapid exhaustion of sugar, shorter duration of acid production and increased base production and a more rapid rise in pH. With sugar concentrations higher than 0·5% this factor increases acid production and its effect on base production is masked. It is likely that the salivary supernatant factor(s) known for many years to stimulate acid production are similar or identical to the pH rise factor or are its precursors.

Factors in plaque which may influence its caries-producing powers

It has been realized for many years that acid production and pH changes in the innermost layers of plaque, where it is in contact with the enamel surface, were probably the decisive factors in caries. The question of the differences between *saliva* in caries-active and caries-free subjects (see p. 348) may therefore have been misdirected—the real question is how does *plaque* in a caries-active mouth differ from that in a caries-free mouth? This raises another question which has been much neglected, namely that in a mouth with caries, plaques form on all the teeth but only some of them produce caries. In other words, in a caries-active mouth there may be two sorts of plaque—those which do, and those which do not, cause caries. A third type which forms calculus might be added. The whole question is inadequately studied but present evidence (discussed more fully by Jenkins, 1965) suggests: (1) that samples of plaque removed from caries-active or caries-free mouths and incubated with sugar *in vitro* produce similar quantities of acid; (2) the general bacterial counts are similar but the plaque from caries-free subjects tend to contain lower counts of *Lactobacillus acidophilus* and *Streptococcus mutans*; (3) there is agreement that the fasting plaque pH is higher in caries-free mouths than in caries-active mouths; and (4) acid production after eating or rinsing with sugar is greater in caries-active than in caries-free mouths, so that in the latter the final pH is also higher. Owing to the logarithmic nature of pH the actual change in pH may be greater in the caries-free—for example, a fall from 7·0 to 6·0 represents less acid production than a fall from 5·8 to 5·0, these being typical ranges respectively for subjects who are caries-free or are suffering from rampant caries (Englander *et al.* 1956).

(5) Ashley (1975) reported that the plaque calcium and phosphate were inversely related both to the total carious experience and to the caries increment during 2 years confirming similar findings by Kleinberg *et al.* (1969). Although these minerals are not all present in ionic forms, the proportion that is ionic (and this increases as the pH falls) will tend to lower the critical pH and thus protect the teeth against acid.

More work is needed before any firm conclusion can be drawn.

Turning now to the question of why within a caries-active mouth some plaques do, and others do not, produce caries, the following differences have been found between areas which are usually caries resistant (for example, lower incisors) and those which are often caries-prone (molars and upper incisors)—but their importance must still be speculative.

(1) The resting or fasting pH tends to be higher in the caries-resistant than in the caries-prone areas (Kleinberg & Jenkins 1964). The pH values reached after sugar rinses are related to the resting pH (if the resting pH is high the pH after the sugar rinse is also higher because the factors tending to maintain a high resting value also tend to prevent a large fall after the ingestion of

sugar). (2) The calcium and phosphate concentrations are higher in caries free areas.

Although much more work is needed, these results suggest that a combination of the calcium and phosphate content of plaque, and of the range of changes in pH value, both influenced largely by the accessibility and composition of saliva, are related to the power of plaque to produce caries. Many other factors not yet studied in plaque may also be involved.

In view of the differences between the composition of plaque and saliva, in particular the calcium and phosphate concentrations and the buffering power, it might be expected that the critical pH at which demineralization begins in plaque would differ from that of saliva. Because of uncertainties about the proportion of these substances present as ions in plaque, this is a difficult point to decide. In practice, however, the pH changes in plaque from caries-active and caries-free subjects do support the idea that caries does not develop unless the pH falls below about 5·2 (Englander *et al.* 1956).

THE EFFECT OF PLAQUE ON THE GINGIVAE

Until recently it was believed that mechanical irritation from calculus initiated gingivitis which, if allowed to progress for years, led to periodontal disease— a condition responsible for the loss of more teeth than caries. Experiments in which human volunteers were asked to refrain from tooth-brushing showed, however, that gingivitis developed in some subjects within a few days —long before the plaque could be fully coverted into calculus (Loe *et al.* 1965). This observation was put on a quantitative basis by Lang *et al.* (1973) whose subjects first carried out very thorough oral hygiene so that their plaque score and gingival index (a measure of gingivitis) was near zero. The subjects were divided into four groups who cleaned their teeth at intervals of 12, 24, 48 and 96 hr for 6 weeks. The first two groups developed no gingivitis, the third group (48 hr) had a measurable score and in the fourth group (96 hr) the score was highest (Fig. X.20). Evidently, plaque has to be 48 hr old before it develops sufficient concentrations of the toxic material to affect the gingivae. Thus, provided tooth cleaning is really thorough, once every other day is sufficiently frequent to prevent gingivitis. Unfortunately, no precise figures can be given for the minimum age at which plaque can produce pH conditions damaging to the enamel surface. It is certainly much shorter than 24 hr and, in some subjects, plaque even a few hours old is potentially able to lower the pH to levels capable of dissolving the enamel at least locally in small areas, if saliva cannot reach it. In spite of this change of emphasis from calculus to plaque, Mandel (1974b) pointed out that the roughened surface of calculus encourages plaque formation and that calculus limits self-cleansing mechanisms by blocking the gingival pocket, and making oral hygiene more difficult. This implies that in spite of recent emphasis on the importance of plaque, the removal of calculus is still clinically desirable.

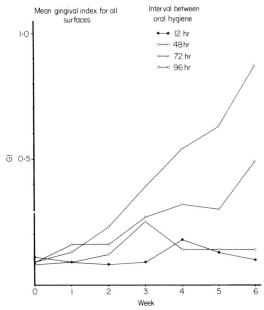

FIG. X.20. The effect on gingivitis index (G.I.) of tooth brushing at intervals of 12, 48, 72 or 96 hr for 6 weeks. The G.I. did not change with tooth brushing at 12 or 48 hr but rose markedly when plaque was allowed to collect for 72 or 96 hr throughout the 6 weeks.

THE NATURE OF THE TOXINS IN PLAQUE WHICH PRODUCE GINGIVITIS

Two views are held about the nature of the response of the gingivae to plaque. The first is that plaque contains substances which diffuse into the gingival tissues and irritate them directly. Evidence for this view is provided by experiments in which HeLa cells have been incubated in a standard medium containing various concentrations of extracts of plaque and the growth rate has been measured and compared with saline controls (Levine *et al.* 1974). If the extract contained the equivalent of more than 1 mg ml^{-1}, growth was inhibited, and if above 2 mg ml^{-1} growth creased altogether (Fig. X.21). Fractionation of the extracts showed that it contained two active constituents: a thermolabile, nondiffusible substance which tends to form polymers but with a monomeric mol. wt. of about 30 000 and a stable substance of mol. wt. about 225. While it cannot be certain that artefacts have been avoided, it seems likely that the toxic effect of these extracts is relevant to gingivitis.

Macrophages (obtained from mice by peritoneal lavage) have been incubated in media with or without suspensions of freeze-dried, sterilized plaque for up to 2 days. Amounts of plaque equivalent to as little as 1–25 μg ml^{-1} led to three- to four-fold increase in cell size and increased release into the medium

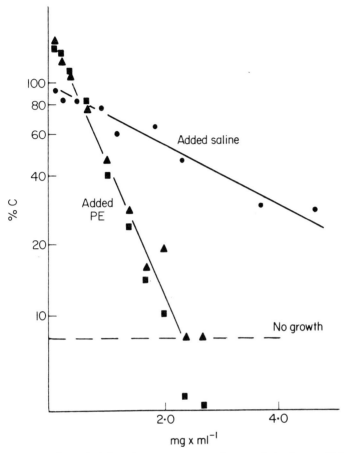

FIG. X.21. The effect of adding plaque extracts on the growth *in vitro* on HeLa cells (cells cultured from human cancer) as a percentage of growth in culture medium only: if the extract was equivalent to more than 2 mg ml^{-1} of medium, growth ceased.

of certain lysosomal enzymes (which are concerned with tissue destruction). If these plaque constituents diffuse into the gingivae and induce similar enzymic release *in vivo*, they could contribute to its breakdown (Page *et al.* 1973).

Plaque contains proteolytic enzymes of bacterial origin (Frostell & Soder 1970; Mäkinen 1966) and the amino acids they release are broken down further into amines, ammonia, H_2S and mercaptans, all of which are potential irritants and some may contribute to halitosis (p. 350). These enzymes are said to be more active in older than in younger people which might be related to the greater incidence of periodontal disease in older people.

Extracts of plaques from adults with radiological evidence of alveolar bone loss and also from children without bone loss led to increased osteoclastic resorption *in vitro* of embryonic bone (Hausmann & Weinfield 1973). The reason for a bone response *in vitro* even from plaque taken from children whose gingivae were healthy is probably that their younger epithelial tissues were more successful in preventing toxic substances from reaching the under-lying structures than in older people. The bacteria in children's plaque are not known to differ from those of adults and, as this experiment shows, are equally capable of producing toxic substances.

Although it is by no means certain that these constituents of plaque do diffuse into the gingivae and, if so, that they are active *in vivo*, it is reasonable to suggest that they may have deleterious effects such as the cell damage, the enzymic destruction of tissues and the increased bone resorption, which were produced *in vitro*.

Another view on the means by which plaque produces gingivitis, is that plaque antigens such as bacterial endotoxins enter the gingivae and induce antibodies in the local lymph tissues. The imediate interaction between the antibodies and the antigens may be beneficial but the union of antibodies with antigen activates complement which in turn causes the release of substances contracting the smooth muscle of arterioles and increasing vascular perme-ability. This results in oedema, inflammation and destruction of bone and periodontal fibres (Mergenhagen *et al.* 1970; Lehner 1975).

Dental Calculus

Dental calculus, or tartar, may occur either above the gum (supragingival calculus) or below (subgingival calculus) and as the two forms differ in proper-ties as well as in position, it is generally supposed that they are formed by different processes. Supragingival calculus is friable, readily removed by scaling and usually unpigmented, whereas the subgingival variety is much harder and often green in colour. Supragingival calculus forms in greatest amounts on the lower incisors and upper molars, i.e. near the orifices of the main salivary ducts and its composition varies in different sites in the mouth. Subgingival calculus is usually present in smaller deposits; they show no tendency to be localized near the salivary ducts and their composition is less dependent on the site. It becomes exposed if the gums recede. Its position, apparently out of contact with saliva, suggested that it was formed by precipi-tation of constituents of serum (hence its former name 'serumnal calculus') rather than from saliva. Although some years ago most workers favoured a salivary origin for both, a good deal of recent evidence justifies a return to the older view. The existence of the gingival fluid and the similarity of the compo-sition and location of subgingival calculus at different distances from salivary ducts all point to a non-salivary origin. Also, Waerhaug (1955) found by experiments with dyes that saliva appeared to have no access to the sites of deposition of subgingival calculus. Subgingival calculus docs not form on experimental strips (described below) within the time required for an abundant deposit of supragingival calculus. Calculus does not form as readily in children as in adults.

Composition

Calculus is variable in composition but always has a preponderance (about 80%) of inorganic material containing calcium, magnesium, phosphate and carbonate. It contains fluoride up to about 400 ppm or even more in old calculus (Jenkins & Speirs 1954; Grøn *et al.* 1967). Analyses of calculus from

TABLE X.4

Range of composition of supragingival and subgingival calculus (percentage of dry weight)

Density	*Org. matter*	*CO_2*	*Ca*	*P*	*Na*
(A) Supragingival					
High (1·33)	11	2	28	16	2·09
Low (1·09)	20	3·7	26·9	14·9	2·58
(B) Subgingival					
High	17	1·3	31	16	1·77
Low	29	3·6	25	14·6	1·26

(Data from Little *et al.* 1961, 1963.)

about 200 subjects (Table X.4) refer to the most and the least radiopaque samples and presumably give the extreme limits of the range of composition. Studies by X-ray diffraction and the electron microscope of the stages of calculus formation on plastic strips show that the first crystalline mineral to be detected is brushite ($CaHPO_4 \cdot 2H_2O$). This is present in 3-day-old plaque in some very rapid calculus formers and detectable in all deposits after 14 days of development; its proportion gradually declines and is not present at all in about half of specimens more than 1 year old. Octacalcium phosphate (OCP): $Ca_8(HPO_4)_2(PO_4)_4$ is also formed in early calculus and some remains even in old deposits. It is thought that brushite is gradually converted into either OCP or, in the presence of high magnesium concentrations, into whitlockite (Ca_3PO_4 with some of the calcium replaced by magnesium). Both of these may change into apatite, especially in the presence of fluoride. Whitlockite occurs rarely compared with apatites, and calculus is the only place in nature where high concentrations of octacalcium phosphate are found, although it may be present in mineralizing tissues as a transitional stage before apatite is formed. It has been speculated that a substance in saliva inhibits apatite formation and favours the deposition of these less usual crystalline forms; it is thought that magnesium ions, by substituting for some of the calcium in whitlockite and forming a more stable crystal, play some part in this process but their concentration in saliva is too low to account for the whole of it. The proportions of the different crystalline forms in calculus differ from one geographical area of Britain to another.

It is not possible to identify the matrix of calculus with any clear chemical compound which is not surprising since it probably consists of varying proportions of material derived from the saliva and bacteria. However, it is largely protein, which has been reported to contain 12–20% carbohydrate, including 6% of various hexoses, 4% fucose (Hampar *et al.* 1961; Little *et al.* 1961), 2–3% hexosamine (mainly glucosamine but with some galactosamine) and GAGs (chondroitin sulphate, hyaluronic acid and heparan sulphate). The GAGs are not present in saliva or plaque but are contained in gingivae and they presumably arise in calculus from this source (Osuoji & Rowles 1972). Calculus also contains 3% of lipid, higher than would be expected from the concentrations in saliva and with a different composition, suggesting a bacterial origin.

Histological examination has shown that many filamentous bacteria are present, probably *Leptotrichia buccalis*. In some specimens, lamination is visible, suggesting that formation is intermittent.

In an attempt to explain why the removal of calculus during scaling was in some cases easy and in others difficult, Zander (1953) studied its mode of attachment to cementum in demineralized and ground sections and Selvig (1969) extended it by electron microscopy. He described four types of attachment: (1) to the pellicle then known as the secondary cuticle; (2) if the pellicle were absent it was attached to minute irregularities in the cementum; (3) masses of organisms which penetrated the cementum were continuous with those in the calculus in what were presumably arrested carious lesions. The crystals of the original tissue were larger than usual and resembled those of the calculus indicating that remineralization had occurred; and (4) calculus was in some places locked into areas of resorption which electron micrographs show are frequent on cementum.

Theories of formation

The older theories of calculus formation, like contemporary theories of mineralization in bone, concentrated on factors concerned with releasing calcium or phosphate ions or which changed the ability of saliva to retain its saturation with calcium and phosphate (plaque was not considered because its composition was not known). More recently, attention has been turned to the matrix and to the possibility that it contains seeding substances.

(1) CARBON DIOXIDE LOSS
The fact that the saturation of saliva may depend on complex formation with other constituents such as CO_2 (see p. 298) suggests that changes in the concentration of these substances might lead to precipitation of calcium phosphate. One of the older ideas was that loss of CO_2 from the saliva, as it equilibrated with the relatively low tension of CO_2 in the mouth, resulted in the precipitation of the calcium salts. This theory offers an explanation for the tendency of calculus to form on the teeth nearest to the salivary ducts because they would be the first teeth to meet the saliva in its unstable condition. The finding that carbonic anhydrase may favour calculus formation *in vitro* and that a high CO_2 tension may lower it (McConnell & Frajola 1961; von der Fehr & Brudevold 1960) is compatible with this theory.

(2) pH CHANGE BY AMMONIA FORMATION
Ammonia formation from urea raises salivary pH *in vitro*, and possibly *in vivo* during periods of reduced salivary flow such as sleep. This might be expected to favour the precipitation of calcium phosphate. Mandel & Thompson (1967) found that rapid calculus producers have a higher than average urea concentration in saliva which might be expected to increase ammonia levels in plaque.

(3) THE PHOSPHATASE THEORY
Although plaque contains both bacterial acid and alkaline phosphatase they are no longer considered to play any significant role in calculus production. PP_i is formed in plaque by bacteria provided the saliva is allowed access to the plaque; its production is reduced if plaque is covered or if saliva is drained from the mouth by cannulae so that it does not reach the plaque. The concentration in plaque has been reported to be higher in slow rather than rapid calculus formers (Edgar & Jenkins 1972) suggesting that it prevents the mineralization of plaque, although exactly the opposite role has also been suggested, namely that it is broken down by bacterial pyrophosphatase and by raising the concentration of P_i encourages mineralization.

(4) SEEDING THEORY
None of these theories is now considered to provide an adequate explanation of how calculus forms. At the same time it has never been proved that they play no part in the process. A seeding process is now thought to be mainly responsible for the formation of calculus but this evades one of the chief practical problems in calculus, namely, why do some people form it more quickly than others? There must, therefore, be factors which control either

the amount of seed formed or its effectiveness or the rate at which the first seeded crystals grow. The actions suggested by the above theories may possibly work in these ways. The evidence for seeding theories is presented in the next few paragraphs.

In vitro studies on calculus formation

Earlier methods of studying the nature of calculus formation and the factors which control it consists of a rocking or dipping device by which teeth can be immersed in saliva, then withdrawn, each cycle lasting for about 1 min. Plaque and calculus-like material collect on the teeth within a few days. Glass slides, cover-slips or glass pellets have been used instead of teeth since the progress of the deposits is then much easier to see and their changes in weight can be more readily detected than with deposits on teeth. It is, of course, uncertain to what extent these deposits resemble true calculus.

Calculus formation on celluloid strips

Calculus formation involves two stages—matrix deposition and its later mineralization. It is reasonable to suppose that the matrix is derived from dental plaque whose formation is discussed on pp. 374–8.

In the experiments with celluloid strips which were attached to the teeth (p. 369) for longer than 3 days, changes in the microscopical appearance and composition were found. Mineralized areas began to form (identified by von Kossa's stain or by radiography) on or near the strip (Fig. X.22). Changes in the staining of the deposits occurred associated with the mineralization.

FIG. X.22. Five-day deposit on strip showing dark staining areas of mineralization at inner surface (bottom) and many filamentous organisms.

The presence of the strips increases calculus formation; for example, it forms on strips in children who did not form it normally, and on teeth with strips when it did not form on adjacent teeth without strips.

The most striking change occurring about the same time as the mineralization was the gradual increase in the proportion of filamentous organisms which eventually equalled or exceeded the number of rods and cocci. This may be the result of the anaerobic conditions developing on the inner plaque as it thickens.

Following the growth of filamentous bacteria, possibly as a result or possibly quite independently, some constituent of plaque matrix or bacteria changes and can act as a seeding substance which, in the salivary environment of a supersaturated solution, results in the crystallization of calcium phosphate.

As mentioned above (p. 372) the concentrations of calcium and phosphate in early plaque are high, indicating either that it already contains areas of crystalline calcium phosphate or that these ions are bound to other substances in the plaque. The latter possibility seems more likely because calcium and phosphate may be extracted from plaque in different proportions at different pH values; this would not be expected if all the calcium and phosphate were present as apatite. Some workers have reported an X-ray diffraction pattern of apatite in early plaque but this may be an artefact following the drying of the plaque.

Some electron micrographs show crystals forming first in the matrix from an unidentified seed (the possibility of the crystals being formed during the preparation of the specimen cannot be ignored). A number of plaque organisms (*Bacterionema matruchotii*, *Actinomyces israelii* and *Streptococcus salivarius*) become mineralized when placed in suitable saturated solutions and substances with seeding properties can be extracted from them by acid. These organisms do not represent a high proportion of those in plaque, however. Other organisms (Veillonellae and diphtheroids) which are present in greater number in plaque mineralize on their surface, i.e. in the plaque matrix.

Pure cultures of bacteria isolated from calculus and placed in dialysis bags were implanted into the peritoneal cavity of rats. After 14 days, the bacteria remained viable and were found to contain apatite crystals. Evidently, the bacteria can form apatite from tissue fluid which increases the probability that they can also do so from saliva or plaque fluid (Rizzo *et al.* 1962).

One objection to the view that mineralization of calculus depends upon formation of apatite within bacteria is that calculus has been found in germ-free animals although in much smaller amounts and differing in appearance from calculus in normal animals on the same diet, suggesting that calculus formation *can* be a purely chemical process not involving enzymes or seeding substances from bacteria. This does not prove that bacterial activity when present does not play a part in calculus formation but merely shows that (at least in the rat) it is not essential. Probably more than one substance can act as a seed and seeding substances are present both in these bacteria and in rat saliva.

Calculus, especially supragingival, is reported to be higher in smokers than in non-smokers, there being no consistent difference between heavy and light smokers (Kowalski 1971).

Individual variation in calculus formation

One of the biggest problems in the calculus field is the cause of the variation between different people in the amount of calculus formed. Although attempts have been made to relate saliva composition to rate of calculus formation it could hardly be expected that the two would be closely associated since the latter is almost certainly a highly localized process. It is quite common to find calculus (indicative of deposition of calcium phosphate) on teeth with active carious cavities (indicating the dissolving of calcium phosphate) only a few millimetres away from where it is being deposited. Obviously, saliva taken from the mouth as a whole could not possibly indicate the causes of both removal and deposition of calcium phosphate.

Turesky *et al.* (1962) investigated the individual factors concerned in calculus formation as follows. They wired three celluloid strips to the lower incisors of a group of five slow calculus formers and a control group of nine rapid calculus formers. Unfortunately, the two groups were not well-matched in age, the slow calculus formers covering a younger range (4–21 years) than the other group (21–43). In other words, the comparison was a somewhat confused mixture between a young group (who tend to form less calculus) and an older group (who form it more readily) rather than between older people who are slow or rapid calculus formers. After 2 days, one of the strips was interchanged from each member of one group into the mouths of the other group for a further 5 days and another strip remained in the original mouth for a second period of 5 days, The 2-day strips from both groups were similar except that some mineralization had already begun in the rapid calculus group. After the transfer, the rate of mineralization was greater in the mouths of the rapid formers, whether the 2-day matrix had formed in their own mouths or in those of slow calculus formers. As in natural calculus, the mineralization occurred deep in the plaque near the strip—not on the surface. The mineralized material was, therefore, mostly the plaque which had been formed by the first subject.

This experiment indicates that the first stage of calculus formation (plaque or matrix formation) occurs as readily in slow calculus formers as in rapid calculus formers and the difference seems to lie in their powers of mineralizing the plaque. It is not clear, however, whether (1) the plaque formed in the slow calculus formers' mouths become modified and more receptive of mineralization (a more efficient seed?) or (2) whether the calcium salts precipitate more readily from the saliva of the rapid formers.

In a later experiment on similar lines, some of the strips from the two groups (slow and rapid calculus formers) were cut in half—one half being incubated in saliva from the same group and the other half in saliva from the other group. All the plaques mineralized after 5 days' incubation in saliva irrespective of whether the saliva came from a rapid calculus or a slow calculus former. Evidently mineralization is so rapid *in vitro* that differences were obscured.

DIFFERENCES IN PLAQUE COMPOSITION BETWEEN LIGHT AND HEAVY CALCULUS FORMERS

Mandel (1974) compared the composition of plaque and saliva from groups of sixteen light and heavy calculus producers matched for sex and age. The main

TABLE X.5

Differences (percentage dry weight) between plaque composition of light and heavy calculus producers

	Light	*Heavy*
Soluble in water		
Maxillary plaque		
Calcium	1.6 ± 0.3	2.3 ± 0.6 ($p < 0.05$)
Inorganic phosphorus	0.5 ± 0.2	1.1 ± 0.2 ($p < 0.05$)
Total phosphorus	1.2 ± 0.2	2.0 ± 0.6
Hexosamine	4.3 ± 0.2	3.5 ± 0.3 ($p < 0.05$)
Lingual mandibular plaque		
Calcium	5.0 ± 0.6	9.0 ± 1.0 ($p < 0.01$)
Inorganic phosphorus	1.4 ± 0.2	5.0 ± 0.4
Total phosphorus	2.6 ± 0.3	6.6 ± 0.7
Potassium	1.4 ± 0.2	0.6 ± 0.1)
Methyl pentose	3.9 ± 0.3	2.3 ± 0.5 ($p < 0.02$)
Hexosamine	3.9 ± 0.5	2.3 ± 0.2 ($p < 0.02$)
Insoluble in water		
Calcium	2.4	10.0
Inorganic phosphorus	1.0	4.2
Total phosphorus	6.3	4.8
Methyl pentose	0.5	3.3
Hexosamine	4.1	3.8

differences are given in Table X.5. Extracts of the lower anterior plaques showed that much more calcium (but less phosphate) was soluble in the heavy formers, and the differences between the calcium and phosphate of light and heavy formers was even more marked in the insoluble fraction. These differences were well established in plaque collected 3 days after a prophylaxis and, when enough plaque was available, were detected even in plaque 1 day old. The high mineral content of plaque in heavy calculus formers is presumably the result of the rapidity with which it forms rather than being a causal factor. The lower concentrations of hexosamine and methyl pentose in heavy formers might suggest that their removal favours mineralization but there is no direct evidence for this. It is quite possible that differences exist which have not been looked for. Although the plaque weights were not given, Mandel (1974) did state that the amounts were smaller in the light formers (samples had to be pooled whereas the samples from the heavy formers could be analysed individually), suggesting, contrary to the results of Turesky *et al.* (1962) that the early stages, rather than the later mineralization, differed in the two groups.

DIFFERENCES IN SALIVA

Early work on mixed saliva, and often without controlling rate or duration of flow, indicated that saliva from heavy formers was higher in protein, calcium and phosphate concentrations, but other results contradicted this (for references see Schroeder 1969 and Mandel 1974). Higher activities of acid phosphatase, pyrophosphatase and esterase have been reported in the unstimulated saliva of calculus formers compared with non-formers. A higher urea concentration was reported for heavy producers. A more careful study by Mandel confirmed a higher protein and calcium concentration in submandibular, but not parotid, saliva of heavy formers but found no difference in phosphate. This higher phosphate in calculus arises presumably by more powerful fixation into mineralization crystals rather than greater availability. The importance of protein is still uncertain. Mandel (1974) found no consistent differences in the types of protein present as shown by electrophoresis and immunodiffusion, but light formers had a higher lysozyme activity in submandibular saliva. Ericson (1968), however, reported in saliva from heavy formers a low molecular weight protein which adsorbed on to apatite and which might conceivably act as a seed, and it is difficult to see why this protein was not detected by Mandel's very sensitive methods. The effect of the lysozyme can only be speculative; possibly, if bacterial cell walls are disrupted, mineralization is reduced. Another possibility is that the acidic protein of saliva believed to prevent the precipitation of calcium (p. 298–9) is either deficient or more rapidly broken down by bacteria in rapid calculus formers (Hay & Grøn 1975). Mandel did not apparently measure urea levels in his later work in spite of its potential importance in raising plaque pH to levels favouring mineralization. There is no doubt that calculus tends to form most readily in plaques with the highest pH.

A number of studies indicate that resting saliva with a high viscosity is associated with a tendency to form calculus more slowly (Schroeder 1969). Since the main event in the early increase in the weight of calculus is the deposition of brushite, it seems probable that some substance or circumstance related to salivary viscosity inhibits the formation of this crystal form. A possible explanation is that the high viscosity arises because the proportion of the viscous saliva from the submandibular and sublingual glands is above average and that, for some reason (perhaps associated with its capacity for supersaturation of this saliva) deposition of brushite is delayed.

References

Reviews:

KLEINBERG I. (1970) Biochemistry of the dental plaque. *Adv. oral Biol.* **4**, 43

McHUGH W.D. (Ed.) (1969) *Dental Plaque.* Livingstone, London

MELCHER A.H. & ZARB G.A. (Eds.) (1976) *Oral Science Reviews* 9. Preventive dentistry: nature, pathogenicity and clinical control of plaque. BOWEN W.H., THEILADE E., THEILADE J. & LOESCHE W.J. Munksgaard, Copenhagen

ASHLEY F.P. (1975a) Calcium and phosphorus concentrations of dental plaque related to dental caries in 11- to 14-year-old male subjects. *Caries Res.* **9**, 351

ASHLEY F.P. (1975b) Calcium and phosphorus levels in human dental plaque variations according to site of collection. *Archs oral Biol.* **20**, 167

ARMSTRONG W.G. (1966) The composition of organic films found on human teeth. *Caries Res.* **1**, 89 (see also *Archs oral Biol.* (1970) **15**, 1001)

ARMSTRONG W.G. (1971) Characterisation studies on the specific human salivary glycoproteins absorbed *in vitro* by hydroxyapatite. *Caries Res.* **5**, 215

BISWAS S.D. & KLEINBERG I. (1971) Effect of urea concentration on its utilisation, on the pH and the formation of ammonia and carbon dioxide in a human salivary sediment system. *Archs oral Biol.* **16**, 759

CIMASONI G. (1974) *The Crevicular Fluid.* Karger, Basel.

CLARKE N.G. & FANNING E.A. (1971)

Plaque pH and calcium sucrose phosphate: telemetric study. *Austral. dent. J.* **16**, 1; (1973) **18**, 229

CRITCHLEY P. (1969) The breakdown of the carbohydrate and protein matrix of dental plaque. *Caries Res.* **3**, 249

DARLING A.I. (1943) The distribution of the enamel cuticle and its significance. *Proc. Roy. Soc. Med.* **36**, 499

DAWES C. (1964) Is acid-precipitation of salivary proteins a factor in plaque formation? *Archs oral Biol.* **9**, 375

DAWES C. & JENKINS G.N. (1962) Some inorganic constituents of dental plaque and their relationship to early calculus formation and caries. *Archs oral Biol.* **7**, 161

DAWES C. *et al.* (1963) The nomenclature of the integuments of the enamel surface of teeth. *Brit. dent. J.* **115**, 65

EASTOE J.E. & BOWEN W.H. (1967) Some factors affecting pH measurements on tooth surfaces in monkeys. *Caries Res.* **1**, 59

EDGAR W.M. & JENKINS G.N. (1972) Inorganic pyrophosphate in human parotid saliva and dental plaque. *Archs oral Biol.* **17**, 219

EDGAR W.M. & TATEVOSSIAN A. (1971) The aqueous phase of plaque. In *Tooth Enamel II*, p. 229, Eds FEARNHEAD R.W. & STACK M.V. John Wright & Sons, Bristol

ENGLANDER H.R. *et al.* (1956) The formation of lactic acid in dental plaque. *J. dent. Res.* **35**, 792 (see also pp. 778, 786)

ENGLANDER H.R. *et al.* (1959) The effects of

saliva on the pH and lactate concentration of plaque. *J. dent. Res.* **38**, 848

Fox D.J. & Dawes C. (1970a) The extraction of protein matrix from human dental plaque. *Archs oral Biol.* **15**, 1059 (see also (1970b) 1355

Frank R.M. & Brendel A. (1966) Ultrastructure of the approximal dental plaque and the underlying normal and carious enamel. *Archs oral Biol.* **11**, 883

Frank R.M. & Houver G. (1970) The structure of microbial dental plaque. In *Dental Plaque*. Ed. McHugh W.D. Livingstone, Edinburgh

Frostell G. & Soder P.O. (1970) The proteolytic activity of plaque and its relation to soft tissue pathology. *Int. dent. J.* **20**, 436

Geddes D.A.M. (1972) Plaque acids produced during *in vitro* sucrose fermentation. *J. dent. Res.* **51**, 1284

Gibbons R.J. & Socransky S.S. (1962) Intracellular polysaccharide storage by organisms in dental plaque. *Archs oral Biol.* **7**, 73 (see also *Archs oral Biol.* (1963) **8**, 319; (1964) **9**, 91)

Gibbons R.J. & Spinell D.M. (1970) Salivary-induced aggregation of plaque bacteria. In *Dental Plaque*. Ed. McHugh W.D. Livingstone, Edinburgh

Gibbons R.J. *et al.* (1964) Studies of the predominant cultivable microbiota of dental plaque. *Archs oral Biol.* **9**, 365

Golub L.M. *et al.* (1971) Urea content of gingival crevicular fluid and its relation to periodontal disease in humans. *J. periodont. Res.* **6**, 243

Graf H. & Mühlemann H.R. (1966) Telemetry of plaque pH from interdental area. *Helv. Odont. Acta* **10**, 94

Grøn P. *et al.* (1967) Inorganic chemical and crystallographic composition of calculus. *Archs oral Biol.* **12**, 829

Grøn P. & Hay D.I. (1976) Inhibition of calcium phosphate precipitation by human salivary secretions. *Archs oral Biol.* **21**, 201

Guggenheim B. (1970) Enzymatic hydrolysis and structure of water-insoluble glucan produced by glucosyltransferases

from a strain of *Streptococcus mutans*. *Helv. odont. Acta.* **14**, 89

Hampar B. *et al.* (1961) The carbohydrate components of supragingival calculus. *J. dent. Res.* **40**, 752

Hausmann E. & Weinfield N. (1973) Human dental plaque: stimulation of bone resorption in tissue culture. *Archs oral Biol.* **18**, 1509

Hay D.I. (1973) The interaction of human parotid salivary proteins with hydroxyapatite. *Archs oral Biol.* **18**, 1517, 1531

Hay D.I. & Grøn P. (1975) Identification of $CaHPO_4 \cdot 2H_2O$ stabilizing factors in human saliva. *Amer. Ass. Dent. Res. Ab.* 267, 268

Hayes M.L. & Hyatt A.T. (1974) The decarboxylation of amino acids by bacteria derived from human dental plaque. *Archs oral Biol.* **19**, 361

Hillman J.D. *et al.* (1970) The sorption of bacteria to human enamel powder. *Archs oral Biol.* **15**, 899

Hotz P. *et al.* (1972) Carbohydrates in pooled dental plaque. *Caries Res.* **6**, 103

Houte J. van & Jansen H.M. (1968) Levan degradation by streptococci isolated from human dental plaque. *Archs oral Biol.* **13**, 827

Jenkins G.N. (1965) The equilibrium between plaque and enamel in relation to caries resistance. *Ciba Symposium: Caries-resistant Teeth*, p. 192.

Jenkins G.N. (1971) Plaque formation and metabolism. In *The Prevention of Periodontal Disease*, p. 34. Eds. Eastoe J.E., Picton D.C.A. & Alexander A.G. Kimpton, London

Jenkins G.N. & Dawes C. (1964) Experiments on the chelating properties of saliva and dental plaque. *Brit. dent. J.* **116**, 435

Jenkins G.N. & Kleinberg I. (1956) Studies in the pH of plaque in interproximal areas after eating sweets and starchy foods. *J. dent. Res.* **35**, 964

Jenkins G.N. & Speirs R.L. (1954) Some observations on the fluoride concentration of dental tissues. *J. dent. Res.* **33**, 734

Jones S.J. (1972) A special relationship between spherical and filamentous microorganisms in mature human dental plaque. *Archs oral Biol.* **17**, 613

KARRING T. *et al.* (1974) Histochemical study of the formation of dental plaque in artificial fissures. *Scand. J. dent. Res.* **82**, 471

KESEL R.J. (1958) Further studies on lactobacilli counts after elimination of carious lesions. *J. dent. Res.* **37**, 50

KIRKEGAARD E. *et al.* (1975) Fluoride uptake in plaque-covered enamel *in vitro*. IADR Abstracts L543

KLEINBERG I. & JENKINS G.N. (1964) Influence of saliva and meals on plaque pH. *Archs oral Biol.* **9**, 493

KLEINBERG I. & SANDHAM H.J. (1964) Effect of fluoride on carbohydrate accumulation in salivary sediment. *J. dent. Res.* **43**, 843 (see also **43**, 745)

KLEINBERG I. *et al.* (1969) Relation between plaque ash, calcium and phosphorus levels on dental caries. *Internat. Ass. Dent. Res. Abs.* 635

KLEINBERG I. *et al.* (1973) Effect of salivary supernatant on the glycolytic activity of the bacteria in salivary sediment. *Archs oral Biol.* **18**, 787

KLEINBERG I. *et al.* (1977) Effects of fluoride on the metabolism of the mixed oral flora. *Caries Res.* **11** (Suppl. 1), 292

KOWALSKI C.J. (1971) Relationship between smoking and calculus deposition. *J. dent. Res.* **50**, 101

KREMBEL J. *et al.* (1969) Fractionation of human dental plaque. *Archs oral Biol.* **14**, 563

LANG N.P. *et al.* (1973) Toothbrushing frequency as it relates to plaque development and gingival health. *J. Periodontol.* **44**, 396

LANKE L.S. (1957) Influence on salivary sugar of certain properties of foodstuffs and individual oral conditions. *Acta odont. Scand.* **15**, Supp. 23

LEACH S.A. (1964) Some observations on the state of sialic acid in human saliva. *Archs oral Biol.* **9**, 461

LEHNER T. (1975) Immunological aspects of dental caries and periodontal disease. *Br. Med. Bull.* **31**, 125.

LEVINE M. *et al.* (1974) Human dental plaque extracts: their crude chemical composition and toxicity to cultured HeLa cells. *Archs oral Biol.* **19**, 583

LILIENTHAL B. (1955) An analysis of the buffer system in saliva. *J. dent. Res.* **34**, 516

LITTLE M.F. *et al.* (1961) The organic matrix of dental calculus. *J. dent. Res.* **40**, 753

LITTLE M.F. *et al.* (1963) Dental calculus composition. I. Supragingival calculus. *J. dent. Res.* **42**, 78; (1964) II. Subgingival calculus. *J. dent. Res.* **43**, 645

LÖE H. *et al.* (1965) Experimental gingivitis in man. *J. Periodont.* **36**, 177

LÖE H. *et al.* (1973) An *in vitro* method for the study of the microbiology of occlusal fissures. *Caries Res.* **7**, 120 (see also *Caries Res.* **7**, 130; (1974) *Scand. J. dent. Res.* (1974) **82**, 471

LOESCHE W. & GREEN E. (1972) Comparison of various plaque parameters in individuals with poor oral hygiene. *J. periodont. Res.* **7**, 173

LUDWIG T.G. & BIBBY B.G. (1957) Acid production from different carbohydrate foods in plaque and bacteria. *J. dent. Res.* **36**, 56, 61

MCCONNELL D. & FRAJOLA W.J. (1961) The chemistry of calculus formation. *J. dent. Res.* **40**, 753

MCDOUGALL W.A. (1963) Studies on the dental plaque. *Aust. dent. J.* **8**, 261, 398, 463; (1964) **9**, 1

MCHUGH W.D. (Ed.) (1970) *Dental Plaque*. Livingstone, Edinburgh

MÄKINEN K.K. (1966) Studies on oral enzymes. *Acta odont. Scand.* **24**, 605, 619, 709, 723, 733

MANDEL I.D. (1974a) Biochemical aspects of calculus formation. *J. periodont. Res.* **9**, 10

MANDEL I.D. (1974b) Relationship of saliva and plaque to caries. *J. dent. Res.* **53**, 246

MANDEL I.D. & THOMPSON R.H. (1967) The chemistry of parotid and submaxillary saliva in heavy calculus formers and non-formers. *J. Periodontol.* **38**, 310

MANDEL J.D. *et al.* (1957) Histochemistry of calculus formation. *J. Periodontal.* **28**, 132; **29**, 145 (also *Oral Surg., Med., Path.* **10**, 874)

MANNERBERG F. (1960) Appearance of tooth surface as observed in shadowed replicas. *Odontol. Revy* **11**, Supp. 6

MAYHALL C.W. (1970) Composition and source of acuired enamel pellicle. *Archs oral Biol.* **15**, 1327

MECKEL A.M. (1965) The formation and properties of organic films on teeth. *Archs oral Biol.* **10**, 585

MERGENHAGEN S. *et al.* (1970) Immunologic reactions and periodontal inflammation. *J. dent. Res.* **49**, 2561

MORENO E.C. *et al.* (1974) Inhibition of *in vitro* enamel demineralisation by salivary pellicles. *J. dent. Res.* **53**, Special Issue, Abstract 187

MÜHLEMANN H.R. & SCHNEIDER U.K. (1959) Early calculus formation. *Helv. odont. Acta*, **3**, 21

OSUOJI C.I. & ROWLES S.L. (1972) Isolation and identification of acid glycosaminoglycam in oral calculus. *Archs oral Biol.* **17**, 211

PAGE R.C. *et al.* (1973) Effects of dental plaque on the production and release of lysosomal hydrolases by macrophages in culture. *Archs oral Biol.* **18**, 1481

RITZ H.L. (1967) Microbial population shifts in developing human dental plaque. *Archs oral Biol.* **12**, 1561

RITZ H.L. (1970) The role of aerobic Neisseriae in the initial formation of dental plaque. In *Dental Plaque.* Ed. McHUGH W.D. Livingstone, Edinburgh

RIZZO A.A. *et al.* (1962) *In vivo* mineralization of bacteria isolated from calculous [*sic*] plaques. 40th meeting of *I.A.D.R. Abs.* 59

ROLLA G. (1977) Effects of fluoride on initiation of plaque formation. *Caries Res.* **11** (*Suppl.* 1) 243

RÖLLA G. *et al.* (1975) Sulphated macromolecules in monkey dental plaque. *Archs oral Biol.* **20**, 341

RÖLLA G. & MATHIESEN P. (1970) The absorption of salivary proteins and dextrans to hydroxyapatite. In *Dental Plaque.* Ed. McHUGH W.D. Livingstone, Edinburgh

SAXTON C.A. (1969) An electron microscope investigation of bacterial polysaccharide synthesis in human dental plaque. *Archs oral Biol.* **14**, 1275

SAXTON C.A. (1973) Scanning electron microscopic study of the formation of dental plaque. *Caries Res.* **7**, 107

SAXTON C.A. (1975) Determination by electron microscope autoradiography of the distribution in plaque of organisms that synthesise intracellular polysaccharide *in situ. Caries Rev.* **9**, 418

SCHLATTER P.A. *et al.* (1961) Changes in the depth of artificial marks on tooth surfaces after certain time intervals. *Helv. odont. Acta.* **5**, 43 (see also (1962) **7**, 30)

SCHROEDER H.E. (1969) *Formation and Inhibition of Dental Calculus.* Hans Huber, Berne

SCHROEDER H.E. & BOEVER J. DE (1969) The structure of microbial dental plaque. In *Dental Plaque.* Ed. McHUGH W.D. E. & S. Livingstone, London

SCHROEDER H.E. & BOEVER J. DE (1970) The structure of microbial dental plaque. In *Dental Plaque*, p 49. Ed. McHUGH, W.D. E. & S. Livingstone, Edinburgh

SCHÜLE H. (1961) Chemical composition and physical properties of enamel cuticle. *Archs oral Biol.* **4**, 40

SCHÜLE H. (1962) *Das Schmelzöberhuchäten.* Thieme, Stuttgart

SCOTT D.B. *et al.* (1949) Replica studies of changes in tooth surfaces with age. *J. dent. Res.* **28**, 37

SELVIG K.A. (1969) Biological changes at the tooth–saliva interface in periodontal disease. *J. dent. Res.* **48**, 846

SILVERMAN G. & KLEINBERG I. (1967) Fractionation of dental plaque and the characterisation of its cellular and accellular components. *Archs oral Biol.* **12**, 1387, 1407

SONJU T. & RÖLLA G. (1973) Chemical analyses of the acquited pellicle formed in two hours on cleaned human teeth *in vivo. Caries Res.* **7**, 30

STEPHAN R.M. (1940) Changes in the hydrogen-ion concentration on tooth surfaces and in carious lesions. *J. Amer. dent. Ass.* **27**, 718 (see also *J. dent. Res.* **22**, 63; **24**, 202)

STRÅLFORS A. (1948) Studies on the microbiology of caries. II. The acid fermentation in the dental plaque *in situ* compared with *Lactobacillus* counts. *J. dent. Res.* **27**, 576. III. The buffer capacity of the dental plaque. *J. dent. Res.* **27**, 587

STRÅLFORS A. (1950) *Investigations into the Bacterial Chemistry of Dental Plaques.* Thule, Stockholm

TATEVOSSIAN A. & GOULD C.T. (1976) Method for sampling and analysis of the aqueous phase of human dental plaque. *Archs oral Biol.* **21**, 313; also **21**, 319

THEILADE E. *et al.* (1973) Microbiological studies of plaque in artificial fissures implanted in human teeth. *Caries Res.* **7**, 130

TURESKY S. *et al.* (1962) The effect of changing the salivary environment upon the progress of calculus formation. *J. Periodont.* **33**, 45 (see also (1962) **32**, 7; (1964) **34**, 322)

TURNER E.P. (1958) The integument of the enamel surface of the human tooth. *Dent. Prac.* **8**, 341, 373

VON DER FEHR F. & BRUDEVOLD F. (1960) *In vitro* calculus formation. *J. dent. Res.* **39**, 1041

WAERHAUG K. (1955) The source of mineral salts in subgingival calculus. *J. dent. Res.* **34**, 563

ZANDER H.A. (1953) The attachment of calculus to root surfaces. *J. Periodont.* **24**, 16

CHAPTER XI

SOME PHYSIOLOGICAL ASPECTS OF DENTAL CARIES

There are numerous references to dental caries scattered throughout this book and in the present chapter they will be collected and presented in a more logical order along with additional points.

The Acid Theory of Caries

The experiments of W. B. Miller carried out towards the end of the last century have dominated views on the nature and cause of dental caries. Miller had shown that when teeth were incubated with saliva and carbohydrates, acid was formed and that some of the calcium phosphate of the teeth dissolved. On the other hand, he found that when teeth were incubated with saliva in the absence of carbohydrate they were not attacked. He concluded that acid formed from carbohydrate by salivary bacteria was the cause of caries (the so-called 'chemico-parasitic theory'). Miller clearly recognized that the structure of the teeth affected their resistance to acids but this point was largely ignored by later exponents of this theory. A reprint of Miller's classical book was published in 1973.

The evidence for this theory has steadily accumulated and, in particular, the finding that pH in the plaque after eating sugar may be lower than the critical value at which enamel dissolves (p. 388) has given it overwhelming support.

Histology of the Early Caries Lesion

The nature of the changes in the enamel in early caries has been studied by a variety of methods which have given broadly consistent results although differing in detail; they do agree in showing that these changes are complicated.

414

In the most informative method ground sections of teeth with early carious lesions have been studied by transmitted and polarized light and by micro-radiography. The use of polarized light provides information about the 'birefringence' of a substance which is a property of materials, like crystals or fibres, which are arranged in an orderly fashion with an orientation in one direction. Two types of birefringence are known: 'intrinsic birefringence' dependent on molecular structure, and 'form birefringence' related to the orientation of the crystal as a whole and dependent upon the refractive index of the medium in which the particles are immersed. In enamel, the study of form birefringence has been linked with another property, namely that enamel behaves as a molecular sieve, i.e. allows some molecules below a certain size to enter it but excludes larger molecules. For example, in a quinoline medium, certain markings in the enamel (for example, the striae of Retzius and the cross striations) are prominent but become invisible in Thoulet's medium (an aqueous medium with the same refractive index as enamel). The interpretation is that water molecules are small enough to pass through the 'sieve' and enter the spaces so that the spaces and the enamel itself then have the same refractive indices and hence the spaces become invisible. When the enamel is placed in quinoline (which also has the same RI as enamel) it cannot enter the enamel because the molecules are too large, hence the spaces remain filled with air with a different refractive index from both enamel and quinoline. The light is then refracted in passing through the spaces which, therefore, become visible. As caries develops in enamel, spaces develop which become progressively larger and thus the pores in the 'sieve' become bigger. Studies of the form birefringence of sections immersed ('imbibed') in substances of known molecular size and different refractive index can determine the extent to which the substance has entered the spaces and thus the size of the pores. For full accounts of the procedure see Darling (1956, 1958) and for a critique of the method see Houwink (1969).

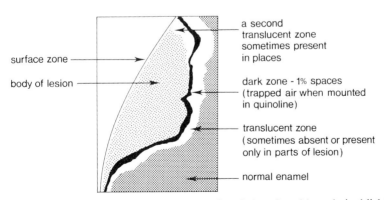

surface zone

body of lesion

a second
translucent zone
sometimes present
in places

dark zone - 1% spaces
(trapped air when mounted
in quinoline)

translucent zone
(sometimes absent or present
only in parts of lesion)

normal enamel

FIG. XI.1. Diagram of the zones in an early carious lesion viewed by polarized light.

These methods have shown that the early lesion consists of a series of zones with different optical properties, analysis of which has given information about the chemical changes in each zone. These zones (Figs XI.1 and 2) have

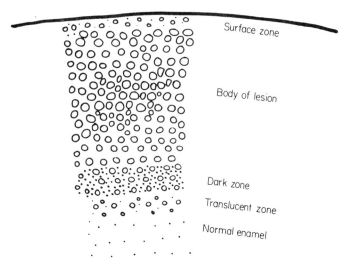

FIG. XI.2. Diagram of the size of spaces in the zone of a carious lesion.

the following properties listed below, contrasting with normal enamel which has spaces representing only 0.1% of the volume and of a size approximating to that of a water molecule.

Starting from the normal inner enamel and working outwards the zones are as follows:

(1) The translucent zone is the first recognizable change at the advancing front of the lesion but is sometimes absent, or present along only part of the lesion. It contains larger spaces, estimated by optical methods as 0.3% of the volume and $1–2\%$ by direct measurement of density. Chemical analysis of pieces of enamel microdissected from sections of carious teeth (p. 61) show that the main differences from normal enamel are a rise in fluoride concentration and an average fall of 12% in magnesium and a more variable loss of carbonate (Hallsworth *et al.* 1973). The mineral removed is, of course, mostly calcium phosphate but it is much richer in magnesium and carbonate than is intact enamel. The sections which provided these analyses were more permeable to dyes than normal at the rod borders suggesting that this was the site of loss of mineral; however, in very thin sections of enamel, the rods are liable to dry and shrink and thus form spaces at their border which are artefacts. Contrary to earlier results by optical methods, there is no chemical evidence of loss of protein in this zone.

Fig. XI.3. Ground section of a carious lesion in quinoline viewed with polarized light. × 35.

(2) The dark zone has spaces estimated by optical methods to constitute 2–4% of its volume and 5–7% of its mineral matter. Some of these spaces are quite large but many are smaller even than those in the translucent zone, suggesting that some remineralization has occurred. If this zone is narrow it is thought to indicate that the advance of the lesion has been rapid but a slower demineralization gives a more gradual change spread over a wider zone.

(3) Some workers have described a third zone running along part of the outer edge of the dark zone, but it is not always detectable.

(4) The body of the lesion has lost a much larger proportion of its mineral matter, the spaces being estimated as occupying between 5 and 25% of the total volume. The apatite crystals are larger than the average in normal enamel suggesting that the smaller crystals are dissolved first.

(5) The surface zone over an early lesion shows surprisingly little change, averaging a fall from the normal 87 to 83% mineral by volume. A complication in deciding on the nature of the changes is that the outer surface of normal intact enamel is markedly different from the deeper layers, being for example approximately 40% lower in magnesium and higher in fluoride and protein. It has usually been assumed that the outer enamel over a lesion remains fairly intact because its composition, for example the high fluorine and protein concentration, provide a higher resistance. The question then arises as to how the attack breaches the outer enamel and can develop within. Darling

(1958) concluded that the lesion entered via the striae of Retzius but this is disputed (Mortimer 1968; Crabb 1966). Sections of carious enamel taken just below the base of a fissure have indicated numerous independent areas of advancing caries (shown by their low density) not associated with any detectable histological structure and cutting across the striae (Mortimer 1968). These results suggest that there may be areas of the enamel surface which, perhaps from their chemical structure (low in fluoride and protein, high in magnesium and carbonate), rather than from a morphological defect, are less resistant to acid then neighbouring areas.

An alternative explanation of the relatively undamaged surface zone to a lesion is that it represents a reprecipitation of material dissolved at an earlier stage of the lesion. The evidence for this is that in artificial lesions on teeth from which the outer enamel with its resistant layer had been ground away still showed less removal of mineral on the artificially formed outer layer than within the enamel.

Remineralization

It has been widely reported that carious lesions up to the white spot stage (but before enough enamel has been lost to form a cavity) may cease to develop, become smaller or even disappear completely, but systematic study of this regression is quite recent. Backer-Dirks (1966) followed the course of white spot carious lesions on buccal surfaces of teeth in 8-year-old children. Out of the 72 white spots observed at 8 years of age, 7 years later 9 had cavitated, 26 remained unchanged but 37 had regressed to become indistinguishable from the surrounding sound enamel. If fluoride is added to an unstable saturated or supersaturated solution of calcium phosphate (a 'mineralizing solution'), apatite is precipitated and if an etched surface of enamel is placed in this solution the apatite will be deposited in the damaged area, presumably by a seeding process. Remineralization was first demonstrated by treating extracted teeth with acid and measuring the reduction of surface hardness, then exposing them to the mineralizing solution and noting that the hardness increases (Koulourides 1968). *In vivo*, saliva alone (as a solution saturated with enamel mineral) brings about remineralization but it may be accelerated or intensified if accompanied by sodium fluoride mouth-rinse (Levine 1975).

Mineral deposition, even in normal enamel, can be detected by studies with polarized light of extracted teeth exposed to mineralizing solutions. Unerupted teeth take up more than erupted teeth probably because many of the minute spaces between the apatite crystals of the enamel, which later become filled by substances diffusing in from the saliva, are still vacant before, or shortly after, eruption.

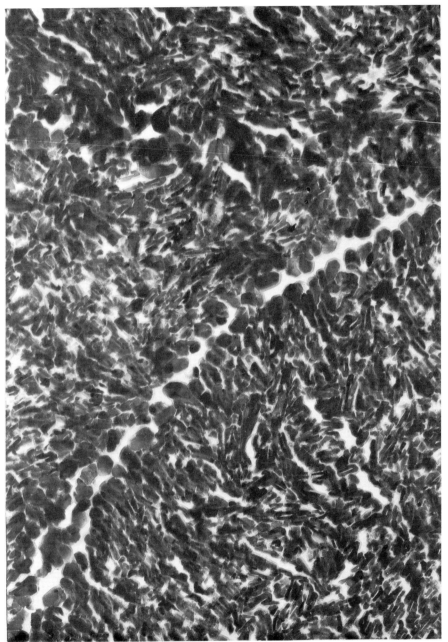

FIG. XI.4. Electronmicrograph of enamel after mild treatment of the surface with acid. The crystals on the outside of the rods are larger than those within, the usual explanation being that they have been formed by remineralization from calcium phosphate dissolved in other parts of the enamel. Note that some of the crystals within the rod are damaged by acid shown by a white line running down the middle of the crystal.

It is believed that caries progresses by alternate demineralization, when plaque pH falls after eating carbohydrates, and partial remineralization when the pH rises. As some of the calcium and phosphate ions dissolved off the enamel probably diffuse away from the inner layer of plaque or the phosphate is taken up by bacteria, it is not all available for remineralization, consequently the lesion progresses. If fluoride in the plaque acts in the same way as in test-tube experiments, it would favour remineralization, as well as increase the formation of fluorapatite in preference to other crystalline forms of calcium phosphate. Presumably, fluoride ions in the plaque as well as fluoride released from enamel (including any fluoride introduced artificially from dentifrice or mouth-rinses) would all contribute to this effect which, some workers believe, is the most important action of fluoride.

Electron micrographs of thin sections of enamel in early caries frequently show that the outer edge of enamel rods is lined by much larger crystals than are in the enamel as a whole (Fig. XI.4). A possible explanation is that acid diffuses along the inter-rod spaces causing some crystals to dissolve and, after neutralization, the calcium phosphate is reprecipitated as larger apatite crystals. However, even in parts of the enamel without obvious effects of acid the apatite crystals tend to be larger on the outside of the rods than within (Simmelink *et al.* 1974).

The importance of diffusion in caries

The fact that caries is a penetrating lesion, rather than a destruction of the outer surface of the enamel, shows that inward diffusion of acid must play an important role in caries. Investigations of artificial caries with lactic acid either in a colloid or containing a substance (such as diphosphonate) which reduces the solubility of the enamel surface show that the depth of penetration of the lesion is governed by the concentration of unionized lactic acid outside the enamel much more than by the pH value (Gray 1966; Featherstone 1977). Presumably the unionized acid diffuses more readily than the lactate ion because, being uncharged, it does not react so readily with the apatite. When it has penetrated and become diluted then it will eventually ionize and react with the apatite. The resulting calcium and phosphate ions will then tend to diffuse outwards, driven by the concentration gradients. As this occurs the ions may meet conditions near the enamel surface where they cannot remain in solution and consequently some calcium phosphate is precipitated, probably as $CaHPO_4$ which can be detected in carious enamel. The deposition of this material may explain the apparently intact outer layer of enamel over a carious lesion: as suggested above, it may not be the original undamaged surface but a new layer formed by remineralization.

On this view, the critical pH may not only be the level at which the environment of the enamel becomes unsaturated with apatite but it may also be the pH at which sufficient concentrations of unionized lactic acid exist to ensure its inward diffusion.

Although this approach tends to minimize the importance of acid making the environment unsaturated with apatite it is probable that inward diffusion can only occur after some of the surface apatite has dissolved. Electron-microscopy of very early lesions (Frank & Brendel 1966) suggest that this occurs in a few isolated points, perhaps more soluble than the outer enamel as a whole, 1 μm or less in thickness but adequate to expose the subsurface enamel directly to acid formed in the plaque.

Alternatives to the acid theory

(1) THE PROTEOLYTIC THEORY
When a carious cavity reaches the dentine, acid alone could not account for the removal of the collagen of the matrix because (unlike the proteins of enamel) it is insoluble in acid and retains its shape after demineralization. The action of proteolytic bacteria is, therefore, required to produce caries in the dentine. In 1947 Gottlieb emphasized the possibility that the *initial attack* on the enamel might be on the protein of the enamel matrix rather than by acid on the apatite and this idea received some support from other workers. The evidence was never fully sifted but recent results have produced much evidence against it.

(2) THE PHOSPHOPROTEIN THEORY
A hypothesis based on experiments on rats' teeth suggests that an enzyme reported to be in plaque, phosphoprotein phosphatase, releases phosphate from one or more phosphoproteins presumed to be in the enamel matrix (Kreitzman *et al.* 1969, 1974). The purity of the enzyme used in these experiments was not established and there is no evidence that phosphoproteins occur in human enamel in sufficient amounts to play a key role in caries. This hypothesis does not appear to have been tested on human teeth.

(3) THE PROTEOLYSIS-CHELATION THEORY
A third possibility has been raised by Schatz and his colleagues (1957a, b, 1962) in what they call the 'proteolysis-chelation theory' which suggests that some of the products of bacterial action on enamel, dentine, food and salivary constituents may have the property of forming complexes or chelates with calcium. A chelate is a complex formed between a cation such as calcium and two or more groups of the complexing compound leading to a ring structure and sometimes incorporating the elements of water. Fig. XI.5 shows the suggested structure of the chelate compounds formed between calcium and lactic acid and glycine. Many substances, including some in the plaque, may form complexes or chelates at neutral or alkaline pH values and in an environ-

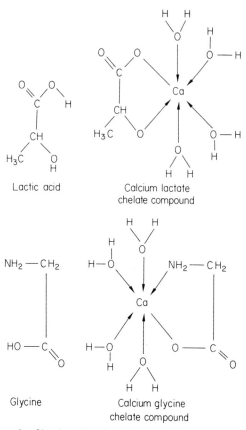

Lactic acid   Calcium lactate
chelate compound

Glycine   Calcium glycine
chelate compound

FIG. XI.5. The formula of lactic acid and glycine and of the calcium chelate compounds which they form.

ment saturated with calcium and phosphate ions. They may combine directly with the calcium of enamel or, by 'mopping up' calcium ions in the plaque may reduce its concentration below that required to maintain saturation. If chelation occurred in this way the enamel could be attacked without acid formation and the concept of a critical pH would be invalid. Chelate formation can also occur under acid conditions, however, and when calcium phosphate dissolves in lactic acid part of the calcium goes into solution as calcium and lactate ions (which occurs in saliva only below the critical pH) and part as the chelate compound with lactic acid (which can occur also above the critical pH).

The theory is somewhat misleadingly named because many substances which form complexes with calcium are not of proteolytic origin, nor are all the complexes necessarily chelates (that is, ring compounds). The term 'complexing theory' would be more accurate but to avoid confusion the usual term 'chelation' will be used here.

The evidence for and against these theories about the initiation of caries may be briefly summarized as follows.

Evidence for the acid theory

(1) There is no doubt that the pH may fall intermittently below what in saliva is the critical demineralization level, in the thick plaque formed after several days' abstention from tooth-brushing. The same is assumed to be true, in places where plaque and food debris cannot be removed by the toothbrush, and where even saliva may have difficulty in reaching.

The original methods of measuring plaque pH did not give information about the inner plaque in contact with enamel which is most relevant to caries. The results from electrodes built into extracted teeth mounted on dentures (p. 389) do show that pH changes occur in this locality and seem to reach lower values and be more prolonged than in plaque as a whole (Fig. XI.4).

(2) The pH values of carious cavities are known to be lower than those in neighbouring tissues (MacGregor 1959; Dirksen *et al.* 1962).

(3) Many workers have found a correlation between the intensity of caries and the numbers in saliva of either (*a*) *Streptococcus mutans*, (*b*) *Lactobacillus acidophilus* or (*c*) of acid production on incubation of saliva and glucose. This point is discussed on p. 432, where the inconclusive nature of this evidence is emphasized.

These points can be expressed most cogently in this form: if the pH falls below the critical value in sheltered parts of the tooth surface, how can it fail to demineralize the enamel?

(4) In germ-free rats, inoculation with some acid-producing organisms without proteolytic activity induced caries but others did not. This proves that acid causes caries in the rat.

CARIES *IN VITRO*

When most of the enamel is covered with wax leaving a small window, through which alone acid can reach its surface (resembling the local build-up of acid in a fissure or contact point), the enamel dissolves away completely causing a cavity of increasing depth with no trace of the complicated zones of natural caries. However, if teeth are subject to acid (pH 4·0) in the presence of a colloid (gelatin, hydroxy ethyl cellulose or cultures of dextran-producing bacteria have been used) for up to 12 weeks, the result is a penetrating lesion with the various zones, described above, reproduced, indistinguishable from natural caries (Fig. XI. 6). A possible explanation of the effect of the colloid is that when the acid dissolves those parts of the outer enamel which are most soluble, the colloid molecules enter the spaces vacated by the mineral and coat

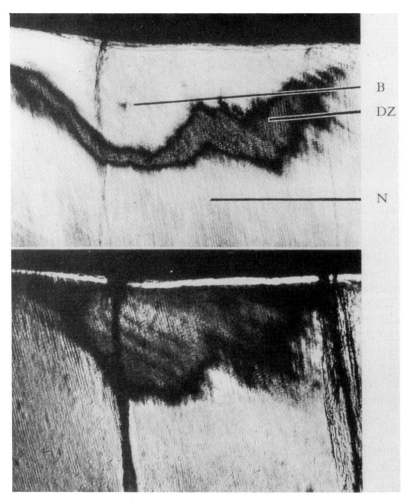

Fig. XI.6. Longitudinal section through an artificial caries lesion after exposure of enamel to acidified gelatin for 20 weeks, ×100; (a) section examined in quinoline showing a well-marked dark zone at the advancing front of the lesion; (b) section examined dry in air with polarized light, the body of the lesion appears black but the surface zone is almost identical to the normal enamel (bottom) showing that the pore volume of this zone is approximately 1%. B = body of lesion; DZ = dark zone; N = normal enamel.

the surrounding crystals which are then protected from further attack. Consequently, the acid diffuses past these crystals and reaches deeper layers still unprotected by colloid. As more dissolves so more colloid enters thus pushing the zone of early demineralization further inwards. Presumably the proteins and polysacharides of the plaque matrix and pellicle act in a similar way thus explaining the shape of the lesion. Diphosphonates, substances which bind to the enamel surface and reduce its solubility, have a similar effect.

SEM Studies on the Effects of Acids and Chelators

When the surface of human enamel is treated with acid and then studied with the scanning electron microscope (SEM) several workers (for references see Mortimer & Tranter 1971) have reported that the cores of the rods dissolved,

FIG. XI.7. Scanning electronmicrograph of enamel treated with acid. × 2500.

leaving the periphery relatively intact (Fig. XI.7). When the same experiment was carried out with the complexing agent, neutral EDTA, the reverse effect

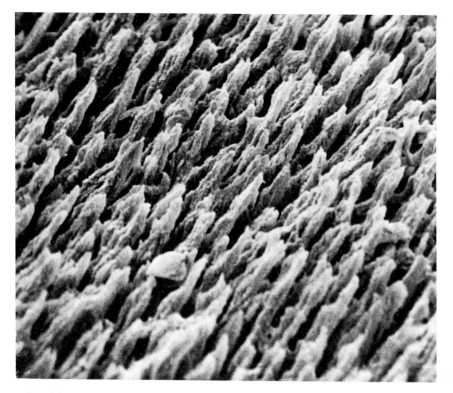

Fig. XI.8. Scanning electromicrograph of enamel treated with a complexing agent, × 2500.

occurred and the periphery of the rods dissolved leaving the core as a solid column (Fig. XI.8). Comparison of these effects with the change occurring in early caries seemed a possible method of deciding whether acid or complexors attacked the enamel.

Later work has shown that this distinction is far from clear-cut, however, and that, although the majority of the rods are dissolved centrally by acids, peripheral attack does occur and in some parts of the tooth no definite pattern is observed (Silverstone *et al.* 1975). There is also uncertainty about the site of the initial attack in caries; some reports with the SEM suggest the periphery of the rod is dissolved first, others the central region. Confusion may arise because if the 'tail' part of the core were dissolved first the removal of this narrow part of the core might give the impression that the periphery of neighbouring rods is attacked. The appearance would then depend on which part of the core was dissolved first.

It is, however, agreed that once caries is sufficiently well established to be detectable by microradiography in ground sections, it affects the rod core preferentially (Miller 1958; Sharpe 1967) suggesting that acid is the most likely agent at this stage. There is no satisfactory explanation of the tendency for acids to attack rod cores rather than the periphery. One suggestion is that the hydrogen ions, being small, can diffuse into the tightly packed crystals of the rod, whereas the large molecules of the complexors can enter only along the larger spaces between the rods. This might explain why chelators preferentially attack the periphery but could hardly explain why hydrogen ions have less effect in the more permeable area.

There is no evidence definitely against the acid theory and most workers regard the accumulation of circumstantial evidence as virtual proof of its validity. The only reasonable question is whether other reactions may supplement the effect of acid.

Evidence for the proteolytic theory

The proteolytic theory has received little attention recently and the validity of the older observations which seemed to support it have not been tested by modern methods.

(1) Histologically it is often found that bacteria (unidentified) are present in the enamel lamellae in early cavities. Since the lamellae consist of organic matter it was concluded that only proteolytic organisms would be capable of invading these structures.

(2) After a certain stage, carious cavities invariably turn a yellow-brown colour owing to the presence of pigments which are believed to be melanin. Protein breakdown products are the usual source of melanin, a fact which suggested that proteolysis must precede the formation of this pigment. It has been stated, however, that similar pigments may be produced in the organic matter of enamel and dentine by treating teeth with methyl glyoxal and acetol, two degradation products of glucose (Dreizen *et al.* 1949) although this does not seem to have been investigated further.

Difficulties of the proteolytic theory

(1) It is now known (see pp. 104–5) that some of the organic matter of enamel is acid-soluble. Its removal during caries does not, therefore, necessarily prove proteolytic activity.

(2) When undemineralized dentine is exposed to a proteolytic enzyme the collagen is unaffected, but if the dentine is first demineralized by acid, and then treated with proteolytic enzymes digestion readily occurs (Evans & Prophet 1950). This means that *in dentine* the calcium salts protect the collagen from enzyme attack and, by analogy, it is argued that probably enamel

protein cannot be digested until the protecting calcium salts are dissolved away by acid.

(3) In germ-free animals, the addition of a proteolytic organism to an acid producer did not intensify the caries attack and a proteolytic organism alone did not produce caries.

Evidence for the proteolysis-chelation theory

(1) Many naturally-occurring substances are known to be capable of complexing calcium and in some cases they may play an important part in biological processes generally. Amino acids, citrate and lactate, are such substances known to be present in the mouth and plaque and it is quite possible that they might contribute to the demineralization of the teeth in caries.

The calcium concentration in plaque and plaque fluid is much higher than would be expected unless complexors, or substances which inhibit crystallization (pp. 298–9) are present. Evidently, much of the complexing power of plaque constituents is already used up, presumably by the cations entering from saliva. The concentration of complexors in the inner plaque is not known and if these substances are produced within the plaque by bacterial metabolism, it is possible that they might build up in concentrations exceeding those which could be reached by calcium diffusing into the plaque from saliva, i.e. some complexing power might remain unused. As already indicated, it can hardly be doubted that acid attacks enamel, but whether any additional effect from chelation is on a significant scale is the point at issue. The shape of the Stephan curve (pp. 387–8) suggests the action of acid is usually intermittent and, in people who do not eat between meals, may be effective for only a few minutes after each meal containing carbohydrate. It is possible that the chelators could act in the intervals between the acid attacks and this weak attack, extending over the greater part of the day, might be as damaging as a more severe acid attack of short duration after meals.

(2) When powdered bone or dental tissues are incubated with certain oral bacteria in pure culture at neutral or alkaline pH values, calcium and phosphate have been found to go into solution (Lura 1957; Stüben 1959; Schatz *et al.* 1957, 1958, 1962). As the media in which these experiments were carried out was not saturated with calcium and phosphate (unlike plaque fluid and saliva) the dissolving of some of the mineral would be expected.

(3) Although in man there is overwhelming proof that acid forms in the plaque and in carious cavities, some pH measurements in animals (monkeys and rats) failed to detect a fall below pH 7, even after food (Ockerse & De Jager 1957; Haldi *et al.* 1960). Later work in monkeys and rodents has, however, shown similar pH changes to those of human plaque (Bowen & Eastoe 1967).

Difficulties of the proteolysis-chelation theory

(1) In the experiments on the incubation of teeth with saliva upon which the concept of a 'critical pH' has been developed no detectable calcium went into solution at or about neutrality. However, in these experiments thymol or toluene was added to the saliva to prevent bacterial action from changing the chemical environment so that the formation by bacteria of possible complexing agents could not have occurred.

(2) The original version of this theory suggested that the products of the breakdown of the organic matrix of enamel provided the chelating agents which dissolved the apatite. The proportion of organic matter in enamel is so small, however (p. 108), that even if it were all capable of forming chelates, the amount of calcium dissolving would be negligible. Schatz suggested that the removal of even a small proportion of the mineral matter from certain key positions could conceivably result in extensive collapse of the enamel, but there is no evidence for this speculation. Of greater importance is the possibility that food debris or plaque might provide a constant source of chelating substances. The crucial experiment is to find out whether there are any natural circumstances under which the tooth can dissolve in saliva above the critical pH. Experiments by Jenkins & Dawes (1964), in which teeth were incubated for several days with saliva in the absence of carbohydrate or toluene, the pH rising to about 8·0, gave no indication that tooth substance dissolved and therefore did not support the theory. It was also shown that salivary extracts of plaque (which would be expected to contain any soluble chelating agents which the plaque contained) did not dissolve any bone labelled with ^{32}P. Somewhat similar experiments by Mørch *et al.* (1971) did suggest that substances formed in saliva by bacteria could dissolve enamel at neutrality and this question urgently requires further investigation.

While the presence of chelators in plaque cannot be doubted, it seems likely that they would have more contact and bind more readily with the soluble calcium compounds of salivary origin in plaque fluid rather than with enamel. Some of this calcium is released as ions when the plaque becomes acid suggesting that, far from damaging the enamel, the chelators may build up a reservoir of calcium which can be released when the plaque becomes acid and thus protect the enamel. The position may be summarized by saying that acid is undoubtedly present providing an environment which would be expected to dissolve the mineral of the tooth and is regarded as the most probable cause of caries. Chelators are also present but probably bound to cations of salivary origin and therefore their power of attacking enamel is problematical. The possibility of some additional solvent action from them, however, perhaps alternately with acid when the plaque is neutral, cannot be dismissed.

The evidence for the proteolysis-chelation theory has been discussed in detail (Jenkins 1961).

Salivary tests for caries activity

Certain tests on saliva have been developed which it was hoped would be of value in predicting the future carious activity.

The most widely used of these tests is the '*Lactobacillus acidophilus* count' which makes use of the fact that an agar medium containing tomato juice and adjusted to pH 5 favours the growth of lactobacilli but few other salivary organisms. If saliva (diluted if necessary) is spread on to agar plates containing this medium and incubated, only those bacteria which can grow at pH 5 will survive. Yeasts, and several species of bacteria other than lactobacilli, will grow but it is generally possible to distinguish colonies of the latter by their appearance when examined under a lens. Various modifications of the tomato agar medium have been suggested to make it more selective for lactobacilli, such as the addition of sodium azide, which is stated to prevent the growth of other aciduric organisms without significantly affecting lactobacilli. Great care is required in homogenizing the saliva before spreading as, even with precautions, duplicates show a large variation. Most workers have found a fair correlation between lactobacillus counts and the extremes of caries activity; the count is low or may be zero on 'caries-free saliva' and may reach a figure of over 1×10^{-6} ml^{-1} in saliva from highly caries-active people, although some exceptions are found. Some have been unable to find any correlation whatever, but errors in technique or in assessing caries may be responsible.

A group of tests based on the same underlying idea consists of measuring the fall on pH (either electrically or by titrating with N/100 alkali), of a sample of saliva incubated at 37° C for 4 hr with glucose solution. The greater the fall in pH, the greater is thought to be the caries activity. In Snyder's test, the saliva is incubated for 96 hr with a glucose-agar medium containing the indicator bromo cresol green; the colour of the indicator is taken as a measure of acid production.

The methyl red test of Hardwick & Manley (1952) is an application *in vivo* of the same idea. A 0·1% solution of methyl red (an indicator which is yellow at or above pH 6·3 and red at or below pH 4·2) is placed on the surface of the teeth with a dropper pipette, at least 1 hr after the last meal. Usually the tooth surfaces remain yellow but active carious cavities may immediately become red. The teeth are then sprayed with 1% glucose solution followed by a second application of the indicator. Areas where acid is produced from the glucose, and where caries is likely to develop, then become red within a few minutes. The test is valuable in predicting the site of future cavities as well as indicating, from the number and intensity of the red spots, the general susceptibility of an individual to caries.

A third test is Fosdick's 'calcium solubility test' in which 100 mg of ground enamel (or calcium phosphate) is shaken at 37° C with saliva containing

7% glucose. As the pH falls owing to the conversion of some of the glucose to acid by the bacteria, some of the enamel dissolves, the amount depending on the initial concentrations of calcium and phosphorus, the buffering power of saliva and the amount of acid formed. By estimating the calcium in solution before and after incubation, the amount dissolved from the enamel can be found by subtraction, and this figure is the basis of assessing the result.

Experiments in which several of the tests have been carried out repeatedly on the same subjects have shown that the tests agree with each other but not necessarily with the caries susceptibility of the subjects as measured by clinical examination. The differences between the results with caries-free and caries-rampant subjects were significant and gave some indication of the caries activity during the following year, but not longer (Davies *et al.* 1959; Gardner & Snyder 1960). Small differences in susceptibility were not predictable.

THE EMPIRICAL NATURE OF THE TESTS

It must be emphasized that these tests are merely based on the *observation* that their results do show some measure of correlation with clinical caries, and the theoretical basis underlying them is still uncertain. They are in fact testing different factors; for example, the calcium solubility and acid production tests measure the net acid produced from all organisms, whereas the lactobacillus count is a measure of one acid-producing organism only. The calcium solubility tests also takes into account the buffering power of saliva and its degree of saturation with apatite, which will alter the effectiveness of acids in dissolving enamel.

The value of these tests may be summed up as follows: if a consistent result has been given by several repetitions of any of these tests then a prognosis of the susceptibility to caries during the following year can be made if the result suggests very high or very low activity but it useless for dealing with intermediate levels of activity. This may be of some value in treatment planning, in advising patients about the frequency of routine checks by the dental surgeon, or in recommending dietary changes. As the theoretical basis of the tests is still uncertain, they cannot be used as more than circumstantial evidence for any theory of caries.

The bacteria responsible for caries

For over 50 years, many investigators have assumed that caries, like other bacterial diseases, is caused by a specific organism and much work has been devoted to attempts to identify it. It is by no means certain that any one organism is necessary, however. It is quite possible that caries will occur in a suitable biochemical environment (i.e. a sufficiently low pH to make the immediate environment of the enamel unsaturated with apatite) however this is produced. All the recognized histological features of caries can be produced in the absence of bacteria by placing teeth in an acid environment in the presence of a colloid (p. 423). This might imply that any bacteria or combination of organisms able to produce this acid environment could produce caries although, in practice, only a limited number of species may be able to do this in the conditions of the plaque. It is reasonable, therefore, to attempt to identify those organisms which seem, at least in most mouths, to produce caries even if the possibility is considered that if conditions change, then other organisms might assume this role.

In the 1920s two species were isolated from carious mouths and were suggested as the causal organisms: *Lactobacillus acidophilus*, or *odontolyticus* (by McIntosh *et al.* 1922, 1924, 1925) and *Streptococcus mutans* (Clarke 1924). When the statistical association between caries score and the number of lacto-bacilli became established (p. 430) it was somewhat naïvely assumed that these organisms were the cause of caries and methods of inhibiting their growth were sought in the hope that this would also inhibit caries. This is, of course, one possible interpretation of the association although it was realized that lactobacilli represented only about 0.1% of the total salivary organisms and an even lower proportion of plaque organisms. They produce acid more slowly than many streptococci but can survive and continue to produce acid at pH values even below 4·0, an acidity which inhibits most of other acid-producing bacteria. An alternative explanation for their being more numerous in caries-active mouths is that they are the result of caries; the presence of open cavities, which have a low pH, would favour the growth of these organisms. Filling many teeth at once in subjects with rampant caries results in a fall in the lactobacillus counts which supports this interpretation (Becks 1950; Kesel *et al.* 1958).

By instructing subjects to bite into an impression tray containing an agar medium selective for lactobacilli, these organisms are found, after incubation, to be located in those parts of the impression corresponding to the sites of caries.

In the early 1960s, when evidence was accumulating for the importance of dextrans in plaque, the emphasis changed to streptococci, which represent up to 80% of the plaque organisms. *Strep. mutans*, the organism associated with caries in 1924, has since come to be considered as the most likely causative organism. The evidence is as follows:

(1) *Strep. mutans* is a rapid acid-producer and synthesizes copious dextran from sucrose.

(2) When gnotobiotic animals are infected with *Strep. mutans*, very extensive caries is rapidly produced, especially on smooth surfaces; other species (lacto-bacilli and actinomyces) also produce caries but apparently not so vigorously, although no experiment appears to have been done in which the cariogenicity of many species have been directly compared under identical conditions.

(3) A correlation has been reported between the numbers or proportion of *Strep. mutans* in plaque (expressed in various ways) and the presence or

absence of a high DMF score in human subjects. Even within individual mouths, the proportion of *Strep. mutans* on surfaces with caries has been found to be higher than on sound surfaces. In one survey, *Strep. mutans* counts were carried out over 18 months, on selective tooth surfaces in children aged 7–9. The numbers increased over this period, the largest increases occurring on surfaces which later developed caries. Lactobacilli also increased in carious sites, but became a sizeable proportion of the plaque organisms only after caries was clinically evident. On the other hand, a study of the initiation of caries in various sites along with the investigation of the presence of *Strep. mutans* in children showed little correlation and gave no support to the belief that this organism was essential for caries (Hardie 1977). Also Huxley et al. (1975) found in rats that the initiation of caries neither required *Strep. mutans* nor was accelerated by a higher proportion of these organisms in plaque.

There is, therefore, considerable circumstantial evidence that *Strep. mutans* dominates the plaque bacteria and plays an important part in caries in the normal mouth. It does not necessarily follow, however, that this organism is essential for caries or that caries would be prevented if *Strep. mutans* were inhibited as, if this dominant organism were removed, other acid-producing species which are normally unable to compete successfully with it might then assume a leading cariogenic role.

A possible factor in determining the cariogenicity of streptococci, reported so far by only one group of workers, is the presence within the organism of a virus. When nine cariogenic strains were broken up in various ways, virus particles were released but were absent from non-cariogenic strains (Greer *et al.* 1971).

THE POSSIBLE RELATION BETWEEN LACTOBACILLI AND
STREPTOCOCCUS MUTANS

While it is well established that in the gnotobiotic animal infection with *Strep. mutans* alone can produce caries, a combination of streptococci and lactobacilli (although apparently not tested in gnotobiotic animals) would be expected to be more effective in producing a pH sufficiently low to dissolve enamel in the environment of the plaque. Streptococci cease to produce acid at pH values of about 4·3 whereas lactobacilli may continue, but at a reduced rate (although the optimum pH for both species is about 6·0), to below 4·0. The joint effect of the two species would, therefore, be expected to attack the enamel more intensively than streptococci alone or, in very early cavities, perhaps increase the number of occasions when the pH fell below the critical value. Once the cavity is well established and deep, it is probably always acid and too far removed from saliva to show the fluctuations of Stephan curves.

One approach strongly suggests that lactobacilli are concerned with the initial attack, at least when caries reaches the dentine. Extracted teeth with carious cavities were split in half and drilled with sterile instruments from the pulpal surface outwards until the very earliest stage of the advancing lesion was reached. The bacteria in the tissue removed from this carious 'front' were cultured and identified as lactobacilli, in most samples unmixed with strepto-cocci (McKay 1976; Shovlin & Gillis 1969) although it is possible that other organisms were present which did not grow under the cultural conditions used.

The Question of the Special Importance of Sucrose in Caries

Following the discovery of the importance of dextrans, which were thought at first to be formed exclusively from sucrose (cane sugar), in adding bulk to human plaque (p. 385) it became widely believed that sucrose was a carbo-hydrate specifically responsible for caries. This was based partly on the specu-lation that a plaque with much extracellular polysaccharide would retain acids and damage the teeth much more than thinner plaques free from dextrans.

Other evidence for the role of sucrose

Experiments in which germ-free rodents have been infected with various streptococci have shown that some streptococci do, and others do not, produce caries when the animals were fed on cariogenic diets. Ability to synthesize dextran seemed to be the chief factor determining whether the streptococcus was cariogenic. Many animal experiments showed that a higher caries score was produced with a diet containing sucrose than with comparable diets containing other sugars. People suffering from a rare hereditary intolerance of fructose avoid dietary sucrose and are reported to have low caries experience. When food containing added dextranase (see p. 385) was used experimentally in animals caries was reduced, suggesting that when dextran formation was prevented less caries developed. Dextranase, present in the rodents drinking water, was much less effective and when used as a mouth-rinse in human subjects, did not consistently reduce plaque. Evidently, if dextran is allowed to form, it is difficult to break down but if the dextranase is present at the same time as the sucrose, its formation can be reduced. The dextrans are known to vary in molecular weight and in degree of branching so that a mixture of enzymes might be necessary for complete breakdown. Dextrans were first identified as $1:6$ polymers but Guggenheim (1970) produced evidence that some organisms produce a $1:3$ polymer (mutan) and some produce a mixture of both isomers (p. 386). Some experi-ments in rodents suggest that a 'mutanase' ($1:3$ glucan-3-glucanohydrolase) reduces caries more effectively than dextranase but that a mixture of both enzymes is even more active.

Almost all this evidence, which suggested so strongly that sucrose had a special importance in caries has been undermined in various ways by later work or new interpretations of older work, and it is now at least clear that sucrose (and dextrans) are not essential for caries. The evidence against a specific role for sucrose is as follows.

Although dextrans and mutans can only be formed from sucrose other 'slimes' with somewhat similar properties are formed by some organisms from a variety of sugars including glucose (Bowden 1969; van der Hoeven 1974). More careful comparisons of the caries produced in animals by sucrose and other sugars show that the difference, though statistically significant and found in most experiments, is not as marked as had been thought. The main practical emphasis should perhaps be on the fact that most sugars are potentially cariogenic. People with fructose intolerance may tend to avoid all sugars, as they probably associate sweetness with their symptoms, rather than merely omitting sucrose from their diet. There is no experimental evidence that a plaque containing much dextran produces a lower pH or in any other way is in more conducive of caries than plaques low in dextran. A thick layer of dextran formed on teeth *in vitro* does not reduce significantly the access of fluoride to the tooth surface (Kirkegaard *et al.* 1975).

The value of any enzyme, such as dextranase, as an anticaries additive to food is obviously limited because it would not be stable to heat and would therefore operate only in uncooked foods. If used in a mouth-rinse or dentifrice it would not normally be present simultaneously with sucrose, the condition which is necessary for satisfactory effect.

Factors Affecting the Carious Process

The factors which influence the development of a caries cavity may be grouped as follows:

(1) Factors that increase or decrease the bacterial attack.

(2) Factors in the environment of the tooth which tend to reduce the effectiveness of the attack.

(3) The structure of the tooth and its influence on resistance to the attack.

(1) Factors which influence the bacterial attack

(*a*) *Rate of flow and viscosity of saliva.* There is evidence that relative freedom from caries is associated with a rapid rate of flow of saliva although not all the data support this. It seems reasonable to suppose that a rapid flow of highly buffered, mobile saliva would reduce the fall in plaque pH and tend to wash organisms and food debris out of the mouth. Some surveys suggest that a low viscosity in saliva is associated with a low caries rate although there appear to be few recent data collected with satisfactory precautions. A low viscosity is associated with slightly more rapid clearance of sugar from the mouth (Lanke 1957).

(*b*) *Antibacterial activity.* The relation between the antibacterial activity of saliva and caries is in a confused state. Although there is good evidence that the lactobacillus count is very low or zero in saliva from caries-free subjects the reason for this is still uncertain. A globulin which inhibits this organism has been reported in caries-free saliva (Green 1959) but its existence has not been confirmed (Geddes 1972) and, since this substance was stated to attach itself to the lactobacilli, its presence in caries-free saliva could be the result of there being too few organisms to remove it.

It has also been stated that more general antibacterial factors (for example, opsonins and leucotaxin), which would affect all organisms rather than any one species, are more active in saliva from caries-free individuals but this has never been fully investigated. Although data on the total number of bacteria in saliva in relation to caries are limited they do not suggest that they differ according to caries activity. This would minimize the importance of these general antibacterial substances in caries. The immunological approach to caries is discussed below.

(*c*) *Salivary amylase.* There have been many contradictory reports on the relation between the activity of salivary amylase and the intensity of the carious attack and the question is still undecided.

(*d*) *The spacing of the teeth.* If the dental arch is well developed and the teeth are properly spaced and occlude satisfactorily there may be few or no stagnation areas, and therefore less opportunity for bacterial attack although precise clinical data are lacking

THE IMMUNOLOGY OF CARIES AND THE POSSIBILITY OF PREVENTION BY A VACCINE

Kennedy *et al.* (1968) compared the levels of antibody to three of the streptococci associated with caries in the sera from 26 caries-free and 24 caries-active (DMF > 15) youths. The sera of both groups contained antibodies to these organisms, but the caries-free group had significantly higher concentrations to two of the three strains. The results suggest that both groups had been exposed to the cariogenic organisms and that caries had developed in one group in spite of the antibodies in the blood. The caries-free group had produced more antibodies but the difference in concentrations (or 'titre') between the groups were relatively small, whereas the differences between the caries scores were very great. Although the antibodies probably played some part in the freedom from caries they seemed unlikely to account for it entirely. Possibly other factors, such as the composition of saliva or enamel, supplemented the antibodies.

Lehner *et al.* (1975) estimated the concentrations of various types of antibodies, not in groups of caries-active and caries-free subjects, but in groups with the number of decayed, missing or filled teeth (DMFT) of more than or less than 7 (or in one report, of 9). These workers argued that differences were likely to be more significant if antibody titres were plotted against DMF values for the groups of individuals with different levels of active caries (open, untreated lesions involving possible exposure of immunocytes to cariogenic bacteria) rather than for those who were caries-free or had no active caries because their cavities had been filled (Challacombe *et al.* 1973). They suggested that in subjects with open, untreated lesions the bacteria were more likely to reach the cells producing antibodies than if the lesions were filled. They did not indicate the route by which the bacteria might reach the lymphoid tissue from which the antibodies arise.

In one set of data, the concentration of antibodies to nine strains of streptococci and two of lactobacilli in the sera of groups with high and low levels of active caries were compared. Antibodies to all the strains were detected in the high caries group, and although some sera had very low titres to some strains there were significantly higher concentrations to two of the streptococci and to *L. acidophilus*.

Comparisons in saliva and serum of caries-high and caries-low subjects showed that the concentrations of IgA and IgG were higher in the serum of the caries-high, but lower in the saliva of the caries-low group, the differences being significant for IgA.

Tests on human sera and saliva were carried out with antibodies produced in rabbits to an extract of *Strep. mutans* containing glucosyl transferase, the enzyme concerned with dextran synthesis. The results were complicated as they used several different methods for estimating the antibodies (haemagglutination, inhibition of the enzyme by sera, absorption and precipitation tests) and none of the differences was especially dramatic. However, the most striking findings were that in the caries-treated and caries-free groups the titre was lower in the sera from the subjects with a high DMF (i.e. inversely correlated with caries) the reverse being found in saliva (Fig. XI.9). In the active-caries group, the titre in serum was higher with high DMF (positive correlation) and in saliva the correlation was not significant in this group. Similar results were obtained with three other cariogenic strains of *Strep. mutans* but no correlations were found between the DMF and concentrations of antibodies to two non-cariogenic organisms. The antibodies were mainly of the IgG and IgM classes which unfortunately do not enter saliva but reach the mouth in small amounts via the crevicular fluid. The concentrations of IgA in duct saliva (the predominant immunoglobulin in saliva) are only about 3% those of serum but the concentrations in crevicular fluid are approximately one-half to one-third those of serum. This fluid is probably more important than saliva as a source of antibodies in the vicinity of the tooth.

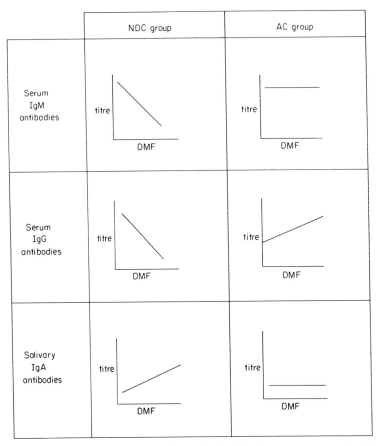

Fig. XI.9. Diagrammatic summary of the relationships between serum and salivary antibodies to glucosyltransferase and DMF index. NDC group = no dental caries (all cavities filled and no open lesions); AC group = active caries (open cavities present). This diagram illustrates the correlation between antibodies and caries but it must be emphasized that they tend to simplify the picture; the individual data show wide variations.

Lehner's group explained the difference between their results and those of Kennedy *et al.* (1968) (which showed higher titres in the caries-free) by the fact that the latter compared sera in caries-rampant and caries-free subjects corresponding to the high DMF of caries-active and the low DMF of treated caries, which in Lehner's subjects showed little difference in antibody titre (Fig. XI.9).

The following interpretation of these results was suggested: if an individual is exposed in early life to cariogenic bacteria, or some fraction from them such as an enzyme, and produces antibodies that may reduce the caries or in rare cases prevent it altogether. Challacombe *et al.* (1973) suggest that most people (the caries-active) suffer from an immunological defect in that they cannot sustain effective levels of antibody throughout life, as shown by the fall in titre when the antigen is removed (as when carious teeth are filled). It seems unreasonable to consider that most people suffer from a defect. It is more likely that caries-active subjects, as the result of early exposure, have become tolerant to the organisms and fail to produce antibodies. The finding that saliva and serum levels have opposite relations to DMF suggests that these levels are under separate control; saliva antibodies may be formed by immunocytes in the oral tissues and have little effect on serum levels and the concentrations of serum antibodies are low in saliva.

These findings undoubtedly suggest that immunological mechanisms do relate, though rather weakly, to caries activity and this had led to the hope that caries might be prevented by a vaccine. There are many difficulties in this approach, however. In the first place, there is no convincing evidence that any one organism, enzyme or other antigen is specifically related to caries, so that there is no clear target to which an antibody should be aimed. The existence of antibodies to glucosyl transferase or *Strep. mutans* in caries-low subjects does not prove that they are operative, but merely that the body has been exposed to this organism and antibodies have been formed. Experiments with germ-free animals have shown that when *Strep. mutans* is present alone, it is more powerfully cariogenic than the other organisms which have been tested. In the normal human mouth, however, there are many organisms capable of producing acid and if one powerful species were inhibited its competitors might become equally effective. The inhibition of glucosyl transferase would only prevent dextran formation (perhaps only one phase of its synthesis, see p. 385) and would be expected, at most, only to reduce caries, since dextrans cannot be regarded as essential for it. A second problem arises from the low concentrations of antibodies in saliva. The concentrations in crevicular fluid are high enough to be effective and antibodies might accumulate in plaque in the cervical region, but they would be greatly diluted and probably ineffective by the time they were carried by saliva to the occlusal surfaces. Another difficulty in relation to the immunology of caries is that of understanding how bacteria in the mouth reach the cells of the lymphoid system responsible for producing antibodies.

Diseases which have been successfully treated by vaccines are those to which there is a natural immunity after one attack, a situation which clearly is not effective for caries (although it is possible that severe caries might provide some immunity for a short period, say of some weeks, which in view of the slowness of caries would not be detectable clinically).

EXPERIMENTAL IMMUNIZATION AGAINST CARIES

Attempts as early as 1940 to immunize human subjects against caries by injecting lactobacilli, the organism then believed to cause caries, were unsuccessful. Immunization of rats and monkeys with *Strep. mutans* or extracts containing glucosyl transferase administered with adjuvant have led to variable results in reducing caries. Some experiments have been entirely negative while others have shown an erratic protection against caries in some immunized animals and not others (reviewed anonymously 1975).

Bowen *et al.* (1975) injected a group of 3 monkeys with cultures of *Strep. mutans* (a total of 12 injections over $5\frac{1}{2}$ years) and after 7 years the immunized animals had a total of fewer than 20 lesions compared with over 50 in the 3 control animals. However, the difference was largely due to one immunized monkey being caries-free and one control having rampant caries, although a second experiment gave more consistent results. Injections of glucosyl transferase tended, inexplicably, to increase the numbers of *Strep. mutans* and of carious cavities. Lehner *et al.* (1975) succeeded in postponing smooth surface caries in 4 out of 12 immunized monkeys for 70 weeks compared with the appearance of similar cavities within 17 weeks in the 11 controls. In the 4 animals in which caries was postponed, serum antibodies were detectable within 4 weeks of the first injection but in those in which caries developed rapidly, antibody production was not evident for 20–48 weeks; caries had begun and progressed before the titre reached effective concentrations. Evidently the great variations in the rate of development of antibodies in individual animals has a decisive effect upon their effectiveness. The proportion of *Strep. mutans* was reduced significantly only in the vicinity of the crevicular fluid, from which it may be concluded that serum antibodies present in this fluid produced these effects.

OTHER METHODS OF REDUCING THE BACTERIAL ATTACK

(*a*) *Detergent diets.* The choice of a tough, fibrous diet increases the volume of saliva and was originally assumed to have a mechanical effect in removing plaque and food debris. Nevin (1954a,b) carried out experiments on the diffusion in narrow spaces resembling the spaces between the teeth. He found that rapid movement (similar to those produced in the mouth by vigorous chewing) favoured the washing out of retained material but pointed out that energetic chewing at the beginning may ram food into the sites of retention.

Observations on plaque stained with disclosing solution clearly show that, although detergent foods may move it from smooth surfaces, they have little or no effect on plaque in contact points, gingival margins and other areas favourable to caries. Of much greater potential importance is the rapid flow of saliva produced in response to the mechanical or gustatory stimuli of tough or highly-flavoured foods. Apples have been suggested for many years as a useful detergent food at the end of a meal but, unfortunately, apple juice is very acid (pH 4) and, while a highly-effective saliva stimulus, its pH is often too low to be neutralized by the alkaline saliva whose beneficial effect is consequently reduced (Fig. XI.10 from Geddes *et al.* 1977). Slack & Martin

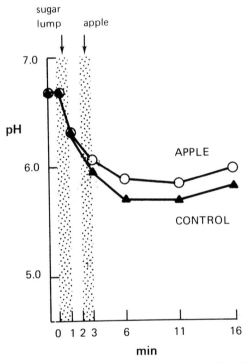

FIG. XI.10. Effect of eating apples after a lump of sugar on the pH changes of the plaque (average of 16 subjects). Note that the apple has only a slight effect on reducing the average pH drop (in some subjects an apple made the pH fall to a lower figure).

(1958) found a smaller increase in caries among a group of children who had eaten a piece of raw apple after each meal for a period of 2 years compared with that in a control group. Owing to differences between the caries incidence in the two groups before the experiment began they were

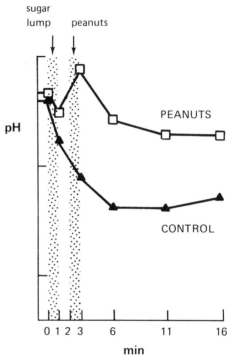

FIG. XI.11. The effect of nuts on the pH change after a lump of sugar. Note that the pH rises during eating the nuts owing to the rapid saliva flow and the subsequent drop is greatly reduced.

cautious in coming to a conclusion but thought it likely that apples with a crisp, firm flesh had had some effect in reducing caries. A few nuts or a small piece of cheese taken immediately after a meal promote a flow of saliva which prevents or reduces greatly the pH drop usually occurring after taking food (Figs XI.11 and 12, Geddes *et al.* 1977; Rugg-Gunn *et al.* 1975). Raw carrots and celery are two other foods with a comparable effect on saliva flow and, being almost neutral, might be expected to reduce caries. However, in one experiment, the provision of raw carrots at the end of school lunch for 2 years had no significant effect on caries (Reece & Swallow 1970), probably because the carrot was given at only one meal a day and only on school days. It has been suggested that the extremely tough foods eaten by man in primitive conditions may cause so much attrition that the occlusal surfaces of the molars become flat and self-cleansing, which could contribute to his low incidence of caries. This is doubtful, however, because caries usually develop within three years of eruption and the removal of pits and fissures by attrition required over ten years even on primitive diets (Hardwick 1960)

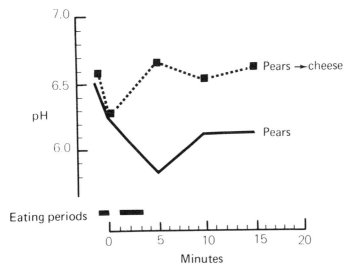

Fɪɢ. XI.12. The effect of cheese in greatly reducing the pH drop in plaque after eating pears.

(*b*) *Oral Hygiene.* It seems reasonable to suppose that tooth-brushing would remove or reduce plaques and oral bacteria and to some extent compensate for a low rate of salivary flow. 'Stephan curves' (pp. 387–93) show that the formation of acid by a thick plaque is extremely rapid after the ingestion of carbohydrate. Therefore, to be really effective, it is probable that tooth-brushing must be carried out immediately after the end of eating as even a few minutes' delay may give time for the plaque pH to fall below the critical figure. Although it has been seldom advocated, there would seem good grounds for brushing the teeth before a meal (to reduce plaques) as well as after a meal (to remove food debris). It seems unlikely that the use of tooth brushes, as made at present, can remove plaque and food debris from all the potential sites of caries, and there is scope for the investigation of brushes with finer, more penetrating bristles. Few satisfactory clinical experiments have been conducted on the efficacy of these measures on caries incidence, the chief difficulty being that of ensuring that the experimental subjects carry out (or that the control subjects do not carry out) the procedure under investigation. Surveys of caries among those who, on their own testimony, brushed their teeth several times a day have shown the same or only slightly less caries than those who did not brush them at all (for references see Bibby 1966). In some surveys, the puzzling observation was made that caries scores were higher among those who brushed more frequently. One experiment in which thorough tooth-brushing (or if not possible, mouth-rinsing) was carried out within 10 min of every meal or sweet did show a significant difference of 63% reduction in caries over

2 years, compared with a group who carried out their normal tooth-brushing practice (Fosdick 1950). As mentioned on p. 397 thorough tooth-brushing every 2 days is adequate to prevent gingivitis but on present knowledge, plaque, even a few hours old, is probably potentially cariogenic.

Although tooth-brushing may have limited effects on plaque in the more frequent sites of caries, use of disclosing solutions show that it does remove plaque from smooth surfaces. Experiments in which volunteers abstain from tooth-brushing for periods of up to 23 days (p. 459) show that demineralization, resembling early caries, could occur during this time. Presumably tooth-brushing does at least prevent this demineralization and the caries which would be expected to develop from it if it were allowed to continue.

Lindhe *et al.* (1973) tested on 192 children aged 7–14 for 3 years the combined effects of two measures: (1) a thorough tooth cleaning, carried out by trained dental personnel (a 'scale and polish' known as a prophylaxis) with an abrasive paste containing 5% sodium monofluorophosphate (MFP), every 2 weeks during the school term but less frequently during the third year, and (2) repeated instructions about tooth-brushing and interdental cleaning with floss. The plaque index and caries and gingivitis scores were all extremely low in the test group compared with the control (0·1 and 3·0 new caries surfaces per year, respectively) even though the controls brushed their teeth with 0.2% NaF solution every 2 weeks, in the third year every 4 weeks (a routine procedure in Sweden). Most of the cavities·in the test group developed in the third year and it is tempting to suggest that this may have arisen because the frequency of the prophylaxes was reduced. Unfortunately, this degree of oral cleanliness is unattainable without the employment of trained personnel and, although these exceptionally good results should not be assessed only in financial terms, the cost was not much less than that of the fillings required by the control group. In a further experiment the effect of frequent prophylaxis with and without the 5% MFP were tested for 1 year (Axelsson & Lindhe 1975). The caries increments were virtually identical in both groups clearly indicating that the prophylaxis was more important than the MFP.

(*c*) *Dentifrices containing antibacterial substances.* Most dentifrices have been designed merely to assist the mechanical action of brushing the teeth in removing plaque and food debris. In recent years, however, dentifrices have been developed containing antibacterial substances which it is thought may reduce bacterial activity in plaque and in the stagnant parts of the mouth. To be effective it is probably important that the substance can diffuse through a plaque even if direct contact with it is limited (it is, of course, the inner part of the plaque which affects the tooth surface) and preferably remain attached to it or to the enamel surface. Among the substances which have been tried are ammonium salts, with and without urea, penicillin, sodium dehydroacetate and sodium N-lauroyl sarcosinate, all of which are very effective in preventing a fall in pH in a 'Stephan curve' but their clinical effectiveness remains to be proved. The only constituents of dentifrice on which extensive clinical trials have been reported are various fluorides. Most of the results have been positive (reviewed by Marthaler 1971, and various authors in the *Brit. dent. J.* **123,** 9, 17, 26, 33, 40) but not necessarily by antibacterial effects and their

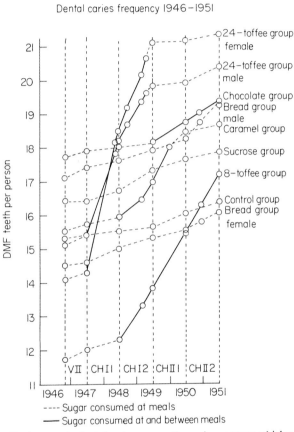

FIG. XI.13. The increase in dental caries among the various groups which received from 1947 to 1951 the carbohydrate supplements named on the right. The parts of the curve with full line represent periods during which the carbohydrates were fed *between* meals; the dotted parts of the curves cover periods during which the supplements were given *with* meals. The dietary arrangements were somewhat complex and the original report must be consulted for details. This diagram clearly shows that the carbohydrate supplements increased caries significantly only if fed during meals. One criticism of the experiment, which is difficult to avoid in investigations on human caries, is also apparent, namely, the great variations in caries incidence among the different groups at the beginning.

introduction means that, contrary to the former results mentioned above, tooth-brushing does now have some effect in reducing caries.

(*d*) *Mouth rinses.* Twice-daily rinses with 0·2% chlorhexidine, a powerful synthetic antibacterial substance, or topical application of up to 2% are very effective, reducing oral bacteria by about 85–90% and preventing plaque and gingivitis. Its continued use is impracticable, however, as apart from its unpleasant taste it binds to proteins of the pellicle on the tooth surface and forms a yellow-brown stain (Löe 1973).

(*e*) *Reduction of dietary carbohydrate.* There are two ways in which carbohydrate restrictions might be effective in reducing caries.

(1) *Reduction of carbohydrate between meals.* The very thorough experiment at Vipeholm Hospital, Sweden, on over 400 mental patients, has shown the importance in caries of sugar taken between meals. The broad plan of the experiment was to take the patients in each of the seven wards as experimental groups and feed them a basal diet extremely low in sugar. To six groups sugar was added to the diet in various forms (as chocolates, caramels, in solution or added to bread) given either with meals or between meals. The seventh group acted as a control and the calories were made up by adding 150 g of margarine daily. The groups which received sugar (in any form) with meals developed less caries than those which had received the sugar between meals, which showed a great increase in caries incidence (Fig. XI.13). The control group had virtually no increase in caries, but this could have arisen either from the low carbohydrate or the high fat content of the diet. The use of different wards as experimental groups meant that neither the ages nor the initial caries of the groups were matched (the variations in the latter can be seen in Fig. XI.13) and these differences probably did affect the results, but not sufficiently to influence the final conclusions (Gustafsson *et al.* 1954). Some of the patients needed help with feeding and tooth-brushing and had difficulty in carrying out instructions; they cannot be regarded as representative of a normal population.

The conclusion was supported by a survey in which the total caries score of about 800 children aged 5–6 in Tennessee correlated well with between-meal eating of carbohydrate-containing foods on the previous day, as recorded by a questionnaire to the parents. This survey was carried out under more natural conditions and with a normal population of suitable age for a caries study but was rather restricted because information on snacks referred to only 1 day, and depended on the parent's memory. The average caries score of 300 children of the staff of British Dental Schools whose between-meal eating was known to be restricted was lower than the national average (Bradford & Crabb 1961). This is not decisive, however, because it is possible that other preventive measures, such as more effective tooth-brushing, may have influenced the result.

Rats given diets high in sugars by a feeding machine which could be programmed to supply the food as a pre-arranged number of meals, showed that increasing the frequency of eating from 12 to 34 times a day trebled the caries score (König *et al.* 1969).

This conclusion is readily explained on a biochemical basis. After eating sugar, the plaque pH drops and may fall below the critical pH at which, in the environment of plaque or saliva, the enamel will dissolve (p. 299). With three meals ending with carbohydrates, the pH will drop three times a day; but with three meals and, say, twenty sweets or sugary snacks spaced between meals it will result in twenty-three occasions when the enamel is at risk.

It is frequently assumed that sweets are the commonest form of sugar consumed between meals and are therefore the chief cause of caries. The importance of sweet-eating has been challenged, however, on the grounds that attempts to relate sugar or sweet consumption with caries scores in the UK have failed to establish a correlation. For example, a survey among 2905 children in Dundee compared the DMF values of groups who, from their answers to questionnaires, consumed various amounts of sweets. The results

TABLE XI.1

DMF values in relation to the amounts of sweets eaten (oz per week)

DUNDEE (2905 children)					
Sweet consumption	< 5	6–11	12–18	19–25	> 25
DMF	9·6	10·5	10·1	9·9	9·3
EDINBURGH (402 children)					
Sweet consumption	< 4	4–7	8–16	> 16	
DMF	9·3	9·7	10·6	11·3	

Mansbridge (1960) & McHugh *et al.* (1964)

(Table XI.1) show a slightly higher DMF amongst the group eating 6–11 oz (170–310 g) compared with less than 5 oz (140 g), but with intakes higher than 11 oz (310 g) the DMF was progressively lower. A similar survey in Edinburgh did show higher DMF values (11·3) with the high sweet intake but the most striking feature is the high DMF values (9·3) with the lowest intake of sweets.

The data collected in surveys of this sort are necesarily inaccurate especially on such topics as sweet-eating which depends on the memory and honesty of the subject. The DMF is a crude measure since it takes no account of the size of cavities and a tiny filling gives the same score as a tooth so severely decayed as to require extraction. Also, DMF scores are a measure of the total accumulated caries whereas the data on sweet-eating referred only to the time immediately preceding the survey. A more critical survey showed that the change in DMF surfaces over the two years (DMFS increment) was significantly higher (10·91) than in schools where sweets were sold than where they were unobtainable (9·34) although again the difference was not large (Fanning *et al.* 1969). The probable explanation of the low correlation between caries score and sweet-eating is that caries is caused largely by sugar in foods and drinks consumed between meals rather than by sweets. Ninety per cent of the sugar consumed in the UK is contained in foods so that on the average sweets merely add a slightly greater challenge though probably greater in children than in adults.

It has also been pointed out that although the average amount of sweets eaten in the United Kingdom is higher than in most comparable countries the average DMF is lower. The DMF figures from the different countries were not standardized, however, and it is doubtful whether comparisons are necessarily valid. If the DMF really is lower in the UK a possible explanation is that most British children drink tea (which contains fluoride) during the years when their teeth are developing or when they can benefit from a topical effect and receive, on the average, enough fluoride to have some protective effect.

Test-tube experiments show that sugar concentrations greater than 20% inhibit acid production by salivary bacteria (a general effect of high concentrations of sugar—hence its preservative value in jams). Consequently, while sweets are being eaten, the pH of plaque does not necessarily fall (unless the sweet is itself acid, as many are). Rapidly flowing saliva, with its high pH and buffering power, secreted in response to a sweet also tends to keep the plaque near to neutrality.

Although the Vipeholm experiment demonstrated the great importance of sugar between meals as a cause of caries, it would be premature to conclude that only foods containing sugar are effective. The experiment did not test the effect of *starchy* food eaten between meals. The importance of starch in caries is almost impossible to test on human subjects because of the difficulty of finding an acceptable diet low in starch. Animal experiments which have included starch diets suggest that it is not highly cariogenic and some workers think that this applies to man also. They suggest that starch is indiffusible and forms acid only on the outer surface of plaque. Although most lines of evidence suggest that starch is not cariogenic, measurement of the pH of inner plaque by built-in electrodes (p. 391) shows a prolonged fall after starchy food contrary to other findings.

(2) *Changes in the order in which foods are eaten.* As already mentioned (p. 392) the pH of plaque does not necessarily fall, and may even rise, during eating (even of sugar), as the high pH and buffering power of stimulated saliva neutralize the acid as it is formed. Telemetric studies show, however, that thick plaques 3 or more days old may fall in pH while a sugar rinse is still in the mouth. The fall in pH usually occurs within a few minutes after eating has finished when the saliva flow subsides. This suggests that if carbohydrate-containing foods are eaten before the end of a meal and sugar-free foods with a powerful stimulating effect on saliva conclude the meal, the fall in pH might be largely prevented, except with very thick plaques. Experiments in which the order of eating different foods has been changed have

confirmed these predictions (Rugg-Gunn *et al.* 1975), but in practice two difficulties arise. The first is that the pH may drop if there is an interval of more than a few minutes between eating a sugar-containing food and the next course, and the second is the established custom of eating the sweet, fruits or sweetened tea or coffee at the end of a meal. If the last items eaten are savoury (cheese for example, preferably without biscuits) or unsweetened tea or coffee, the pH change can be avoided (Figs XI.10, 11, 12). Another point often overlooked is that many foods and most alcoholic beverages are themselves acid and reduce plaque pH without the intervention of bacteria from sugar.

These conclusions are based on pH measurements, mostly of plaque from the more accessible areas, and their application to sites of caries is still uncertain. No clinical trials of the effect on caries of avoiding sugar-containing foods at the end of a meal have been carried out. An effect similar to that of cheese would be expected from any strongly-tasting food or preparation taken immediately after eating. A clinical trial of tablets (Dentabs) containing 3·5% malic acid as a sialogogue and 6% dicalcium phosphate to prevent the erosive effect of the acid, gave significant reduction in caries during the first year but similar caries increments occurred in both the tablet and control groups during the second year of the trial, probably owing to reduced use of the tablet. The result on caries was attributed to the removal of food debris by the saliva rather than to a neutralization of plaque acid; plaque pH was not measured (Slack *et al.* 1964).

(3) *Effect of severe carbohydrate restriction on salivary lactobacilli.* It has been reported in two experiments (Jay 1940; Becks 1950) on about 1600 subjects that if dietary carbohydrates are limited to 100 g per day for 2 weeks (with a corresponding increase in fat consumption) the lactobacillus counts fall and in many subjects the counts remain low even when the carbohydrates are gradually restored to the diet. The long duration of the effect is difficult to explain, since it would be expected that if any lactobacilli at all remained in the mouth (as they did in about half the subjects) they would rapidly multiply as soon as adequate carbohydrate was made available. In the experiment by Becks, the caries rate was reduced but in Jay's work only the lactobacillus count was studied and it was assumed that if it fell, a reduction in caries would follow. In fact, the role of this organism in caries is uncertain.

Another approach is to replace the sucrose of the diet by sugars which are not fermentable. Sorbitol and xylitol are two examples. While it would hardly seem practicable to bring about such a revolution in dietary practice a large scale experiment in Finland with xylitol showed a very marked reduction in caries with no undesirable side effects (Scheinin *et al.* 1975). Some experiments suggest that xylitol increases the peroxidase-thiocyanate anti-bacterial factor in saliva (p. 342) but they have not been confirmed. It is therefore uncertain whether the use of xylitol reduces caries other than by the replacement of fermentable carbohydrate.

(2) Factors tending to reduce the effect of the bacterial attack

It has been emphasized elsewhere that acid production would not itself necessarily cause demineralization of the teeth unless the pH on the enamel surface falls below the critical level at which enamel dissolves. If the fall in pH can be prevented then it would be expected that acid production would be harmless, though the possibility remains of attack by chelating agents formed in the plaque. A high buffering power of saliva may, therefore, be an important factor in preventing acid attack and in at least some caries-free subjects, a high salivary buffering power and consequently high plaque pH seems an adequate explanation for the absence of caries. The average fasting pH of plaque has been found to be higher and the fall in pH after sugar smaller in caries-free than in caries-active subjects.

The critical pH of plaque is governed by its calcium and phosphate concentration, and there is evidence that the concentrations are higher in plaques of caries-free subjects and on the caries-free surfaces in subjects with active caries (p. 396).

ATTEMPTS TO LOWER CRITICAL pH

The addition of 1–2% sodium or calcium phosphate to the caries-producing diets of rodents is highly successful in reducing caries (reviewed by Nizel & Harris 1964). The mode of action is presumably by increasing the buffering power of the saliva and lowering the critical pH by increasing the concentration of calcium and phosphate ions in the plaque although if taken during tooth formation an effect on the morphology of the teeth has been claimed by one group of workers. Several experiments on human subjects have been negative, a possible reason being that human plaque is high in phosphate and when food containing, say, 1% phosphate is in the mouth, the saliva secretion dilutes this to a concentration below that already present in the plaque of most subjects (Tatevossian *et al.* 1975).

Also, the phosphate of saliva usually falls as the flow rate increases reducing still more the phosphate concentration in the environment of the plaque. There is, therefore, in most mouths, no concentration gradient to encourage the diffusion of phosphate into plaque. There is evidence that if the phosphate concentration in the plaque of a particular individual is unusually low, it may be raised by sucking sugar lumps containing 1% sodium phosphate. This suggests that phosphate additives might be effective in those most prone to caries whose plaque are reported to be low in phosphate. In the two experiments in which phosphate did reduce caries, the soluble sodium phosphate was used whereas in the negative experiments, the calcium salt (insoluble in saliva and plaque) was the additive (Stookey *et al.* 1967; Carroll *et al.* 1968).

This raises the question as to why phosphates reduce caries in rodents.

Ericsson (1962) analysed pilocarpine-stimulated saliva from rodents and reported that pH and calcium concentration were much higher and phosphate lower than in human saliva. These results have not been confirmed on samples of unstimulated rat saliva collected by blotting the mouth with filter paper and the effect of phosphate in rodents cannot be readily explained though, as the plaque is presumably thinner than human plaque, diffusion may be easier.

(3) The resistance of the tooth

There are several ways in which the structure of the tooth may modify its resistance to bacterial attack.

(*a*) *The morphology of the tooth.* (1) Teeth with deep pits and fissures are often regarded as being more liable to caries because of the greater opportunities which such teeth provide for the stagnation of food and bacteria although this does not appear to have been investigated statistically. The effect of hypoplasia of the enamel surface as a whole in favouring caries is on a firmer basis (pp. 266–8). (2) The experiments of Kruger (pp. 481–2) show that trace elements may influence the morphology of rodents' teeth and if this applies to man (which has only been shown for fluoride, see p. 481) it could be one possible explanation of the effect of trace elements on caries. (3) The relation of vitamin D to hypoplasia and caries is discussed on pp. 263–269. (4) The very vulnerable fissures may be protected by (i) the insertion of a shallow filling (prophylactic odontotomy) or (ii) a fissure sealant, soon after the posterior teeth erupt and before caries begins (reviewed by Buonocore 1971). Fissure sealants consist principally of synthetic resins and are placed in a clean, non-carious fissure after its surface has been roughened by controlled etching with phosphoric acid (Silverstone 1974). The sealants provide a barrier between plaque and enamel pits and fissures and thus prevent caries provided they remain in place, although there is some evidence that leakage can occur between sealant and enamel. In the hands of some operators, about 80% of sealants remain intact for up to 2 years (Rock 1974).

In view of the suggestion that enamel protein delays the spread of caries, the possible introduction of organic substances into the interstices of the crystals has been considered as an anti-caries measure (Brooke *et al.* 1972; Robinson *et al.* 1976).

(*b*) *The chemical structure of the tooth.* The evidence on the question of chemical composition and caries resistance is discussed more fully on pp. 85 and 241–9.

The position may be summarized by stating that (1) the influence of maternal diet on the caries susceptibility of young experimental animals and (2) the influence of 'war-time' diets which apparently increased the resistance of the tooth (and had a larger influence via the oral environment), have both been interpreted as evidence that the chemical composition of the tooth is important in caries resistance. There are serious weaknesses in this evidence, however. The nature of the difference is still unknown but there are possibilities of variations in the concentrations of trace elements (the evidence is strongest for fluoride, strontium, molybdenum and selenium but others may be involved), carbonates and carbohydrates.

It is likely that the higher concentration of fluoride in teeth formed during residence in 'high fluoride' areas is associated with their lower caries incidence. There is evidence that the fluoride concentration on the enamel surface is related to caries resistance but this requires confirmation (see Chapter XII).

(*c*) *The possible influence of 'vital reactions' of dental tissues in caries resistance.* The gradual hardening of the floor of a cavity and the cessation of its advance, which have been stated to be favoured by the administration of vitamin D, seem to imply some response from within the tooth. If the fluid diffusing through enamel *in vitro* (p. 176) is present *in vivo* then changes in its composition could possibly influence caries. When extracted teeth with a 'window' of enamel exposed were immersed in acetic acid buffer, the demineralization was less when the pulp chamber contained a mineralizing fluid, showing that, at least *in vitro*, protective substances can diffuse from the pulp and reach the enamel (Bergmann & Lindén 1966). The power of the odontoblastic process to reduce the permeability of the dentinal tubules is now well established and could be a factor in delaying the spread of caries. To what extent these reactions are influenced by general systemic changes is not known.

Based on the observation that caries was rare among populations living on food requiring vigorous mastication, Neumann *et al.* (1957) suggested that heavy mastication may build up the resistance of the tooth. The removal of certain teeth from monkeys was followed by a fall in water content and a rise in ^{32}P uptake of their antagonists (which would in these circumstances be subjected to no masticatory stress). The possibility that the additional ^{32}P arose simply from calculus or accumulated debris was eliminated.

These results were never fully established but suggest that the composition of the tooth can be influenced by the amount of masticatory stress it has incurred and might therefore influence caries. The rapid flow of saliva which would follow the vigorous mastication could perhaps explain these effects. Even if vigorous mastication were found to reduce caries it is doubtful whether many would be willing to make the effort required and it would be difficult to find a variety of foods which are sufficiently tough.

(*d*) Animal experiments have shown that saliva increases the resistance of newly erupted teeth, but the constituents concerned are not known (see p. 173).

OTHER DIETARY EFFECTS

The controversial evidence that vitamin D reduces caries is discussed on pp. 263–269. The addition of 1% of calcium sucrose phosphate (CaSP) to sugar and flour has been reported to reduce caries in an experiment lasting 3 years on several hundred children (Harris 1967–9). This substance, like other organic phosphates such as phytate (see later), binds to the tooth surface and reduces its solubility *in vitro* and this is presumed to be one of the ways in which it reduces caries. Commercial CaSP (Anticay) has an alkaline pH and moderate buffering power. Telemetric measurements of plaque pH after rinsing with 10% sucrose containing 1% CaSP show a rise in pH, in place of the usual fall with sugar. With thick, 5-day-old plaques the pH did eventually fall but the minimum reached was much higher than with sugar alone (Clarke & Fanning 1971, 1973).

Epidemiological Evidence for an Influence of Trace Elements

MOLYBDENUM

Adler (1953) found that certain communities in Hungary showed a lower incidence of caries than would be expected from their fluoride intake. The effect was traced to the presence of 0·1 ppm of molybdenum in the water supply. A low caries incidence was also found in Napier, a New Zealand town originally chosen as a control for a fluoridation scheme in Hastings, New Zealand. The vegetables eaten in Napier were grown on a piece of land raised from the sea by an earthquake as recently as 1932 and found by analysis to be unusually high in molybdenum and aluminium. Analysis of whole ground deciduous teeth from these towns showed average molybdenum concentrations of 0·069 and 0·046 ppm. This evidence that molybdenum increases caries resistance has been confirmed in animal experiments, although there is much unexplained contradiction between different workers on such questions as the dosage required or whether the molybdenum is more effective during or after tooth formation (for review see Jenkins (1967)). Other biological effects of molybdenum are greatly influenced by many other ions in the diet (including copper, sulphate, manganese and vanadium) and the dietary levels of these ions have not been controlled in the experiments on caries, which may be one explanation for the contradictory results.

SELENIUM

A study of the caries incidence in children born in various regions of Oregon, USA, revealed that those from the east of the Cascade Range had a lower caries incidence than those from the west of these mountains. Two environmental differences which seemed likely to influence caries were found. First, the east had more sunshine, which has been stated to be associated with a low caries incidence elsewhere, perhaps because it increased vitamin D synthesis in the skin. The second difference was that the urine from residents in the west contained more selenium, indicating that there was a greater intake of this element. Selenium has been found in animal experiments to increase slightly caries incidence, which supports the possibility that selenium favours caries, although the evidence is not decisive (p. 80).

BORON, STRONTIUM AND LITHIUM AND OTHER TRACE ELEMENTS
Three completely independent surveys of caries incidence in such widely separated areas as the USA, New Zealand and New Guinea have demonstrated the presence of boron, strontium and lithium in the environment of populations with unusually low incidence of caries (Table XI.2). In the USA, the childhood residence of 360 caries-free naval recruits was traced and a majority was found to have lived in certain parts of Ohio or in South Carolina. Analyses of the water supplies in these areas revealed the presence of exceptionally high concentrations of boron, lithium, molybdenum and strontium. In New Zealand, Cadell (1964) related caries incidence to the trace elements in the soil and in a strain of sweet vernal, a plant known to reflect the availability of trace elements. He found low caries was associated with residence in areas with soils which were alkaline (known to favour molybdenum uptake by plants) or well drained and high in molybdenum, boron and strontium. In New Guinea, the soil and the sweet potato and sago (staple foods of the area) were analysed by Barmes *et al.* (1969, 1970) and Adkins *et al.* 1974. Low caries was associated with higher concentrations of the alkaline earths (strontium, calcium, magnesium, lithium and potassium) in the soil but not necessarily in the foods (although soil may be present as a contaminant of food) and zinc and boron. The results are summarized in Table XI.2.

A study of the concentrations of trace elements in enamel from teeth with a known caries history and from areas of the USA where the incidence of

TABLE XI.2

Summary of trace elements, with high concentrations in plants, water and soils, associated with low caries experience

New Zealand (plants)	USA (water)			New Guinea (soils)
	Ohio (1)	Ohio (2)	S. Carolina	
B	B	B	B	—
—	Li	Li	—	Li
Mo	Mo	Mo	—	—
Sr	Sr	Sr	Sr	Sr
High pH (soils)	—	—	—	High pH

caries varies was completed by Curzon (1977). The results showed that a high concentration of fluoride and strontium was associated with low caries and high concentrations of copper and manganese were associated with high caries. Contrary to the epidemiological evidence mentioned above a high concentration of selenium was associated with low caries. Other weaker correlations with low caries were high concentrations of boron, potassium and nickel whereas zinc, vanadium and lead were associated with teeth high in caries.

It cannot be assumed that all these trace elements are directly related to caries; it may be that only one or two influence caries but that they all tend to occur together in soils. Apart from the morphological effects on rats' teeth (p. 481) and Curzon's data on enamel (which implies an effect on crystal structure or solubility) there are no other data on suggested mechanisms by which caries is reduced, nor about optimum or potential toxic doses so that this approach to caries does not at present lend itself to practical application. An indication of the extremely complicated relation between trace elements and caries arises from the tendency, found by Barmes, for some elements (lead, strontium and barium) to be associated with low caries when the soil contained high concentrations with the reverse trend when they were abundant in the food.

Practical applications

ADDITION OF FLUORIDE TO WATER SUPPLIES

The most valuable practical measure so far known that can be taken for building up the resistance of the tooth is the addition of 1 ppm of fluoride to drinking water discussed in the next chapter.

Caries-free subjects

About one in 200 young adults in Britain is free from caries and is sometimes described as 'caries immune'. This term is best avoided as it implies that the absence of caries arises from an immunological process, whereas the available evidence suggests that this is, at most, a contributory factor in some subjects. Many comparisons have been made of the composition and properties of enamel saliva (p. 348), and a few of plaque, but no satisfactory explanation for the lack of caries is yet possible. The one fact which is firmly established is that the *Lactobacillus acidophilus* count is much lower than in caries-active subjects and may be zero, and consequently the Snyder test also gives a lower reading.

It seems likely that, in some caries-free subjects, antibodies may inhibit cariogenic bacteria but their effect is supplemented by other factors—for example, some have a highly-buffered saliva with a high pH which prevents plaque pH from falling. In other caries-free subjects, no outstanding differences in any property of saliva have been found. A possible explanation is that many factors are slightly unfavourable to caries with a large cumulative effect but individually these differences are too small to be detected statistically. For example, if the rate of flow of saliva and the concentrations of Ca, PO_4, HCO_3 in saliva and the F/CO_3 of enamel were a few per cent higher than average, they would all be well within normal range but the combined effect of many such small differences might be important.

The evidence suggests that there is no one explanation covering all caries-free subjects but that different factor(s) operate in each subject. The possibility of one over-riding factor that has not yet been discovered must be borne in mind.

Caries as a Disease of Civilization

There is abundant evidence that man in primitive conditions suffers less severely from caries than do the inhabitants of civilized communities and there has been much discussion about the possible reasons. It has been generally supposed that dietary factors are important and there seems little doubt that when primitive groups, originally virtually free from caries, adopt 'civilized' feeding habits, severe caries may ensue. For example, until about 60 years ago, caries was unknown among the Eskimos, whose native diet consists of the flesh of bear and seals and contains little or no carbohydrate, but with increased contact with European trading stations and the consumption of carbohydrate foods, caries is increasing. It is suggested that the introduction of carbohydrates into the diet, virtually for the first time, caused this change. The incidence of caries among the African Bantus who leave their kraals in large numbers to enter the towns of South Africa has also been studied. Although few entirely satisfactory data are on record, caries does occur among the inhabitants of the kraals but there are grounds for believing that the susceptibility to caries increases after some years' consumption of the town diet. The native diet contains carbohydrate and, unlike the Eskimo, there is no evidence of increases in the *amount* of carbohydrate consumed when the Bantu changes his diet. This led Osborn *et al.* (1937) to suggest that unrefined foods (as eaten in the kraals) contain 'protective factors' against caries which are removed during the refinement of foods. A re-investigation of this problem by Jenkins *et al.* (1959) confirmed that brown flour, raw sugar-cane juice and black treacle do contain substances which reduce the solubility of calcium phosphate in test-tube experiments with incubated saliva. Golden syrup and the various forms of brown sugar have a slight protective action. Phytate has been identified as the active substance in brown flour and, along with other organic phosphates which have a similar action, may also contribute to the *in vitro* effect of raw cane juices. The high concentration of calcium is mainly responsible for the very powerful effect of black treacle (this is derived mostly from the lime added to cane juice during sugar manufacture) but buffers and some organic phosphates, including phytate, present in the plant probably play a part in the effect. The outer part of several seeds (oat hulls, peanut hulls, wheat bran) inhibit animal caries and contain antibacterial substances, which are alcohol-soluble, and water-soluble substances which lower the solubility of teeth. A polypentose constituent of the leaves of many plants has been stated to suppress the ability of *Strep. mutans* to form the aggregates which enter plaque (Katz *et al.* 1976). It is not known whether these effects on tooth solubility and bacterial inhibition, so readily observed in test-tube experiments, occur in the mouth, or to what extent they are responsible for the lower caries incidence found with primitive diets. Tests on animal caries with phytates have given some striking reductions, and another organic phosphate, calcium sucrose phosphate, has been reported also to reduce caries in a large-scale experiment with children (Harris *et al.* 1967–9). Phytate may explain the reduced caries in animals fed with seed hulls because it is more likely to be extracted during mastication than the anti-bacterial factors which are insoluble in water. The substances from plant walls which suppress bacterial agglutination do not appear to have been tested on animal caries. There is little evidence in this work on primitive peoples of any permanent resistance as a result of their nutrition during the development of teeth.

Although this work led to the identification of factors with potential protective effects, it is still far from certain that they are extracted from normal foods during mastication in amounts adequate to affect caries or to be responsible for the low caries of primitive man. But the possibility of adding these substances artificially to sugary foods (from which they might be dissolved rapidly during eating) is still inadequately explored although the climate of opinion is unfavourable to additives. The rarity of caries on primitive diets is most simply explained by the virtual absence of free sugar from such diets—starch which is present in many of the diets is believed not to be cariogenic.

When considered along with the work of Sognnaes on the 'war-time diet' effect (see p. 243) it would seem that diet may act partly by influencing the structure of teeth but is more important in altering their environment in various ways and hence the intensity of bacterial attack.

Experimental caries

IN VITRO METHODS

Several techniques have been developed to imitate the caries process under controlled conditions. Teeth have been incubated with saliva and carbohydrates but this results in a more general demineralization of most of the surface not resembling the penetrating lesion of caries. The histological features of caries can, however, be reproduced *in vitro* if teeth are incubated in an acid medium containing a colloid or substances binding to apatite (p. 423).

Various forms of 'artificial mouth' have been devised in which saliva or a bacteriological medium drips over extracted teeth in a closed chamber at 37°C followed by histological study of the demineralization produced (Pigman *et al.* 1952; Sidaway *et al.* 1964; Naylor *et al.* 1969). The most realistic experiments have been carried out *in vivo*. One method is to mount enamel blocks from extracted teeth on to a fixed bridge worn in a subject's mouth for up to 2 weeks. The enamel is covered with 'Dacron' gauze which promotes plaque formation, resulting in a lesion indicated by softening of the enamel; removal of the gauze is followed by rehardening. The response is not consistent in different mouths but shows variations presumably similar to the personal variations in natural caries (Manson-Hing *et al.* 1972).

ANIMAL EXPERIMENTS

For many years, one of the difficulties of caries research was that few species of experimental animals suffer from the disease.

Hoppert *et al.* (1931) discovered that caries could be produced in rats fed on a diet containing corn, ground to a size of 60 mesh. The same diet more finely ground had no caries-producing effect. The critical particle size corresponded with the size of the fissures in rats' teeth and the caries followed the fracture of the cusps as the particles became trapped and were rammed into the fissures. This train of events does not correspond with human caries and it is doubtful whether much of the experimental work on this type of caries is applicable to man.

Later it was discovered that the cotton rat, certain other strains of rats and the golden hamster, if fed on diets high in sugar, may develop cavities very similar to those in human caries. The importance both of the environment and the structure of the tooth have been proved by experiments on these species. When a sugar diet is fed by stomach tube, no caries develops, proving the importance of the local factor. Sognnaes's experiments on the prenatal feeding of purified high sugar diet on the caries susceptibility of the offspring have already been described (p. 244).

Monkeys are susceptible to caries on a refined diet but their high maintenance costs limit their use. Cats and dogs are not susceptible even on diets which are highly conducive of caries in man.

The use of germ-free animals has proved conclusively that caries is a bacterial disease. When rats were born and reared in completely sterile conditions they did not develop caries on diets which are normally highly cariogenic.

Some strains of acid-producing organisms induce caries when present alone. Other acid-producing organisms, including a strain of *Lactobacillus acidophilus*, are unable to induce caries when given in pure culture. The factors which determine whether an organism causes caries or not are not fully known but highly-active acid production and ability to synthesize polysaccharide from sugars, and especially dextran from sucrose and thus build up the plaque (p. 385), are associated, in many organisms, with high cariogenicity.

So far, no proteolytic organism has been found to produce caries *in vivo*.

THE INFECTIVE NATURE OF CARIES IN RODENTS

Many inconsistent results have been obtained in different laboratories on the susceptibility of rodents to caries and erratic variations from one generation to another have sometimes been found even in the same laboratory. One explanarion of these results has been worked out by Keyes (1960). He found that if litters were divided into two groups, one of which was caged alone and the other with caries-active animals, then extensive caries occurred only in the latter group. Also, if the young were inoculated orally during the suckling period with faecal material from caries-active adults, more caries developed than in controls. This result clearly showed that caries does not develop unless the animal acquires a particular flora early in life and in some laboratories this infection does not occur. The young produced from these infected animals were highly susceptible, suggesting that they received these caries-producing bacteria from their mothers. If animals from susceptible parents were fed on a non-cariogenic diet (and remained free from caries) their offspring did develop caries when they received a cariogenic diet—thus the caries-producing flora was still present and could be transmitted to the young even though the animals themselves had no caries since they had been fed a non-cariogenic diet.

Caries susceptibility in animals depends therefore on the interaction of at least three factors: (1) a true genetic factor whose nature is uncertain but which may act through the morphology of the teeth or the composition of the teeth or saliva, (2) the acquisition at the right time of cariogenic micro-organisms, and (3) the feeding of a cariogenic diet.

The importance in man of this work on the infectious nature of caries is unknown, but it might be speculated that cariogenic organisms are so widely distributed that, in modern communities, universal infection occurs at a very early age.

EXPERIMENTAL CARIES IN MAN

Von der Fehr (1966) pinned gold plates to sound teeth which were to be extracted for orthodontic reasons, leaving a narrow space between plate and tooth which became filled with plaque and brought about an experimental white spot after some weeks. When the plate was removed, the area became self-cleansing again and the renewed contact with saliva led to the disappearance or reduction in size of the white spots. This technique provides a means of comparing the effects of various topical applications and other protective measures which may be applied to part of the enamel before the gold plate is attached.

If the outer surface of the enamel under the gold plate was ground off before the experiment began, it showed an outer layer relatively free from attack, as occurs in caries on a normal enamel surface. This supports the suggestion that the apparently almost intact outer layer in a carious lesion results from remineralization and not from an increased resistance of outer enamel.

An even more rapid de- and remineralization, under experimental control was reported by von der Fehr *et al.* (1970). White spot lesions were formed experimentally in subjects abstaining from tooth-brushing and taking frequent rinses with sucrose during 23 days (Edgar *et al.* 1975) found that demineralization was present after only 14 days of this procedure). The white lesions were given a score which, when tooth-brushing was resumed along with daily mouth-rinsing with 0·2% sodium fluoride, reduced considerably within 1 month and reached the original score by 2 months. The importance of the fluoride in promoting remineralization is not clear because no experiments of this type have been carried out from which it has been omitted. The gold plate experiments show that remineralization occurs from saliva alone but it would be expected from the results of *in vitro* experiments that fluoride would accelerate it. This method might lend itself to the testing of anti-caries additives to foods and to comparison of the relative cariogenicity of different carbohydrates. It is, however, subject to the great variability of caries susceptibility shown by different individuals, and groups of at least 12 subjects may be necessary for significant results.

The Multiplicity of Factors

In spite of the uncertainty about many of the ideas outlined above on the cause of caries there is now general agreement that a large number of factors contribute to the disease, some favouring, others hindering its initiation and progress. For this reason the 'cause' of caries will differ from mouth to mouth, possibly even in the same mouth from cavity to cavity. This consideration may go far to explain the discrepancies between the conclusions of different workers in this field. For example, an individual possessing well-spaced teeth with no traces of hypoplasia and who is in the habit of eating a coarse, detergent diet might suffer little caries even if his saliva were relatively small in volume and low in buffering and antibacterial power. On the other hand, the properties of saliva might be decisive in an individual whose teeth had only a moderate degree of resistance. There is therefore little reason to expect that caries incidence can be related, in all subjects, to any one factor such as a single property of saliva, or one constituent of teeth.

It is this multiplicity of factors, along with our inability to control many of the conditions that are believed to influence caries, which makes the prevention of the disease so difficult. As mentioned elsewhere, our knowledge of how to prevent hypoplasia, or to increase the resistance of a tooth by altering its chemical composition, or to modify the protective properties of saliva, is scanty and uncertain. Changes in one factor only (such as reducing sugar intake) may, if the balance is already heavily weighted in one direction by other factors, have no effect whatever on caries, or insufficient effect to warrant the trouble involved.

The rather remote possibility has to be borne in mind that some very important factor remins to be discovered, which would over-ride the many smaller factors which contribute (or are suspected of contributing) to caries. The anti-caries action of fluoride is a moderately powerful factor of this type. Only if such a factor were to be discovered and if it were capable of practical application, would there seem to be much prospect of introducing an effective natural means of reducing caries. Meanwhile the search continues for artificial methods of preventing or resisting the bacterial attack mostly along the lines described earlier in this chapter.

References

The literature on dental caries is extremely large and a full bibliography cannot be given here. The following are general surveys of the subject:

A Survey of the Literature of Dental Caries (1952) Pub. 225 of National Academy of Science. National Research Council, Washington

BAGNALL J.S. (1950) *Bibliography on Caries Research*. National Research Council, Canada, Ottawa

BRISLIN J.F. & COX G.J. (1964) *Survey of the Literature of Dental Caries 1948–1960*. University of Pittsburgh Press, Pittsburgh

JENKINS G.N. (1961) A critique of the proteolysis-chelation theory of caries. *Brit. dent. J.* **111**, 311

SILVERSTONE L. *et al.* (1977) *Dental Caries*. Macmillan Press

The following deal with special aspects of the caries problem:

ADKINS B.L. *et al.* (1974) The aetiology of caries in Papua, New Guinea. The trace element content of urine samples and its relation to individual dental caries experience. *Bulletin of W.H.O.* **50**, Issue 6, 495

ADLER P. (1953) A water-borne caries-protective agent other than fluoride. *Acta Med. Acad. Sci. Hung.* **4**, 221

ANON. (1975) Immunization against dental caries. *Brit. med. J.* **iv**, 424

AXELSSON P. & LINDHE J. (1975) Effect of fluoride on gingivitis and dental caries in a preventive program based on plaque control. *Community Dent. & Oral Epidemiol.* **3**, 156 (see also (1976) **4**, 232)

BACKER-DIRKS O. (1966) Posteruptive changes in dental enamel. *J. dent. Res.* **45**, 503

BARMES D.E. (1969) Caries etiology in Sepik villages—trace element, micronutrient content of soil and food. *Caries Res.* **3**, 44

BARMES D.E. *et al.* (1970) Etiology of caries in Papua, New Guinea. Associations in soil, food and water. *Bull. WHO* **43**, 769

BECKS H. (1950) Carbohydrate restriction in the prevention of dental caries using the *Lactobacillus acidophilus* count as one index. *J. Calif. State Dent. Assoc.* **26**, 53

BERGMAN G. & LINDÉN L.-A. (1966) Effect of an 'internal factor' on enamel decalcification. *Archs oral Biol.* **11**, 943

BIBBY B.G. (1966) Do we tell the truth about preventing caries? *J. Dent. Child.* **33**, 269

BOWDEN G.H. (1969) The components of the cell wall and extracellular slime of four strains of *Staphylococcus salivarius* isolated from human dental plaque. *Archs oral Biol.* **14**, 685

BOWEN W.H. *et al.* (1975) Immunisation against dental caries. *Brit. dent. J.* **139**, 45

BOWEN W.H. & EASTOE J.E. (1967) The effect of sugar solutions containing fluoride and molybdate ions on the pH of plaque in monkeys. *Caries Res.* **1**, 130

BRADFORD E.W. & CRABB H.S.M. (1961) Carbohydrate restriction and caries incidence. *Brit. dent. J.* **111**, 273

BROOKE R.I. *et al.* (1972) Infiltration of carious enamel *in vivo. J. dent. Res.* **51**, 1262

BUONOCORE M.G. (1971) Caries prevention in pits and fissures sealed with an adhesive resin polymerized by ultraviolet light: a two-year study of a single adhesive application. *J. Amer. dent. Ass.* **82**, 1090

CADELL P.B. (1964) Geographic distribution of dental caries in relation to New Zealand soils. *Aust. dent. J.* **9**, 32

CARROLL R.G. *et al.* (1968) The clinical effectiveness of phosphate-enriched breakfast cereals on the incidence of dental caries in adults, results after 1 year. *J. Amer. dent. Ass.* **76**, 564

CHALLACOMBE *et al.* (1973) Antibodies to an extract of *Streptococcus mutans* containing glucosyl transferase activity related to dental caries. *Archs oral Biol.* **18**, 657

CIBA FOUNDATION SYMPOSIUM (1965) *Caries Resistant Teeth.* Churchill, London

CLARKE J.K. (1924) On the bacterial factor in the aetiology of dental caries. *Brit. J. exper. Path.* **5**, 141

CLARKE N.G. & FANNING E.A. (1971) Plaque pH and calcium sucrose phosphate: A telemetric study. *Austr. dent. J.* **16**, 13; also (1973) *Austr. dent. J.* **18**, 229

CRABB H.S.M. (1966) Enamel caries. Observations on the histology and pattern

of progress of the approximal lesion. *Brit. dent. J.* **121**, 115, 167

CURZON M.E.J. (1977) Personal communication

DARLING A.I. (1956) Studies of the early lesion of enamel caries with transmitted light, polarized light and radiography. *Brit. dent. J.* **101**, 289 and 329 (see also *Brit. dent. J.* (1958) **105**, 119 and *J. dent. Res.* (1959) **38**, 1226)

DARLING A.I. *et al.* (1961) Molecular sieve behaviour of normal and carious human dental enamel. *Archs oral Biol.* **5**, 251

DARLING A.I. (1963) Resistance of enamel to caries. *J. dent. Res.* **42**, 458

DAVIES G.N. *et al.* (1959) The relationship between lactobacillus counts, Snyder tests and the subsequent incidence of dental caries. *Archs oral Biol.* **1**, 62

DIRKSEN T.R. *et al* (1962) The pH of carious cavities—I. The effect of glucose and phosphate buffer on cavity pH. *Archs oral Biol.* **7**, 49

DREIZEN S. *et al.* (1949) The *in vitro* production of a 'yellow-brown melanin-like pigment' in the organic matrix of noncarious human tooth crowns by methyl glyoxal (pyruvic aldehyde) and acetol (acetyl carbinol). *J. dent. Res.* **28**, 26 (see also *Oral Surg., Med., Path.* **3**, 1582)

EDGAR W.M. *et al.* (1975) Experimental caries in man. II. The effect of topically applied NaF solution. *J. dent. Res.* **54**, *Special Issue A*, **L76**, Abstract **L306**

ERICSSON Y. (1962) Some differences between human and rodent saliva of probable importance for the different specie reactions to cariogenic and cariostatic agents. *Proc. 9th ORCA Congress, Archs oral Biol.* **7**, Supp. 327

EVANS D.G. & PROPHET A.S. (1950) Disintegration of human dentine by bacterial enzymes. *Lancet*, **i**, 290

FANNING *et al.* (1969) Dental caries in children related to availability of sweets at school canteens. *Med. J. Austral.* **i**, 1131

FEATHERSTONE J.D.B. *et al.* A mechanism for dental caries. *Archs oral Biol.* **22**, in press.

FEHR F.J. VON DER *et al.* (1970) Experimental caries in man. *Caries Res.* **4**, 131

FOSDICK L.S. (1950) The reduction of the

incidence of dental caries. I. Immediate tooth-brushing with a neutral dentifrice. *J. Amer. dent. Ass.* **40**, 133

FRANK R.M. & BRENDEL A. (1966) Ultrastructure of the approximal dental plaque and the underlying normal and carious enamel. *Archs oral Biol.* **11**, 883

GARDNER M.K. & SNYDER M.L. (1960) Acid production in sucrose by oral bacteria as means of estimating caries activity (Rickles test). *J. dent. Res.* **39**, 320

GEDDES D.A.M. (1972) Failure to demonstrate the antibacterial factor of Green in caries-free parotid saliva. In *Host Resistance to Commensal Bacteria. The Response to Dental Plaque.* Ed. MACPHEE T. Churchill Livingstone, London

GEDDES D.A.M. *et al.* (1977) Apples, salted peanuts and plaque pH. *Brit. dent. J.* **142**, 317

GOTTLIEB B. (1947) *Dental Caries.* Lea & Febiger, Philadephia

GRAY J.A. (1966) Kinetics of enamel dissolution during formation of incipient caries-like lesions. *Archs oral Biol.* **11**, 397

GREEN G.E. (1959) A bacteriolytic agent in salivary globulin of caries-immune human beings. *J. dent. Res.* **38**, 262

GREER S.B. *et al.* (1971) Viruses of cariogenic streptococci. *J. dent. Res.* **50**, 1594

GUGGENHEIM B. (1970) Enzymatic hydrolysis and structure of water-insoluble glucan produced by glucosyltransferases from a strain of *Streptococcus mutans.* *Helv. odont. Acta* **14**, 89

GUSTAFSSON B.E. *et al.* (1954) Vipeholm caries study. *Acta odont. Scand.* **11**, 232

HALDI J. *et al.* (1960) pH on the teeth of albino rats under various conditions conducive to caries. *Archs oral Biol.* **2**, 46

HALLSWORTH A.S. *et. al.* (1973) Loss of carbonate during the first stages of enamel caries. *Caries Res.* **7**, 345

HARDIE J.M. *et al.* (1977) A longitudinal epidemiological study on dental plaque and the development of dental caries. Interim results after two years. *Proceedings of 7th International Conference on Oral Biology*

HARDWICK J.L. (1960) The incidence and distribution of caries throughout the ages

in relation to the Englishman's diet. *Brit. dent. J.* **108**, 9

HARDWICK J.L. & MANLEY E.B. (1952) Caries of the enamel. Acidogenic caries. *Brit. dent. J.* **82**, 227

HARRIS R. *et al.* (1967–9) The cariostatic effect of calcium sucrose phosphate in a group of children aged 5–17 years. *Aust. dent. J.* **12**, 105; (1968) **13**, 32, 345; (1969) **14**, 42

HOEVEN J.S. VAN DER (1974) A slime-producing micro-organism in dental plaque of rats, selected by glucose feeding. *Caries Res.* **8**, 193

HOPPERT C.A. *et al.* (1931) The production of dental caries in rats fed an adequate diet. *Science*, **74**, 77 (see also *J. dent. Res.* **12**, 161)

HOUWINK B. (1969) The limited usefulness of Thoulet's solution in imbibition experiments in dental enamel. *Brit. Dent. J.* **126**, 50

HUXLEY H.G. (1975) An investigation into the prevalence of *Streptococcus mutans* in Wistar rats, its relationship to the initiation of dental caries, and the effect upon its presence of the diet fed before weaning. *Archs oral Biol.* **20**, 351

JAY P. (1940) The role of sugar in the aetiology of dental caries. *J. Amer. dent. Ass.* **27**, 393

JENKINS G.N. (1961) A critique of the proteolysis-chelation theory of caries. *Brit. dent. J.* **111**, 311

JENKINS G.N. (1967) Molybdenum and dental caries. *Brit. dent. J.* **122**, 435, 500, 545

JENKINS G.N. & DAWES C. (1964) Experiments on the chelating properties of saliva and dental plaque. *Brit. dent. J.* **116**, 433

JENKINS G.N. *et al.* (1959) The influence of the refinement of carbohydrates on their cariogenicity. *Brit. dent. J.* **106**, 195, 362

KATZ S. *et al.* (1976) Plaque inhibition by plant cell fractions. *Internat. Ass. Dent. Res. Abs.* 827, 828, 829

KENNEDY A.E. *et al.* (1968) Antibodies to cariogenic streptococci in humans. *Archs oral Biol.* **13**, 1275

KESEL R.G. *et al.* (1958) Further studies on Lactobacilli counts after elimination of carious lesions. *J. dent. Res.* **37**, 50

KEYES P.H. (1960) The infectious and transmissible nature of experimental dental caries. *Archs oral Biol.* **1**, 304 (see also KEYES P.H. (1962) *Internat. dent. J.* **12**, 443)

KIRKEGAARD E. *et al.* (1975) Fluoride uptake in plaque-covered enamel *in vitro*. *Internat. Ass. dent. Res. Abs.* 543

KÖNIG K.G. *et al.* (1968) An apparatus for frequency-controlled feeding of small rodents and its use in dental caries experiments. *Archs oral Biol.* **13**, 13

KÖNIG K.G. *et al.* (1969) A strain-specific eating pattern as a factor limiting the transmissibility of caries activity in rats. *Archs oral Biol.* **14**, 91

KOULOURIDES T. (1968) Remineralisation methods. *Ann. N.Y. Acad. Sci.* **153**, 84

KREITZMAN S.N. *et al.* (1969) Enzymatic release of phosphate from rat molar enamel by phospho-protein phosphatase. *Nature (Lond.)* **223**, 520

KREITZMAN S.N. (1974) Enzymes and dietary factors in caries. *J. dent. Res.* **53**, 218

LANKE L.S. (1957) Influence on salivary sugar of certain properties of foodstuffs and individual oral conditions. *Acta Odont. Scand.* **15**, Suppl. 23

LEHNER T. *et al.* (1975) Immunological and bacteriological basis for vaccination against dental caries in rhesus monkeys. *Nature (Lond.)* **254**, 517

LEVINE R.S. (1975) An initial clinical assessment of a mineralising mouthrinse. *Brit. dent. J.* **138**, 249

LINDHE J. & AXELSSON P. (1973) The effect of controlled oral hygiene and topical fluoride application on caries and gingivitis in Swedish schoolchildren. *Community Dent. & Oral Epidemiol.* **1**, 9 (see also (1975) **3**, 150)

LÖE H. (1973) Does chlorhexidine have a place in the prophylaxis of dental diseases? *J. periodont. Res.* **8**, Suppl. 12, 93

LURA H. EGGERS (1957) The non-acid agents in the caries pathogenesis and their relation to the prophylaxis. *Proc. 5th O.R.C.A. Conference, Odont. Revy* **8** 169

MACGREGOR A.B. (1959) Acid production and the carious process. *J. dent. Res.* **38**, 1055

McHUGH W.D. *et al.* (1964) Dental disease and related factors in 13-year-old children in Dundee. *Brit. dent. J.* **117**, 246

McINTOSH J. *et al.* (1922) An investigation into the etiology of dental caries. I. The nature of the destructive agent and the production of artificial caries. *Brit. J. Exptl Path.* **3**, 138. Also II (1924) *Brit. J. Exptl Path.* **5**, 175; III (1925) *Brit. J. Exptl Path.* **6**, 260

McKAY G.S. (1976) The histology and microbiology of acute occlusal dentine lesions in human permanent molar teeth. *Archs oral Biol.* **21**, 51

MANSBRIDGE J.N. (1960) The effects of oral hygiene and sweet consumption on the prevalence of dental caries. *Brit. dent. J.* **109**, 343

MANSON-HING L.R. *et al.* (1972) Microradiographic comparison of artificial caries systems. *J. dent. Res.* **51**, 923

MARTHALER T.M. (1971) Confidence limits of caries tests with fluoride administation. *Caries Res.* **5**, 343

MILLER J. (1958) Note on the early carious lesion in the enamel. *Brit. dent. J.* **105**, 135

MILLER W.B. (1890) Microorganisms of the human mouth. Reprinted 1973. Karger, Basel.

MØRCH T. *et al.* (1971) The possible role of complex-forming substances in the decalcification phase of the caries process. *Caries Res.* **5**, 135

MORTIMER K.V. (1968) The pattern of demineralization of the enamel by dental caries. *Caries Res.* **2**, 180

MORTIMER K.V. (1970) The relationship of deciduous enamel structure to dental disease. *Caries Res.* **4**, 206

MORTIMER K.V. & TRANTER T.C. (1971) A scanning electron microscopy study of carious enamel. *Caries Res.* **5**, 240

MUHLER J.C. *et al.* (1955) Effect of a stannous fluoride-containing dentifrice on caries reduction in children. *J. Amer. dent. Ass.* **50**, 163 (see also *J. dent. Res.* (1956) **35**, 49)

NAYLOR M.N. *et al.* (1969) Mono- and di-saccharide solutions and the formation of plaque *in vitro*. In *Dental Plaque*, p. 41, Ed. McHUGH, W.D., E. & S. Livingstone Edinburgh

NEUMANN H.H. (1957) Radiophosphorus uptake in chewing and nonchewing teeth.

J. Amer. dent. Ass. **54**, 598 (see also *J. dent. Res.* (1953) **32**, 725; (1954) **33**, 677; (1955) **34**, 716; (1957) **36**, 286; (1958) **37**, 978)

NEVIN R.B. (1954a) *The Diet and Mastication; their Effects on Diffusion and on the Inception of Dental Caries.* Progress Printing Co. Ltd., Dunedin

NEVIN R.B. (1954b) *Experimental Observations on the Diet and Oral Hygiene in Relation to Dental Caries.* Progress Printing Co. Ltd., Dunedin

NIZEL A.E. & HARRIS R.S. (1964) The effects of phosphates on experimental dental caries: a literature review. *J. dent. Res.* **43**, 1123

OCKERSE T. & DE JAGER C.L. (1957) Dental caries produced in the vervet monkey. *Brit. dent. J.* **102**, 93

OSBORN T.W.B. *et al.* (1937) A comparison of crude and refined sugar and cereals in their ability to produce *in vitro* decalcification of teeth. *J. dent. Res,* **16**, 165 (see also *J. dent. Res.* **16**, 545; (1941) **20**, 59)

PIGMAN W. *et al* (1954) Caries-like lesions of enamel produced in the artificial mouth. *Oral Surg., Med., Path.* **7**, 427 (see also *J. dent. Res.* (1952) **31**, 627; (1955) **34**, 537)

REECE J.A. & SWALLOW J.N. (1970) Carrots and dental health. *Brit. dent. J.* **128**, 535

ROBINSON C. *et al.* (1976) Arrest and control of carious lesions: A study based on preliminary experiments with resorcinol-formaldehyde resin. *J. dent. Res.* **55**, 812

ROCK W.P. (1974) Fissure sealants. Further results of clinical trials *Brit dent. J.* **136**, 317

RUGG-GUNN A.J. *et al.* (1975) The effect of different meal patterns upon plaque pH in human subjects. *Brit. dent. J.* **139**, 361

SCHATZ A. *et al.* (1957a) The proteolysis-chelation theory of dental caries. *Proceedings of 4th O.R.C.A. Conference, Odont. Revy* **8**, 154; (1957b) *Ann. Dent.* **16**, 37

SCHATZ A. *et al.* (1958) Some philosophical considerations on the proteolysis-chelation theory of dental caries. *Proc. Pennsyl. Acad. Sci.* **32**, 20

SCHATZ A. & MARTIN J.J. (1962) Proteolysis-chelation theory of dental caries. *J. Amer. dent. Ass.* **65**, 368

SCHEINEN A. *et al.* (1975) Turku sugar studies V. Final report on the effect of sucrose, fructose and xylitol diets on the earies incidence in man. *Acta Odont. Scand.* **33**, *Suppl.* **70**, 67

SHARPE A.N. (1967) Influence of the crystal orientation in human enamel on its reactivity to acid as shown by high resolution microradiography. *Archs oral Biol.* **12**, 583

SHOVLIN F.E. & GILLIS R.E. (1969) Biochemical and antigenic studies of lactobacilli isolated from deep dentinal cavities, biochemical aspects. *J. dent. Res.* **48**, 356

SIDAWAY A.B. *et al.* (1964) The artificial mouth in caries research. *Proc. R. Soc. Med.* **57**, 1065

SILVERSTONE L.M. (1974) Fissure sealants. Laboratory studies. *Caries Res.* **8**, 2

SILVERSTONE L.M. *et al.* (1975) Variation in the pattern of acid etching of human dental enamel examined by scanning electron microscopy. *Caries Res.* **9**, 373

SIMMELINK J.W. *et al.* (1974) Theory for the sequence of human and rat enamel dissolution by acid and EDTA: a correlated scanning and transmission electron microscope study. *Archs oral Biol.* **19**, 183

SLACK G.L. *et al.* (1964) The effect of tablets stimulating salivary flow on the incidence of dental caries—a two-year clinical trial. *Brit. dent. J.* **116**, 105

SLACK G.L. & MARTIN W.J (1958) Apples and dental health *Brit. dent. J.* **105**, 366

SOGNNAES R.F. (1962) *Chemistry and Prevention of Dental Caries.* Thomas, Springfield

STOOKEY G.K. *et al.* (1967) Clinical effectiveness of phosphate enriched breakfast cereals on the incidence of dental caries in children: results after 2 years. *J. Amer. dent. Ass.* **74**, 752 (see also (1969) **76**, 564)

STÜBEN J. (1959) Über die Ca-bindende Affinität verschiedener Metallkomplexbildner, ermittelt an Schmelzproben vor und nach Behandlung mit Fluornatrium. *Dtsche Zahnartz* **161. 8**

TATEVOSSIAN A. *et al.* (1975) Changes in the concentrations of phosphates in human plaque after the ingestion of sugar with and without added phosphates *Archs oral Biol.* **20**, 617

CHAPTER XII

FLUORIDE

The Influence of Fluoride on Teeth

In the early years of this century, attention was drawn to the occurrence of 'mottled enamel', an abnormality in which the enamel, usually only of the permanent teeth, acquired an unsightly brown pigment. It became clear that mottling occurred only in people born and spending their childhood in certain areas coinciding with those of water supplies and that a constituent of the water was responsible for the condition (McKay 1916; Ainsworth 1933). An analysis by routine methods failed to detect any constituent common to water supplies which caused mottling, but in 1931—25 years after the search began—fluoride was found in a number of these water supplies (Churchill 1931). Almost simultaneously it was found by Smith *et al.* (1932) that when fluoride was added to rats' diet, the effects on their teeth were similar to those produced by adding water from areas where mottling occurred, which strongly supported the view that fluoride was the element responsible. The rat is less sensitive to fluoride than man, so it was necessary to concentrate the water ten times, that is, give ten times the concentration of fluoride that is effective in man.

'Idiopathic' and fluoride mottling

There are two types of mottling or opacities which have probably been confused in the past. One type occurs in towns with virtually no fluoride in the water (so-called idiopathic mottling) and the other is caused by fluoride but is only of significance where the water contains more than about 1·5 ppm. Idiopathic mottling consists of irregular white flecks randomly distributed, unlike fluoride mottling which is usually considered to be bilaterally symmetrical though this difference was questioned by Al-Alousi *et al.* (1975). One speculation about the causes, discussed by Jackson (1961), of idiopathic mottling is that it follows mechanical damage to the permanent tooth germ from minor blows in the mouth area—for example, from falls (Andreasen & Ravn 1973). Several surveys suggest that the incidence of idiopathic mottling is lower with water-borne fluoride up to 1 ppm (Zimmerman 1954; Forrest

466

1956). Possible explanations of this effect of fluoride are that the opacities are areas of demineralization, perhaps early or arrested caries, and these lesions are naturally less frequent with a high fluoride intake. Alternatively, if the opacities are of developmental origin fluoride may favour remineralization so that small imperfections would disappear and larger ones would become less obvious.

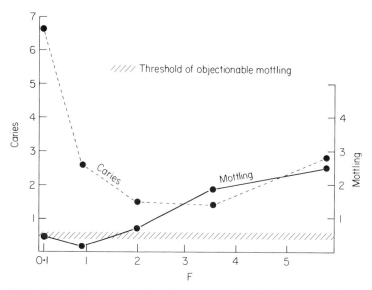

Fig. XII.1. Relation between the fluoride concentration of the water supply, caries incidence and mottling in British towns. The optimum intake is clearly about 1 ppm which causes a great reduction in the caries incidence (but does not give quite the maximal reduction), reduces non-fluoride mottling and has virtually no effect in producing fluoride mottling.

In the early surveys of mottling these two types were not distinguished and the descriptions of the effects of water containing less than 2 ppm of fluoride are confusing.

Although severe fluorosis was first observed in the form of brown stains it is now known that the defect takes different forms at different levels of fluoride intake.

In a study of nearly 6000 children, mostly aged 12–14 years, the relation of dental structure to fluoride intake was as follows (Dean 1942).

Between 0·5 and 1 ppm, 5–10% of the children showed the effect described as 'very mild', characterized by small opaque white areas scattered irregularly over the tooth, but, surprisingly, Dean did not realize that the mottling in this group was not caused by fluoride.

With intakes of 2 ppm, about 10% of the teeth were graded as 'moderate' in which the whole enamel surface showed either the opaqueness or the brown stain. Fewer than 25% of the teeth were free from some defect.

With 4 ppm, only 5% of the teeth were normal and about 25% showed moderate fluorosis. About 12% were graded 'severe' in which all the enamel surfaces were affected either by opacity or brown stain and in addition there was much pitting. Enamel in this grade is also brittle and readily chipped off. At about 6 ppm no teeth were free from symptoms and about 50% showed a severe response.

Higher levels, even up to 14 ppm, did not make the condition appreciably worse than was observed at 6 ppm.

In order to compare the average mottling of whole populations Dean (1942) devised a 'community index' based on the grades of the two most severely mottled teeth in each individual, divided by the number of individuals.

It is not known why at the lower levels of intake only some of the population is affected. It could be either that some people are more sensitive than others or that those who are affected had a greater water intake and therefore received more fluoride during enamel formation.

Although the white patches occur on deciduous teeth they are rare and the brown pigmentation is almost unknown. In permanent teeth fluorosis is apparent on eruption as white chalky areas which, in severe cases, later become pigmented. These observations suggest that the white patches result from the original defect and that the pigmentation is a gradual secondary change, requiring a longer time for its development than the few years during which the deciduous teeth are in the mouth.

The term 'mottling' is only appropriate for the brown stain caused by the higher intakes. 'Fluorosis' is a preferable name to cover all grades of the defect.

In Anglesey (F = 1 ppm) 39% of the incisors of a group of 171 children were mottled compared with 58% among 178 children from Leeds (no fluoride) and 4·2% and 7·5% respectively of the incisors were pigmented. These figures confirm what other surveys based on Dean's index had shown, that fluoride at 1 ppm reduces the mottling index. As a test of the practical importance of mottling under the influence of 1 ppm of fluoride in the water, 10 observers were shown, in a random order, photographs of incisors, 50 from Anglesey and 50 from Leeds and were asked either to identify their origin or state whether their structure was perfect, acceptable, or not acceptable. The observers were not able to identify the teeth from the fluoride area nor did they agree about the acceptability of their structure. It may be concluded that the effect of fluoride intake from 1 ppm in the water on the appearance of the teeth has no practical importance (Al-Alousi *et al.* 1975).

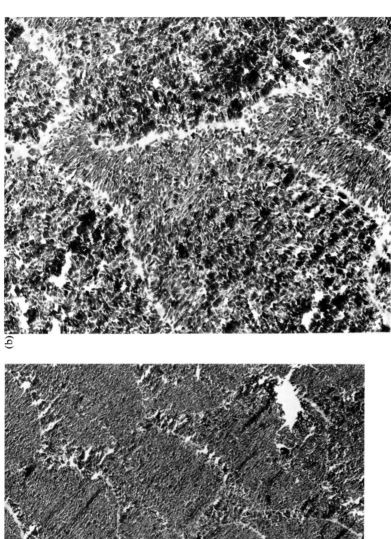

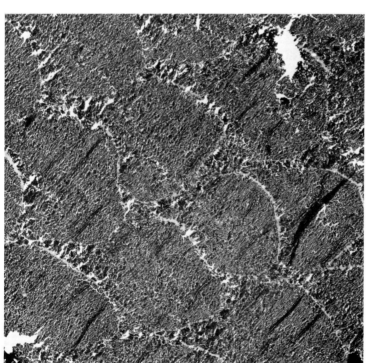

Fig. XII.2 Electronmicrograph of enamel from mildly-fluorosed teeth showing the gaps surrounding the rods.

The nature of fluorosis

Ground sections of fluorosed teeth show that the abnormality extends inwards from the surface but usually reaches only to about one-third of the thickness of the enamel, though occasionally the whole enamel may be involved. If fluorosed teeth are treated with silver nitrate and ground sections are made, the black silver stain is found to permeate through the outer parts of the enamel rods to the same depth as the original abnormality. This suggests that the fundamental defect is in the outer part of the enamel rod which alters the optical properties, and therefore the external appearance, of the enamel and secondarily allows substances from the mouth to diffuse into the enamel and cause the brown pigmentation. Heavily fluorosed teeth contain more manganese than normal teeth although the significance of this is not known (Ockerse & Wasserstein 1955). Measurements of the density of micro-radiographs (by the method described on p. 82), have shown that, except for the outer surface of mottled enamel which is radioopaque (i.e. well minerali-zed) the rest of the outer third, corresponding to the pigmented area, is under-mineralized. At higher levels of intake (5 ppm) half or three-quarters of the thickness of the enamel may be under-mineralized.

Measurements of birefringence (inbibition studies, p. 415) of the affected outer enamel show that, if severely fluorosed (5 ppm in drinking water) larger areas will have spaces with 10% of the mineral missing, and some may be as much as 25% below normal. Less severely affected enamel (from 1·5 ppm F) shows no differences radiologically but the more sensitive inbibition studies showed extensive areas with 1% spaces and small subsurface areas with 5% spaces (Fejerskov *et al.* 1975). The boundary between normal and fluorosed enamel is not sharp and follows neither the incremental lines of matrix formation nor the pattern of maturation.

Electronmicrographs show that the porosity arises from unusually wide gaps between the rods and fewer apatite crystals than usual in the tail of the rods (Fig. XII.2). This could arise from a smaller number of seeding sites or a reduced growth of crystals. In view of the uncertainty about the nature and situation of seeding sites in enamel (if they exist at all, p. 139) it is difficult to predict what the effect would be of interference with their forma-tion. Reduced growth of the crystals, that is impaired maturation, could however, explain why the outer enamel is affected because this is undergoing maturation at about the time when the fluoride concentration of the develop-ing tooth is at its highest.

Experimental fluorosis

To elucidate the mechanisms by which fluorosis is produced the histological changes have been studied in the rodent incisor following the feeding or injection of fluorides. In the earlier work, the dosages were extremely high so that, particularly in view of the specialized nature of the rodent incisor, they are of doubtful relevance to fluorosis in man and will not be discussed (see Moulton 1942 for details).

The injection of fluoride at various doses (including 0·1 mg F/kilo body weight, comparable with those received by children on fluoridated water) into new-born rats lead to distensions of the endoplasmic reticulum of the ameloblasts and reductions in their synthesis of protein, as measured by auto-radiographs after injecting tritiated proline or serine (Kruger 1970). The teeth tended to be smaller and the pits and fissures shallower, probably the result of reductions in matrix production leading to thinner enamel.

Hypomineralization of fluorosed teeth is mostly at the periphery of the rods, what used to be thought of as the interrod substance but is now considered to be a reorientation of the crystals of adjacent rods. This indicates that, in addition to the evidence that protein synthesis is impaired, mineralization (which begins in the core of the rod and spreads outwards) ceases earlier than usual so that insufficient apatite is laid down to fill the rods to the normal extent. Fluoride ions favour the deposition of apatite, so presumably this effect arises from a reduced ability of the cell to carry out mineralization or to changes in the matrix. It may be speculated that fluorosis affects mainly the outer enamel (the part formed and mineralized last) because the fluoride concentration rises during the later stages of enamel formation, in spite of some removal earlier (p. 151), and only at the later stages does it reach concentrations high enough to affect the cell.

In rats, a series of twice daily doses (17 mg F/kilo), a very large dose sufficient to produce a calciotraumatic line in the enamel, resulted in the formation of unidentified spherical bodies in the ameloblast and a 'shredded' appearance of the Tomes's processes, shown in electron micrographs. A zone of the matrix formed after each injection did not mineralize. The boundary between the cells and the matrix was irregular which would possibly lead to micro-irregularities on the enamel surface (Walton & Eisenmann 1974). The ameloblasts recovered rapidly between the injections when they formed matrix which mineralized normally.

No changes were detected in the odontoblasts but there were zones in the dentine which microradiographs showed were alternately hypermineralized and normal. Electron micrographs, on the other hand, showed areas of hypomineralized matrix near the odontoblasts (i.e. recently formed) but deep within the dentine these areas became smaller giving the impression that the defective areas had mineralized at a later stage. It has been speculated that in fluorosis either (1) inhibitors of mineralization such as pyrophosphate (p. 119) are broken down more slowly than usual in fluorotic enamel and dentine or (2) the synthesis of seeding sites in dentine, perhaps phosphoproteins (p. 122), is slower.

Fluoride and dental caries

Because enamel shows an effect of fluoride at lower intakes than other tissues it is usually assumed either that ameloblasts are the most sensitive cells in the body to fluoride or, because of their proximity to enamel with its high concentration of fluoride, are subjected to higher concentrations than other cells. There is no proof of their greater sensitivity, however, because the ultrastructure of cells other than ameloblasts does not appear to have been examined after exposure to low doses of fluoride.

It was realized early in the study of mottled enamel that, in spite of their apparently defective structure, mottled teeth were no more liable to caries than were unmottled teeth. It was not until the 1930s, however, that Trendley Dean, in a survey of caries among some 8000 children in 21 American cities with fluoride in their water supplies ranging from 0 to 2 ppm, showed a clear inverse relationship between caries and water-borne fluoride (Fig. XII.3) confirmed in Britain by Weaver (1944, 1950). This suggested that fluoride acts as an anti-caries agent and the finding that the addition of fluoride to drinking water has virtually the same effect on caries as fluoride occurring naturally (see Moulton 1942, 1946; McClure 1962, 1970) proves that fluoride is responsible and not some substance which accompanies it in the water. The average reduction obtained from water containing 1–2 ppm fluoride is approximately 50%. It appears to affect caries at all levels of severity as the

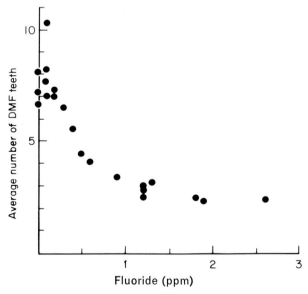

Fig. XII.3. The relationship between caries in 14-year-old children and the fluoride in their drinking water as reported by Dean.

percentage of subjects with very high DMF values falls and the percentage with lower values or who are caries-free increases.

To obtain the maximum reduction in caries, fluoride must be taken during enamel formation and continued after the teeth have erupted. For the deciduous teeth the pre-eruptive systemic effect seems most important but for the permanent teeth some surveys have suggested that the greatest effect is exerted after eruption.

The optimum dose is accepted as about 1 ppm in temperate climates because, although the anti-caries action is slightly increased with higher levels, the risk of unaesthetic mottling is too great. The evidence, indicated in Fig. XII.1, that water containing more than 4 ppm increases caries, has been substantiated (Ericsson 1977).

The addition of fluoride to the water supply of several towns in the USA showed it to have the same effect as fluoride present naturally. By 1975, fluoridated water was available to about half the American population (100 m). In the UK, three demonstration areas were set up (part of Anglesey in 1955, Kilmarnock and Watford in 1956) and in 1975 about 3 m people received artificially fluoridated water.

THE AGE GROUP BENEFITING

Although newborn animals contain some fluoride in their skeletons, auto-radiographs of the entire bodies of pregnant mice after injection of ^{18}F show that it accumulates in the placenta which is therefore reducing free diffusion into the foetus. Chemical analyses of placental tissue confirm that it is higher in fluoride than most other soft tissues. Increasing the fluoride intake of pregnant women would not therefore be expected to have much effect in raising the fluoride concentration in the teeth of the offspring. Clinical trials have shown either no effect or at most a small effect of prenatal fluoride on caries reduction (Marthaler 1971). The fluoride concentration in human milk is also very low, usually less than 0·05 ppm, and sometimes below 0·01 ppm; as in plasma, a high proportion of the fluoride is bound, similar to that of blood and raised only slightly by feeding extra fluoride to the mother (Ericsson 1969;). Cows' milk is reported to be higher, about 0·10 ppm of which 16% is ionic (Backer-Dirks 1974) but the reasons for this are unknown. If fluoride is received during childhood and continued during adult life, its effect is detectable throughout the whole life span provided adequate numbers of people are studied. This has been shown in surveys in the USA, Hungary and the UK. There are, of course, difficulties in measuring caries among mature adults as they lose many teeth from causes other than caries such as periodontal disease, and the DMF becomes increasingly inaccurate as a measure of caries after the age of 25. Jackson (1961) suggested the following method for estimating the proportion of extracted teeth which had been removed for caries. From large collections of teeth extracted at different ages he diagnosed the reason for extraction for each type of tooth (molars, premolars, etc.) from which the proportions removed for caries and other reasons could be calculated. For example, at age 42, the DMF of upper incisors was 62 per 100, but only 44 were carious so the correction factor was (44/62) = 0·7.

The reduction in caries in the later age groups is quite obvious even when the observed figures are compared (Fig. XII.4) but became more marked with the corrected figures (Fig. XII.5) (Murray 1976). Studies on adults are necessarily based on areas with natural fluoride because the practice of adding fluoride to the water started only in the mid 1940s and even in the longest scheme no elderly people have had fluoride throughout their lives. Most other results on adults refer to a population which had received higher concentrations than the 1 ppm which is officially recommended and it is possible that

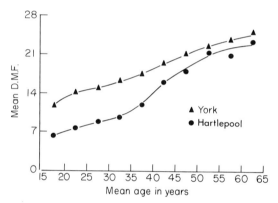

FIG. XII.4. Observed DMF values at different ages in Hartlepool (fluoride originally about 2 ppm reduced to 1·5 ppm a few years before these data were collected) and of York (0·1 ppm) showing that the effect of fluoride is still detectable in the later age groups. The marked rise in DMF in Hartlepool after age 35 is probably due mainly to periodontal disease which is not prevented by fluoride; the more gradual rise in York probably occurs because more teeth are lost from caries at an earlier age so fewer survive to the later years when periodontal disease occurs.

with 1 ppm the effect on adults might be smaller than shown in Figs XII.4 and 5. Since the rate of caries attack falls off after age 30–40, if caries in a tooth can be postponed till this age there is a good chance that it will not occur at all (Figs XII.4 and 5). The situation has been confused in the UK because the earlier surveys among groups of adults (too small in number to be a reliable sample) did suggest that the effect of a life-long intake of fluoride from water containing about 1 ppm on the DMF was of little practical value by the age of 40 and this has given rise to the widespread belief that adults get little or no benefit from fluoride. The proportion of missing to filled teeth (i.e. the proportion of teeth so severely attacked as to require extraction to those which could be saved) is usually lower in fluoride than in control areas

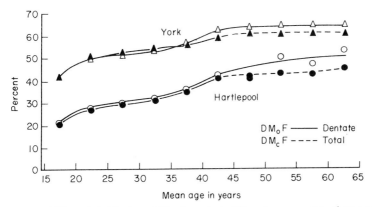

FIG. XII.5. DMF teeth in York and Hartlepool at different ages expressed as a percentage of 28 (that is erupted teeth excluding the third molars) corrected for loss from causes other than caries. The dotted lines represent data based on the general population and are comparable with Fig. XII.4; the full line excludes edentulous subjects.

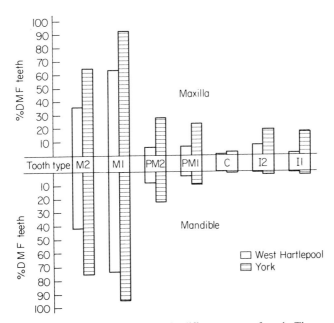

FIG. XII.6. The effect of fluoride on caries in different types of teeth. The percentage reduction in DMF (the difference between the highest part of each pair of columns) is much greater in anterior than in posterior teeth.

and, at comparable ages, the cavities are smaller showing that fluoride not only reduces the numbers of teeth affected but also the rate of caries development.

Fluoride is more effective in reducing caries in anterior teeth than on the occlusal surfaces of molars (Fig. XII.6). Two possible explanations are: (1) anterior teeth receive more fluoride after eruption from direct contact with fluoride-containing drinks than do the fissures of molars, or (2) perhaps fluoride has a more marked effect on teeth fairly resistant to caries (such as incisors) but is not sufficiently powerful to exert so great an effect on surfaces very prone to caries, such as molar fissures. In practice, this difference is not as serious as it might seem because caries in fissures is much easier to treat than in approximal surfaces.

The discovery of the unique property of fluoride in reducing caries so markedly had led to a great deal of research on its concentration in the oral structures and the effects which it exerts upon them. The fluoride content of enamel and dentine depends on the amount of fluoride ingested in food and drinking water (also tea), mainly during their mineralization. The concentration in dentine is between two and three times that in enamel (Table XII.1).

TABLE XII.1

Fluoride concentration (ppm) in permanent teeth in relation to fluoride of water supply

Fluoride concentration of water (ppm)	0·0–0·3	1·1–1·2	2·5–5·0
Enamel	100	130	340
Dentine	240	360	760

(Data from McClure & Likins 1951.)

The concentrations in deciduous teeth are lower than in permanent teeth formed under the same conditions.

The concentration of fluoride on the extreme outer surface of the enamel is ten times higher than that of the enamel as a whole (Fig. XII.7). This is true even in areas where fluoride is absent from the tap water. Unerupted teeth, which of course have had no contact with the fluids in the mouth, also possess a high concentration of fluoride on their surface, but it is not as high as for comparable erupted teeth and the fluoride-rich layer is thinner. These results confirm that the fluoride is deposited partly before eruption and partly after, from contact with fluoride in plaque, saliva and drinks.

The fluoride concentration of surface enamel has been measured in biopsy samples obtained by grinding or dissolving off minute samples from teeth in the mouth. The latter method can be carried out by placing either a drop of acid (4–6 μl) on the enamel for 3 s or a filter paper disc soaked in acid for 6–7 s

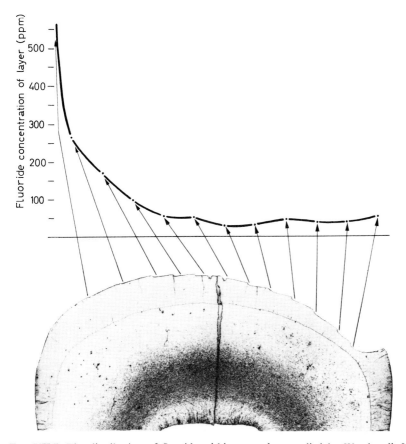

Fig. XII.7. The distribution of fluoride within enamel as studied by Weatherell & Hargreaves (1965). Successive layers of enamel were dissolved off by exposure to acid for periods of between 5 and 80 s and analysed for fluoride (upper). After each exposure, nail varnish (impermeable to acid) was placed over a strip of enamel to prevent further dissolution at that spot. A series of steps resulted corresponding with the depth of each layer from which the thickness of enamel removed by each exposure could be estimated. The very high fluoride concentration of the extreme outer layer (removed after only 20 s exposure to acid) is clearly shown and the low but fairly uniform concentration of the deep enamel.

(Hotz *et al.* 1970; Munksgaard & Bruun 1973). The slightly roughened and dull surface produced is readily polished leaving no perceptible defect.

Typical results by the grinding method from the outermost 0.5μm of incisor enamel are: 2100 ppm from subjects with low fluoride in the water and 3000 ppm with 1 ppm. The concentration was about 1000 ppm lower in the next 1.5μm under the surface.

The fluoride concentration in incisors is reported to be higher than in molars but highest in canines, with buccal and lingual surfaces higher than mesial or distal surfaces. Some of these differences may arise after eruption by uptake of fluoride from oral fluids partly balanced by the removal of outer enamel by abrasion. The major difference, however, probably depends on the time required for the formation of enamel, especially the interval between formation and eruption, during which fluoride is taken up from the tissue fluid.

The fluoride concentration in enamel is reported to be about 10% higher for boys than for girls. The main factor is probably the later eruption in boys (averaging among American children 3·3, 4·2 and 7·3 months for the maxillary central incisor, lateral incisor and canine, respectively). Possible additional factors are a greater intake of food and fluid by boys and the established fact that girls clean their teeth more thoroughly than boys and may remove more fluoride by abrasion (Aasenden 1974).

The earlier work comparing the fluoride concentration of teeth of different ages suggested that a steady rise occurred with increasing age, especially on the outer enamel and inner dentine, the surfaces in contact with saliva and tissue fluid. In view of the high uptake *in vitro* of fluoride by apatite, it was widely assumed by most workers that the rise occurred by a gradual partial conversion of hydroxyapatite into fluorapatite. However, Little *et al.* (1967) reported that when completely sound, non-pigmented outer enamel at different ages were compared the average rise in fluoride was only from about 250 ppm (age <20) to 500 ppm (at age 50). If areas of the older enamel which had become pigmented were included, a much greater increase, up to 3000 ppm by age 50, was detected. They concluded that fluoride increased only after the enamel had been made permeable, presumably by demineralization, and after organic matter had entered. Later, from studies on the nuclear magnetic resonance of fractions of the organic matter of enamel, these workers concluded that some of the fluoride was organically bound (Little *et al.* 1971) but this requires further investigation.

The effect of age on the fluoride concentration of dentine has not been studied with modern methods but early work suggested that it rises with age, partly because primary dentine gradually acquires it and partly because secondary dentine (which with increasing age becomes a higher proportion of the whole) is richer in fluoride than is primary dentine. This probably arises because it forms more slowly and each successive layer has a longer contact with tissue fluid, from which it takes up fluoride, than in primary dentine.

When the effect of age on the fluoride concentrations of different parts of the outer surfaces of teeth were studied the results showed that near the biting surface the fluoride fell with increasing age (Fig. XII.8) but in the cervical region it rose (Weatherell *et al.* 1972). Other studies, based on biopsies of

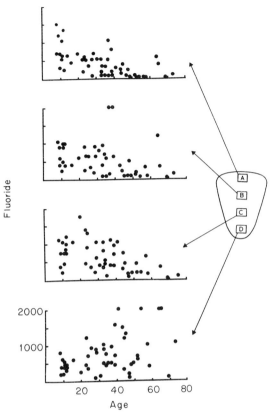

Fig. XII.8. Changes in the fluoride concentration on the surface of enamel with age: there is a marked tendency for the fluoride concentration to fall in three of the areas tested but it tends to rise near the gingival margin (D).

enamel, suggest a fall in fluoride even between the average ages of 8 and 17 (Aasenden 1975). This result is unexpected in view of the steady rise which had been found with earlier, much cruder methods. A tentative explanation for the effect of age is that attrition and abrasion from tooth-brushing gradually removes the high fluoride layer from incisal areas but that it increases in the presence of plaque (which is high in fluoride (p. 486) and tends to have a low pH, favouring fluoride uptake by apatite). Fig. XII.8 also illustrates the tremendous variation in enamel fluoride concentrations. The reasons for the rise in fluoride with age reported in earlier studies are not clear but the whole surfaces of the enamel were used in which at least some surfaces would not have been subjected to abrasion and no account was taken of uptake in demineralized areas (see later). A high concentration of fluoride was found on the incisal part of newly-erupted teeth although only a small group were studied. This might be explained by the fact that this part of the tooth forms and erupts first and therefore has the longest time of exposure to tissue fluid before eruption and to oral fluids after eruption (Weatherell 1975).

There is considerable loss in the outer fluoride-rich enamel during a prophylaxis with pumice paste and even with abrasive dentifrices. However, prophylaxes with an abrasive paste every 2 weeks during the school year for the greater part of 3 years decreased caries and the presumed loss of surface fluoride showed no undesirable effects (Axelsson & Lindhe 1975).

Armstrong & Brekhus (1938) suggested that enamel from non-carious teeth contained a higher fluoride content (an average of 0·0111%) than that from the surviving part of carious teeth (average of 0·0069%); the dentine showed no difference. These figures were widely quoted as being the only established difference between carious and non-carious enamel. It is now realized that the non-carious teeth came from a group averaging 16 years older than the control group (Armstrong & Singer 1963) and the accumulation of fluoride with age which had been reported was thought to explain this difference. The question has been re-opened by the more recent results showing that, over much of the enamel surface, the fluoride concentration falls with age; the absence of any difference in the fluoride of the dentine is another difficulty in explaining these differences as age effects. Several groups of analyses have shown that there is no difference between the fluoride concentration in the enamel as a whole (as opposed to the fluoride on the surface) in a caries-free tooth and the surviving parts of a carious tooth. The fluoride concentration is *higher* in the carious cavity itself because it accumulates in areas where the enamel is defective and more permeable.

One of the ways in which fluoride enters the tissues is by replacing carbonate (see p. 78); this led Nikiforuk (1961) to estimate the fluoride and carbonate concentrations in carious and non-carious teeth. There was no difference between the carbonate of the carious and non-carious teeth in a town with 0·1 ppm of fluoride in the water but the fluoride of the outer third of the enamel was higher in non-carious than in carious deciduous enamel. The carbonate also showed a relation to caries in a town with 1 ppm of fluoride in the water. If the CO_3:F ratios were compared, a marked difference was found between carious and non-carious teeth (Table XII. 2).

The low carbonate associated with high fluoride concentrations was not confirmed by Cutress (1972) in a study of the minor constituents of surface enamel from several widely-scattered population groups. He did find that the solubility of enamel was related directly to the CO_2 concentration ($P < 0.01$) and its CO_2:F ratio ($P < 0.001$) and was weakly related inversely to its fluoride concentration (P between 0·1 and 0·05). There was no correlation between the solubility and the concentration of any other trace element on the surface.

A correlation has been found between the average fluoride concentration in surface enamel (from biopsy samples) and the caries experience in groups of residents of towns with varying fluoride concentrations in their water supplies (DePaola *et al.* 1975). This indicates that the fluoride of enamel is related to caries resistance but so many other factors influence caries that the correlation is not significant unless fairly large groups with wide variations in fluoride intake are considered. When DMFS was plotted against mean enamel fluoride a curve was obtained similar in shape to that in Fig. XII.3 relating caries to fluoride in the water. The maximal protection was associated with 3000 ppm of fluoride on the enamel surface and the association was presumably causal. However, the correlation was not apparent in a population on the same water supply and consequently with a narrower range of variation in fluoride concentration.

TABLE XII.2

Carbonate-fluoride ratios on outer enamel from towns with high and low fluoride levels in water

F of water (ppm)	1	0·1
Non-carious	0·53	1·52
Carious	0·93	2·34

The ratio was calculated as $\dfrac{\%CO_2}{ppm\ F} \times 100$.

(Data from Nikiforuk 1961. A similar trend was noted by Nikiforuk & Grainger 1965.)

MODE OF ACTION OF FLUORIDE IN REDUCING CARIES

As already mentioned, the full effect of fluoride on caries seems to depend on an increased intake both before and after eruption, indicating a multiplicity of actions.

(1) Morphological changes in the tooth

Animal experiments have shown that fluoride (and some other trace elements) taken during tooth formation may reduce the size or alter the shape of the tooth (Kruger 1961, see Fig. XII.9). The enamel and dentine are thinner, presumably owing to a smaller amount of matrix formation, which would result in wider fissures and perhaps smaller teeth (Kruger 1968, 1970). The effect is probably similar to the action on protein synthesis which leads to mottling.

Studies on human teeth formed in areas with varying fluoride intakes have shown they tend to be smaller than in controls and with shallower fissures (for references see Lovius & Goose 1969). These differences were small and not always statistically significant but the overall tendency would be to reduce the size and number of places where food debris and plaque could accumulate. This effect could play some part—though probably a small one—in the anti-caries effect of fluoride.

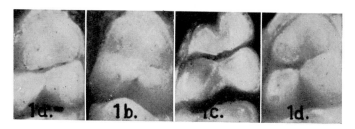

FIG. XII.9 Mesial fossa of mandibular molars of rats given varying supplements of trace elements during enamel formation; (1a) control; (1b) boron; (1c) fluorine; (1d) molybdenum.

(2) Effects of fluoride in enamel

The concentration of fluoride in teeth is higher if there is a greater intake during their formation (see p. 476) and it would be reasonable to suppose that this higher concentration is, at least partly, responsible for the reduction in caries.

(A) POSSIBLE INFLUENCES ON SOLUBILITY

The most widely-discussed hypothesis of the effect of fluoride in enamel is that it reduces its solubility. It was based on the discovery many years ago that if dental tissues are treated *in vitro* with fluoride, even in solutions as dilute as 1 ppm or less, the fluoride becomes incorporated in the tooth substance and they then dissolve more slowly in acid. The practical question is whether an intake of fluoride from water containing 1 ppm raises the fluoride concentration of the enamel sufficiently to influence the solubility.

The few direct comparisons of the acid solubility of enamel from subjects with or without fluoridated water show a tendency for the enamel with the higher fluoride to dissolve more slowly but the differences are small and do not always correspond to differences in fluoride concentration (Isaac *et al.* 1958; Jenkins 1963; Healy & Ludwig 1966; Cutress 1972).

The greatest differences in fluoride concentrations occur on the extreme outer surface of the enamel, which (assuming solubility is a factor) might affect the initiation of caries, but the levels within intact enamel seem too low to influence solubility. However, areas of damaged enamel, including early caries, take up fluoride throughout the damaged areas and the solubility in buffers of carious enamel is considerably less than that of intact enamel from the same teeth (Dowse & Jenkins 1957). This difference between carious and sound enamel is accentuated in teeth from fluoridated areas.

The data as a whole suggests that water-borne fluoride does make the outer intact enamel slightly less soluble and has a larger effect in early caries.

When the fluoride concentration in enamel reaches about 3000 ppm (equivalent to the substitution of less than 10% of its OH groups) its effect in reducing caries is maximal. There have been two explanations offered for this. First, this concentration may be adequate to convert the outer part of the apatite crystals to fluorapatite which then exert a protective action on the unsubstituted hydroxyapatite within. Secondly, the entry of fluoride has been pictured as the filling of holes in the apatite crystal arising from the occasional absence of OH groups, as explained on p. 72, an effect which would affect its stability and decrease its solubility.

COMPLICATIONS IN THE SOLUBILITY OF APATITE

Unfortunately, these experiments are misleadingly simple when applied to the effect of acids on the enamel surface in the plaque environment. One confusion arises because some test-tube experiments measure the solubility of enamel when equilibrium is reached, whereas others measure the *rate* at which equilibrium is approached. It is uncertain which is relevant to the caries because it is not known whether equilibrium is reached during the short periods of acid dissolution occurring, at least during the early stages of caries. In view of the usually short duration of the low pH in plaque (p. 388) and the lack of stirring, it might be speculated that equilibrium is not reached.

Another complication in these solubility studies is that several different crystalline forms of calcium phosphate exist (for example brushite, octacalcium phosphate and the two biological apatites) and a buffer solution may be unsaturated to one form (which dissolves) and supersaturated to another (which consequently separates out) (Rootare *et al.* 1962; Larsen & Thorsen 1974). If partial remineralization occurred during the measurement of solubility it would reduce the net amount dissolved and would be recorded as a reduced solubility.

With apatites, the question of solubility is further complicated by the effect of pH which changes the nature of the phosphate ion from PO_4^{3-} at high pH values to HPO_4^{2-} and $H_2PO_4^-$ at low values. The influence of this factor is best considered by constructing phase diagrams, i.e. graphs relating the concentrations of the ions concerned in the precipitation, and therefore the solubility, of a salt (for a full discussion, see Brown *et al.* 1977). With hydroxy-apatite (HA) the solubility involves three constituents: $Ca(OH)_2$, H_3PO_4, H_2O, but with fluorapatite (FA) a fourth constituent (HF) is involved which makes graphical representation impossible on a single two-dimensional graph. Phase diagrams of FA can only be represented either on complicated three-dimensional diagrams or by a series of graphs for different HF concentrations. An additional complication in relation to HA and FA is that HA releases OH^- as it dissolves thus tending to raise the pH. This does not occur when FA dissolves, but conversely the F ions released act as an acid by conversion to HF:

$$Ca_5(PO_4)_2F + 10\ H_2O = 5\ Ca(OH)_2 + 3(H_3PO_4) + HF$$

When HA and FA are dissolved in such amounts as to provide equal concentrations of calcium and phosphate ions, the pH of the FA solution will be lower and the effect of the fluoride would be to ensure that, in spite of the lower pH (which would be expected to dissolve more apatite) no more would be dissolved. This effect on pH would not occur in test-tube experiments with buffers which are designed to reduce or prevent changes in pH. Such experiments would suggest differences in solubility which would be absent from a less buffered medium. In view of the small amounts of enamel dissolved at any one time into the heavily-buffered plaque environment, it might be speculated that the pH would not change and the effect of fluoride on solubility will be maximized under conditions in the plaque.

A further complication in studying the solubility of apatites is that the amount dissolving increases with an increase in the amount of solid (or of surface exposed) in a given volume of solvent (the solid:solution ratio). This occurs because apatites react with the water in the solvent in ways which increase their solubility.

Phase diagrams of HA and FA confirm the lower solubility of FA but emphasize that the difference seems too small to make a significant contribution to the reduction in caries produced by fluoride. This seems even more obvious when account is taken of the low proportion of the apatite in enamel present as FA (even the 3000 ppm of fluoride on the outer enamel in fluoride areas represents less than 10% of the OH ions substituted by fluoride).

An important point which emerges from the analysis by Brown (1974, 1977) of the phase diagrams of apatite is based upon the additional concept that the development of caries depends on the rate of outward diffusion of the dissolved calcium and phosphate ions. The lower pH produced when FA dissolves would tend to lower the activity of $Ca(OH)_2$ and therefore lower the driving force for its outward diffusion but favour inward diffusion from plaque (i.e. remineralization). Conversely, the lower pH would increase activity of

H_3PO_4 and would suppress its ionization. The activity, and therefore outward diffusion, of phosphate ions would be less in spite of higher concentrations of total H_3PO_4. According to Brown, these effects on diffusion exceed in importance the reduced common ion effect from the low concentration of phosphate ions but, as mentioned above, it is doubtful whether these considerations are valid in the plaque with its high buffering power.

In summary, most of the evidence does support the hypothesis that intake of fluoride reduces the solubility of enamel but owing to the great complexity of the chemistry of the calcium phosphate it is not certain that simple tests of solubility are valid.

(B) POSSIBLE WAYS IN WHICH FLUORIDE MIGHT LOWER THE SOLUBILITY OF ENAMEL

(1) The above considerations apply to pure HA and FA but enamel contains other constituents such as carbonate which modify its properties. Fluoride enters the apatite of enamel during its formation at the expense on carbonate and a low carbonate is thought to reduce solubility (see pp. 242 and 480).

(2) The concentration of fluoride in a medium in which apatite crystals are forming may affect their 'crystallinity', i.e. increase their size and reduce the defects in the crystals (Grøn *et al.* 1963), and both of these tend to lower the solubility of the crystal. Increased fluoride intake certainly has this effect in bone but it has not been established for enamel and as apatite crystals in enamel are always larger than in bone (p. 65) this effect may not be possible in enamel.

(3) Very low concentrations of fluoride, even 0·1 ppm, favour the precipitation of apatite from unstable supersaturated solutions such as saliva. Brudevold (1965) concluded that, in the absence of fluoride, apatite crystals do not precipitate from saturated solutions but more soluble substances such as octacalcium phosphate are formed. The higher the concentration of fluoride the greater the tendency for an apatite (not necessarily fluorapatite) to be deposited. Fluoride released from the enamel or stored in plaque may have this effect in the remineralizing phase of caries (p. 418) and thus slow up the rate of development of a cavity.

There is still no final decision on the relative importance of these possibilities, several of which may operate.

(3) Effects of fluoride in plaque

(A) INHIBITORY EFFECTS ON BACTERIA

The fluoride ion is an inhibitor of many enzymes so that it could conceivably exert its anti-caries action by reducing the effectiveness of the bacterial enzymes which are responsible for the attack on the tooth. In order to test this theory, two pieces of information are necessary. First, the concentration of fluoride needed to inhibit acid production by the dental plaque must be known and, secondly, the concentration of fluoride ions present in the plaque. If fluoride is added to saliva-glucose mixtures before incubation, it is found that the concentration necessary to cause the smallest detectable reduction in bacterial acid production by saliva (a measure of bacterial metabolism) is 1–2 ppm and 10 ppm are necessary for a moderately large inhibition. Much higher levels, up to 100 ppm, are required to reduce bacterial growth. Salivary bacteria are much more sensitive to fluoride at pH 5·0 than at neutrality and if the experiment just mentioned is modified and fluoride is added to saliva adjusted to a pH of 5, much lower concentrations inhibit and as little as 6–8 ppm will completely stop any further acid production. The fluoride concentration of fasting saliva, estimated by the specific ion electrode, is lower than 0·02 ppm (considerably less than earlier estimations) and shows only a slight rise after the ingestion of 1 mg of fluoride (as NaF). The effect of drinking fluoridated water (equivalent to 1 mg of fluoride spread over many hours) on salivary levels is probably too small to detect.

It seems most unlikely, therefore, that the fluoride of the saliva can inhibit bacteria. The fluoride of the dental plaque, however, is not only very much higher in concentration but has been shown to be affected by the fluoride intake.

In some early estimations in a town with no fluoride in its water the average fluoride of plaque was about 25 ppm and with a water supply containing 2 ppm the plaque averaged 47 ppm (wet wt). Later estimations with more accurate methods have given lower values (10–20 ppm) but there is no doubt that the plaque does store fluoride. Only about 1% of these values are obtained when the concentration is measured with the fluoride electrode (which detects only fluoride ions) and the remainder must be bound in some way. When certain bacteria are grown in media containing fluoride they take up high concentrations (for example, 12 ppm from a medium containing 5 ppm) and there is evidence that much of the bound fluoride of plaque is present in bacterial cells. Earlier work suggested that the fluoride in the bacteria inhibited acid production but this has not been confirmed. Nevertheless, some of the fluoride of plaque can exert an inhibitory effect as shown by the finding that acid production by plaque, measured *in vitro*, is slightly but significantly lower in higher fluoride areas.

This is found when plaque from high and low fluoride areas are compared (Jenkins *et al.* 1969) and also in one town when plaques were studied before and after fluoridation (Edgar *et al.* 1970). The effect, although small, is consistent and statistically significant and indicates enzymic inhibition in the plaque bacteria. Other studies have shown that the proportion of organisms storing polysaccharides is lower in plaques from high fluoride than from control areas. Either fewer polysaccharide-storing bacteria are present or those present store less polysaccharide than usual. This may be an additional reason for the reduced pH drop.

Birkeland (1973) in a series of studies in which fluoride has been added to saliva has shown that its concentration falls and that it binds and precipitates with inorganic substances, probably calcium phosphate, rather than with bacteria. In the presence of citrate which complexes divalent cations including calcium (p. 421) and prevents their precipitation, the concentration of fluoride ions did not fall. The fluoride in plaque, like that stored in certain bacteria, exists in two forms. One fraction is readily extracted by dilute acids and detected as fluoride ions but the remainder requires more powerful reagents for its release as ions. The fact that both plaque and bacteria contain these two forms provides further evidence that part of the plaque fluoride is attached to the bacteria (Jenkins & Edgar 1977).

(B) EFFECTS ON ENAMEL SOLUBILITY IN A BUFFER

Concentrations of fluoride as low as 0·1 ppm may reduce the amount of HA dissolving in a buffer (Manly & Harrington 1959). The fluoride probably converts the outer layers of the HA into FA after which the crystals as a whole acquire the solubility properties of FA (Brown *et al.* 1977). The free fluoride ions present in plaque would be expected to exert this effect on enamel when it is attacked by bacterial acids.

(C) EFFECTS ON REMINERALIZATION

Fluoride ions in plaque would favour remineralization after acid dissolution, as discussed on p. 418.

(D) A SOURCE OF ENAMEL FLUORIDE

The fluoride concentration of enamel (at least in incisors, there are few data on other teeth) rises with age in areas covered with plaque, in contrast to the fall on areas free from plaque (p. 479 and Fig. XII.8). Some of this fluoride is probably incorporated into apatite during minor episodes of de- and re-mineralization and will have a protective effect on the enamel. There is evidence that some of the fluoride is organically bound (p. 478) and its effects are uncertain.

The Source of Plaque Fluoride

The source of the fluoride present in all plaques, even from subjects with no fluoride in their water, ought probably to be considered separately from the additional fluoride present in areas with fluoridated water. Plaque fluoride might be derived from (1) the enamel surface; (2) food or drinks; and (3) saliva and gingival fluid.

It is most unlikely that the fluoride-rich layer of the outer enamel contributes a regular supply of fluoride to plaque because if it did the fluoride concentration would rapidly fall, whereas on plaque-covered enamel it tends to rise with age as mentioned above. Drinks are also an unlikely source because, apart from tea, they are usually low in fluoride and in contact with plaque only for short periods. In the few foods containing high concentrations of fluoride (for example, fish skin), it is not freely soluble. By elimination, the most likely source is therefore saliva and gingival fluid, but since bacteria cannot build up the high levels of fluoride in plaque from salivary concentrations (less than 0·02 ppm) it is speculated that some constituent of plaque, possibly apatite, concentrates fluoride which is released when plaque pH falls following carbohydrate ingestion. A rise in the ionic concentration of fluoride in plaque occurs when it is extracted with acids which, by diluting plaque, favour the dissolving of its constituents. It is not known whether a similar release occurs when the plaque pH falls *in vivo* that would be unaccompanied by dilution with an extractant. The binding of salivary fluoride to calcium phosphate reported by Birkeland (1973) may be a transitional stage for the uptake by plaque bacteria.

The additional plaque fluoride in high fluoride areas is probably derived from direct contact of the plaque with drinks. Salivary fluoride concentrations are only very slightly raised by ingesting 1 mg of fluoride in tablet form so that the effect of fluoridated water (i.e. 1 mg spread over many hours) is likely to be even smaller. Although the effect of a very slight rise in salivary fluoride over the greater part of the day cannot be dismissed entirely, the contact of plaque with about 1 ppm in drinks, in spite of its short duration, would seem a more likely source.

Occurrence of Fluoride

Fluoride is present in concentrations of up to 0·5 ppm in many foods but the total daily intake from this source rarely exceeds 1 mg. It has often been stated that fish is high in fluoride but only the skin and bone are unusually high (typical values are 8 and 700, respectively) the flesh being not more than about 1 ppm. Tinned fish, in which the skin is present and the bones are often edible, may provide more. The only other common dietary source is tea which averages about 1·5 ppm (if made with water containing negligible fluoride), the dry leaves containing between 100 and 300 ppm, depending on the blend.

Total fluoride intake is clearly very variable but ranges from about 1 mg a day in an individual with low tea consumption and negligible fluoride in the water, to about 3 mg in a heavy tea drinker (15 cups per day). With fluoridated water, these values are approximately doubled and in exceptionally heavy tea drinkers may reach from 8 to 10 mg daily. The fluoride concentration of processed foods tends to be higher if they are manufactured with fluoridated water; this may be significant in the USA where a high proportion of cities (including some with food industries) have fluoridated water. Foods grown in fluoridated areas do not take up significantly more fluoride than controls. In most diets, the fluoride intake is dominated by the concentration in the water and the amount of tea consumed. The high contribution from water has led to the erroneous view that water determines the intake of trace elements in general—fluoride is probably the only element provided in greater abundance in water than in food.

Metabolism of Fluoride

Fluoride absorption is rapid and begins in the stomach and upper intestine. The fluoride of the faeces is usually about 10% of that ingested and is presumably unabsorbed dietary fluoride although excretion via the intestine may possibly contribute. If the fluoride is taken with a great deal of calcium (as in fish bones) much less is absorbed because calcium fluoride or fluorapatite is formed, both of which have a very low solubility and enter the faeces. Concentrations in the plasma are low, about 0·1 ppm. Taves (1968) showed that only 10–20% of plasma fluoride is present as free ions; the rest is bound, though the nature of the binding is uncertain; protein binding has been suggested but also disputed. It is presumed that concentrations in tissue fluids resemble those of plasma although no direct estimation appears to have been made. The concentrations in saliva and milk follow those of plasma and show very small changes after ingestion of low doses (say 1 mg); no consistent rise is detectable in human milk if fluoride is taken on a full stomach.

The explanation of the low plasma concentration and the smallness of the increase after ingesting fluoride is that the skeleton takes up fluoride by ionic exchange and the kidney excretes it very rapidly (30% of a dose of up to 5 mg is excreted within 3 hr). Storage in the skeleton occurs normally so that urinary excretion of fluoride is usually lower than absorption. As the concentration of fluoride in the skeleton rises with age, it tends to approach an

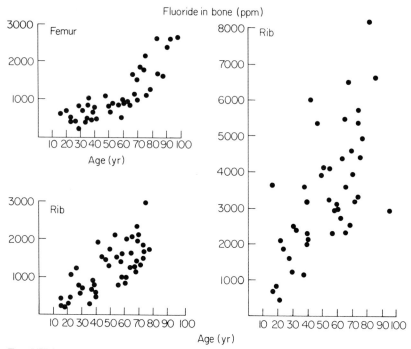

Fig. XII.10. The concentration of fluoride, from the non-fluoridated area of Leeds, England, in bones from different parts of the skeleton in relation to age. Note that the fluoride concentration increases steadily and in the ribs may exceed 5000 ppm in elderly people.

equilibrium with plasma concentrations so that less is stored and a higher proportion of the amount ingested enters the urine. The evidence on this point is not entirely consistent, however; some data suggest that equilibrium is reached within a few years (or even months) so that eventually the urine contains almost the whole of the intake. However, there is no doubt that skeletal levels increase throughout life (Fig. XII.10) reaching concentrations of 2000–3000 ppm or, in spongy bone with its richer blood supply, even 6000–8000 ppm, by the age of 80–90 years, which clearly implies continued storage at all ages. An earlier belief, that no further increase occurred after the age of 50 or so, is erroneous and based on too few samples.

The Effect of Fluoride on Enzymes

Fluoride inhibits several groups of enzymes (reviewed by Wiseman 1970), including many whose action depends on divalent metals such as magnesium (enolase, phosphatases) or trivalent metals (catalase, peroxidase). In acid production from sugar (glycolysis) the most sensitive enzyme is enolase which is inhibited by 45% with about 10 ppm fluoride (0.5×10^{-3} M). The sensitivity of enolase is low in the absence of phosphate which led to the mistaken view that fluorophosphate (thought to have been formed spontaneously from fluoride and phosphate) was the real inhibitor. Fluorophosphate does not form at room temperatures and, when pure, has no inhibitory action. When used in dentifrices, there is evidence that its action depends on the release of fluoride by a slow spontaneous breakdown (Pearce & Jenkins 1976). Enolase is also concerned with the uptake of glucose by bacteria and it is probably inhibition at this level, rather than in the course of glycolysis, that occurs in the bacteria of saliva or plaque.

The concentration required to inhibit enzymes at physiological pH values are very much higher than those in plasma (about 0.1 ppm total fluoride or 0.02 ppm fluoride ions). Only in mineralized tissues (including those with pathological calcification, such as artery walls or kidney stones) do the concentrations exceed about 1 ppm. The cells associated with bones and teeth (especially the ameloblasts) seem to be those most easily affected by fluoride but it is not known whether they have a greater sensitivity or whether they take up more fluoride merely because they are exposed to higher concentrations as a result of their close contact with apatite. It would not be expected that fluoride bound in apatite would affect enzymes or that fluoride would diffuse out of the apatite in enamel. Apatite in bone is dissolved in the course of remodelling so that bone cells are probably subjected to higher concentrations of fluoride released into tissue fluid than cells elsewhere.

Fluoride has been reported to accelerate a few enzyme reactions but this has not been thoroughly studied on pure enzymes. Some of the effects reported arise indirectly because one pathway is inhibited by fluoride making more substrate available for other pathways which thus appear to be enhanced. Purified preparations of the enzyme adenyl cyclase, which converts ATP into cyclic AMP and is a key reaction in many hormonal effects, are stimulated by fluoride and higher concentrations of cAMP have been reported in the liver, heart and submandibular glands of rats receiving as low a dose as 1 ppm in their drinking water (Allman & Benac 1976). The effect of fluoridated water has not been tested on the levels of cAMP in human tissues or body fluids but feeding 3.76 mg of fluoride to human experimental subjects increased urinary excretion of cAMP by 25% during the following 6 hr (Mornstad *et al.* 1975).

A Summary of the Main Objections to Fluoridation

The fluoridation of water has been opposed on three major grounds, namely, that it is not sufficiently effective to justify the cost or alleged risk, that there are doubts about its safety and that it interferes with the liberty of the subject.

ITS EFFECTIVENESS

Some critics have emphasized that the effect on caries in the UK (DHSS 1969) for children aged 8–11 years represents a delay in DMF of only one tooth per year and that the *rate* of caries is not reduced. This overlooks two points: (1) fluoride has a smaller proportional effect on the occlusal surfaces of molars where most caries occurs at ages 8–11, than on the incisors, so that this age group shows a smaller benefit than at ages 5 or 15; and (2) the DMF score underestimates the effect on caries because it does not show that the progress of caries is slower as well as that the number of cavities is smaller. Some critics have quoted figures referring to children who have not received fluoride throughout their lives and would not be expected to show the full effect.

It is also stated that the fluoride only benefits children whereas all surveys show some benefit to adults, although admittedly the effect becomes smaller by middle age (p. 474). The evidence on this point can only be derived from natural fluoride areas as none of the artificial schemes have been in existence for more than 30 years.

SAFETY

The main objection is doubt about the safety of ingesting fluoridated water throughout a lifetime, especially in Britain where much fluoride is already consumed in tea. No consistent differences in vital statistics have been established for high and low fluoride areas which, within the rather high error of public health statistics, show that 1 ppm fluoride has no detectable effect on the length of life or on the incidence of fatal diseases. It is more difficult to decide whether minor illnesses, which are not recorded statistically, are affected by fluoride. From the known effects of chronic fluorosis, the earliest expected symptoms would be stiffness and pain in the joints, especially of the spine and this has not been observed by medical practitioners in fluoridated areas or in either of the two surveys so far conducted on joint pains in fluoride areas. Much confusion has arisen because of the failure by the opponents of fluoridation to distinguish between the effects of high doses (which are known to be toxic) and of the intake from water fluoridated at 1 ppm.

Some reports state that a minority of individuals have an immediate unfavourable reaction to fluoridated water (i.e. different from the effects following years of intake) resembling an allergic reaction or, more precisely, a hypersensitivity (Waldbott 1955 ab; Grimbergen 1974). The symptoms described include rashes, tremors, diarrhoea, stomatitis, visual disturbances, tinnitis, mental depression—all non-specific, subjective and difficult to measure. The validity of this conclusion could be studied by double-blind tests or by comparing the incidence of these symptoms among residents of high and low fluoride areas. Tests which were regarded as double-blind have been attempted but in all the published reports some features of these tests prevented their being truly double-blind, for example in one test the fluoride was a solution containing 5000 ppm delivered to the patient who made his own dilution to 1 ppm. This concentration can be detected in various ways, for example by taste and it leaves a visible residue on evaporation. The existence of hypersensitivity to fluoride has, therefore, never been established.

The question of the long-term safety of fluoridation can be approached by considering the intake of fluoride which has been associated with the first signs of undesirable effects. In Bartlett, Texas (fluoride in water 8 ppm until it was reduced), a detailed medical examination showed that 10–15% of the inhabitants did show radiological evidence of some thickening of the bone although this was not accompanied by any disability or symptoms. This suggests that 12–16 mg a day (the probable minimum intake from water containing 8 ppm) is enough to produce very early, but still unimportant, changes in some of the population. In Britain, the intake on fluoridated water rarely exceeds 5 mg a day and is usually much less. One individual in fluoridated Newcastle drank 22 cups of tea and 4 pints of beer a day, providing a probable 8–9 mg (his urine contained 6 mg per day) so that even this extreme intake is within acceptable limits. In Britain, most children drink some tea from an early age and the average intake up to the age of 7 is 2·5 cups providing about 0·5 mg of fluoride. This may account for the lower caries figures reported for Britain compared with some continental countries although no strictly comparable figures, collected by the same group of observers, are available.

It is also questioned whether natural and artificial fluoride have the same effects on the body and whether the health records of areas with natural fluoride necessarily apply to artificial fluoridation. Critics argue that the sodium fluoride usually added artificially may differ from the natural salt which they describe as calcium fluoride since it often occurs in hard water. At 1 ppm, all salts are fully ionized so that, on theoretical grounds, the concentration of fluoride ion at 1 ppm would be expected to be identical. This is confirmed by the specific ion electrode, which measures only ionic fluoride, and also in experiments in which natural and artificially-fluoridated water have been given to rats and the skeletal uptake of fluoride was virtually the same in both (Wagner & Muhler 1957). As mentioned on p. 489, it is true that in the presence of high calcium intake in the diet, less fluoride is absorbed but this requires much higher concentrations than are present in hard water.

In summary, no undesirable effects have been established nor would be expected when the intakes recorded in fluoridated areas are related to levels known to be of borderline safety. On the other hand, vigilance should continue, especially with regard to minor effects not easy to measure and not contained in any official statistics. The undoubted dental benefits far out-weigh the hypothetical risk of minor harmful effects to a small minority.

THE ETHICAL QUESTION

The ethical objection that fluoridation interferes with the liberty of the subject is not a scientific question and is outside the scope of this book.

ALTERNATIVES TO THE FLUORIDATION OF THE PUBLIC WATER SUPPLY

The fluoridation of salt at 250 ppm (Toth 1973) is effective and milk has been proposed as a vehicle but only limited clinical data exist on its effectiveness. The calcium of milk reduces only slightly the availability of fluoride. The difficulty with fluoridated milk is that of distributing it to children during the pre-school years when its effect on the developing teeth might be expected to be greatest. However, the fluoridation of the water supply to some schools in the USA (at 4·5 or 6·3 ppm—levels which take into account the proportion of total fluid which was drunk at school) reduced caries markedly even though the fluoride was not taken until the age of 6. Milk distributed to school-children would therefore seem to be a potentially effective vehicle for fluoride.

Fluoride can be given as tablets containing 1 mg or 0·25 mg fluoride with the following doses: after birth, 0·25 mg fluoride is recommended daily for the child during his first 8 months, 0·5 mg fluoride from 8 to 16 months; 0·75 mg fluoride from 16 to 24 months and 1 mg fluoride daily after 2 years of age. Once the teeth are erupted the tablets should be sucked rather than swallowed whole, to allow a topical effect followed by a systemic effect after swallowing.

TOPICAL APPLICATION OF FLUORIDE

Another method of utilizing the anti-caries action of fluoride is the technique known as 'topical application', i.e. painting the teeth—usually with a 2% solution of sodium fluoride or stannous fluoride. Widespread success has been claimed for this method, although some results have been negative. The mode of action of these very high concentrations of fluoride in reducing caries is probably similar to those of water-borne fluoride but the relative importance of the various actions may differ, for example effects on solubility may be more prolonged than effects on plaque.

Most of the experiments have been carried out on children but clinical trials on young adults have given positive results. Topical application does not appear to have been tested experimentally in middle-aged subjects but would be expected to reduce the rate on development of cavities present at the time of treatment.

Treatment of dental tissues *in vitro* with strong sodium fluoride solutions reduces their solubility and it was natural to suspect that the mechanism of action of topical application of fluoride was through a reduction in the solubility of the tooth and hence an increased resistance to acid attack. High concentrations of fluoride become attached to the enamel surface during these treatments, partly in a stable form by ionic exchange with hydroxyl ions in apatite (as occurs from fluoride in tissue fluids) and partly by the formation of adsorbed calcium fluoride. The latter is formed only with concentrations greater than 100 ppm and may be brushed off within a few days (Zwemer 1957) or dissolved, perhaps into plaque where it may reduce bacterial acid production (Houte *et al.* 1969; Loesche *et al.* 1973, 1975; Woolley & Rickles 1971). The uptake is greatest in early caries lesions where the enamel has become permeable and allows the fluoride to reach the deeper parts of the lesion and this occurs irrespective of the age of the subject.

Fluoride complexors, such as aluminium, also increase both the uptake and retention of fluoride by enamel. The effectiveness in caries reduction of some of these methods is not as great as would be predicted from the fluoride uptake, suggesting that only certain types of fluoride binding are associated with high caries resistance. Fluoride solutions at different pH values have been tested as well as other salts of fluoride such as stannous, ammonium, titanium and amine fluorides. Retention of fluoride (as calcium fluoride) is more prolonged from ammonium fluoride (at pH 4·4) than from other treatments; the reason for this is unknown.

Acidified solutions of sodium fluoride reduce solubility more effectively than do neutral solutions and favour the uptake of fluoride by enamel *in vitro*, suggesting that acid solutions would be more effective against caries. An objection to acid solutions is that they might dissolve some of the enamel. Brudevold *et al.* (1963) attempted to overcome this difficulty by using a solution of 2·0% NaF (= 1·23% F) in 0·1 M H_3PO_4 (acid phosphate fluoride or APF). The high phosphate concentration was designed to reduce the solvent action of the acid by a common ion effect. A 70% reduction in caries was reported in the first experiments but the superiority of this mixture compared with neutral solutions has not been confirmed in the large number of later clinical trials. In order to reduce the time required for topical application, gelling agents have been added to APF which the subject then applies to the teeth by means of mouth trays. Substances which reduce solubility do not necessarily protect against caries, for example, topical application of indium nitrate or zinc salts reduce solubility but have no effect on caries and lead fluoride reduces solubility more than does sodium fluoride but has a smaller effect on caries.

Fluoride mouth rinses reduce caries and are used quite extensively where fluoridation is impracticable. Several techniques have been tested, such as holding in the mouth for 2 min 10 ml of either 0·05% NaF daily or 0·2% NaF fortnightly. Both have been shown to be effective but only the daily rinse has been reported to have a marked action, about 50% reduction (Torell &

Ericsson 1965). Rinses are unsuitable for children younger than 3 years because they cannot be relied upon to inhibit swallowing and the amount of fluoride in the rinse is undesirably large for ingestion by young children which, if swallowed frequently, might lead to mild fluorosis (mottling).

Dentrifices containing various fluoride compounds have been extensively tested and found to reduce caries by up to about 30%. They seem particularly effective on teeth erupting during the trial, presumably because fluoride uptake is probably greater before posteruptive maturation (p. 173) has occurred and maturation can then be more effectively accelerated or increased by fluoride itself. In dentifrices containing stannous fluoride the stannous ion probably plays some part in the reaction with enamel or the pellicle and tends to produce a yellow-brown stain after long use (Naylor & Emslie 1967).

Children under the age of 4 have difficulty in spitting out a dentifrice and may therefore ingest some fluoride from it. Although individual children do not invariably swallow it, most children do on some occasions. Even if the dentifrice were swallowed daily the amount of fluoride concerned is most unlikely to lead to any result more serious than mild mottling and even this has not been reported. As a precaution Ericsson & Forsman (1969) recommend that the amount of toothpaste used on each occasion by children under 4 years should not exceed the size of a pea, especially in areas with fluoridated water.

The effect on caries of fluoride in dentifrices or topically applied are additive to those of water fluoridated at 1 ppm. Either the high concentrations on fluoride in the former have qualitative effects additional to those of water or they may increase the effects of the water which, at 1 ppm, are not maximal. The effects are not large, however, and it is doubtful whether the results of methods involving professional personnel would justify the expense, except perhaps with subjects very prone to caries.

Koch (1969, 1970) showed that, 2 years after stopping the use of a fluoride rinse or dentifrice, the difference between the caries increments of test and control groups virtually disappeared. The value of these procedures at school is therefore limited at least in Scandinavia where the caries rate is high, although some postponement of caries by a few years may mean that cavities form more slowly with increased prospects that the teeth will be saved.

References

General Reviews:

Brown W.E. & König K.G. (Eds) (1977) Cariostatic mechanisms of fluorides. Proceedings of a Workshop organized by the American Dental Association Health Foundation and the National Institute of

Dental Research, Naples, Fla., 1976. *Caries Res.* **11,** Suppl. I

Jenkins G.N. (1963) Theories on the mode of action of fluoride in reducing dental decay. *J. dent. Res.* **42,** 444 (see also (1969) *Archs oral Biol.* **14,** 105)

McClure F.J. (1962) (Ed.) *Fluoride Drink-*

ing Waters. U.S. Dept. of Health, Education and Welfare, Bethesda, Maryland

MCCLURE F.J. (1970) *Water Fluoridation. The Search and the Victory*. National Institute of Dental Research, Bethesda, Maryland.

MOULTON F.R. (1942) (Ed.) *Fluorine and Dental Health*. Amer. Ass. Adv. Sci., Washington

MOULTON F.R. (1946) (Ed.) *Dental Caries and Fluorine*. Amer. Ass. Adv. Sci., Washington

MURRAY J.J. (1976) *Fluorides in Caries Prevention*. Wright & Sons, Bristol

ROYAL COLLEGE OF PHYSICIANS (1976) *Fluoride Teeth and Health*. Pitman Medical, London

WISEMAN A. (1970) Effect of inorganic fluoride on enzymes. In *Handbuch der experimentallen Pharmakologie*. (Eds) EICHLER O., FARSH A. & WELCH A.D. Springer-Verlag, Berlin

The toxicity of fluoride is discussed in the quarterly journal *Fluoride* published by The International Society for Fluoride Research, P.O. Box 692, Warren, Michigan

AASENDEN R. (1974) Fluoride concentration in enamel of males and females. *Archs oral Biol.* **19**, 647

AASENDEN R. (1975) Post-eruptive changes in the fluoride concentrations of human tooth surface enamel. *Archs oral Biol.* **20**, 359

AINSWORTH N.J. (1933) Mottled teeth. *Brit. dent. J.* **15**, 233

AL-ALOUSI W. *et al.* (1975) Enamel mottling in a fluoride and in a non-fluoride community. *Brit. dent. J.* **138**, 9, 56

ALLMANN D.W. & BENAC M. (1976) Effect of inorganic fluoride salts on urine and tissue $3'5'$ cyclic AMP concentration *in vivo*. *Internat. Ass. Dent. Res. Abs.* 523

ANDREASON J.D. & RAVN J.J. (1973) Enamel changes in permanent teeth after trauma to their primary predecessors. *Scand. J. dent. Res.* **81**, 203

ARMSTRONG W.G. & BREKHUS P.J. (1938) Chemical composition of enamel and dentine. II. Fluorine content. *J. dent. Res.* **17**, 27

ARMSTRONG W.D. & SINGER L. (1963) Fluoride contents of enamel of sound and carious human teeth: a reinvestigation. *J. dent. Res.* **42**, 133

AXELSSON P. & LINDHE J. (1975) Effect of fluoride on gingivitis and dental caries in a preventive program based on plaque control. *Community Dent. & Oral Epidemiol.* **3**, 156

BACKER-DIRKS O. *et al.* (1974) Total and free ionic fluoride in human and cow's milk as determined by gas-liquid chromatography and the fluoride electrode. *Caries Res.* **8**, 181

BIRKELAND J.M. (1973) The effect of pH on the interaction of fluoride and salivary ions. *Caries Res.* **7**, 11

BIRKELAND J.M. & CHARLTON G. (1976) Effect of pH on the fluoride ion activity of plaque. *Caries Res.* **10**, 72

BIRKELAND J.M. & RÖLLA G. (1972) *In vitro* affinity of fluoride of proteins, dextrans, bacteria and salivary components. *Archs oral Biol.* **17**, 455

BROWN W.E. (1974) Physicochemical mechanism of dental caries. *J. dent. Res.* **53**, 204

BROWN W.E. *et al.* (1977) Effects of fluoride on enamel solubility and cariostasis. *Caries Res.* **11** (Suppl. 1), 118

BRUDEVOLD F. *et al.* (1956) The distribution of fluoride in human enamel. *J. dent. Res.* **35**, 420

BRUDEVOLD F. *et al.* (1959) A comparison of the increment of fluoride in enamel and the reduction in dental caries resulting from topical fluoride applications. *J. dent. Res.* **38**, 672

BRUDEVOLD F. *et al.* (1963) A study of acidulated fluoride solutions. *Archs oral Biol.* **8**, 167, 179, 183

BRUDEVOLD F. (1965) Ciba Conference: The caries resistant tooth. Eds WOLSTENHOLME G.E.W. & O'CONNOR M. Churchill, London

CHURCHILL H.V. (1931) Occurrence of fluoride in some waters of the United States. *Ind. Eng. Chem.* **23**, 996

CUTRESS T.W. (1972) The inorganic

composition and solubility of dental enamel from several specified population groups. *Archs oral Biol.* **17,** 93

DEAN H. *et al.* (1942) Domestic water and dental caries. V. Additional studies of the relation of fluoride domestic waters to dental caries experience in 4425 white children, aged 12 to 14 years, of 13 cities in 4 States. *Pub. Health Rep.* **57,** 1155 (see also (1941) *Pub. Health Rep.* **56,** 761)

DEAN H.T. (1942) The investigation of physiological effects by the epidemiological method. In MOULTON F.R. (1942) *Fluorine and Dental Health*, p. 23. The Science Press Printing Company, Lancaster, Pennsylvania

DE PAOLA P.F. *et al.* (1975) A pilot study of the relationship between caries experience and surface enamel fluoride in man. *Archs oral Biol.* **20,** 859

DEPARTMENT OF HEALTH AND SOCIAL SECURITY (1969) The fluoridation studies in the United Kingdom and the results achieved after eleven years. *Reports on Public Health and Medical Subjects No. 122.* Her Majesty's Stationary Office, London

DOWSE C.M. & JENKINS G.N. (1957) Fluoride uptake *in vivo* in enamel defects and its significance. *J. dent. Res.* **36,** 816

EDGAR W.M. *et al.* (1970) Inhibitory action of fluoride on plaque bacteria. *Brit. dent. J.* **128,** 129

ERICSSON Y. (1969) Fluoride excretion in human saliva and milk. *Caries Res.* **3,** 159

ERICSSON S.Y. (1977) Cariostatic mechanisms of fluorides: clinical observations. *Caries Res.* **11** (Suppl. 1), 2

ERICSSON Y. & FORSMAN B. (1969) Fluoride retained from mouth rinses and dentifrices in preschool children. *Caries Res.* **3,** 290

FEJERSKOV O. *et al.* (1975) The ultrastructure of fluorosed human dental enamel. *Scand. J. dent. Res.* **82,** 357

FORREST J.F. (1956) Caries incidence and enamel defects in areas with different levels of fluoride in the drinking water. *Brit. dent. J.* **100,** 195

GRAY J.A. (1962) Kinetics of the dissolution of human dental enamel in acid. *J. dent. Res.* **41,** 633

GRIMBERGEN G.W. (1974) A double blind test for determination of intolerance to fluoridated water. (Preliminary report.) *Fluoride* **7,** 146

GRØN P. *et al.* (1963) The effect of carbonate on the solubility of hydroxylapatite. *Archs oral Biol.* **8,** 251

GRON P. (1977) Chemistry of topical fluorides. *Caries Res.* **11** (Suppl. 1), 172

HARGREAVES J.A. *et al.* (1972) A gravimetric study of the ingestion of toothpaste by children. *Caries Res.* **6,** 237

HEALY W.B. & LUDWIG T.G. (1966) Enamel solubility studies on New Zealand teeth. *N.Z. dent. J.* **62,** 276

HOTZ P. *et al.* (1970) A new method of enamel biopsy for fluoride determination. *Helv. odont. Acta.* **14,** 26

HOUTE J. VAN *et al.* (1969) Idophilic polysaccharide-producing bacteria and dental caries in children consuming fluoridated and non-fluoridated drinking water. *Caries Res.* **3,** 178

ISAAC S. *et al.* (1958) The relation of fluoride in the drinking water to the distribution of fluoride in enamel. *J. dent. Res.* **37,** 254, 318

JACKSON D. (1961) A clinical study of non-endemic mottling of enamel. *Archs oral Biol.* **5,** 212

JENKINS G.N. *et al.* (1952) Laboratory investigations on the relation of fluorine to dental caries on Tyneside. *Proc. Roy. Soc. Med.* **45,** 517

JENKINS G.N. & SPEIRS R.L. (1953) Distribution of fluorine in human enamel. *Archs oral Biol.* **6,** 305

JENKINS G.N. *et al.* (1969) The distribution and metabolic effects of human plaque fluorine. *Archs oral Biol.* **14,** 105

JENKINS G.N. & EDGAR W.M. (1977) Distribution and forms of F in saliva and plaque. *Caries Res.* **11** (Suppl. 1), 226

KOCH G. (1969) Caries increment in school-children during and 2 years after the end of supervised rinsing of the mouth with sodium fluoride solution. *Odont. Revy* **20,** 323 (also (1970) *Caries Res.* **4,** 149)

KRUGER B.J. (1968) Ultrastructural changes

in ameloblasts from fluoride treated rats. *Archs oral Biol.* **13**, 969

KRUGER B.J. (1970) The effect of different levels of fluoride on the ultrastructure of ameloblasts in the rat. *Archs oral Biol.* **15**, 109 (see also (1972) **17**, 1389)

LARSEN M.J. & THORSEN A. (1974) Fluoride and enamel solubility. *Scand. J. Dent. Res.* **82**, 455

LITTLE M.F. *et al.* (1967) Site of fluoride accumulation in intact erupted human enamel. *Archs oral Biol.* **12**, 839

LITTLE M.F. *et al.* (1971) Inorganic-organic interactions in human dental enamel. In *Tooth Enamel*, Vol. II, p. 100, Eds FEARNHEAD R.W. & STACK M.V. John Wright, Bristol

LOESCHE W.J. *et al.* (1973) The effect of topical acidulated fluoride on percentage of *Streptococcus mutans* and *Streptococcus sanguis* in interproximal plaque samples. *Caries Res.* **7**, 283

LOESCHE W.J. *et al.* (1975) Effect of topical acidulated phosphate fluoride on percentage of *Streptococcus mutans* and *Streptococcus sanguis* in plaque. II. Pooled occlusal and pooled approximal samples. *Caries Res.* **9**, 139

LOVIUS B.B.J. & GOOSE D.H. (1969) The effect of fluoridation of water on tooth morphology. *Brit. dent. J.* **127**, 322

MANLY R.S. & HARRINGTON D.R. (1959) Solution rate of tooth enamel in an acetate buffer. *J. dent. Res.* **38**, 910

MCKAY F.S. (1916) Investigation of mottled teeth. *Dental Cosmos*, LVIII

MCCLURE F.J. & LIKINS R.C. (1951) Fluorine in human teeth in relation to fluorine in the drinking water. *J. dent. Res.* **30**, 172

MARTHALER T. (1971) Confidence limits of results of clinical caries tests with fluoride administration. *Caries Res.* **3**, 343

MINISTRY OF HEALTH (1962) The conduct of the fluoridation studies in the United Kingdom and the results achieved after five years. *Reports on Public Health and Medical Subjects, No. 105.* Her Majesty's Stationery Office, London

MORNSTAD H. *et al.* (1975) Increased urinary excretion of cAMP following administration of sodium fluoride. *J. dent. Res.* **54**, Special Issue A, L39, Abstract

MUNKSGAARD E.C. & BRUUN C. (1973) Determination of fluoride in superficial enamel biopsies from human teeth by means of gas chromatography. *Archs oral Biol.* **18**, 735

NAYLOR M.N. & EMSLIE R.D. (1967) Clinical testing of stannous fluoride and sodium monofluorophosphate dentifrices in London schoolchildren. *Brit. dent. J.* **123**, 17

NEWBRUN E. (Ed.) *Fluorides and Dental Caries.* Thomas, Springfield

NIKIFORUK G. (1961) Carbonates and fluorides as chemical determinants of tooth susceptibility to caries. In *Caries Symposium Zurich*, p. 62. Haber, Berne (see also (1962) *J. dent. Res.* **41**, 1477)

NIKIFORUK G. & GRAINGER R.M. (1965) Fluoride-carbonate-citrate interrelations in enamel. In *Tooth Enamel*, p. 26. Eds STACK M.V. & FEARNHEAD R.W. Wright, Bristol

OCKERSE T. & WASSERSTEIN B. (1955) Stain in mottled enamel. *J. Amer. dent. Ass.* **50**, 536

PEARCE E.I.F. & JENKINS G.N. (1976) The inhibition of acid production in human saliva by monofluorophosphate. *Archs oral Biol.* **21**, 617

RAMSEY A.C. *et al.* (1975) Fluoride intakes and caries increments in relation to tea consumption by British children. *Caries Res.* **9**, 312

ROOTARE H.M. *et al.* (1962) Solubility product phenomena in hydroxyapatite-water systems. *J. Colloid Sci.* **17**, 179

SMITH M.C. *et al.* (1932) The cause of mottled enamel. *J. dent. Res.* **12**, 149

TAVES D.R. (1968) Evidence that there are two forms of fluoride in human serum. *Nature (Lond.)* **217**, 1050 (see also **220**, 582)

TAVES D.R. (1971) Comparison of 'organic' fluoride in human and nonhuman serums. *J. dent. Res.* **50**, 783

TORELL P. & ERICSSON Y. (1965) Two-year clinical tests with different methods of local caries-preventive fluoride application in Swedish schoolchildren. *Acta odont. Scand.* **23**, 287

Toth K. (1973) Fluoridation of domestic salt after three years. *Caries Res.* **7**, 269

Wagner M.J. & Muhler J.C. (1957) The metabolism of natural and artificial fluoridated waters. *J. dent. Res.* **36**, 552

Waldbott G.L. (1955) Insipient fluorine intoxication from drinking water. *Acta med. Scand.* **156**, 157

Waldbott G.L. (1955) Chronic fluorine intoxication from drinking water. *Int. Arch. Allergy* **7**, 70

Walton R.E. & Eisenmann D.R. (1974) Ultrastructural examination of various stages of amelogenesis in the rat following parenteral fluoride administeration. *Archs oral Biol.* **19**, 171

Walton R.E. & Eisenmann D.R. (1975) Ultrastructural examination of dentine formation in rat incisors following multiple fluoride injections. *Archs oral Biol.* **20**, 485

Weatherell J.A. (1975) Composition of dental enamel. *Brit. Med. Bull.* **31**, 115

Weatherell J.A. & Hargreaves J.A. (1965) The micro-sampling of enamel in thin layers by means of strong acids. *Archs oral Biol.* **10**, 139

Weatherell J.A. *et al.* (1972) Changes in the labial enamel surface with age. *Caries Res.* **6**, 312

Weatherell J.A. *et al.* (1973) The effect of tooth wear on the distribution of fluoride in the enamel surface of human teeth. *Archs oral Biol.* **18**, 1175

Weaver R. (1944) Fluorosis and dental caries on Tyneside. *Brit. dent. J.* **76**, 29; **77**, 185

Weaver R. (1950) Fluorine and war-time diet. *Brit. dent. J.* **88**, 231

Woolley L. & Rickles N.H. (1971) Inhibition of acidogenesis in human dental plaque *in situ* following the use of topical sodium fluoride. *Archs oral Biol.* **16**, 1187

Zimmerman E.R. (1954) Fluoride and enamel opacities. *Publ. Hlth Rep.* **69**, 1115

Zwemer J.D. (1957) Lactic acid formation by Lactobacilli exposed to fluoridized enamel. *J. dent. Res.* **36**, 182

CHAPTER XIII

MASTICATION AND DEGLUTITION

The Mechanics of Mastication

The active components of mastication are the reflexly controlled and co-ordinated muscles whose contraction results in rhythmic movements of the passive parts of the masticatory (stomatognathic) system. These are the mandible, the temperomandibular joint and the teeth.

Lateral movement of the mandible is, in most subjects, accompanied by a lateral translation of the condyle on the same side of up to 1·4 mm (mean of 27 subjects, 1·04 mm) but is absent in some subjects. This movement (Bennett movement) had been suspected for years but was finally proved by measurements of the reflection of ultrasound from the condyle when the mandible was centrally or laterally placed (Preiskel 1972).

The temporomandibular joint

In man the temporomandibular joint allows movements of three types. First, it has a hinge-like movement which is used during the biting of food and corresponds with the only movement of which the mandible is capable in carnivores. A second possible movement which may be employed in the early stages of mastication is the protrusion and withdrawal of the mandible corresponding with the main masticatory movement of rodents. The hinge movement, preceded by slight protrusion to place the cutting edges of the incisor teeth nearer to each other, is used in biting soft foods. For tougher foods it may be necessary to produce a tearing action by following the hinge-like closure of the jaw with a sharp movements of the second type in a posterior direction. Also with tough foods, the cutting edges of the incisor teeth may be brought directly opposite each other, requiring a greater degree of protrusion of the mandible. The third action is the lateral movement of the mandible which is used during mastication proper and results in a grinding action of the teeth on the food. It is accompanied by vigorous hinge-like movements which cause crushing to occur along with the grinding. In most individuals, the lateral movement is approximately symmetrical, but the presence of a tender tooth, among many other causes, may lead to the establishment of habits of unilateral chewing. Such habits may persist indefinitely, long after the original cause has been removed.

Four types of nerve receptors have been described in the temperomandibular joint. The most numerous in the joint capsule are clusters of small globular corpuscles (Type I). They are of low threshold and slowly adapting, so that even when the mandible is at rest the tension is sufficient to excite them. They are the principal source of the impulses concerned with the perception of mandibular position. Type II are encapsulated, conical end-organs with a similar distribution but are fewer in number. They have a low threshold, adapt readily and are stimulated briefly immediately after movement of the joint. Type III are high threshold and respond only to excessive tension in the lateral ligament and Type IV are pain receptor consisting of free nerve endings and plexuses of unmyelinated fibres (Clark & Wyke 1974, Harris & Griffin 1975).

The Muscles of Mastication

The muscles of mastication can be classified into those concerned with opening or with closing the mouth and their actions are illustrated in Fig. XIII.1. The former consist of the external pterygoid, the digastric and the infrahyoid while the latter are the temporalis, used in quick closure and gentle biting, while the masseter and internal pterygoid produce more powerful crushing antigens. The muscles of the lips, tongue and cheek also take part in mastication. There is evidence of reciprocal innervation of the masticatory muscles; when the mandible is depressed the masseter muscles are inhibited and the digastric stimulated (Carlsöö 1952).

A study of the events during the mastication of natural food was made by Jankelson *et al.* (1953) on thirty-five subjects by radiographic cinematography along with records of tooth contact and jaw movement. They found that details of the biting stroke ('incision') varied with the toughness of the food. With resistant foods like meat, the biting was rarely carried out by the teeth alone but movements of the whole head and shoulders, and a twisting motion of the hand and arm, co-operated in the incisal movement. The masticatory movements showed no regular pattern, but were adapted to the particular food.

Another method of recording the movements of mastication is by cinematography of subjects with a marker, such as a small metal ball, attached to the incisor teeth. Ahlgren (1966, 1967) reported a very thorough investigation of the masticatory movements in thirty-five children by this method. As markers, two metal balls 1·5 mm in diameter attached to 1 cm of wire were soldered on to orthodontic bands on an upper and lower incisor. The move-

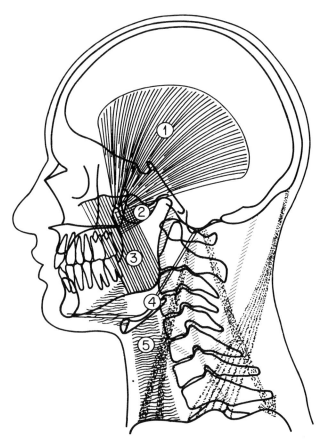

FIG. XIII.1. Muscles of the head and neck. The main muscles of mastication have been marked: (1) the temporal muscle; (2) the external pterygoid; (3) the masseter and internal pterygoid muscles; (4) the digastric muscle; (5) the infrahyoid muscles.

ment of the lower marker with reference to the upper, as recorded on the film, indicated the movements of the mandible. He found great variations within and between subjects but with the two test materials (chewing-gum and carrot) each child had a characteristic pattern—those with malocclusion being less symmetrical and more complicated with paths which often criss-crossed (Fig. XIII. 2). The mean vertical and lateral movements were 19·1 and 5·3 mm, respectively, and the average speed of movement was 6·4 cm s^{-1} for chewing-gum and 7·5 cm s^{-1} for carrots and the average durations of the cycles were 0·77 and 0·58 s, respectively.

If the bolus was transferred from one side to the other the pattern of movements on the two sides was different (Fig. XIII.3).

Masticatory cycles

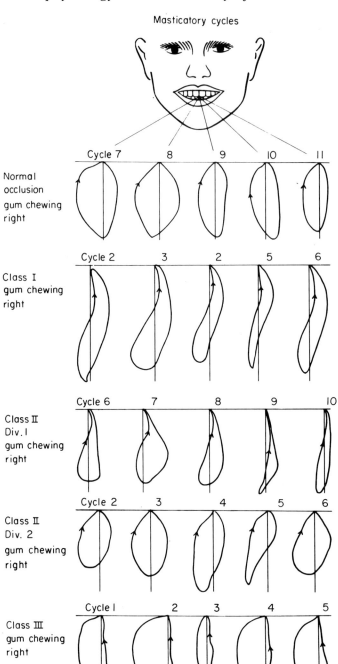

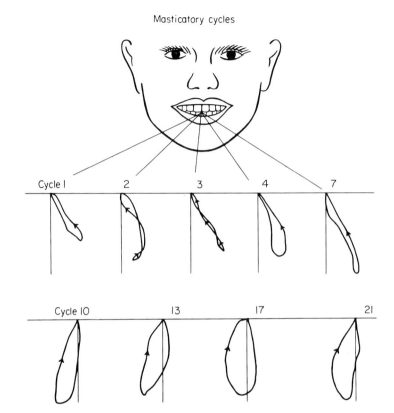

Masticatory cycles

Cycle I 2 3 4 7

Left side

Cycle 10 13 17 21

Right side

FIG. XIII.3. Masticatory movements when the bolus is transferred from one side of the mouth to the other.

The role of the tongue

The functions of the tongue in mastication are numerous. First, it may have a direct crushing effect on food by pressing it against the hard palate. This function is assisted by the roughness both of the anterior portion of the dorsum of the tongue (caused by the papillae) and of the hard palate (caused by the rugae) which prevents the slipping of the food mass. Secondly, the tongue pushes the food on to the occluding surfaces of the teeth, transfers it from one occluding surface to another, and helps to mix in the saliva. Thirdly, the sensory endings of the tongue and of the posterior part of the mouth enable it to select those parts of the food mass which are sufficiently well

FIG. XIII.2. Masticatory cycles with chewing gum in subjects differing in occlusal conditions, as recorded by cinematography of metal balls attached to the incisors.

masticated to be ready for swallowing and to separate them from parts requiring further mastication. This selection may continue in the pharynx and within the region of the upper oesophagus where its muscles are voluntary because even within 1 or 2 s after swallowing, a bolus can be regurgitated if its 'feel' suggests that it has not been sufficiently broken up. The middle part of the oral cavity, the dorsum of the tongue and the molar teeth are less sensitive. After eating is finished, sweeping movements of the tongue help to remove food residues which have become trapped between the cheeks and the gingivae and elsewhere.

These functions which require delicate and skilful movements of the tongue are controlled by neural feed-back mechanisms. The nature of the sensory endings involved has been controversial, however, as it has frequently been stated that muscle spindles are absent from the tongue. This seems to be true of some species but muscles spindles have been clearly detected in the human tongue by several workers (Cooper 1953).

These functions require movements of the tongue as a whole which are brought about by the extrinsic muscles (which are inserted into structures outside the tongue itself) and also changes in the shape of the tongue for which the intrinsic muscles, which connect one part of the tongue to another, are responsible.

The hard palate

The function of the hard palate as a surface against which the tongue works has been mentioned above. Another function follows from the high sensitivity of the epithelial surface of the hard palate to touch. Food which is harsher than usual is detected mostly by this surface. The loss of 'taste' often reported by denture wearers partly arises from the loss of this sensation of touch and of the reduced ability to judge the texture and temperature of food (but see p. 544).

The cheeks and lips

It is doubtful whether the cheeks play an important part in mastication in civilized man. If the mouth is overfull, however, food in the course of mastication may escape from between the teeth into the vestibule (the space between the lips and cheeks and the teeth and the alveolar margins) and remain there until the central part of the mouth can accommodate it.

The functions of the lips are partly sensory and their great sensitivity to touch and temperature helps to prevent the entrance of unsuitable material into the mouth. They also have a mechanical function in the transfer of food and especially drink into the mouth and in preventing the loss of food from the mouth during mastication.

The asymmetry of mastication

Cinematography of the skull during the mastication of test foods containing radiopaque material have shown that few people chew symmetrically. In one study on twenty-five subjects, the bolus was divided and simultaneously chewed on both sides in one-third of the total of 1039 masticatory strokes. The bolus was chewed on the left more frequently than on the right but usually it was changed from one side to the other, although five subjects chewed exclusively on the left and two on the right. In twenty-five edentulous patients without dentures more (46%) of the 890 strokes recorded were on the right side than on the left (36%) and 16% were central—between the tongue and the hard palate and avoiding the use of what, in normal subjects, would be the occlusal areas—patients with teeth rarely used this procedure (Sheppard *et al.* 1968). Watson (1972) showed that the commonest pattern of chewing in subjects with teeth is for food to be broken up in the molar and premolar region and some of it is then pushed forwards to the incisor region for several masticatory strokes, then to be withdrawn and either divided, not necessarily equally, between the two sides or transferred from one side to the other at different stages of the mastication (Figs. XIII.4 and 5).

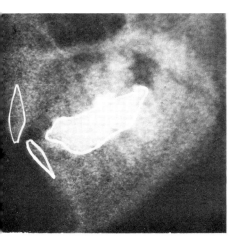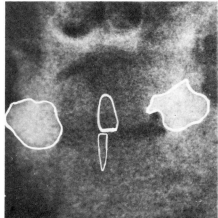

Fig. XIII.4. Radiographs of an individual chewing radiopaque material showing how the bolus may be divided and placed on both sides of the mouth.

Occlusal contact during mastication

Anderson & Picton (1957) in experiments on ten subjects during mastication of foods, recorded simultaneously contacts between the teeth and electro-myographs of the masseter muscle. Occlusal contact was recorded by arranging that a low voltage electrical circuit through the teeth was completed

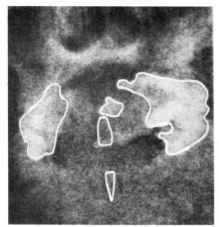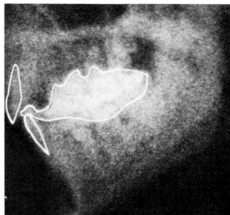

FIG. XIII.5. Radiograph showing the pushing of food towards the incisors.

when the opposing teeth touched. The proportion of masticatory strokes in which the teeth came into contact varied with different foods—for example with bread or meat about half the subjects made contact with every chew, but with biscuits the proportion of contacts was much less. In general they found that about half the masticatory strokes led to occlusal contact. Other workers have found a much smaller proportion but their results seem to have been based on more limited data. Jankelson *et al.* (1953), for example, found that food was between the teeth almost throughout mastication so that the teeth came into contact very infrequently but did during swallowing, though even then not always at the first swallow of a mouthful.

In a small number of subjects wearing dentures, the duration of contact varied between 0·02 and 0·37 s. The frequency of contact increased as the mastication proceeds and the food is broken up and offers less resistance. Chewing tends to be unilateral and more frequent contacts were made on the non-chewing side. The chewing time for apple varied between 11 and 34 s (16 and 46 chews) and for a meat sandwich between 9 and 43 s (12 to 57 chews) (Neill 1967).

Studies of muscular activity and tooth contact during sleep show that contacts of up to about 0·5 s occur when the subject turns over and during the periods of rapid eye movements (the phase of sleep, lasting from several minutes to an hour, occurring several times during a night and associated with dreaming).

Tooth movements during mastication

During mastication, slight movements of the teeth occur, but one is not usually aware of them unless mastication is powerful. If the teeth were absolutely

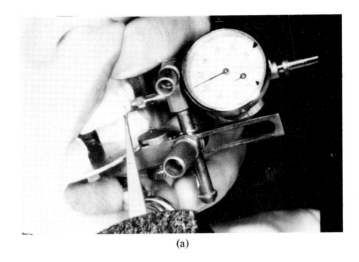

(a)

(b)

FIG. XIII.6. The apparatus used by Mühlemann in his studies of tooth mobility. A known force is developed by the graduated dynamometer (shown separately in (b)) and transmitted through the projecting metal arm which can be seen behind the upper tooth in (a). The movement of the tooth is measured on the gauge at the right in (a) which is made rigid by attachment to the lower teeth.

rigid they would be less capable of withstanding sudden occlusal stress, as all the stress would be applied to the tooth thus increasing the tendency to damage. When some of the energy is absorbed in causing slight tooth movements, damage is less likely.

THE MEASUREMENT OF TOOTH MOBILITY DURING MASTICATION
Mühlemann (1954, 1960) measured the buccolingual movements of teeth by applying a known static force, usually up to 500 g for 2 s, to a tooth by means of a graduated dynamometer and recording the movement by a measuring gauge with a contact point placed on the tooth (Fig. XIII.6(a) and (b)). Movements in a lingual and labial direction can be measured by suitable placing of the instrument. In a survey including about 10 000 measurements he showed that the movement of both single and multi-rooted teeth occurred

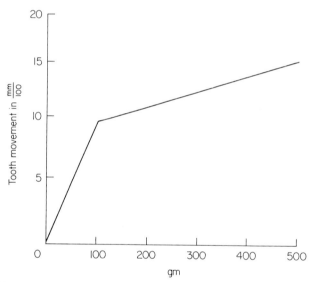

Fig. XIII.7. Graph showing the effect of the application of increasing force on tooth movement.

in two phases (Fig. XIII.7)—with forces up to 100 g the movement per unit of force was greater than when this force was exceeded. A point was reached at a force of about 1500 g at which no further movement occurred and pain was felt. The forces actually applied during normal mastication are discussed on p. 518.

He also applied static forces to monkey teeth by inserting screws through the alveolar bone after which the animals were killed and histological sections of the teeth and supporting structures were made. It was thus possible to measure the compression and stretching of the fibres of the alveolar bone associated with a measured amount of tooth displacement. He concluded that the first phase in Fig. XIII.7 occurred when the periodontal fibres were stretched. This movement was small in abraded teeth (i.e. teeth in heavy function and therefore with well-developed periodontal membranes) and larger in erupting teeth where periodontal achorage is incomplete. The second phase represented an elastic deformation of the alveolar bone and could be measured on the outside of the bone through an incision in the mucosa. This phase of tooth mobility decreased with age, as the elasticity of the tissues decreases.

The tooth movements in response to loads applied to the incisors of anaesthetized rats were considerably larger than in the same rat immediately after death and before any post-mortem changes occurred in the fibres of the periodontium. This implies that the capillary blood flow in the periodontium contributes to the dissipation of forces acting on the tooth.

Factors affecting tooth mobility

Tooth mobility varies during the day, being highest in the morning just after waking and lowest in the evening. It is greater in children than in adults and slightly greater in females than in males. Incisors are more mobile than multi-rooted teeth. Measurements of tooth mobility are very sensitive and can be used to detect pathological conditions in the supporting tissues and to follow the response to therapeutic measures (Mühlemann 1960).

In a study of tooth mobility in two pregnant women, mobility rose markedly as the pregnancies proceeded and in one case fell steadily during lactation. In the other, death of the foetus occurred at about 35 weeks and the tooth mobility fell at a rapid rate at this time to the values in early pregnancy. These results suggest that the supporting structures of the teeth are sensitive to female sex hormones. Storey (1953) has also obtained evidence for this in his finding that tooth movement in orthodontic patients is greater during the second half of the menstrual cycle than during the first half. No change in horizontal mobility of the teeth occurs during the various phases of the menstrual cycle (Friedman 1972).

It was found in monkeys that if measurements were made repeatedly over a period of 2 h or after a 15-min period of masticating hard food, the mobility increased but returned to normal within 30 min. The presence of contact points had no effect on the first phase of mobility but reduced the second phase.

Picton (1962a, b, 1963) and Parfitt (1960) studied the vertical movement of teeth which might be expected to be the most important component of tooth movement during mastication. Their results were similar to those of Mühle-mann in showing that the movement varies with the force in two phases: at first small forces cause relatively large movement but when the force exceeded a certain figure (which they found to be higher than the 100 g observed by Mühlemann, even up to 300–600 g) the movement decreased.

Picton (1962c) found that neither chronic marginal gingivitis nor experi-mentally-induced gingivitis affected vertical movement. Inflammatory changes in the deeper supporting tissues, however, were accompanied by an increased mobility, especially in the first rapid phase.

With teeth not in occlusion, in which condition the periodontal membranes and alveolar bone have been stated to be thinner than in teeth with normal occlusion (p. 530), Picton found that mobility was within the normal range. When occlusal changes were brought about experimentally by placing an onlay 0·5 mm thick on the occlusal surface of the first molar for 3 weeks so that the rest of the teeth were out of occlusion, the mobility of the first molar greatly increased from 13 days, then gradually decreased over the next 4 weeks. At the end of the 3 weeks, the remaining teeth had reached occlusion (either by supra-eruption or, more likely, by the depression of the test tooth).

If thrusts were applied to the teeth in quick succession (at say, 5-s intervals) so that there was insufficient time for the return of the tooth to the resting position, the movement produced by each thrust diminished. Only if the intervals between thrusts were from 1 to 1·5 min, did the movement of teeth show no reduction.

Picton (1962a) found that during biting the teeth also tilted vertically (in a mesial direction) and transmitted this tilt to adjacent mesial teeth, provided there was a good mesial contact. The vertical movement was reduced in monkeys after local injection of noradrenaline—presumably the blood flow is reduced and hence the refilling of the vessels between thrusts (Slatter & Picton 1972). Picton suggested that this constant tendency towards tilting during biting could be a major cause of physiological mesial drift although he later rejected this suggestion (p. 210).

When normal biting forces were applied to the teeth on one side of the mouth, slight movements could be detected in teeth on the opposite side (Picton 1962b). Since this occurred in most subjects, even with teeth missing from the dental arch, Picton considered that these movements occurred as a result of distortion of the jaw. Vigorous contraction of the masticatory muscles with the mouth open (so that force was applied to the jaw bones but none was applied to the teeth) also caused tooth movement, again owing to bone distortion.

The reflex control of mastication

Although the existence of reflex actions controlling mastication has been known for many years the more recent work (reviewed by Kawamura 1974) on the details and the nature of the afferents are controversial and somewhat confused by species differences.

Mastication is brought about by voluntary muscles and it is possible, therefore, for it to be controlled entirely by the will but, like other complicated muscular activities, its control is normally exercised by sub-cortical centres.

Three possibilities have been suggested about the nature of the reflex control of mastication (reviewed in depth by Thexton 1973–4). The first is based on the observations of Sherrington (1916, 1917) on reflexes in anaesthetized cats. Sherrington found that a reflex closing of the jaw is caused by mechanical irritation of the tongue and accompanies the swallowing reflex. A reflex opening of the jaw follows mechanical stimulation of the gums, the anterior part of the hard palate, or the occlusal surfaces of the teeth. When the stimulus for the jaw-opening reflex is withdrawn, the jaws close with a powerful snap (an example of the phenomenon of 'rebound' in reflex action, a powerful reflex response immediately after an inhibitory influence is removed). Sherrington pictured the reflex mechanism as follows. When the jaw is closed voluntarily on a piece of food, the force applied to the gums, teeth and hard palate provides a stimulus for the jaw-opening reflex and reflexly inhibits the jaw-closing muscles. The jaw opening then causes a rebound of the original jaw-closing reflex which is followed by a repetition of the whole cycle until the masticated material is removed.

The second view is that the rhythm originates from the cerebral cortex or some sub-cortical centre. Different types of movements of the jaw, mostly contralateral but some ipsilateral (reviewed by Kawamura 1974) are produced in animals by stimulating different cortical areas. Masticatory movements can also be evoked in animals by stimulation of the basal ganglia (amygdala), the limbic areas and the lateral hypothalamus. Somewhat diverse movements have been recorded during stimulation of quite large areas of the human cerebral cortex (precentral and postcentral gyri) exposed at operations (Penfield & Boldrey 1937). Rhythmic masticatory movements are more difficult to produce than many other activities, however, and decerebrate animals are capable of mastication, so these higher centres are evidently not essential for this action.

The third possibility is that some areas of the brain stem act as what Dellow & Lund (1971) call a 'pattern generator' which may send out rhythmic impulses in response either to cortical or intra-oral stimuli. They found that stimulation of the putamen and corticobulbar pathways in rabbits caused rhythmic movements which were not abolished by blocking afferent impulses from the proprioceptive nerve-endings by gallamine triethiodide, so were not dependent on a sensory impulse from the muscles. Nevertheless, the nature of the activity would normally be modified by stimuli from the mouth and their intensity, site and total area of stimulation would control the various patterns of mastication produced by different foods and at different stages of mastication of a food.

OTHER REFLEXES INVOLVING THE MUSCLES OF MASTICATION

In one series of experiments, in which cats' teeth were tapped, a jaw-opening reflex resulted lasting 100 ms. This response was unaffected by removal of the pulp or of neighbouring gingival tissue but was rapidly abolished when the periodontal tissue was anaesthetized, proving the importance of the periodontal receptors in this reflex (Hannam & Matthews 1969).

When the right upper central incisor of human subjects was tapped with a light hammer while maintaining a steady activity of their elevator muscles by biting on a hollow rubber bung, an inhibition (a 'silent period') of the masseter was produced preceded by a brief stimulation. Unlike the reflex in the cat, this inhibition was not abolished by local anaesthesia (although its duration may have been reduced) and was also observed in edentulous subjects wearing full dentures and could not therefore involve the periodontal receptors. The latent period and duration of the stimulation resembled those of a jaw-jerk (the reflex response of a tap on the chin) and it was finally suggested that the tap on the tooth caused a vibration, via the bones of the skull, in neighbouring muscles which stimulated their muscle spindles or Golgi tendon organs and triggered off the reflex inhibition (Hannam *et al.* 1970).

Similar experiments by Sessle & Schmitt (1972) with controlled stimuli applied electronically to human subjects confirmed the existence of the inhibition and its preceding stimulation but the inhibition was abolished by local anaesthesia and was presumably mediated by the periodontal ligaments. They suggested that the results of Hannam *et al.* arose because their stimulus (a tap with a hammer) was uncontrolled in strength.

Inhibition of the masseter muscle also occurs when painful or mild electrical stimuli are applied to the upper lip or on various sites within the mouth. The response to pain is presumably protective but the importance of the reactions to mild innocuous stimuli is unknown.

Electrical stimulation of oral mucosa in man causes reflex inhibition of the masseter and temporalis muscles (Yemm 1972a,b) and mouth-opening but the threshold stimulus is high suggesting that this is a protective reflex against excessive stimuli rather than being concerned with normal mastication. The opening was not produced by activity of the mouth-opening muscles which remained quiescent and no simple explanation can be provided for the observed sequence.

A jaw-closing reflex can be elicited in man and animals by rubbing the mucosa of the hard palate or between the incisors of either jaw. If there is already activity in the jaw-closing muscles, as produced by biting on a rubber bung, mechanical stimulation of the mucosa inhibits their action (Achani & Thexton 1974).

Numerous muscle spindles have been detected histologically in the jaw-closing muscles but there are few or, in some species, none in the jaw-opening muscles. The role of stretch reflexes in jaw-opening is, therefore, uncertain and since these reflexes are not readily produced by mild stimuli, they may be concerned only with protection rather than mastication. Powerful stimuli to the pharynx produce jaw-opening, probably concerned with retching and vomiting—mild stimuli initiate swallowing and apparently the strength as well as the sites of these stimuli partly determines whether the response is swallowing or retching.

Electromyography

If electrodes are held in place by an adhesive on the skin over a muscle, or if needle electrodes (a small bore hyperdermic needle with an insulated silver wire running through it) are inserted into a muscle, it is possible to record the electrical activity (electromyography, EMG). By this means the relative importance of the various muscles involved in a complicated action like mastication and their timing can be measured. The method is illustrated in Fig. XIII.8 from Greenfield & Wyke (1956) who made simultaneous records on the anterior and posterior parts of the masseter and temporal muscles taking great care to standardize the condition of the experiment. Ahlgren (1966), Møller (1974) and Munro (1975) have reviewed in detail the application of this technique to mastication. Among the many factors influencing the activity of the muscles during mastication is the position of the head. If the head is turned to the left or the right during mastication, the activity of the various

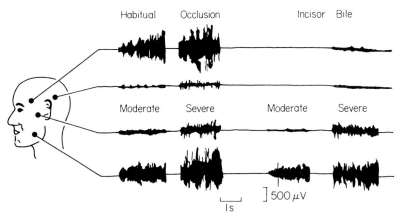

Fig. XIII.8. Diagram of the action potentials recorded from needle electrodes, placed in the positions shown, during moderate and vigorous chewing movements in the position of normal occlusion (left-hand pair of records) and with incisal biting (after Greenfield & Wyke 1956).

muscles change, presumably by the action of sensory impulses from the neck muscles (Kawamura 1974).

REST POSITION (POSTURAL POSITION) AND THE FREEWAY SPACE
The rest position is that taken up by the mandible without any conscious control when mouth movements are absent. The mandible tends to fall under its own weight but this is opposed, mostly by contraction of the temporalis muscle, reflexly controlled by afferent impulses from the muscle spindles and Type I receptors in the temporomandibular joint. The tone and co-ordination of the muscles is maintained by impulses from the cerebellum to the motor nucleus of the fifth cranial nerve which supplies these muscles. The elastic properties of the muscle and connective tissue may contribute passively to the rest position and, according to Yemm & Nordstrom (1974), may (at least in the rat) be a major factor since the forces required to maintain various jaw positions remained the same when muscular activity ceased following the death of the rat. Wyke (1972) points out that in man muscle tone is essential for maintaining mandibular posture. The mandible drops during sleep in the upright position or in patients with damage to the motor branch of the trigeminal nerve.

The teeth are not in contact in the rest position but are separated by a wedge-shaped space of between 2 and 8 mm (but usually between 2 and 4 mm) in the incisal region but narrowing towards the molars—the freeway space (or interocclusal distance). This space exists even before the eruption of the deciduous teeth so that a radiograph of the skull of a young baby gives the impression of its having a gaping mouth. With a healthy subject in the normal upright position the freeway space is fairly constant because anything which tended to increase it would lead to a stretching of the muscles which, via the stretch reflex, would restore the position by increasing muscle tone.

However, many factors do influence the freeway space. The following will increase it: changing the position of the body with the head bent backwards, inspiration especially in mouth breathing, emotion (his 'face fell') and it will decrease when the head is bent forward, during exertion, stress or pain in the oral cavity (when muscle tone increases) or arthritis of the temporomandibular joint. It may change in either direction during sleep depending on the position of the head and the tone of the muscles.

Gnathodynamics

The measurement of masticatory force

The earliest recorded measurements of the force of mastication were made by Borelli in 1681. His method was a simple one of attaching various weights to a

loop of cord passed over the molar teeth and finding the maximum weight
that could be lifted by mandibular movements. The strength of the bite and
the factors which affect it have been studied in more recent times by instruments known as gnathodynamometers.

There are many forms of gnathodynamometer but essentially they consist
of two pads, on which the teeth are placed, either made of rubber or covered
with some soft material like felt or rubber to prevent damage to the teeth (see

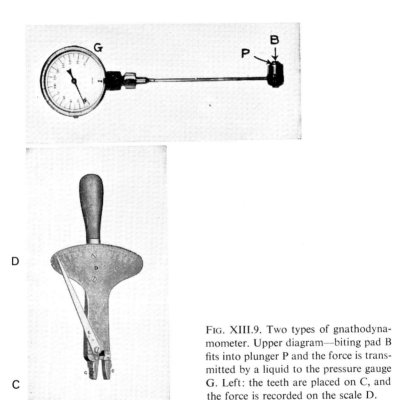

Fig. XIII.9. Two types of gnathodynamometer. Upper diagram—biting pad B
fits into plunger P and the force is transmitted by a liquid to the pressure gauge
G. Left: the teeth are placed on C, and
the force is recorded on the scale D.

Fig. XIII.9). Either the pads are of such size that the force exerted by single
pairs of teeth is measured or they may be designed to measure the force
produced by all the teeth simultaneously. The pads are attached to a device
for measuring the force put on to them. In some instruments one of the pads is
a calibrated spring the end of which acts as a pointer on a scale to indicate the
force applied. In another form, the force applied to the plates is transmitted
to a hydraulic pressure-gauge and, more recently, an electronic measuring

device has been used. Various types of gnathodynamometers are reviewed and a new design described by Duxbury *et al.* (1973).

It is important to appreciate that the bite is measured as a force and not as a stress (that is, force per unit area). The force which is measured over the whole surface of the gnathodynamometer is, in normal chewing, concentrated on to the small area of occluding surface. Another point to be borne in mind is that whereas the gnathodynamometer measures static forces with the jaws at rest, mastication is brought about by dynamic forces, since the mandible is moving. The energy involved is, therefore, greater than might be thought from gnathodynamometer measurements.

Factors controlling the strength of the bite

Studies by various workers have found the biting force among young people eating civilized food to be about 45 kilo for molar teeth. The average figure for women is lower than that for men. Among athletes it is no greater than among non-athletes in spite of the general superiority of their muscles and their neuromuscular control. The force used for ordinary mastication is, on the average, about one-third of the maximum that can be exerted.

The first molar exerts the greatest biting force (usually about 45 kilo) with the other molars slightly less, but the pre-molars and incisors are capable of developing only about one-third of the force produced by the molars. These facts are illustrated by the individual curves in Fig. XIII.10. The greater area of attaching surface possessed by the posterior teeth (thus distributing the tension more widely), and their position in relation to the insertion of the muscles may be factors concerned in these differences. Much of the variation between the performance of individuals is explicable on an anatomical basis, such as the length of the mandible. Although there is a considerable sex difference in the force developed by the molars (the female producing only about two-thirds of that of the male), the incisors and canines produce almost identical forces in both sexes.

EFFECT OF PRACTICE

An experiment by Brekhus *et al.* (1941) in which two groups of fifty subjects (one group of each sex) chewed a $\frac{1}{2}$-inch cube of paraffin wax for an hour a day for 50 days, showed an increase in their biting forces. After 30 days, biting force in the male subjects rose from an average of 53 k to 63 k but after 50 days there was practically no further increase (average 64 k). In the female subjects the biting force rose from 35 k to 45 k, and the rise was more gradual. Within 2 weeks of the end of the experiment the biting forces had fallen again almost to the initial figures. This experiment illustrates the undeveloped condition in which the masticatory apparatus exists in

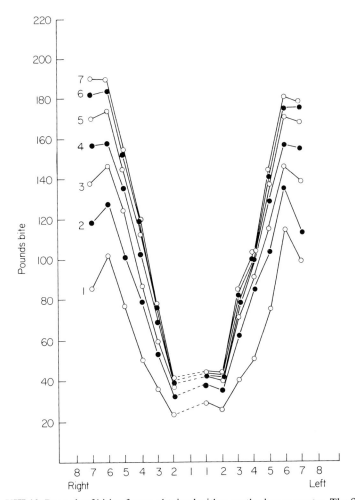

FIG. XIII.10. Records of biting forces obtained with a gnathodynamometer. The figures on the abscissa refer to the individual teeth. Each curve represents the record of all the teeth of the subject (3rd molars and upper right central incisor missing) and show the much greater force exerted by the molars than by the anterior teeth.

The successive curves 1–7 show the effect on the strength of the bite of 3, 4, 7, 9, 11 and 14 days' practice respectively. Note that the forces are approximately doubled in curve 7 (after 14 days' practice) compared with curve 1.

civilized man. The results of a similar experiment by Worner & Anderson (1944) in which the biting forces of individual teeth were tested every day for a fortnight are shown in Fig. XIII.10. Other evidence of the importance of exercise is provided by the observation that individuals who habitually chew on one side of their mouths show a biting force for that side of more than double the value on the unused side. It is of interest that measurements on the molars of male Eskimos who were living on an extremely tough diet requiring very vigorous mastication, gave values of about 140 k with a maximum of 158 k. For females the figures were only slightly lower. It must not be necessarily assumed that this powerful masticatory mechanism follows the use of a tough diet, as it is equally possible that the racial inheritance of the powerful jaws permits the use of the tough food. It is also possible that these high values may have been partly caused by unskilled use of the gnathodynamometer. If the instrument is placed so that two pairs of teeth press on the pads the reading is much higher than if they are accurately placed between one pair.

Two factors might be involved in the improvement with practice of the biting force. The first is the strength of the muscles of mastication and the second is the sensitivity of the periodontal membrane to pain. As the force applied to the teeth increases, more and more tension is applied to the periodontal membrane until, at a certain threshold, pain is felt. The evidence is confused on the role of the periodontal receptors in controlling mastication. In an experiment on one subject (Schroder 1927), anaesthesia of the periodontal region led to an increased strength of the bite, from which it was concluded that pain from this region limited the masticatory force. In a more thorough investigation of this point on nine subjects Lund and Lamarre (1976) found that anaesthesia of the periodontium reduced masticatory force to 60% of normal. These workers speculated that impulses from the periodontal receptors might reach both bulbar and cortical levels of the central nervous system. They suggest that during jaw-closing, periodontal impulses reaching the cortex overcome bulbar inhibition of jaw-closing motoneurones. Very sudden stimulation of these receptors (such as would occur by biting unexpectedly on a hard object) might, however, stimulate the bulbar region and cause a jaw-opening reflex before the impulses reached the cortex and produce the more normal jaw-closing effect.

Circumstantial evidence that the periodontal receptors may limit jaw-closing arises from the observation that the force which, when applied to a tooth, just causes a load to be detected is least with the incisors and increases progressively to the molars, that is, the incisors are most sensitive and the molars least sensitive to stress and therefore probably to pain. This corresponds to the order of the force which each tooth can exert (Fig. XIII.10).

The distance between the jaws is another factor altering the strength of the bite. If the latter is measured with the jaws at different distances apart, as may be done with special gnathodynamometers in which the vertical dimension is adjustable, it is found that there is a particular distance at which the biting strength is optimal. It has been suggested that this finding is related to the well-known fact that stretching a muscle increases its strength of contraction, although this explanation seems to imply that muscular strength, and not the pain threshold of the periodontal membrane, controls the strength of the bite.

Wearers of full or partial dentures are found to be capable of exerting not more than one-third of the biting forces developed by those with well occluding natural teeth. This means that denture wearers, perhaps sub-consciously, must be selective in their foods since the forces required to crush many normal foods are much higher than the average biting forces developed by these subjects. The reason for the low biting force of denture wearers is probably fear of the dentures slipping, because higher forces have been recorded when slipping was prevented by holding the denture with the fingers on the opposite side.

Individual teeth which are loose from periodontal disease, or in which the pulp is dead, or which are out of alignment, are found to be incapable of transmitting normal biting forces. A good state of oral hygiene and of dental attention appears to favour high bite forces. The gnathodynamometer may be used to diagnose some of these conditions and to study the response to treatment.

The touch receptors in the mucosa monitor the masticatory movements in denture wearers and these have a higher threshold than the receptors in the periodontal ligament which operate when the teeth are present. A higher pressure must therefore be exerted before a comparable sensation arises. This means that denture wearers have a less delicate control of mastication. Edentulous patients tested without their dentures did not show gross over-closure but the jaws moved haphazardly when they reached what had been the contact position when their teeth were present; evidently some afferent impulses (from muscle spindles?) were monitoring their position and pre-venting overclosure.

BITING LOADS DURING NORMAL MASTICATION
Anderson (1953) worked out a method in which the biting loads developed during normal mastication can be measured. It consists of a small wire strain gauge placed inside an occlusal inlay in a molar tooth with a wire lead leaving the inlay through a lingually placed hole and passing between the teeth on the opposite side of the mouth to a recording oscilloscope (Fig. XIII.11). The device is calibrated by applying known forces outside the mouth. Normal foods are masticated and the records show the loads developed at each stroke. The results of measurements of normal chewing loads show much lower figures than the maximal static found with the gnathodynamometer, the loads being up to 6 kg (Anderson 1956). There was a tendency for the recorded load to increase towards the end of each chewing sequence and for the last one or two loads to be longer and larger than the others (Fig. XIII.12). The reason

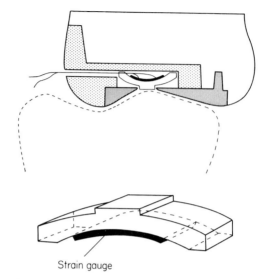

Fig. XIII.11. Anderson's method for measuring occlusal force during normal eating. The strain gauge (shown enlarged below) is inserted into an inlay in the tooth.

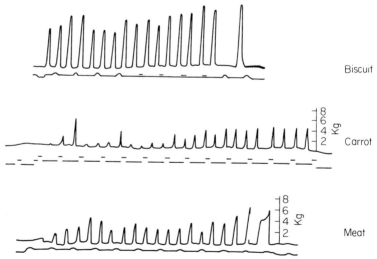

Fig. XIII.12. Oscilloscope records of stresses on teeth during the mastication of three foods. The lower tracing in each record shows 1-s intervals.

for this gradual increase throughout chewing is uncertain, but the high readings at the end were caused by the clenching of the teeth when swallowing.

Bruxism

The non-functional grinding or gnashing of the teeth and the pressing of the teeth together in nervous tension or to suppress emotion are called 'bruxism'. Bruxism is caused by occlusal disharmony combined with nervous tension. It has been produced experimentally in monkeys by inserting high amalgam fillings in the lower molars—vigorous gnashing occurred until the amalgam was worn down (Ramfjord 1961).

Tests on Masticatory Efficiency

Comparatively little accurate work has been carried out on the effectiveness of mastication in breaking up food and the factors which control it.

The method which has been used to study this problem is to take a weighed quantity of some hard food (nuts have frequently been used) and ask the subject to masticate it, either for a standard time or for a standard number of chews, or till he feels it is ready for swallowing. The food is then spat out into water which is poured onto a series of sieves of decreasing mesh size placed on top of each other, and is washed through them with water. The more efficient the mastication, the greater the proportion of food which will pass through the smallest mesh sieve. If the amount of food retained by each sieve is weighed (preferably after drying) and expressed as a percentage of the total weight, a measure of masticatory efficiency is obtained. Much of the early work was inadequately controlled or carried out on too few subjects to lead to conclusive results. Dahlberg (1942) carried out the most thorough investigation along these lines. He used gelatine, hardened by treatment with formalin, as his test material and separated the chewed particles into groups of uniform size by means of a specially designed apparatus containing ten sieves with holes ranging in diameter from 1 to 10 mm. He also studied the increase in surface area during mastication of pieces of hardened gelatine and has used this figure as a mastication coefficient.

By these methods, the importance of a good dentition for mastication has been demonstrated, although if the number of occlusal points is reduced, there is a smaller proportionate reduction in the efficiency of mastication. For example, subjects with good dentitions were able to increase the surface area of the hardened gelatine by eleven times as a result of mastication, the average figure for those with poor dentitions being about seven times (64%). The numbers of occlusal points were approximately eighteen and five respectively, that is, those with poor dentitions had only about 27% of the occlusal contacts of the group with good dentitions. Some workers have found the poor occlusal contacts can be compensated for by increasing the number of chews but, as stated below, in practice those with poor dentitions do not, on the average, chew for a greater number of times than do those with perfect dentitions. Dahlberg (1942) in a study of subjects with poor dentitions stated that they displayed 'a more skilful management of the mouthful' and used their incisors (which have a greater survival rate than molars even in poor dentitions) for grinding as well as incision. Older men were found to have a higher mastication coefficient than younger men with dentitions in similar condition, the probable reason being that abrasion grinds down occluding teeth till they match more closely and therefore offer a greater surface. Dahlberg found that the average occluding area for a group of sixty-three young men was 435 mm^2 compared with 532 mm^2 in a group of fifteen older men; a difference which is statistically significant. Within each of the groups, that is, those with either good or poor dentitions, there was considerable variation between individuals in the masticatory coefficients, which were accounted for partly by differences in the number of chews and partly in the number and surface areas of the occlusal contacts. The masticatory coefficients of the same individual measured on different occasions were very constant as would be expected from the observation that the numbers of chews also show little variation, since clearly the occlusal surface would not vary appreciably over a short time. Other factors, such as the strength of mastication and the skill in managing the bolus, play some part in accounting for individual variation.

Number of chewing movements

Dahlberg (1942) has also made a thorough statistical study of the factors controlling the number of chewing movements. His main conclusion was that each individual tends to form a fixed habit of the number of chewing movements. For example, no significant difference was observed between those with good and poor dentitions though it might have been expected that the latter would chew more thoroughly as a compensation for their smaller occlusal area. Women were found to make slightly fewer masticatory movements than men, and 7-year-old children fewer than adults. The number of chewing movements was not altered by small changes in the consistency of the food although with large changes (for example, when comparisons were made of the mastication of white of egg and India-rubber) the number of movements was adjusted to suit the material. The mean number of masticatory strokes is about 80 min^{-1} (Neil 1967); it did not differ in normal and denture wearers.

It might have been expected that the number of chews and the efficiency of mastication would be related. However, Neil (1967) found no relation between the efficiency of 3 chews in a subject and the number of chews he normally carried out. For example, two subjects both chewed 13 times for a standard piece of ham sandwich; in one, 3 chews produced 23% efficiency and in the other 56% efficiency, whereas 56% efficiency was achieved by another subject who chewed 51 times.

The Importance of Mastication in Digestion

The problem of the value of mastication for enhancing the digestibility of food has been approached by microscopical examination or chemical analysis of the faeces either of patients whose masticatory efficiency is impaired by a poor dentition, or of normal subjects who have deliberately bolted food as an experiment. The results seem to indicate that in people with normal digestive systems, mastication of modern cooked foods of ordinary consistency has little influence on their utilization, although no definite agreement had been reached. One difficulty in the use of microscopic examination of faeces follows from the observation that human faeces contain so many enzymes, presumably mostly bacterial, that even if unmasticated food reached the large intestine without being digested, the faecal enzymes might bring about sufficient digestion to make microscopical identification difficult or impossible. Since the absorption of foods from the large intestine is extremely limited, few of the products of this breakdown would be available for absorption. Chemical analysis of the faeces of people who are eating the same foods with and without normal mastication for periods of, say, 1 week would seem to be a possible, but unwieldly, method of deciding the question.

Farrell (1956) studied this problem in volunteers who swallowed two small cotton net bags tied together, one containing about 1 g of masticated food and the other a similar quantity of the same food before mastication. The bags were removed from the faeces and their contents weighed, thus making possible a comparison of the proportion of the masticated or unmasticated foods which had been digested. Twenty-nine foods were tested and the results made it possible to divide them into three groups: (1) foods which are likely to leave large residues if swallowed without chewing and which may leave some residues even if chewed, (2) foods which may leave some residue when unchewed but are usually digested when chewed, and (3) foods which are likely to be fully digested, whether chewed or not. The main foods from each class are shown in Table XIII.1.

Farrell also carried out some experiments by this method on subjects who had poor masticatory efficiency as a result of the loss of teeth. He found that even the slight degree of mastication which they could achieve was enough to ensure maximal digestion. The general conclusion is that for

TABLE XIII.1

Foods classified according to the effect of mastication on the digestion

Class 1 Mastication essential for digestion	Class 2 Mastication improves digestion	Class 3 Digestion complete even without mastication
Roast and fried pork	Roast chicken	Fried and stewed beef fat
Fried bacon	Stewed lamb	Fried and boiled cod
Roast, fried and stewed beef		Fried kipper
Roast and stewed mutton		Hard-boiled egg
Roast and fried lamb		Boiled rice
Fried and boiled potatoes		White and wholemeal bread
Boiled garden peas		Cheddar cheese
Boiled carrots		

certain foods, some mastication is necessary for full digestion, but that very thorough mastication appears to offer no advantage.

Sognnaes (1941) observed that the removal of the maxillary molars from rats fed on a diet containing 60% of coarsely ground corn caused a very large fall in their masticatory efficiency, as measured in one group of rats by killing them immediately after a meal and studying the particle size of the stomach contents. In another group of rats from which the teeth had also been extracted, the faeces were examined and the number of large particles was found to be high, thus showing that digestion had been impaired, but no significant change in their growth rate or general health was apparent. Either the rats were eating more to compensate for their impaired digestive efficiency or they were selecting a larger proportion of the finer parts of the diet. In a similar experiment (Gyimesi & Zelles 1972) the extraction of the molars in rats did lead to a slower growth rate.

There are three reasons for expecting that poor mastication might delay digestion. First, it is obvious that large lumps of food present a smaller surface area to the enzymes and the digestive juices than does the same food finely masticated. Secondly, thorough mastication and the more powerful stimulation of taste which results, increases the flow of saliva and gastric juice. Thirdly, the size of the particles in the stomach may control its emptying time of the stomach; large particles being retained in the stomach whereas fine particles leave the stomach rapidly. This factor may account for the surprising observation in dogs that digestion is more complete when large lumps of meat are eaten than when the meat is finely ground. The large lumps are held by the stomach and the products of gastric digestion are gradually supplied to the intestine in small lots. Ground meat leaves the stomach in an almost unaltered form which the intestine may be less able to digest completely.

Although, for these reasons, it is obvious that large lumps of food would not be digested so rapidly as the same food thoroughly masticated, the important question is whether they would reach complete digestion before entering the large intestine. If digestion, although delayed, can eventually occur while the food is in an area from which absorption takes place (and this is the point upon which Farrell's work is so revealing) then thorough mastication would not seem to be important from the standpoint of nutrition.

Effect of poor mastication on the digestive tract

Another possible influence of poor mastication which is often mentioned but has not been thoroughly investigated is that large pieces of unmasticated food might irritate the stomach and be a factor in the causation of other disturbances of the digestive tract. Mumma & Quinton (1970) compared the number of digestive symptoms (epigastric distress, nausea, vomiting and anorexia) among two groups of hospital patients with or without posterior teeth (graded as efficient or inefficient masticators, respectively). There was a tendency which just failed to reach significance ($p = 0.06$) for a higher proportion of the thirty-five inefficient masticators to suffer from one or more of these symptoms than among the ninety-five efficient.

Intestinal obstruction owing to the impaction of large masses of indigestible or poorly masticated food, although rare, has been recorded and gives rise to severe symptoms.

An increased volume of secretion, acidity and buffering power of histamine-stimulated gastric juice has been reported in patients 15–30 days after bilateral extraction of the molars. This requires confirmation and, in any case, the duration of the effect was not measured.

Extraction of molars in old rats, although causing a loss of weight in some groups and an increase in the percentage of coarse food particles in the stomach, was associated with microscopically detectable lesions in the stomach in only three animals out of thirty. The affected rats were those with the highest percentage of coarse particles in their stomachs except for one control animal which had the highest percentage of all and some lesions in the stomach; evidently rats, like men, vary in the thoroughness of mastication (Kapur & Okubo 1970).

Effect of dentures on nutrition

Lack of teeth leads to changes in the selection of foods, the intake of fruits, vegetables and meat being reduced and of soft foods such as porridge increased. Full dentures restored the selection to normal in 70% of the subjects studied by Bates & Murphy (1968). Mäkilä (1968) estimated plasma levels of thiamine, riboflavin and ascorbic acid in normal and edentulous subjects with and without dentures and found slight reductions in the edentulous (which was significant with ascorbic acid) one year after using their dentures. No differences were found in the bone density of groups of dentate or edentulous patients with or without satisfactory dentures and all groups were receiving nutritionally adequate diets.

Effect of Vigorous Mastication on the Oral Tissues

Although mastication has little or no effect on the digestibility of many modern foods, there is good evidence for the beneficial effects of vigorous mastication on the growth and maintenance of the oral tissues.

Experiments in which young growing rats have been fed for 4 months either on hard food, or on the same food finely ground and mixed with water, have shown that the total volume, weight and thickness of the mandibles were greater in the group with the hard diet. Although the density of the bone as measured or judged by radiographs was unaltered this technique cannot be relied upon to exclude small changes. Similar, though not quite such marked results, were obtained on adult rats. The conclusion is that both during and after growth, the size and shape of the mandible is dependent on the vigour of mastication. However, a similar experiment in which the number of mitotic divisions (labelled by tritiated thymidine injected 1 hr before death) in six types of cell in various parts of the supporting structures of rats' teeth (fifteen comparisons in all) were compared on hard or powdered food showed no significant differences except in the epithelium of the alveolar crest and the fibroblasts of the bone between the roots (Weiss *et al.* 1969).

In animal experiments in which the muscles of mastication have been either denervated or removed on one side the growth of the skull differed considerably on each side, again showing the importance of masticatory forces on bone growth.

It has been thought for many years that the adherence of food debris, plaques and calculus is reduced when a tough diet which requires vigorous mastication is eaten but controlled trials on this point have only been attempted since 1955.

Egelberg (1965) measured gingival exudate (a measure of gingival inflammation) in groups of dogs fed a hard or soft diet (bovine trachae either whole or finely minced) for 14 days which showed that the rate of exudation was reduced to approximately half when the hard diet replaced the soft diet, indicating that the hard diet reduced gingival inflammation.

Tests with disclosing solution on plaque removal have shown however, that although coarse foods may remove plaque from the smooth surfaces of the teeth they have little or no effect on those areas (fissures, contact points and the gingival margins) in which plaque is clinically important.

The effect of eating raw carrots for 2–3 min three times a day for 18 days was found by Lindhe & Wicen (1969) to have no effect, compared with controls, on the gingival index (a measure of gingivitis), the amount of gingival fluid and of plaque in students who abstained from tooth-brushing during the experiment. Slack & Martin (1958) tested the effect of eating a ring of hard apple after every meal and reported some reduction in caries (although there were uncertainties owing to differences between the caries scores of the experimental and control groups at the beginning), and significant improvement in the gingival condition. In an experiment with students who were encouraged to eat apples after the evening meal, no effects either on caries or oral hygiene status were observed except for a reduction in calculus (Lindhe & Wicen, 1969). A piece of raw carrot given to schoolchildren after the midday meal at school had no significant effect on caries, plaque or gingival condition (Reece & Swallow 1970) in agreement with some earlier experiments.

These studies all agree in showing that these fibrous foods have much less effect than had been supposed and they gave discrepant results on details, partly because their procedures were different. Experiments of this type are very difficult to conduct—it is not easy to match the two or more groups at the beginning or to guarantee that the particular food will be taken (or not taken in the control group). Also, the fact that the subjects are taking part in such an experiment may alter their attitudes to tooth cleaning and other measures which may affect oral health.

King (1948) showed that the chewing of sugar cane by human subjects, or the feeding to ferrets of bones to which meat was attached (the latter being an incentive to gnawing), greatly influence the health of the gingivae and periodontal membrane. The mechanism seemed to be chiefly the effect of friction on the removal of plaque and the prevention of calculus. King stated that if the calculus was not removed by the vigorous mastication, either because of its hardness or inaccessibility, little improvement in the condition of the tissue was noted.

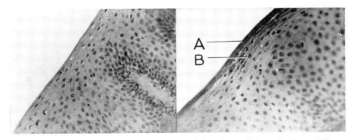

Fig. XIII.13. Effect of brushing on the keratinization of the gingivae. Photomicrographs of biopsy specimens taken before experiment (left), and after 60 days' brushing (right). (a) Keratinized surface, (b) stratum granulosum.

A carefully controlled experiment on forty young men on the effect of massaging the gums with a toothbrush was carried out by Robinson & Kitchin (1948), who found by biopsy before and after 60 days' massaging that the keratinization of the epithelium had clearly improved (Fig. XIII.13). Keratinization of scrapings from the gingivae was significantly greater after 4 weeks' brushing with a hard, compared with a soft brush. A brush which is too hard may, however, damage both the gingivae and the hard dental tissues.

Castenfelt (1952) was, however, unable to confirm that massaging increased the keratinization of the gingivae although it did decrease the depth of pockets and the tendency for bleeding.

Effect of mastication on periodontal ligament

The effect of mastication on the structure of the periodontal ligament has been studied by several workers. For example, Coolidge (1937) in post-mortem measurements on 172 teeth in fifteen jaws found the average thickness of the periodontal ligament in teeth with heavy masticatory functions to be 0·18 mm compared with 0·13 mm in teeth without antagonists. This implies that with powerful mastication, movements of the teeth had enlarged the alveolar space by bone resorption resulting in compensatory thickening of the periodontal ligament. The mandibular teeth were extracted from monkeys which were killed at intervals up to 561 days later. The supporting tissues of the surviving non-functioning teeth showed severe atrophy and loss of orientation of the fibres of the periodontal ligament. The thickness of the cementum was greater on the non-functioning side and the gingivae were more inflamed (Pihlstrom & Ramfjord 1971). Alexander (1970) found more subgingival calculus and a higher degree of gingival inflammation in the vicinity of non-functioning human teeth compared to functioning teeth in the same mouth.

Similar changes have been found experimentally in human subjects by placing an onlay on one tooth, thus increasing occlusal stress, and examining the supporting structures after extraction of the tooth and the accompanying alveolar bone. The corresponding tooth on the opposite side acted as a control. Unilateral chewing, as shown by unequal attrition on the two sides of fifteen human skulls, was associated with greater deposits of calculus and more severe bone loss on the side with least attrition (Larato 1970).

The soothing effect of mastication

Many activities of the body are accompanied by voluntary muscular movements (such as finger tapping, leg swinging, pipe smoking) which are not in any direct way connected with the activity. The subjective impression of the value of such movements is usually stated to be an increased feeling of relaxation or in the common phrase 'it soothes the nerves'.

An extensive study by Hollingworth (1939) showed that during the mastication of chewing gum there was a fall both in muscular tone and in these fidgeting activities. This work, by demonstrating the influence of chewing movements on muscular tone, has shown that mastication is one method of achieving greater muscular relaxation.

Physiology of suckling

(1) BOTTLE FEEDING

Ardran & Kemp (1958) studied by cineradiography in thirty-five babies the muscular movements occurring during the bottle feeding of milk containing radiopaque barium salts. The jaws are alternately raised and lowered and, when raised, the neck of the teat is compressed between the upper gingivae and the tip of the tongue which lies on the lower gingivae. The contents of the bulb are moved, some being forced back into the bottle and some into the mouth. The tongue is then pressed on the teat, from before, backwards which forces its contents into the mouth. The posterior part of the tongue is in contact with the soft palate, thus closing off the mouth from the pharynx. When the teat is emptied, the tongue and soft palate come apart and the soft palate is elevated, the free end reaching the posterior pharyngeal wall, and the upper surface makes contact with the adenoidal pad on the posterior pharyngeal wall. Ardran & Kemp (1958) suggest that the bolus is directed into the low pharynx by the tonsils which they believe limit the backward spread of the food. They suggest that the lymph tissue (both tonsils and adenoids) play an important part in deglutition in the suckling infant.

(2) BREAST FEEDING

Breast feeding has been studied by Ardran & Kemp (1958) by placing small tin discs on the areolae and barium-lanoline cream on the nipples of lactating women and taking radiographs while the infant was suckling. The shadows of the tin and barium cream showed that the greatly elongated nipple and part of the areola was drawn into the baby's mouth and incorporated into the teat which was about twice as long as the nipple at rest. The nipple was grasped by sucking it into the mouth. In spite of the term 'sucking', the milk is delivered from the mammary ducts largely by the contraction of the myoepithelial cells under the influence of oxytocin from the posterior pituitary in response to mechanical stimulation of the nipple. Active suction by the infant probably plays only a small part. During the feeding, the jaw was alternately raised and lowered in a cycle of about 1·5 s. When it was lowered, the teat was about three times as long as the resting nipple, with its orifice placed near the junction of the hard and soft palates, and its neck between the tip of the tongue and the upper gum. The lowering of the jaw reduces the pressure in the mouth and presumably exerts a suction. When the jaw was raised the tongue pressed on the lower surface of the teat to reduce it to about half its previous width. Observations on an infant with a bilateral hare lip showed that during suckling the tongue is grooved longitudinally and a peristaltic wave moving backwards obliterates the groove, presses on the teat and expresses the milk from it. The milk is then swallowed. The grooving of the tongue during the swallowing of liquids has also been observed in adults (Whillis 1946).

The role of the lips is controversial. It is not clear whether their main function is to envelop the areola to form an airtight seal or whether they assist in the rhythmic pressure on the teat.

Deglutition (Swallowing)

The details of the process of deglutition are still controversial. Parts of this complicated act are so rapid that it is impossible to follow with the eye all the movements when observing radiologically the deglutition of radiopaque material, and even cinematography has not cleared up a number of points.

When the food in the mouth, or part of it, has been masticated the chain of reflexes involved in deglutition is begun by a voluntary act. Although mastication and deglutition are really one continuous action it has been customary to regard mastication as a separate process and to divide deglutition into three stages.

The decision to swallow depends on several factors: the degree of fineness of the food, the intensity of the taste extracted and the degree of lubrication of the bolus (Neill 1967). Some people continue chewing until the particles are as small as they can be made, 0·8 mm being reported as the lower limit (Manly & Vinton, 1951), others are content to bolt their food with a minimum of mastication.

The first stage

The first stage is voluntary and consists of forming the selected part of the masticated food into one mass called a bolus, placing it on the dorsum of the tongue and pressing it lightly against the hard palate. The tip of the tongue touches the hard palate just behind the incisors. Thexton (1973) described a reflex wave of contraction passing backwards from the tip of the tongue when the mucosa is diffusely stimulated as would occur when food is finally divided and made up into a bolus contacting a large area.

Two mechanisms have been suggested by which the bolus is transferred from the back of the tongue into the pharynx. The first is the contraction of the mylohyoid muscle which pushes the bolus backwards by raising the back of the tongue. This is followed by a peristaltic wave caused by the contraction of the pharyngeal constrictors. The soft palate is raised by the action of the levator and tensor palati muscles and touches the posterior pharangeal wall, thus sealing off the nasal passage.

The second mechanism was suspected by Barclay (1936) from radiological studies. He concluded that the rapid relaxation of the muscles of the tongue and pharynx causes the creation of a space while the airways are still closed leading to a negative pressure which he thought sucked the bolus from the mouth into the pharynx. Barclay supported his theory by publishing tracings showing a transient negative pressure in the pharynx. Others have either failed to detect a negative pharyngeal pressure during deglutition or found, at most, a very short and negligibly small phase of negative pressure (Fyke & Code 1955). Most workers have found that the pressure in the pharynx is positive; for example, during over 100 swallows in eight subjects, the pressure varied between 4 and 10 cm Hg. Only in the anterior part of the mouth was a negative pressure ever found (Rushmer & Hendron 1951). It is known that swallowing occurs readily in subjects in whom, as a result of accidents to the neck tissues, air can enter the pharynx freely and the creation of negative pressure would be impossible.

The movement backwards of the bolus (barium meal) as a result of the upward and forward pressure of the tongue on the hard palate was described by Ardran & Kemp (1951) as like toothpaste being pressed from a tube. Others have described its movement more as a jerk but all agree about the rapidity with which the bolus is propelled from the mouth.

In the normal act of swallowing solid food the lips form a seal, the tongue is contained within the dental arches and the teeth come into occlusion. Variations occur in this general pattern. For instance, if the individual does not have a 'lips together' resting posture then circum-oral muscular contraction will be required to form a lip seal. If the upper incisors are prominent the individual may posture the mandible downwards and forwards to facilitate the formation of a lip seal; as a part of this adaptive activity the tongue may be extended between the incisors to contact the lips. If the individual has an endogenous tongue thrust the tongue will be forcibly thrust forwards between the incisors to contact the lips. Whilst in the normal act of swallowing the teeth are usually in occlusion, electrical methods of detecting occlusal contact have confirmed that this does not always occur. Rix pointed out that in some children swallowing is performed with the teeth apart ('abnormal swallow'), which he believed is a survival of the swallowing mechanism used during sucking and leads to abnormal pressures conducive of malocclusion (Ballard 1955, 1962, Straub 1961, Rix 1952, 1953). Cleall (1965) found that the resting posture and movements in deglutition were very variable but characteristic of each individual and dictated largely by the shape of the palatal vault. Cleall found that many subjects with excellent occlusion swallowed without tooth contact and disputed that this was abnormal or a cause of malocclusion.

THE PRESSURES EXERTED BY THE TONGUE DURING SWALLOWING

By incorporating transducers (instruments which convert a physical condition, in this case pressure, into an electrical impulse which can be accurately measured) in different areas of an acrylic dental plate, it has been possible to measure the pressures developed by the tongue during swallowing (Kydd & Toda 1962). The results show that the pressures on the anterior and lateral areas of the palate (average for fifteen subjects: 112 g cm^{-2}) were higher than in the central area (average 67 g cm^{-2}). The pressures were less than half these values when they were recorded for spontaneous swallowing under relaxed conditions with no observer present (52 and 20 g cm^{-2}). During the swallowing of water, the pressures were less than with saliva. The shape of the palate was found to be an important factor, since this affected the closeness of contact of the tongue with the different parts of the palate. For example, the pressure developed on the anterior and lateral surfaces of a 'peaked' palate was greater than on a flat palate but, as would be expected, the reverse was true of the central areas—as clearly, the centre of the tongue could contact a flat palate more readily than one with a peaked contour. These pressures exerted by the tongue on the palate are low when compared with those exerted

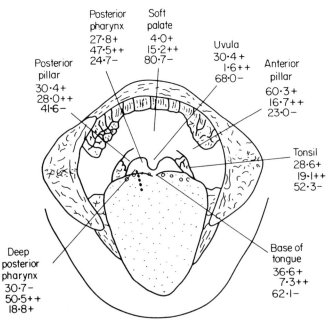

Fig. XIII.14. The area of the mouth which on stimulation cause swallowing. The figures are the percentages of the subjects who gave a response (+); a powerful response (+ +); or no response (−). Note that no area gave a response in all subjects.

on the teeth during swallowing, which ranged from 41 to 709 g cm^{-2} (Winders 1958). It is not surprising that excessive tongue pressure on the teeth is a factor in malocclusion.

The second stage

The second stage begins by the contacts of the bolus with the mucosa in certain parts of the mouth and pharynx, which act as the stimuli to a series of reflexes whose main function is to ensure that the bolus descends into the oesophagus and does not enter the trachea or nasopharynx.

The exact location of the sensitive areas has been studied in a large group of subjects by applying a glass rod to various parts of the mouth and pharynx and noting which produces a swallowing reflex (Pommerenke 1928). Great variation was found amongst different individuals and no single area was found, stimulation of which invariably causes swallowing in all subjects (Fig. XIII.14). The most sensitive area was found to be anterior pillars of the fauces, but even here 23% failed to respond to the stimulation. The side of the posterior wall of the pharynx is also sensitive. The soft palate and uvula were insensitive in 81% and 68% of the subjects respectively. Anaesthesia of the sensitive areas was found to impair swallowing in response to a mechanical stimulation and, in some subjects, also affected voluntary swallowing. Complete inhibition of swallowing was obtained only with anaesthesia of the anterior pillars, thus confirming the results of the stimulation experiments.

THE MOVEMENTS AND POSSIBLE FUNCTIONS OF THE EPIGLOTTIS
The movements and role of the epiglottis are perhaps the most controversial points of all. It was at first thought that the epiglottis moved downwards and acted as a lid to the larynx, but direct observation on a subject who, following a severe surgical operation, had a large opening through the tissues of the neck into the pharynx, suggested that the epiglottis remained upright during swallowing (Stuart & McCormick 1891–2). The radiological observations of Barclay (1936) led him to support this view and he described the position of the epiglottis during swallowing as standing erect 'like a rock sticking out under a waterfall'. His published radiographs, however, gave little clear indication of the epiglottis at all. It is known that removal of most of the epiglottis does not make swallowing impossible, and it has been suggested that this structure is vestigial in man and, since it contains taste-buds, that its original function had been concerned with taste. Other radiological studies have shown that the epiglottis does descend during swallowing (Johnstone 1942–3). This was particularly well demonstrated by serial radiographs at the rate of 25 s^{-1} of a subject who volunteered to have a silver clip put on the tip of his epiglottis which showed that this structure does turn down during swallowing (Kemp 1950). Its movements were found to be extremely rapid

which probably accounted for the difficulty which previous workers had experienced in deciding this tissue. Another report, on a patient whose pharynx could be viewed from outside following surgical removal of tissues from the neck, also stated that the epiglottis was observed to move downwards during swallowing (Syrop 1953).

The radiological studies of Ardran & Kemp (1952) suggest that the epiglottis does not close the entrance of the larynx effectively until *after* the bolus has passed. They suggest several functions for the epiglottis: (1) before it descends it acts as a ledge which prevents the entry of food into the larynx; (2) later, the sides form a chute from which the bolus can be seen to enter the food channels on one or both sides, rather than gliding over it; and (3) when it descends after the bolus has passed it acts as a cover to prevent food from being sucked in as the airway of the larynx is re-established. When several swallows follow in rapid succession, the epiglottis may not return to the rest position until after the series is complete (Rushmer & Hendron 1951).

THE PROTECTION OF THE RESPIRATORY TRACT

Several other mechanisms help to prevent the entry of food into the trachea. The larynx is raised and is closed off against the back of the tongue. This movement of the larynx also has the effect of stretching the anterior wall of the upper oesophagus thus dilating it and making it easier to receive the bolus. A sphincter—the cricopharyngeal sphincter—at the mouth of the oesophagus is normally closed and has the effect of preventing inspired air from descending the oesophagus (Negus 1949). This sphincter can be detected in two ways. First, an obstruction can be felt when an oesophagoscope is pushed down the oesophagus. Secondly, when the pressure is measured at various levels of the oesophagus a band of high pressure (between 20 and 60 cm of water) has been found for a width of about 30 cm at the level of the cricoid cartilage. The pressure of a bolus reflexly releases the sphincter. The larynx is also closed by bringing together the true and false vocal cords. This protection of the respiratory tract from invasion by food perhaps represents the more primitive function of the larynx. Its function in phonation is probably a later evolutionary development. Respiration is inhibited during the second stage (apnoea of deglutition) thus preventing the possible sucking of food into the respiratory passages by inspired air.

During deglutition, the Eustachian tubes whose pharyngeal orifice is normally closed, are opened by the contraction of the salpingopharyngeus and dilator tubae muscles.

The first and second stages of deglutition together last only about 1 s.

The third stage

The third stage consists of a peristaltic wave which forces the bolus down the oesophagus and which, on arrival at the cardiac sphincter, causes its relaxation. This wave takes about 6 or 7 s to force the solid bolus along the whole length of the oesophagus, but the rate is not uniform in different parts. In the upper section where the muscle is voluntary the rate is much more rapid than in the lower, where the muscle is mostly or entirely involuntary. While the bolus is in the upper part of the oesophagus it is possible to return it to the mouth by a powerful voluntary effort.

When liquids are swallowed, the process is slightly different in that the liquid flows down the oesophagus by gravity, ahead of the peristaltic wave, although its entrance into the stomach is held up until the cardiac sphincter opens after the arrival of the peristaltic wave.

Although it has been stated that the time required for the passage of a solid bolus from the mouth to the stomach is greater than normal when the body is inverted, changes of position within the normal range do not have much influence on the time required for swallowing. It may be concluded, therefore, that gravity plays little part in swallowing except in liquids.

In order to study the number of times swallowing occurs at different times during the day a small microphone was worn round the neck attached by a long lead to a tape recorder so that the sound of swallowing could be recorded without restricting normal movements. In a typical 24-h cycle 590 swallows were recorded, 146 while eating, 394 between meals while the subject was awake and 50 during sleep. The infrequency of swallowing during sleep is of interest and corresponds with the finding (p. 320) that saliva flow during sleep almost ceases. Most of these swallows were in the later hours of sleep as sleep became increasingly light (Flanagan *et al.* 1963). This figure is much lower than previous speculative estimates of up to 2400 swallows a day. A survey on small numbers of normal (5) and abnormal (6) swallowers showed that the latter have a much lower rate of swallowing than the former (Kydd & Neff 1964).

The volumes of fluid swallowed with each act of deglutition have been measured in groups of about a dozen subjects and found to average: adult female 14 ml, males 21 ml and children (1·25 to 3·5 years old) 4·5 ml (Jones & Work 1961).

References

Reviews:

Anderson D.J. & Matthews B. (Eds) (1976) *Mastication—A symposium on the Clinical and Physiological Aspects of Mastication.* John Wright, Bristol

Bosma J.F. (1957) Deglutition: pharyngeal stage. *Physiol. Rev.* **37**, 275

Griffin C.J. & Harris R. (1975) *The Tem-*poromandibular *Joint Syndrome.* Karger, Basel

Kawamura Y. (1974) (Ed.) *Physiology of Mastication.* Karger, Basel

Matthews B. (1975) Mastication in *Applied Physiology of the Mouth*, p. 199. Ed. Lavelle C.L.B. John Wright, Bristol

Posselt U. (1968) *Physiology of Occlusion and Rehabilitation.* Blackwell, Oxford

SILVERMAN S.I. (1961) *Oral Physiology.* Mosby, St Louis

ACHANI N.K. & THEXTON A.J. (1974) A masseteric reflex elicited from the oral mucosa in man. *Archs oral Biol.* **19**, 209

AHLGREN J. (1966) Mechanism of mastication. *Acta odont. Scand.* **24**, Supp. 14

AHLGREN J. (1967) Pattern of chewing and malocclusion of teeth: a clinical study. *Acto odont. Scand.* **25**, 3

ALEXANDER A.G. (1970) The effect of lack of function of teeth and gingival health, plaque and calculus accumulation. *J. Periodont.* **41**, 438

ANDERSON D.J. (1953) A method of recording masticatory loads. *J. dent. Res.* **32**, 785

ANDERSON D.J. (1956) Measurement of stress in mastication. *J. dent. Res.* **35**, 664, 671

ANDERSON D.J. & PICTON D.C.G. (1957) Tooth contact during chewing. *J. dent. Res.* **36**, 21

ARDRAN G.M. & KEMP F.H. (1951) The mechanism of swallowing. *Proc. Roy. Soc. Med.* **44**, 1038

ARDRAN G.M. & KEMP F.H. (1952) The protection of the laryngeal airway during swallowing. *Brit. J. Radiol.* **25**, 406

ARDRAN G.M. & KEMP F.H. (1958) A cineradiographic study of bottle feeding. *Brit. J. Radiol.* **31**, 11

BALLARD C.F. (1955) A consideration of the physiological background of mandibular posture and movement. *Dent. Practit.* **6**, 80

BALLARD C.F. (1962) The clinical significance of innate and adaptive postures and motor behaviour. *Dent. Practit.* **12**, 219

BARCLAY A.E. (1936) *The Digestive Tract. A Radiological Study of its Anatomy, Physiology and Pathology.* Cambridge University Press

BATES J.F. & MURPHY W.M. (1968) A survey of an edentulous population. *Brit. dent. J.* **124**, 116

BREKHUS P.J. *et al.* (1941) Stimulation of the muscles of mastication. *J. dent. Res.* **20**, 87

CARLSON G.E. (1974) Bite force and masticatory efficiency. In *Physiology of Masti-cation*, p. 265. Ed. KAWAMURA Y. Karger, Basel

CARLSÖÖ S. (1952) Nervous co-ordination and mechanical function of the manibular elevators. *Acta odont. Scand.* **10**, Suppl. 11

CASTENFELT F. (1952) Toothbrushing and massage in periodontal disease. *Dent. Dig.* **58**, 505

CLARK R.K.F. & WYKE D.B. (1972) Contributions of temporomandibular articular mechanoreceptors to the control of masticatory system: an experimental study. *J. Dent.* **1**, 121

CLARK R.K.F. & WYKE B.D. (1974) Arthrokinetic reflexogenic systems in the temporomandibular joint. *J. Anat. (Lond.)* **117**, 216

CLEALL J.F. (1965) Deglutition: a study of form and function. *Amer. J. Orthodont.* **51**, 566

COOLIDGE E.D. (1937) The thickness of the human periodontal membrane. *J. Amer. dent. Ass.* **24**, 1260

COOPER S. (1953) Muscle spindles in the intrinsic muscles of the tongue. *J. Physiol.* **122**, 193

DAHLBERG B. (1942) The masticatory effect. *Acta med. Scand.* Supp. 139

DELLOW P. & LUND J.P. (1971) Evidence for a central rhythmic drive of jaw muscles. *J. Physiol. (Lond.)* **215**, 1

DUXBURY A.J. *et al.* (1973) An instrument for the measurement of incisive bite force. *J. Dent.* **1**, 246

EGELBERG J. (1965) Local effect of diet on plaque formation and development of gingivitis in dogs. *Odont. Revy* **16**, 31, 42, 50

FARRELL J.H. (1956) The effect of mastication on the digestion of food. *Brit. dent. J.* **100**, 149

FLANAGAN J.B. *et al.* (1963) The 24-hour pattern of swallowing in man. *I.A.D.R. Abs.* no. 165

FREIDMAN L.A. (1972) Horizontal tooth mobility and the menstrual cycle. *J. periodont. Res.* **7**, 125

FYKE F.E. & CODE C.F. (1955) Resting and deglutition pressures in the pharyngo-esophageal region. *Gastroenterology* **29**, 24

GREENFIELD B.E. & WYKE B.D. (1956) Electromyographic studies of some of the muscles of mastication. *Brit. dent. J.* **100**, 129

GRIFFIN C.J. & HARRIS R. (1974) Innervation of human periodontum. *Aust. Dent. J.* **19**, 51, 255 (see also **19**, 174, 326)

GYIMESI J. & ZELLES T. (1972) Effect of removal of molars on weight increase and food intake in albino rats. *J. dent. Res.* **51**, 897

HANNAM A.G. & MATTHEWS B. (1969) Reflex jaw opening in response to stimulation of periodontal mechano-receptors in the cat. *Archs oral Biol.* **14**, 415 (see also (1970) **15**, 17)

HANNAM A.G. *et al.* (1970) Receptors involved in the response of the masseter muscle to tooth contact in man. *Archs oral Biol.* **15**, 17

HARRIS R. & GRIFFIN C.J. (1975) *Neuromuscular Mechanisms and the Masticatory Apparatus. Temporomandibular Joint Syndrome*, p. 45. Karger, Basel

HOLLINGWORTH H.L. (1939) Chewing as a technique of relaxation. *Science* **90**, 385

JANKELSON B. *et al.* (1953) The physiology of the stomatognathic system. *J. Amer. dent. Ass.* **46**, 378

JOHNSTONE A.S. (1942–3) A radiological study of deglutition. *J. Anat. Lond.* **77**, 97

JONES D.V. & WORK C.E. (1961) Volume of a swallow. *Amer. J. Dis. Child.* **102**, 427

KAPUR K.K. & OKUBO J. (1970) Effect of impaired mastication on the health of rats. *J. dent. Res.* **49**, 61

KAWAMURA O. (Ed.) (1974) *Frontiers of Oral Physiology. Physiology of Mastication.* Karger, Basel

KEMP F.H. (1950) Movements of the epiglottis during deglutition. *J. Physiol.* **112**, 11P

KING J.D. (1948) The influence of diet on paradontal disease. *Nutrit. Abstr. Rev.* **17**, 569

KYDD W.L. & NEFF C.W. (1964) Frequency of deglutition of tongue thrusters compared to a sample population of normal swallowers. *J. dent. Res.* **43**, 363

KYDD W.L. & TODA J.M. (1962) Tongue pressures exerted on the hard palate

during swallowing. *J. Amer. dent. Ass.* **65**, 319

LARATO D.S. (1970) Effects of unilateral mastication on tooth and periodontal structures. *J. oral Med.* **25**, 80

LINDHE J. & WICEN P.-O. (1969) The effects on the gingivae of chewing fibrous foods. *J. periodont. Res.* **4**, 193

LUND J.P. & DELLOW P.G. (1971) The influence of interactive stimuli on rhythmical masticatory movements in rabbits. *Archs oral Biol.* **16**, 215

LUND J.P. & LAMARRE Y. (1976) The importance of positive feedback from periodontal pressoreceptors for voluntary isometric contraction of jaw closing muscles in man (in press)

MÄKILÄ E. (1968) Effects of complete dentures on the dietary habits and serum thiamine riboflavin and ascorbic acid levels in edentulous persons. *Suom Hammaslaak* **64**, 105

MANLY R.S. & VINTON P. (1951) Factors influencing denture function. *J. Prosth. Dent.* **1**, 578

MØLLER E. (1974) Action of the muscles of mastication. In *Frontiers of Oral Physiology. Physiology of Mastication*, p. 121. Ed. KAWAMURA O. Karger, Basel

MÜHLEMANN H.R. (1954) Tooth mobility. *J. Periodont.* **25**, 22, 125, 128, 198, 202

MÜHLEMANN H.R. (1960) Ten years of tooth-mobility measurements. *J. Periodont.* **31**, 110

MUMMA R.D. & QUINTON K. (1970) Masticatory efficiency and gastric distress. *J. dent. Res.* **49**, 69

MUNRO P.R. (1975) *Electromyography of the Muscles of Mastication*, p. 87. In Temperomandibular joint syndrome. The masticatory apparatus of man in normal and abnormal funtion. Eds GRIFFIN, C.J. & HARRIS, R. *Monographs in Oral Science* **4**. Karger, Basel

NEGUS V.E. (1949) *The Mechanism of the Larynx.* Heinemann, London

NEILL D.J. (1967) Studies of tooth contact in complete dentures. *Brit. dent. J.* **123**, 369

NEILL D.J. & PHILLIPS H.I.B. (1970) The masticatory performance, dental state and dietary intake of a group of elderly army pensioners. *Brit. dent. J.* **128**, 581

O'ROURKE J.T. (1951) *Oral Physiology*. Ed. MINER L.M.S. Kimpton, London

ÖWALL B. (1974) Oral tactility during chewing. *Odont. Revy* **25**, 135, 327

PARFITT G.J. (1960) Measurement of the physiological mobility of individual teeth in an axial direction. *J. dent. Res.* **39**, 608

PENFIELD W. & BOLDREY E. (1937) Somatic motor and sensory representation in the cerebral cortex of man as studied by electrical stimulation. *Brain* **60**, 389

PICTON D.C.A. (1962a) Tilting movements of teeth during biting. *Archs oral Biol.* **7**, 151

PICTON D.C.A. (1962b) Distortion of jaws during biting. *Archs oral Biol.* **7**, 573

PICTON D.C.A. (1962c) A study of normal tooth mobility and the changes with periodontal disease. *Dent. Practit.* **12**, 167

PICTON D.C.A. (1963) Vertical movement of cheek teeth during biting. *Archs oral Biol.* **8**, 109

PIHLSTROM B.L. & RAMFJORD S.P. (1971) Periodontal effect of nonfunction in monkeys. *J. Periodont.* **42**, 748

POMMERENKE W.J. (1928) A study of the sensory areas eliciting the swallowing reflex. *Amer. J. Physiol.* **84**, 36

PREISKEL H. (1972) Observations on Bennett movement. *Dent. Pract. Den. Rec.* **22**, 179

RAMFJORD S.P. (1961) Bruxism: a clinical and electromyographic study. *J. Amer. Dent. Ass.* **62**, 21

REECE J.A. & SWALLOW J.N. (1970) Carrots and dental health. *Brit. dent. J.* **128**, 535

RIX R.E. (1946) Deglutition and the teeth. *Dent. Rec.* **66**, 103; (1953) **73**, 427

RIX R.E. (1952) Some observations upon the environment of the incisors. *Trans. Brit. Soc. for the Study of Orthodont.* **75**

ROBINSON H.B.G. & KITCHIN P.C. (1948) The effect of massage with the tooth-brush on keratinization of the gingivae. *Oral Surg., Med., Path.* **1**, 1042

RUSHMER R.F. & HENDRON J.A. (1951) The act of deglutition: a cinefluorographic study. *J. appl. Physiol.* **3**, 622

SESSLE B.J. & SCHMITT A. (1972) Effect on controlled tooth stimulation on jaw muscles in man. *Archs oral Biol.* **17**, 1597

SHEPPARD I.M. *et al.* (1968) Bolus placement during mastication. *J. pros. Dent.* **20**, 50

SHERRINGTON C.S. (1916) Some observations on the bucco-pharyngeal stage of reflex deglutition in the cat. *Quart. J. exp. Phys* **9**, 147

SHERRINGTON C.S. (1917) Jaw reflexes. *J. Physiol.* **51**, 420

SHRODER H. (1927) *Lehrbuch der Technicher Zahnheilkunde*. Bd. 1 Leiferung 2. Meusser, Berlin

SLACK G.L. & MARTIN W.J. (1958) Apples and dental health. *Brit. dent. J.* **105**, 366

SLATTER J.M. & PICTON D.C.A. (1972) The effect on intrusive tooth mobility of noradrenaline injected locally in monkeys. *J. periodont. Res.* **7**, 144

SOGNNAES R.F. (1941) Studies on masticatory efficiency. I. Review of literature. II. Masticatory efficiency in rats. III. Muscle strength of normal and fluorosed rats. IV. Mastication and experimental rat caries. *Amer. J. Orthodont. and Oral Surg. (Oral Surg. Sect.)* **27**, 309, 383, 458, 552

STOREY E. (1953) Bone changes associated with tooth movement. *Aust. J Dent.* **57**, 57; **59**, 147, 209, 220 (see also **58**, 80; **59**, 147, 209, 220); see also RATEITSCHAK K.H. (1967) *J. periodont. Res.* **2**, 199

STRAUB W.J. (1960) Malfunction of the tongue. *Amer. J. Orthodont.* I **46**, 404; II (1961) **47**, 596

STUART T.P.A. & McCORMICK A. (1891–2) The position of the epiglottis in swallowing. *J. Anat. Lond.* **26**, 231

SYROP H.M. (1953) Motion picture studies of the mechanism of mastication and swallowing. *J. Amer. dent. Ass.* **46**, 495

THEXTON A.J. (1973–4) Some aspects of neurophysiology of dental interest. *J. Dent.* **2**, 49, 131

WATSON R.M. (1972) Masticatory ability: cineradiographic observations. *J. Dent.* **1**, 54

WEISS R. *et al.* (1969) Effects of diets of different physical consistences on the periodontal proliferative activity in young adult rats. *J. periodont. Res.* **4**, 296

WHILLIS J. (1946) Movements of the tongue in swallowing. *J. Anat. Lond.* **80**, 115

WINDERS R.V. (1958) Forces exerted on the dentition by the perioral and lingual musculature during swallowing. *Angle Orthodont.* **28,** 226

WORNER H.K. (1939) Gnathodynamics. *Aust. J. Dent.* **43,** 381; (1944) **48,** 1

WORNER H.K. & ANDERSON M.N. (1944) Biting force measurements on children. *Aust. J. Dent.* **48,** 1

WYKE B.D. (1972) Neuromuscular mechanisms influencing mandibular posture: a neurologist's review of current concepts. *J. Dent.* **1,** 111

YEMM R. (1972) The response of the masseter and temporal muscles following electrical stimulation of oral mucous membrane in man. *Archs oral Biol.* **17,** 23 (see also p. 513)

YEMM R. & NORDSTROM S.H. (1974) Forces developed by tissue elasticity as a determinant in the rat. *Archs oral Biol.* **19,** 347

CHAPTER XIV

SENSATIONS ARISING IN THE MOUTH

Taste

In the lower animals, the functions of taste are probably of greater importance than in civilized man. Animals have been shown to develop a craving for some nutrients in which they happen to be deficient (for example salt), and the mechanism for this control of intake probably involves the sensation of taste. For example, the effect of body requirements on the sensitivity of taste is shown by the experiments of Richter who found that adrenalectomized rats (which require more sodium chloride for survival than do normal rats) could detect salt by taste in lower concentrations than could normal rats, a fact which is probably connected with their craving. Taste is not a reliable guide to the edibility of materials, since not all toxic substances are unpalatable and not all unpalatable substances are toxic.

The sensation of taste can be regarded as sensitivity to chemical substances in solution. Taste sensitivity can be measured at two levels. The first is by finding the concentration of a sapid (i.e. having a taste) substance which can just be detected as different from water (detection threshold)—some workers measure this by placing only one drop of a solution on the tongue but lower concentrations can be detected by allowing 5–10 ml of solution to be moved over the whole surface of the mouth.

The second method is to find the minimum concentration which can be identified as sweet, sour, etc. (the 'recognition threshold' which requires higher concentrations than detection). Confusion can arise because some authors quote results as thresholds, others as sensitivities. It must be emphasized that the lower the threshold concentration the greater is the sensitivity.

At least some of the nerve endings responsible for converting the chemical stimulus into a nerve impulse are situated within structures known as taste-buds, found on the tongue, soft palate and epiglottis. The taste-buds are embedded within the stratified epithelium associated with the fungiform and circumvallate papillae and are absent from the middle of the dorsum and the under surface of the tongue. Electron microscopy has failed to confirm the existence of 'taste hairs', the small projections from the sensory cells of the taste bud seen in the light microscope, but has established that the sensory cells end in numerous microvilli.

Light microscopy indicates that two types of cell are present in the taste buds, referred to as sensory and sustentacular (or supporting) cells and some electron micrographs have confirmed this distinction. The taste buds are constantly undergoing a life cycle and some workers suggest that what were thought to be distinct cell types are different stages in this cycle. Experiments with tritiated thymidine suggest that the cells of the taste bud have a life span of about 10–12 days and are constantly replaced by cell divisions in the neighbouring epithelial cells. It has been known for many years that the taste buds degenerate if their nerve supply is cut and reform when the nerve regenerates. An intact innervation is required in at least two points in the life cycle—for mitosis of the epithelial precursor and maintenance of the mature cell. The nature of the presumably chemical factor responsible is not known.

In addition to nerves ending in the taste buds, papillae contain unmyelinated nerve fibres which end as free nerve endings in the epithelium surrounding the taste buds. Like free nerve endings elsewhere they probably subserve pain and common chemical sensibility (see p. 550). The following evidence suggests that they contribute to the discrimination of tastes (Henkin 1970a). In a rare hereditary condition known as familial dysautonomia, taste is virtually absent and examination of the tongue, including some biopsy specimens, has failed to detect any taste-buds, although unmyelinated nerves with free endings are present. After injection of methacholine, salt and sweet tastes became detectable with almost normal thresholds—in other words, taste sensitivity exists in the apparent absence of taste-buds.

Nerve fibres lead from the sensory cells within the taste-buds of the posterior third of the tongue to join the glossopharyngeal nerve and those from the anterior two-thirds to the lingual nerve, the taste fibres of which enter the chorda tympani.

The basic tastes

Experiments in which small areas of the tongue are stimulated with, for example, a fine camel hair brush, dipped in various substances, have led to the view that there are only four (or some say, six) basic tastes. These are sweet, sour, bitter and salt and the two doubtful tastes are alkaline and 'metallic'. All bitter or sweet substances do not taste the same, however. The sensitivity of the tongue to these sensations varies markedly from region to region. The tip is more sensitive to sweet than to the other tastes, the circumvallate area to bitter, and the side to acid and salt, although there is some individual variation.

Further evidence for the independent existence of mechanisms for different tastes is provided by observing the effect of certain local anaesthetics. Cocaine, for example, abolishes the taste sensations in the following order: bitter, sweet, salt, sour. Gymnemic acid abolishes the sweet taste and leaves the other three tastes relatively unaffected—earlier results suggesting that it reduces the bitter taste arose because, as a bitter substance itself, it produces adaptation (see p. 546) to this taste. A constituent of a West African shrub, miraculin, changes the acid taste to sweet.

Alkali appears to have a distinctive taste and some have included it among the basic tastes while others have regarded it either as a general irritant or as acting by the release of volatile amines which are detected as odours. The tip of the tongue is more sensitive to alkali than the dorsum suggesting that it is detected by the taste mechanism rather than by less specific nerve endings. Study of the action potentials in nerves from the cat's tongue have shown that endings sensitive to water (which must therefore be presumed to have a specific taste in cats), salt and sometimes to bitter substances all respond to alkali. It is apparently a true taste which, like others, stimulates several types of ending. Acid and alkali also change the physical properties of the mucous surfaces of the mouth, which contributes to their overall effects. Acid gives rise to a rough sensation and alkalies to a feeling of smoothness.

The sensitivity to taste of areas outside the tongue

Henkin (1970b) showed that if the tongue is completely anaesthetized and the sensitivity to detection of the basic tastes is determined over the whole mouth, the subject becomes less sensitive to salt and sweet but is completely unchanged from normal values for acid and bitter (Fig. XIV.1). If the palate was anaesthetized, Henkin found that sensitivity to salt and sweet was essentially normal but the sensitivity to acid and bitter was reduced. Evidently the sensation of acid and bitter are detected mainly on the hard palate. When both palate and tongue were anaesthetized, no tastes were detectable in the mouth but if the solutions were swallowed, so that they made contact with the epiglottis and other pharyngeal structures, detection was within the normal range. Further analysis shows that the junction of the hard and soft palate is the area more sensitive to acid and bitter than is the tongue. These findings explain the frequent reports that taste is impaired in patients wearing upper dentures and improved when their dentures are removed. Henkin states that after wearing dentures for many years impairment of taste was reported by some patients even after they had removed their dentures and speculates that some degeneration of the palatal taste endings occurs as a result of the prolonged mechanical irritation of the denture. In other patients, an apparent adaptation to the presence of the dentures occurred which might possibly arise because the patient gradually learned how to apply sapid substances to the most sensitive areas by modified tongue movements.

Murphy (1971) compared the sensitivities to sweet taste of denture-

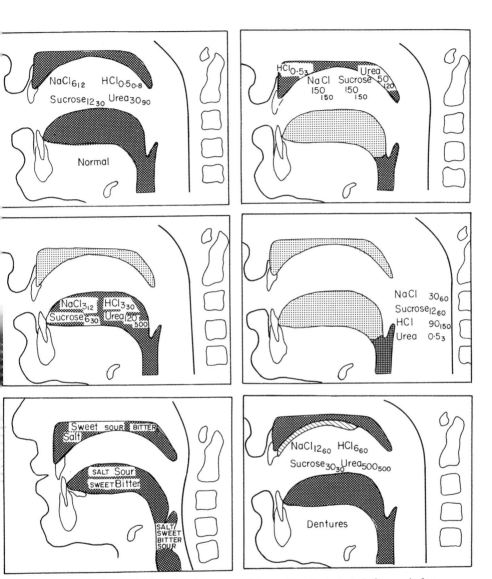

FIG. XIV.1. The sensitivity of various parts of the oral cavity to taste before and after the anaesthesia of selected areas (shaded). The bold figures are the concentrations (mmol/l) required for detection, the smaller figures give the higher concentrations required for recognition of each taste. Top left—no anaesthesia; top right—tongue anaesthetized; middle left—hard palate anaesthetized; middle right—hard palate and tongue anaesthetized but threshold found after swallowing; bottom left—summary of distribution of sensations; bottom right—thresholds with upper denture in place.

wearing patients with or without their dentures. He found that patients who were first tested without dentures showed greater sensitivity without their dentures although the results were not statistically significant for detection but approached significance for identication. When the order of testing was reversed (with dentures first, then without) again the sensitivity for detection was greater without but, for identication, it was greater with the dentures, i.e. the denture appeared to increase identification sensitivity (measured as a decreased threshold). Frequently the identification was wrong at the detection level, the sweet solution often being described as sour or bitter. There is no obvious explanation of the enhancement of taste identification with dentures although this has been described before (Kapur *et al.* 1967).

Dentures may reduce sensitivity immediately after a patient begins to wear them because they stimulate saliva and this dilutes sapid substances. This provides an alternative explanation of the adaptation of taste to the presence of dentures as described above since the stimulation of saliva would diminish with time and also explains why dentures which cover only a small area of the palate may affect taste.

Adaptation

Taste and smell show rapid adaptation, that is, the intensity of sensation diminishes even if the stimulus continues unchanged. If a sweet is placed on the tongue and left in position for more than half a minute, one's awareness of its taste gradually fades, but is instantly renewed when the sweet is moved so that it comes into contact with a part of the tongue which has not been stimulated. Adaptation arises because, even with a constant simulus, the number of nerve impulses ascending the nerve decreases rapidly within a second or two then remains steady at the low frequency (Beidler 1953). Action potentials have been recorded in the human chorda tympani exposed during surgical operations. The prolonged application of a taste stimulus show a rapid decline within a few seconds followed by a slower reduction eventually reaching zero, thus showing that adaptation occurs at the peripheral nerve ending. In animals, the response falls off to a steady state but does not reach zero—either adaptation to taste is much less marked or it is a central phenomenon. If the tongue adapts to one acid substance it is found to be adapted to other acids as well (cross adaptation) but may become more sensitive to other tastes (for example, after acids water tastes sweet and adaptation to sweet intensifies the bitter taste). With bitter and sweet stimuli, however, adaptation to one substance does not necessarily involve adaptation to other substances with the same taste.

In animal studies on salts some results have reported cross adaptation especially to cations, others have failed to detect it. These contradictory results probably arise because some workers measure adaptation as changes in the first response of high frequency action potentials, others have judged adaptation by changes in the much lower frequency at the steady state. Cross adaptation can be demonstrated to the immediate high frequency response but does not usually occur to the steady state. Since animals appear to identify tastes with stimuli of very short duration it seems likely that the initial high frequency discharge is more important than the steady state (Frank *et al.* 1972).

Salts have a bitter as well as a salty taste and adaptation reduces the salty but enhances the bitter taste. Many human subjects might tend to confuse these two sensations and not observe the adaptation to salt.

The Mechanisms for Discriminating Between Different Tastes

The obvious question that arises is: if the taste mechanism can detect so few basic tastes, how can we explain the great variety of tastes which we are able to

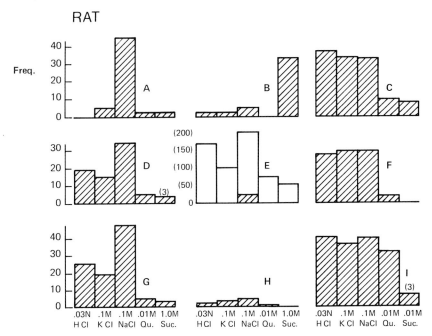

FIG. XIV.2. The frequency of action potentials in eight single nerves from taste receptors in the rat when stimulated by various sapid substances (indicated at the bottom of the diagram). Most of the nerves respond to all five stimuli but to varying degrees, but nerve A is insensitive to HCl and nerve B to quinine (bitter).

perceive? Consideration of the intimate nature of the responses of individual taste receptors along with the action of other types of nerve ending has offered a tentative answer.

Recordings of the action potentials in single nerve fibres from the taste receptors shows that some of them respond to all four of the basic tastes but that some are insensitive to one taste and have low sensitivity to others (Fig. XIV.2). Even individual taste-bud cells usually fire off nerve impulses with several different tastes. There is no finally agreed interpretation of these findings which seem to cast doubt on the existence of separate types of receptors corresponding to each of the basic tastes but two suggestions have been made.

INTERPRETATION OF STIMULATION EXPERIMENTS

The first is referred to as the 'pattern theory' but would be better called the 'ratio theory'. It suggests that discrimination depends on the relative rather than the absolute number of impulses in a group of nerves, for example, one ending (*A*) may be extremely sensitive to sugar and discharges with low concentrations and be slightly sensitive to salt and therefore require salt in high concentrations before being stimulated. An adjacent ending (*B*) may have the reverse sensitivities. A larger number of impulses in *A* than in *B* would be interpreted by the central connections in the nervous system as sweet whereas if the number in *B* exceeded that in *A* the sensation would be salty.

The second suggestion was made by von Békésy (1964, 1966) who developed a technique for applying sapid substances to individual papillae of the human tongue with a micro-pipette and concluded that papillae were, in general, sensitive to one taste only but the sensation produced tended to be 'flat' and lacking in overtones. The only papillae responding to more than one taste (invariably salt and sour) were unusually large and looked like two or more separate papillae which had grown together. From these results he was able to identify individual papillae on a human tongue which were sensitive to each taste and he confirmed the identification by electrical stimulation of single papillae for 0·5 ms by gold electrodes 0·3 mm in diameter, which also produced one rather flat taste for each papillae. He also concluded that the papillae sensitive to each of the four basic tastes had a different shape (Fig. XIV.3). von Békésy reconciled these results with the conclusion from the study of action potentials (which indicated that all papillae are sensitive to several basic tastes) as follows. He suggested that sapid substances possess multiple tastes (for example a substance which is predominantly sweet may produce slight stimulation of bitter and sour receptors in addition to more intense stimulation of sweet receptors). This would also explain why most sweet or bitter substances differ slightly in their overall taste by varying the extent to which they stimulated the other tastes. A simple experiment supports this concept. If the mouth is rinsed with a mixture of substances with salt, sour

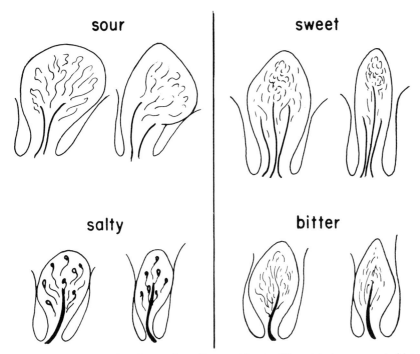

Fig. XIV.3. The varying shapes of papillae sensitive to different tastes as reported by von Békésy.

and bitter tastes for about a minute, so that the receptors become adapted to those tastes, then spat out and immediately followed by a sweet substance, the latter resembles the flat taste produced by electrical stimulation of sweet receptors; also, sugars which normally are recognizably different became much more alike. In the absence of the other components pure sweet was detected. Confirmation of this concept arisês from observations on two subjects who were incapable of recognizing the taste of any sweet substance. Sugars tasted either sour (sucrose) or bitter (glucose).

An attempt by Harper *et al.* (1966) to repeat von Békésy's observations on stimulation of individual papillae with sapid substances on four subjects was only partially successful. Although some papillae responded only to one taste, others responded to several. However, it is possible that those sensitive to more than one taste corresponded to double papillae described by von Békésy. Also, many individuals have poor discriminative powers for taste and are especially liable to confuse acid and bitter. In experiments on taste, it is desirable to select subjects who have good discrimination but this does not seem to have been done by Harper *et al.*

Other stimuli associated with taste

Many other factors enter into what we normally regard as taste and which supplement the responses of the small number of types of taste receptors.

The most important of these is undoubtedly smell. The sensation that is called taste is in fact compounded of true taste and smell and is technically known as 'flavour'. The importance of smell is illustrated by the effects of a common cold, in which access to the olfactory epithelium is blocked by mucous secretion, resulting in a great loss of subtlety in detecting and appreciating flavours. An even more striking way of demonstrating the double nature of flavour is by holding the nose when some strongly-flavoured food (for example raw onion) is in the mouth. Almost all flavour disappears, and returns immediately when nose-breathing is resumed. This observation implies that the volatile material is carried by expired air from the mouth to the olfactory epithelium via the posterior nares. It would appear that the air containing the odour must be in motion for it to stimulate the olfactory epithelium as otherwise when the nose was held the odoriferous substances already in the nasal cavity would be detected.

Other sensations which contribute to flavour are touch (whether a food is smooth or rough, hard or soft) and temperature. These sensations are perceived partly on the hard palate, and may become dulled in denture wearers if a plate prevents access of food to this surface which contributes to the impairment of taste. The oral mucosa, like the subcutaneous tissues, the cornea, and some other mucous surfaces is also sensitive to general chemical stimulation by irritants ('common chemical sensibility') which accounts for the pungency of mustard, pepper, ginger, etc. The receptors for this sensation are not taste-buds, but free nerve endings which are distributed throughout the oral mucosa and are connected, like the touch and pressure receptors, to the trigeminal nerve.

Stimulation of the tongue by one taste alters its sensitivity to others. For example, bitter substances taste more bitter if eaten immediately after sweet substances. If such contrast effects occur when other mixtures are applied simultaneously then they may contribute to the variety of tastes which can be perceived. Such interactions are readily explained on von Békésy's theory since, if a particular taste depends on stimulation of several types of endings, reduced sensitivity of one type after prolonged stimulation would modify the complex.

It has been stated that any taste can be imitated by mixtures of suitable substances possessing the four basic tastes. In view of the effects of other sensations described above, there would seem no reason to expect that *all* tastes can be produced by mixing basic tastes.

Taste and chemical structure

There has been much study of the relation between taste and chemical structure, but there would seem to be little in common between the structures of sucrose, lead acetate, glycine and saccharine, yet all taste sweet. Shallenberger & Acree (1967) suggested that a grouping common to many sweet substances with very diverse structures is a pair of electro-negative atoms (which they call *A* and *B*) between 2·5 and 4 Å apart and with a hydrogen atom attached to one of them at a distance of 3 Å which makes H-bonding impossible (the 'AH–B system'). This grouping is presumed to bind with the appropriate receptor and the complex then stimulates the nerve ending in such a way that it leads to the entry of sodium and loss of potassium ions which accompanies the nerve impulse (Fig. XIV.4).

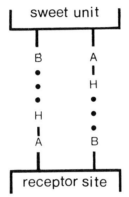

FIG. XIV.4. A diagram of a suggested structure associated with the sweet taste and which combines with a protein on the taste receptor.

The bitter taste of a considerable number of plant constituents has been related to similar groups but at a distance not exceeding 1·5 Å, i.e. making it possible to form an intramolecular H^- bond. They suggest that to combine with the bitter acceptor substance the proton donors must be strong enough to sever the H-bonding of the bitter substance.

Acids share the property of releasing hydrogen ions and this is believed to account for their similarly in taste. There is no exact correlation between the degree of dissociation of an acid and the strength of acid taste and it is clear that some other factor may play a part (diffusibility into the sensory cells is among the several suggestions). Any differences between the tastes of two acids, for example acetic and citric, could be accounted for by the taste of the anion superimposed on that of the hydrogen ion (acetate ion is bitter but citrate ion is sweet). The receptor for the sour stimulus may be the phosphate groups on the phospholipids of the cell membrane. When changes of one physico-chemical parameter (surface pressure) of phospholipids extracted from bovine fungiform papillae were plotted against pH following addition of hydrochloric or acetic acids, the curves were almost identical to that relating the neural response in the tongue of the rat to these acids over the same pH range (Koyama & Kurihara 1972). The salt taste is produced largely by anions, although either the cation or possibly undissociated salt molecules must play some part because, for example, all chlorides do not taste exactly alike.

The intimate nature of taste

Many attempts have been made to explain the means by which stimuli from different sapid substances initiate a nerve impulse by the nerve endings of the taste-buds. In view of the speed at which taste is perceived, it is likely that the reaction occurs between sapid substances and the surface of the receptor cell. Extracts of the epithelium of bovine tongues have been made containing the soluble proteins. Fractionation by ammonium sulphate has revealed a protein which forms complexes with sweet substances, as detected by a change in its UV spectrum when mixed with sugars, saccharine and sweet amino acids, displaying an affinity proportional to their taste intensity. It is not confined to taste buds so that if it really is concerned with taste this supports the belief that cells other than taste buds may detect sweet. A bitter sensitive substance has also been isolated.

The testing of possible binding substances to salt and sour is difficult because most salts and the hydrogen ion affect the conformation of proteins and many bitter substances themselves absorb strongly in the UV range. One report has shown a good correlation between the taste intensity of a number of bitter substances and their ability to activate phosphodiesterase, the enzyme concerned with the hydrolysis of cAMP. If this work is confirmed it suggests that cAMP is involved in the excitation of the receptor cells for the bitter taste, although, if so, it is subject to the criticisms of Baradi & Bourne's theory mentioned below (Price 1973).

Baradi & Bourne (1951) showed by histochemical tests that several phosphatases which are specific for splitting various organic phosphatates exist in the taste-buds, or neighbouring tissues, and that the activities of some of these enzymes are altered by the presence of sapid substances. The activity of each enzyme could theoretically either be increased, decreased or unaffected by other substances, and examples of these three actions have been found. For instance, vanillin (the substance responsible for the flavour of vanilla) inhibits glycerophosphatase; quinine also inhibits this enzyme and the enzymes 5-nucleotidase and esterase as well, but greatly increases the activity of ribonuclease. These enzyme reactions will alter in different ways the concentrations of ions and organic compounds in the several places where the enzymes are found. Thus each substance would produce its own pattern of reactions which might stimulate the various nerve endings in a specific way. With six enzymes, the activities of which are capable of being affected in three ways, placed in four sites, hundreds of patterns could be envisaged. One gap in this theory is that there is no evidence that the products of these enzymes really do have any influence on nerve endings. The enzymes were also found to have a specialized distribution in the olfactory epithelium, suggesting that a similar theory might explain the sensation of smell.

These observations do not appear to have been repeated by others although some evidence has implicated enzyme activity leading to the production of ATP as a factor in triggering the nerve impulse from taste buds (Duncan 1964). The enzyme theory has not been widely accepted, among its objections being: (1) the rapidity with which action potentials can be detected after applying sapid substances suggests that the receptors must be on the cell surface without involving passage through a membrane; (2) enzyme inhibitors have been found not to affect sensitivity to taste; and (3) the sensitivity to taste is not greatly affected by the temperature of the solution (if applied locally and for a short time to avoid gross cooling of the tongue as a whole) whereas if taste were dependent on enzyme action it would be expected to be highly sensitive to temperature.

Some substances, for example monosodium glutamate (MSG) and 6-hydroxy-5-nucleotides, enhance the taste of other substances and of each other. MSG is used for this purpose in food manufacture. The number of action potentials in the nerves from taste receptors is increased when these substances are added to other sapid substances (for example sodium chloride) applied to the receptor thus showing that their action is on the receptor. Experiments of this type show that they suppress the bitter flavour.

EFFECT OF AGE, MENSTRUATION AND SMOKING
The sensitivity of taste falls with advancing age, for example, in one experiment a group aged over 80 required about five times the electrical stimulation which was effective in subjects aged 20. There does not appear to be a steady decline with age since a group of 3- to 5-year-old children had sensitivities similar to those of their parents.

Tests with solutions have shown that the sensitivity to sweet, sour and bitter is lower in a 48–60 year age group than in younger age groups but that no change occurred to the salt taste (over 60s were not tested). This age change can be related partly to reductions in the number of taste-buds with advancing age. The number of taste-buds has been estimated at about 8000 in young adults but the number in the circumvallate papillae of the elderly is only about 80% that of children. Changes in the interpretation of taste have also been reported suggesting that the effect is partly at the central, presumably cortical, level.

Increased sensitivity to both smell and taste (bitter) have been reported during menstruation compared with those in the pre- or post-menstrual phases although one-third of the twenty-three subjects showed either no change or a decrease in sensitivity.

Heavy smokers have a reduced sensitivity to taste but it is not known whether this arises from toxic constituents of tobacco damaging the taste buds or whether smokers are more or less permanently adapted to certain tastes. The effect on salt taste was reported to raise the threshold from about N/2 in controls to about 7N—a fourteen-fold rise (Jackson 1967). It was speculated that this would be likely to lead to increased salt consumption which in turn might be a possible reason for the greater tendency for heavy smokers to suffer from cardiovascular diseases (salt intake influences blood volume and hence blood pressure).

Curiously enough, if an individual smokes while his taste sensitivity is being tested the sensitivity increases (unpublished observations by the author).

A solution of a sweet substance which is pleasant to a fasting subject may be described as unpleasant after the intake of a large dose of glucose (50 g in 200 ml). Incidentally, this changed reaction to excessive sweet taste is much reduced or absent in patients suffering from some forms of obesity, suggesting that their condition may be linked to an unawareness of internal signals.

The Sense of Smell

As already mentioned, the sense of smell makes an important contribution to flavour and therefore merits some description in a book on the physiology of the mouth.

In man, olfaction is insensitive and unimportant compared with its status in many of the lower animals in which it may be the dominating sensation.

Like taste, smell is a chemical sense, but whereas taste requires contact of the receptor with a solution of the substance tasted, smell detects airborne volatile substances and has been loosely described as 'taste at a distance'. The sense endings are in the olfactory epithelium, which is an area pigmented yellowish-brown, of about 240 mm^2 situated in the epithelium between the upper part of the nasal septum, the roof of the nose and the superior nasal conchae. This area is not normally traversed by inspired air and consequently only a small part of the odoriferous material in inspired air reaches the olfactory epithelium by diffusion. By sniffing, the course of the inspired air is diverted and some of it does come into direct contact with the olfactory epithelium.

The olfactory epithelium is normally covered by a thin layer of watery mucus. The molecules responsible for odour must dissolve in this layer before reaching the sensitive cells; this consideration is a difficulty for theories of olfaction 'at a distance' based on radiation from odoriferous molecules.

The sense of smell is equally sensitive in both sexes and is not reduced among smokers, except immediately after smoking. As with most sensations, there is a gradual decline in sensitivity with age estimated to be 50% loss in 22 years, somewhat more rapid than for taste. The range of sensitivity among normal subjects is very wide, the highest and lowest of the normal range being ten times and one-tenth as sensitive as the mean.

Mechanism of olfaction

Many theories of olfaction have been suggested over the last few decades, reviewed by Moncrieff (1967) but most of them are now merely of historical interest. Baradi & Bourne (1951) demonstrated histochemically the presence of a variety of phosphatases in the olfactory epithelium and sugested that, as in their hypothesis of taste, their action might be modified by odoriferous substances and that the products would stimulate the nerve endings. The objections mentioned on p. 553 apply to olfaction as well as to taste and this hypothesis is virtually abandoned. Three other hypotheses have replaced it. The first is based on studies of 'molecular profiles' or 'molecular silhouettes' and has been developed by Amoore (1971). He classified more than 600 organic compounds into groups which had similar odours. Three-dimensional models of representative members of these groups were constructed and photographed from various directions and the silhouettes of substances with similar smells were found to be strikingly similar. Amoore concluded that there were seven groups of substances with similar odours and he suggested that the olfactory receptors contained cavities with shapes corresponding to those of the odoriferous molecules. He described these basic odours as ethereal, camphoraceous, musky, floral, minty, pungent, and putrid, and was able to suggest which particular shapes corresponded with each odour (Fig. XIV.5). Some molecules might fit several receptors but on a probability basis they would be expected to be less common than those which fitted only one. He did find groups of substances with less common odours which did not fit into the above groups, for example aromatic and aniseed were quite rare and he suggested that they might fit into two receptors and thus stimulate two sets of nerve endings— which would be interpreted as these odours. 'Garlic' and 'rancid' were very rare and he suggested they were probably capable of fitting into several receptors. This could explain how a small number of receptors could perceive the large number of odours. This theory has successfully predicted the odour quality of new compounds.

It is not definitely known how odoriferous substances stimulate the nerve

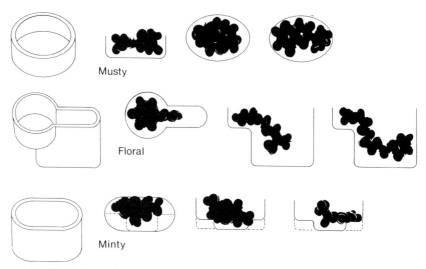

Fɪɢ. XIV.5. The profiles from different angles of models of substances with different odours and the suggested shapes of the olfactory receptors which they stimulate.

endings. It has sometimes been thought that the substances had to be soluble in both water and fat solvents. Solubility in water is of doubtful importance and if aqueous solutions of odoriferous substances are placed on the olfactory epithelium they do not always produce their characteristic odour. Solubility in fat solvents does seem to be important and suggests that permeability through the lipid layers of the cell membrane is necessary for stimulation to occur. In the frog, different parts of the olfactory epithelium differ in their sensitivity to specific odours, suggesting some localization of function comparable with that in the tongue (Kauer & Moulton 1974).

The atoms in a compound are vibrating so that the outlines of a large molecule are constantly changing and do not have a fixed shape. Although Wright (1966) suggested that this might increase the specificity—not only the shape but also the vibrations of a substance and the receptor would have to match—he has now developed an alternative hypothesis based largely on the study of odoriferous substances which attract insects. Some evidence suggests that radiation (probably infra-red) emitted by a molecule might be related to its odour. The presence of pigment in the olfactory epithelium leading to the old belief, probably incorrect (Ottoson 1963), that albinos have no sense of smell, supports the idea that absorption is important in olfaction. At least some of the pigment is accounted for by the presence of carotenoids or vitamin A in the olfactory mucosa. These substances are, of course, important in the absorption of light energy and the stimulation of the nerves in the retina.

Wright has drawn attention to the similarities between peaks and troughs in the infra-red spectra of sixty-seven substances which attract a particular insect, the Medfly, even though they may differ in shape. It is not necessarily thought that the receptors accept these particular vibrations (although they may do) but that they are merely a property which is conveniently recorded, indicating some common factor which the receptor can recognize. Wright suggests three ways in which the molecules might influence the receptors: an interaction at very close range but not involving attachment, a brief adsorption and rapid release, and an adsorption of indefinite duration. He gives cogent reasons for preferring the second mechanism and suggests that with differential stimuli to about twenty types of receptors, over one million (2^{20}) odours could be detected. A striking relation has been found in some substances between the Raman shift of a substance and its odour although some exceptions have also been found. When monochromatic light is scattered by a pure substance, the emerging light is no longer monochromatic but consists of both longer and shorter wave-lengths than the original. This change in wave-length is called the Raman shift and depends on the molecular vibrations of a substance. Correlations between certain odour factors and the Raman spectra yielded significant values but not as highly significant as Amoore's results on molecular shape. It has, however, been shown that the response to odoriferous substances is prevented if the nasal mucosa is covered by a thin plastic membrane which transmits infra-red radiation but impedes direct contact between the receptors and the stimulating substance. This is compatible with Wright's suggestion that the vibrations of a molecule, and not the radiation which it emits, determine its ability to combine with the olfactory receptor. Ash (1968) reported the isolation of a protein from rabbit olfactory epithelium which combines with a perfumery ingredient with a lavender odour which suggests that the primary odours are associated with acceptor proteins.

A third hypothesis (Davies 1962) suggests that odour stimulation depends on the ability of a substance to penetrate the cell membrane and leave a gap permeable to ions which trigger off the impulse. Substances which diffuse slowly and leave a gap which fills slowly would be effective stimulants whereas small, very permeable molecules would require large large numbers (i.e. a high concentration indicating low sensitivity) to have a similar effect. There is little evidence for this hypothesis and it does not explain how similar molecules (for example isomers) may have very different odours.

Like taste, olfaction is rapidly adapted. Thus people who have been in a room containing, say, strongly-perfumed flowers for some time, may be unaware of any odour which is very strong to a newcomer. Studies in animals of the action potentials after prolonged stimulation of the olfactory epithelium do not show a steady decrease in the rate of discharge—after a small initial fall in frequency, the rate remains almost constant. In other words, the odour receptors do not show the rapid adaptation which might have been expected from the subjective decrease in intensity of an odour. It is concluded that the adaptation so readily observed in man probably arises mostly from inhibition of the impulses in the central system rather than from adaptation in the receptor itself.

The nasal epithelium as a whole, and not only the olfactory region, is sensitive to irritants, such as pepper, acid or ammoniacal fumes.

Discussion of the electrophysiological changes in the olfactory epithelium (the electro-olfactogram, EOG), along the nerve and in the olfactory bulb are beyond the scope of this book. For detailed reviews see Hayashi (1967).

Sensations from Teeth

Pressure

It has already been mentioned that pressure and pain can be detected in the periodontal ligament when pressure is applied to a tooth and that these sensations play a part in the control and limitation of mastication. A generous nerve supply has been found in the periodontal ligament and at least four types of sensory endings have been described (for references see Harris 1975). These endings are probably sensitive to deformation (a change in their shape) which will result when pressure is applied to the periodontal fibres. The nerves from the periodontal region contain fibres whose diameters are 10–12 μm in addition to finer fibres of about 6 μm in diameter. It is probable that these are concerned with conducting impulses for touch and pain respectively.

No sensation can be elicited directly from the enamel and pressure on this tissue, and even crude localization, is perceived in the periodontal ligament as a result of slight movements of the tooth (reviewed by Crum & Loiselle 1972). This has been confirmed by oscillographic records of impulses in the nerves from the teeth pioneered by Pfaffmann (1939). The nerve endings adapted slowly as the number of impulses decreased slowly over 2–3 min. By applying pressure to the tooth so that a particular nerve ending was alternately stretched and compressed, it seemed that the endings were sensitive only to one type of deformation, probably pressure. Nevertheless, these movements might stimulate the mucosa surrounding the tooth, possibly the periosteum of the alveolar bone and even nerve endings in the pulp via the dentine. When the pulp was destroyed, this response was affected little or not at all, strongly supporting the view that the impulses arose from the periodontal tissues and not from within the tooth. On the other hand, some experiments have suggested that the touch thresholds are higher in pulpless teeth and were raised by capping the enamel, which would reduce stimulation of the tooth itself but not affect the periodontal nerves. These experiments have not been repeated and their validity is unknown and they do not fit into most other data. The threshold pressure for the tooth of an adult cat was between 2 and 3 g (compare with the threshold for the mucosa of the gum which was below 0·25 g). Very weak stimuli affected few, and sometimes only one, nerve fibre, which may explain the ability to locate a stimulus on the tooth, as follows. If a pressure were applied at one side, the tooth would be displaced very slightly in its socket which would cause pressure, and therefore a nerve stimulation, in part of the periodontal ligament only. This would be interpreted as a local stimulation of the enamel although in no way implying that the enamel itself is sensitive. Correlation of nerve discharge with tooth movement suggests that an average threshold movement of 2–3 μm is required (Yamada 1967).

Touch threshold in man

In man the threshold forces have been determined as well as the discriminating power (the minimum increase of a force which is just detectable, sometimes called the Weber ratio). Known forces were applied from different directions to different teeth and the individual was asked to say which of two forces was the greater. Discrimination was poor with forces lower than 50 g but between 100 and 500 g the Weber ratios for the maxillary central incisor were between 0·105 and 0·137 (i.e. a difference of between 10·5 and 13·7% could be detected on an arbitrarily chosen basis of 7 out of 10 trials), irrespective of whether the direction was parallel or at right angles to the axis of the tooth (in contrast to the results on the cat, mentioned above). When several teeth were compared the maxillary canine showed greatest discrimination, the ratio being below 0·1. There were differences between the ranges of the forces at which different teeth had their optimum power of discrimination—the maxillary incisor could discriminate best with forces between 100 and 500 g, whereas the figures for the mandibular canine were 500–2000 g (Bowman & Nakfoor 1968).

Another method consists of testing the ability of subjects to distinguish between wires or pieces of metal foil of different thickness by biting on them. Subjects with normal occlusion could distinguish 0·2 mm differences but those with maloccluded incisors could not detect differences of less than 0·4 mm.

The presence of foil 0·02 mm thick between the natural posterior teeth can be detected but for denture wearers the detection thickness is six times greater. Discrimination is reduced but not abolished by anaesthesia of the periodontal ligament (Öwall 1974).

Tactility has been measured by embedding steel balls, graded in size from 0·2 mm and upwards in 0·1-mm increments, into peanuts which the subjects then chewed. The size of ball which the subject could detect during chewing was recorded as a measure of sensitivity. The average size of about 0·7 mm was required for detection, some thirty-five times greater than that detectable by static biting. In denture wearers the average threshold for detection was 1·4 mm. There are several reasons for the much lower threshold during chewing. The teeth are depressed into the socket during chewing and do not fully recover in the interval (0·3 and 0·4 s) between thrusts. Adaptation of the mechanoreceptors occurs with stimuli more frequent than 1 in 10 s so that the much more rapid masticatory strokes would certainly be expected to cause some adaptation. The focusing of attention on a single pair of occluding teeth (as in the biting test) as opposed to sensations arising from the dentition as a whole may also increase the sensitivity to bite. Conversely, an inhibition of sensitivity (corticofugal inhibition) owing to its adjustment to the relatively large force involved in mastication may occur (Öwall & Møller 1974).

Pain

Pain is not detectable from normal enamel but when damaged appears to be sensitive, presumably by opening up channels reaching the dentine. Pain and the causes of toothache are reviewed by Anderson (1976) and Mumford (1973). Dentine is extremely sensitive to the stimuli of touch, heat, cold and osmotic pressure. Some reports state that the first three can be identified as such when they are mild, but others have denied this and state that all stimuli above the threshold are perceived as pain. Anderson (1976) points out that most observations have been made on teeth with hyperaemia pulps and states that normal dentine is insensitive.

The area of dentine from which pain can be most readily elicited is usually considered to be the amelodentinal junction, although there do not appear to be any quantitative data on the point. The pulp is highly sensitive, all four stimuli resulting in pain. It is a common clinical observation that the sensitivity of dentine varies in different individuals and, although critical proof is lacking, the clinical opinion has been expressed that dentine is more sensitive when it is soft and poorly calcified than when it is hard. Another common observation is that whereas most carious teeth are painful, a large cavity may sometimes develop so painlessly that the subject is unaware of its existence. The presence or absence of pain probably depends on the rate of development of the cavity and on the extent to which an impermeable barrier is formed on the inner side of the dentine.

Dentine which is exposed as a result of attrition loses its sensitivity, otherwise mastication would be prohibitively painful. The sclerosed dentine which is formed under dentine exposed by attrition is less sensitive than normal dentine presumably because the means of transmitting the sensation is cut off by the mineralization of the tubules which causes the reduced permeability of this tissue.

Experimental findings on pain in dentine

Studies of the changes in the action potentials in the nerves of the pulp in anaesthetized animals have made it possible to study quantitatively the effects of cold, heat, touch, or various chemicals, applied to the dentine. The threshold temperature has been found, by recording the temperature in the pulp at which the nerve discharge begins, to be rather variable (between 42 and 62° C in one series of sixteen nerves studied in eight dogs) and it may be that the *rate* of heating or cooling, rather than any particular temperature, acts as a stimulus. The threshold for cold was found to be 7° C. The fact that no increase in the frequency of the nerve impulses occurred with temperatures between 7 and 42° C is against the view that true temperature endings are present. In man the thresholds of pain are closer, about 45 and 27° C (Matthews 1977). The effect of drilling seemed to be related to heating of the pulp as the nerve response did not begin until the temperature reached 45° C and ceased when the pulp cooled (for details of these experiments see Anderson 1963).

Anderson *et al.* (1958) showed that when sucrose, acetylcholine or KCl solution (substances known to stimulate exposed nerve endings in the skin) were applied to freshly exposed dentine, a pain response was produced more frequently by sucrose than by the others (out of forty-eight trials on twenty-four subjects, the number of times pain was produced was: sucrose, twenty-three; acetylcholine, three; KCl, six). It seemed possible, however, that the dentinal tubules might be partly blocked in freshly-drilled cavities and that some of the chemical stimuli did not reach the sensitive nerve. In separate experiments the effect of grinding a cavity in dentine reduced its permeability to dyes—compared with the permeability of fractured dentine—thus confirming that ground cavities may be unsuitable for testing chemical stimuli on the pain mechanism. Application of local anaesthetics to dentine did not abolish pain. Silver nitrate and strontium chloride, salts reported to desensitize exposed dentine, did not affect the number of cavities which were sensitive but strontium chloride was reported by the subjects to reduce the severity of the pain.

With solutions of calcium chloride as a stimulus the number of painful responses was related to the osmotic pressure of the solution but this relationship was not consistently shown with other substances. When cavities in dentine were tested immediately after drilling and 1 week after the cavity had been filled with gutta percha, it was more sensitive on the second occasion. This increased sensitivity may have occurred because gutta percha causes inflammation of the pulp and inflamed tissues elsewhere are found to be more sensitive to painful stimuli

The sensitivity to pain decreased during an experimental session, lasting an hour or so—evidently the pain mechanism becomes temporarily impaired after repeated stimulation (this change seems to be quite different from the adaptation which occurs to nerve endings generally after prolonged stimulation). Measurements *in vitro* of fluid movements within the tooth when calcium chloride was applied to cavities cut in the dentine also declined, suggesting that some impairment in this movement might be related to sensation (Anderson *et al.* 1967).

Theories of pain perception in dentine

There has been much discussion about the physiological mechanism by which pain is perceived in dentine and the following possibilities have been considered.

(1) NERVES IN DENTINE

The most obvious mechanism would be that dentine contains nerves with free endings similar to the pain endings found elsewhere. Arwill (1958) reviewed over 150 publications on this question which have appeared during the previous hundred years. About two out of three workers who have studied this question by the more refined methods available during recent years have found what they believe to be nerve fibres in at least some parts of the dentine, but few have claimed a widespread innervation of this tissue. Unfortunately, most of the staining methods used do not differentiate with certainty between fine non-medullated nerve and connective tissue fibres. To prove that a fibre is a nerve it is necessary to show (*a*) that it does lead to or from a nerve bundle which is sufficiently large to be recognized with confidence and (*b*) that the fibre is absent after the main nerve is cut and time is allowed for degeneration, or (*c*) its highly-characteristic structure in electron micrographs which show that nerves contain more mitochondria, neurotubules and other organelles than the odontoblastic processes but, even so, identification is not always certain.

Mummery (1924) and several others have shown that fibres enter the tubules from the pulp but Bradlaw (1939) showed that they were still present in teeth examined some time after section of their nerves, thus proving that these particular fibres are not nerves and their nature is unknown. Many workers have shown indisputably that nerve fibres do pass between the odontoblasts into the predentine and on occasion they have been shown to enter the tubules. According to Fearnhead (1963), the nerve fibres are found in the predentine and dentine only after the age of 20 and even then the number of fibres shows great variability from tooth to tooth and from place to place in the same tooth, contrasting with the sensitivity to pain which is present from an early age. Fearnhead (1961) showed with the light microscope that the fibres which he took to be nerves disappeared after nerve section but this does not seem to have been repeated with electron microscopy. Electron micrographs have shown that the fibres in the predentine degenerate when the inferior alveolar nerve was cut in mice but this work does not appear to have been extended into the dentine as a whole (Byers & Kish 1976).

Frank (1968) showed by electron micrographs that fibres are present at least in the inner part of the dentine. They run within the tubules and parallel to the process in inner dentine but, more peripherally, they follow a corkscrew course around the process giving the impression, perhaps erroneously, that they are nerve endings on or within the odontoblastic process. Close association of what appear to be nerve fibres and the bodies of the odontoblasts have been described (Anderson 1975). Tritiated proline was injected into the right trigeminal ganglion of rats and the distribution of the label in the dentine was studied at intervals of up to 21 days by electron micrographs, it being assumed that any label reaching the dentine from the ganglion must be transported along nerves. After 3 hr label was detected on the subodontoblastic plexus, the odontoblasts of the molar crowns (but not the molar roots) and spirally round their processes up to one-quarter or one-half of the thickness of the dentine. Label was absent from the left molars showing that the stain was not generally distributed by the blood and very little reached secondary dentine (Byers & Kish 1977). Assuming that this method of identification of nerve is valid these results suggest a distribution of nerves similar to those found by the electron micrographs of Fearnhead and Anderson.

Nevertheless it is difficult to believe that, if these structures are nerve fibres, they can function as such because they are deeply embedded in dentine and are far removed from sources of oxygen and nutrients which, one would expect, are essential for the nerve activity. In any case there is agreement that even if dentine does contain nerve fibres they do not reach the outer half although this part of the dentine is usually regarded as being sensitive.

Anderson *et al.* (1958), as mentioned above, show that the sensitivity of dentine is not destroyed by silver nitrate or by the direct application of a local anaesthetic. This evidence suggests that sensitivity to pain is independent of living cells in the dentine.

Scott & Tempel (1965) detected a variety of electrical impulses from electrodes placed on the dentine of cats' incisors and were of greater amplitude if recorded from the floor of deep cavities cut into the dentine. Some discharges occurred without any obvious stimulation, others often appeared when stimuli (hot, cold or touch) were applied to the dentine or (with hot and cold) on the enamel. They believed that these impulses were derived from nerves stimulated within the dentine either directly or by conduction of temperature changes from the enamel, and, if so, provided evidence for the existence of receptors in the dentine. These conclusions were challenged by Horiuchi & Matthews (1974) who produced very similar records from dentine with the pulp partly removed and replaced by a piece of the radial nerve which was stimulated electrically outside the tooth. They argued that since impulses within the pulp (in this experiment, conducted artificially into the pulp) could be picked up from the dentine, this explained the findings of Scott & Tempel (1965) and that they did not necessarily support the existence of dentinal receptors.

Some impulses arose from artefacts such as the coalescence of air bubbles around the tip of the electrode or slight movements of the electrode which might explain the spontaneous discharges observed by Scott & Tempel, and which were never observed from pulpal nerves by Horiuchi & Matthews (1974) or when electrodes were used which avoided these complications. The impulses might also arise from antidromic impulses from the nerves in the pulp and these impulses are not necessarily all sensory—they might be vasomotor.

Later work, in which nerve impulses were recorded from the dentine of cats' canine teeth when the pulp nerves were stimulated electrically or by sodium chloride solution and vice versa suggest that the impulses were not artefacts. They may arise from conduction of action currents from the nerve endings in the odontoblastic region. The close association of what appear to be nerve endings with the odontoblastic process described by Frank (1968) suggest that the process might, in some undefined way, act as a receptor and pass on its stimulus to the nerves linked with the deeper part of the process.

(2) CONDUCTION ALONG THE ODONTOBLASTIC PROCESS

Those workers who have concluded that the innervation of dentine as a whole is quite inadequate to explain its great sensitivity have usually supposed that the odontoblastic process is a route by which stimuli might reach the nerves which, all workers agree, exist in pulp near the odontoblasts.

Avery & Rapp (1959) detected in the odontoblastic processes, by the non-specific methods then available, choline esterase, an enzyme known to be associated with the transmission of nerve impulses. This observation supported the idea of conduction of impulses via the process but they have not been confirmed by more specific methods, although the enzyme was clearly detected in nerves in the pulp (Ten Cate & Shelton 1966). On general physiological grounds, it is most unlikely that any structure other than a nerve ending could initiate an impulse resembling a nerve impulse, but it is possible that the process might transmit a mechanical pressure to nerve endings near the odontoblasts.

(3) MOVEMENT OF THE ODONTOBLASTIC PROCESSES

Brännström (1963) showed that certain painful stimuli (reduced pressure, a blast of air and heat) applied to cavities in dentine all resulted in the movement ('aspiration') of odontoblasts into the dentinal tubules which was detectable histologically (Fig. XIV.6). He suggested that the evaporation of water from the tubule in some of the above conditions, as well as during the heating caused by the grinding of dentine, might cause the displacement (the 'hydrodynamic theory'). Evidence which supports this theory is his finding that placing absorbent paper on a cut dentine surface (which would withdraw water from the open tubules and thus resemble evaporation) was painful in all

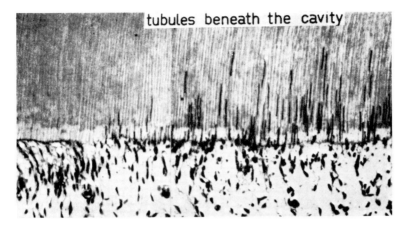

Fɪɢ. XIV.6. Pulp and dentine adjacent to cavity exposed to reduced pressure for 2 min resulting in the drawing up of many of the nuclei of the odontoblasts into the tubules.

of fifty-two applications but placing of similar paper soaked in isotonic potassium chloride (which would not be expected to soak up moisture) was painful in only four out of fifty-four tests and the pain was very brief. Displacement of the contents of the odontoblastic tubules may stimulate nerve endings (mechanoreceptors?), which, as mentioned on p. 563, probably exist in the region of the odontoblasts and thus give rise to pain. Although in most of the examples given above displacement was outwards, a positive pressure applied to a cut surface of dentine was also painful and this would probably drive the contents of the tubule inwards—it may be that movement in either direction can stimulate the nerve endings.

A possible factor is suggested by the finding that hydrostatic pressure applied to dentine of freshly-extracted teeth resulted in the development of an electric potential across the dentine, presumably owing to the movement of fluids along the tubules. If this occurs *in vivo*, it could explain how movement of tubule contents results in a stimulus (Mumford & Newton 1969).

Caution is necessary in interpreting the histological results because nuclei and organelles of odontoblasts have been observed in the tubules of normal mice teeth as an artifact where the beaks of the extraction forceps were placed. This may be linked to the finding that pressure applied to a cavity caused pain in about half of the human subjects tested. In a few subjects pain was felt when the pressure was released. Both procedures might be expected to cause displacement of odontoblastic nuclei (Robinson 1964).

An observation made by Kramer (1955) seems, at first sight, to disprove this theory. He found that although certain operative procedures caused the entry of odontoblasts into the tubules, there was no correlation between those teeth in which pain was felt during the operation and those in which the movement of the odontoblasts had occurred. Brännström's (1963) theory could be reconciled with Kramer's work if it is supposed that movement of tubule contents may act as a stimulus even if they are too small to be detectable histologically. When aspiration of the odontoblasts occurred in teeth in which no pain had been felt Brännström speculates that the rate of movement may have been too slow to act as a stimulus.

A number of teeth were extracted and examined by Brännström at intervals (up to 2 months) after a cavity had been exposed to a blast of air. Most of the odontoblastic nuclei had disappeared from the tubules within a week although the dentine became more sensitive. Thus, the sensitivity of dentine appears to be independent of the existence of the odontoblasts. If Brännström's theory is correct then it is not necessarily the movement of the odontoblasts themselves which is the stimulus but their movement is merely visible evidence of a disturbance of the tissues in the pulpodentinal region which stimulates nerve endings in that area.

The effect of temperature changes and of solutions of different substances on pulp pressure or fluid movement in the dentinal tubules has been studied by Brännström *et al.* (1967) and Horiuchi & Matthews (1973). They measured pressure changes in the pulp chamber when the solution was placed in cavities in the dentine of extracted human teeth. All the solutions tested caused some flow, usually outwards, but some substances (for example, urea) often caused slight inward flow. Successive applications of the same solutions produced smaller responses on each application, presumably because as the substance diffused into the dentine it would alter its osmotic pressure. For any one substance, the pressure changes increased with increased concentration (and therefore osmotic pressure) but the behaviour of different substances was not predictable from their osmotic pressure. This fact, and the finding that the fluid could move in either direction, showed that the effects could not be explained entirely on an osmotic basis; in other words, dentine does not behave as an ideal semipermeable membrane. Cooling or warming the cavity also caused fluid movement into and out of the dentine respectively.

These data support the hydrodynamic theory on the whole, particularly as the concentrations which caused pain produced similar rates of flow and a fall in temperature of $7°$ C (the threshold for pain) produced a similar movement to 3 ml of dextrose (also the threshold). One observation that did not fit in, however, was that water (which is not painful) produced a flow of the dentine towards the pulp chamber. Even more puzzling was the finding that 4 M NH_4Cl applied to exposed dentine produced a much greater nerve discharge than glucose solutions of the same osmotic pressure, although the fluid movement was much greater with the glucose solution.

Naylor (1963) investigated whether the sense endings for pain were situated inside the dentine or in the outer regions of the pulp by the following method. First, he measured the time elapsing between the application of cold water to a cavity in dentine and the perception of pain. In experiments on extracted teeth he then measured the time taken for water, at the same temperature as used previously, to cool the dentine throughout its thickness so that the cold stimulus reached the pulp. He found that a cold stimulus caused pain in a shorter time than it took for the stimulus to reach the pulp and concluded that some receptor within the tooth was affected before the stimulus reached the pulp. Brännström & Åström (1964) suggest as an alternative explanation that if the pulp behaves as a mechanoreceptor it could respond to volume changes in the odontoblastic tubules produced by local cooling and before the cooling had reached the pulp.

Horiuchi & Matthews (1973) point out that although the hydrodynamic theory is probably correct for some stimuli other mechanisms of detecting pain may exist. Some results of stimulation with NaCl solutions suggest that changes in the ionic environment, rather than movement of the contents of the tubules, might trigger a nerve impulse.

EVIDENCE AGAINST AN IMPORTANT ROLE FOR THE ODONTOBLASTS
Winter *et al.* (1963) studied the resting potentials of odontoblasts by introducing microelectrodes, by means of a micromanipulator, into the odontoblasts of extracted dog and human teeth and of dog teeth in the anaesthetized animal. The results showed an average potential of about 30 millivolts, but this did not change when the tooth was stimulated by a current sufficiently strong to increase the electrical activity in the mandibular nerve. If this work is confirmed the conclusion would be that the odontoblast does not play any part in transmitting sensation from the dentine and this implies that no stimuli resembling nerve impulses pass along the odontoblastic process. Brännström found that the sensitivity of dentine increased in the week following the cutting of a cavity although during this time the odontoblasts degenerate. As mentioned above, the sensitivity of the dentine increased during a week in which the odontoblasts degenerated following cavity preparation.

The position may be summarized as follows. The hydrodynamic theory seems the most probable and is supported by many of the experiments but they also strongly suggest either that other mechanisms exist or that unknown factors influence the effectiveness of fluid movement to stimulate the nerve endings, wherever they may be.

Sensitivity of cementum

Clinical evidence shows that a root exposed as a result, for example, of gingival recession is often sensitive to various stimuli which are perceived as pain. This might suggest that cementum is sensitive but the apparent absence of nerves or other structures which could respond to stimuli makes this explanation unlikely. Although there appear to be no data on the point, it is probable that when an exposed root is sensitive there is a gap between the edges of the enamel and the cementum which leaves a layer of sensitive dentine uncovered.

Sensation from Oral Mucosa

Sensitivity to touch can be studied either by testing with a series of mounted bristles which can just be felt when pressed against the surface being tested, or by finding the smallest difference between two points (as in a pair of dividers) at which the points can be perceived separately. On both these tests the tip of the tongue, lips, gingivae and hard palate are found to be among the most sensitive structures in the body. The inner surface of the cheek is much less sensitive. A thorough investigation of the physiology of sensation in the oral mucosa does not appear to have been carried out.

Certain areas of mucosa in the pharynx and at the back of the mouth give rise to nausea when touched and others described on p. 534 produce the swallowing reflex.

References

General reviews

ADEY W.R. (1959) The sense of smell. In *Handbook of Physiology*, Sect. I. Neurophysiology. Ed. FIELD J. p. 535 Amer. Physiol. Soc., Washington

ANDERSON D.J. (1963) (Ed.) Chemical and osmotic excitants of pain in human dentine. In *Sensory Mechanism in Dentine*, p. 88. Pergamon Press, Oxford

ANDERSON D.J. *et al.* (1970) Sensory mechanisms in mammalian teeth and their supporting structures. *Physiol. Rev.* **50,** 171

HAYASHI T. (Ed.) (1967) *Olfaction and Taste*. Pergamon Press, Oxford

MONCRIEFF R.W. (1967) *The Chemical Senses* (2nd edn.) Ed. FIELD J. Leonard Hill, London

MUMFORD J.M. (1973) *Toothache and Related Pain*. Churchill Livingstone, London

OTTOSON D. (1963) Some aspects of the function of the olfactory system. *Pharmacol. Rev.* **15,** 1

PFAFFMANN C. (1959) The sense of taste. In *Handbook of Physiology*, Sect. I, p. 507.

Neurophysiology. Amer. Physiol. Soc., Washington

SYMONS N.B.B. (1968) (Ed.) *Dentine and Pulp*. E. & S. Livingstone, Edinburgh

WRIGHT R.H. (1964) *The Science of Smell*. Allen & Unwin, London (see also *Nature* (*Lond.*) **209,** 551, 571)

The following refer to special aspects of the subject:

AMOORE J.E. (1971) Stereochemical and vibrational theories of odour. *Nature* (*Lond.*) **233,** 270

AMOORE J.E. (1970) *Molecular basis of odor*, Charles C. Thomas, Springfield, Illinois

ANDERSON D.J. (1975) Pain from dentine and pulp. *Brit. Med. Bull.* **31,** 111

ANDERSON D.J. & MATTHEWS B. (1966) An investigation into the reputed desensitizing effect of applying silver nitrate and strontium chloride to human dentine. *Archs oral Biol.* **11,** 1129

ANDERSON D.J. *et al.* (1958) The sensitivity of human dentine. *J. dent. Res.* **37,** 669

ANDERSON D.J. *et al* (1967) Fluid flow

through human dentine. *Archs oral Biol.* **12,** 209

ANDERSON D.J. (1976) The nature of pain. In *Scientific Foundations of Dentistry*, p. 267, Eds COHEN, B. & KRAMER, I.R.H., Heinemann, London

ARWILL T. (1958) Innervation of the teeth. *Trans. Royal School of Dentistry.* Stockholm and Umeå

ASH K.O. (1968) Chemical sensing: An approach to biological molecular mechanisms using difference spectroscopy. *Science,* **162,** 452

AVERY J.K. & RAPP A. (1959) Mechanism of neural impulse transmission in human teeth. *Oral. Surg., Med., Path.* **12,** 190

BARADI A.F. & BOURNE G.H. (1951) Localization of gustatory and olfactory enzymes in the rabbit, and the problems of smell and taste. *Nature (Lond.)* **168,** 977

BEIDLER L.M. (1953) Properties of the chemoreceptors of tongue of the rat. *J. Neurophysiol.* **16,** 595; (1955) A theory of taste stimulation. *J. gen. Physiol.* **38,** 131

BEIDLER L.M. & TUCKER D. (1955) Response of nasal epithelium to odor stimulation. *Science* **122,** 76

VON BÉKÉSY G. (1964) Sweetness produced electrically on the tongue and its relation to taste theories. *J. App. Physiol.* **19,** 1105; (1966) **21,** 1

BOWMAN D.C. & NAKFOOR P.M. (1968) Evaluation of the human subject's ability to differentiate intensity of forces applied to the maxillary central incisors. *J. dent. Res.* **47,** 9

BRADLAW R.V. (1936) The innervation of the teeth. *Proc. Roy. Soc. Med., Lond.* **29,** 507; (1939) **32,** 1040

BRÄNNSTRÖM M. (1963) A hydrodynamic mechanism in transmission of pain-producing stimuli through the dentine. In *Sensory Mechanisms in Dentine*, p. 13. Ed. ANDERSON D.J. Pergamon Press, Oxford

BRÄNNSTRÖM M. & ÅSTRÖM Å. (1964) A study of the mechanism of pain elicited from dentine. *J. dent. Res.* **43,** 619

BRÄNNSTRÖM M. *et al.* (1967) The hydrodynamics of the dentinal tubule and of pulp fluid. *Caries Res.* **1,** 310

BYERS M.R. & KISH S.J. (1976) Delineation of somatic nerve endings in rat teeth by radioautography of axon-transported protein. *J. dent. Res.* **55,** 419

CRUM R.J. & LOISELLE R.J. (1972) Oral perception and proprioception: a review of the literature and its significance to prosthodontics. *J. prosthet. Dent.* **28,** 215

DAVIES J.T. (1962) The mechanisms of olfaction. *Symp. Soc. Expt. Biol.* **16,** 170

DUNCAN C.J. (1964) The transducer mechanism of sense organs. *Die Naturwissenschaften* **7,** 172

FEARNHEAD R.W. (1961) The neurohistology of human dentine. *Proc. R. Soc. Med.* **54,** 877

FEARNHEAD R.W. (1963) The histological demonstration of nerve fibres in human dentine. In *Sensory Mechanisms in Dentine,* p. 15. Ed. ANDERSON D.J. Pergamon Press, Oxford

FRANK R.M. (1968) Ultrastructural relationship between the odontoblast, its process and the nerve fibre. In *Dentine and Pulp,* p. 115. Ed. SYMONS N.B.B. E. & S. Livingstone, Edinburgh

FRANK M. *et al.* (1972) Cross-adaptation between salts in the rats chorda tympani response. In *Oral Physiology,* p. 227. Eds EMMELIN N. & ZOTTERMAN Y. Pergamon Press, Oxford

HARPER H.W. *et al.* (1966) *Physiol. Behaviour* **1,** 319

HARRIS R. (1975) Innervation of the human periodontium In *The Temporomandibular Joint Syndrome*, pp. 27–44. Ed. GRIFFIN C.J. & HARRIS R. Karger, Basel

HENKIN R.I. (1970a) The role of unmyelinated nerve fibers in the taste process. In *Second Symposium on Oral Sensation and Perception,* p. 80. Ed. BOSMA J.F. Charles C. Thomas, Illinois

HENKIN R.I. (1970b) Taste localization in man. In *Second Symposium on Oral Sensation and Perception,* p. 43. Ed. BOSMA J.F. Charles C. Thomas, Springfield, Illinois

HORIUCHI H. & MATTHEWS B. (1973) Fluid flow through human dentine. *Archs oral Biol.* **18,** 275

HORIUCHI H. & MATTHEWS B. (1974) Evidence on the origin of impulses recorded from dentine in the cat. *J. Physiol.* **243**, 797

JACKSON J.A. (1967) Heavy smoking and sodium chloride hypogeusia. *J. dent. Res.* **46**, 742

KAPUR K.K. *et al.* (1967) The effect of denture factors on the gustatory sensitivity of denture wearers. In *Olfaction and Taste* 2. Ed. ZOTTERMAN Y. Pergamon, Oxford

KAUER T.S. & MOULTON D.G. (1974) Responses of olfactory bulb neurones to odour stimulation of small nasal areas in the salamander. *J. Physiol.* **243**, 717

KOYAMA N. & KURIHARA K. (1972) Receptor site for sour stimuli. *Nature* (*Lond.*) **239**, 459

KRAMER I.R.H. (1955) The relationship between dentinal sensitivity and movements in the contents of the dentinal tubules. *Brit. dent. J.* **98**, 391

MATTHEWS B. (1970) Nerve impulses recorded from dentine in the cat. *Archs oral Biol.* **15**, 523

MATTHEWS B. (1977) Responses of intradental nerves to electrical and thermal stimulation of teeth in dogs. *J. Physiol.* **264**, 641

MUMFORD J.M. & NEWTON A.V. (1969) The transduction of hydrostatic pressure to electrical potential in human dentine. *J. dent. Res.* **48**, 226

MUMMERY H. (1924) Nerve supply of the dentine. *Proc. Roy. Soc. Med.* **17**, 35

MURPHY W.M. (1971) The effect of complete dentures upon taste perception. *Brit. dent. J.* **130**, 201

NAYLOR M.N. (1963) Studies on the mechanism of sensation to cold stimulation of human dentine. In *Sensory Mechanisms in Dentine*, p. 80. Ed. ANDERSON D.J. Pergamon Press, Oxford

NAYLOR M.N. (1968) The effect of silver nitrate and the uncooled high-speed bur on dentine sensitivity. In *Dentine and Pulp*. Ed. SYMONS N.B.B. Livingstone, Edinburgh

OTTOSON D. (1963) Some aspects of the function of the olfactory system. *Pharmacol. Rev.* **15**, 1

ÖWALL B. (1974) Oral tactility during chewing. II. Natural dentition. *Odont. Revy* **25**, 135

ÖWALL B. & MÖLLER E. (1974) Tactile sensibility during chewing and biting. *Odont. Revy* **25**, 327

PFAFFMANN C. (1939) Afferent impulses from the teeth due to pressure and noxious stimulation. *J. Physiol.* **97**, 207 (see also *J. Physiol.* **97**, 220)

PRICE S. (1973) Phosphodiesterase in tongue epithelium: activation by bitter taste stimuli. *Nature* (*Lond.*) **241**, 54

ROBINSON A.D. (1964) A preliminary investigation of the pain responses to mechanical deformation of the teeth. *Archs oral Biol.* **9**, 281

SHALLENBERGER R.S. & ACREE T.E. (1967) Molecular theory of sweet taste. *Nature* (*Lond.*) **216**, 488

SCOTT D. & TEMPEL T.R. (1965) Responses from single receptors in cat teeth. *J. dent. Res.* **44**, 20

TEN CATE A.R. & SHELTON L. (1966) Cholinesterase activity in human teeth. *Archs oral Biol.* **11**, 423

WINTER H. *et al.* (1963) Transmembrane potentials of odontoblasts. *J. dent. Res.* **42**, 594

WRIGHT R.H. (1972) Stereochemical and vibrational theories of odour. *Nature* (*Lond.*) **239**, 226

YAMADA M. (1967) Interactions between the tactile sense and the mobility of the tooth. *J. dent. Res.* **46**, 1256

CHAPTER XV

SPEECH

Before discussing the mechanism of speech it is important to make clear a few fundamental points about the physics of sound.

Sounds may differ from each other in four ways. (1) Sounds vary in loudness, which in physical terms means that the amplitude of vibration of the source of the sound may vary. (2) Variations in pitch are the ear's interpretation of variations in the frequency of the vibration. For example a frequency of 261 Hz (cycles per second cps) is heard as middle C, double this frequency is C an octave higher, half this frequency is C an octave lower. (3) Variations in quality, such as the differences between the sounds of different musical instruments, are caused by differences in the shape of the waves. When a musical instrument plays a particular note, say middle C, which is called the fundamental, many other pitches are simultaneously sounded extending for many octaves above middle C ('overtones' or 'harmonics'). Some overtones are more accentuated than others and what we call the 'quality' of a sound depends on the pattern of overtones produced by that particular source of sound. The various frequencies of the overtones are superimposed, resulting in one wave with an extremely complicated pattern. (4) The duration of the sound is the fourth way in which sounds may vary. In speech, all four variations play a part.

Resonance is a phenomenon exhibited by sound and other forms of waves and is of great importance in speech. If sound waves of a particular pitch are conveyed through a medium, usually air, and meet a structure or cavity whose natural frequency of vibration is the same as that of the sound, it too will begin to vibrate. This means that a feeble sound may be reinforced if it succeeds in causing a large structure to vibrate or resonate. Resonators may be highly sensitive in the frequencies to which they respond (as in an organ pipe) or they may respond to a wide range of frequencies (as in a megaphone).

Speech may be described briefly as the production of sound by the larynx (phonation) and its modification by the resonance of the air in various spaces between the larynx and the lips (articulation). Both processes are under voluntary control and both contribute to the considerable variety of sounds

571

which go to make up speech. It is clear that there are great difficulties in deciding the contributions of each, because of the impossibility of finding out on the living subject what the laryngeal sounds are like before they are modified by the resonators.

The range of the singing voice is divided into 'registers', the three main ones being known as the chest, middle and head registers, to which some would add the 'upper thin' or 'whistle' register and the bass register. Each register covers the portion of the scale which a given singer can produce without altering the quality of the tone, and it is likely that different mechanisms come into play to contribute to these different pitch ranges. The name head register has been given because when high notes are sung there is a subjective impression that structures in the skull are vibrating and contributing to the sound production. The bones of the skull may, in fact, resonate at high pitches and the ribs at low pitches but this is probably of minor importance.

The pitch of the fundamentals of the human voice vary between about 90 Hz (in a man with a deep voice) and 300 Hz (in a woman with a shrill voice).

Respiration and speech

It can easily be observed that during speech the regular rhythm of inspiration and expiration is disturbed. Inspiration occurs rapidly at the ends of sentences or at pauses between sections of sentences; expiration is prolonged to last from pause to pause.

Respiration provides the means by which the loudness of the voice may be controlled. As the pressure of expired air increases so does the loudness of speech or song.

Phonation

The vocal 'cords' (also known as the vocal 'bands' or 'folds') are flaps containing the thyroarytenoid muscle, the inner edge of which is sometimes regarded as a separate muscle, the vocalis muscle. The cords also contain elastic tissue covered by stratified epithelium at their free edge and when in contact they cover the entrance to the trachea (Fig. XV.1).

The actions of the vocal cords have been studied by various forms of laryngoscope, by the stroboscope and by cinematography. An instrument known as the laryngograph records the movements of the vocal cords from two electrodes placed on the surface of the skin on either side of the larynx. As the cords move to and fro the electrical impedance of the instrument varies and is recorded (Abberton *et al.* 1972). During normal respiration, the

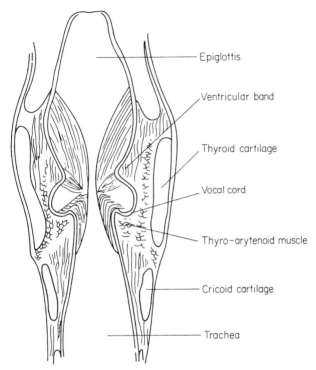

F<small>IG</small>. XV.1. The anatomy of the vocal cords and neighbouring structures.

cords are relaxed and the space between them (rima glottidis) is wide open but may narrow a little during expiration. Considerable widening can be observed during powerful inspiration.

The voice has generally been thought to be caused by the passive vibration

F<small>IG</small>. XV.2. Diagram of the movements of the vocal cords. The ellipse represents approximately the movement of one point. Note that the horizontal component greatly exceeds the vertical (after Curry 1940).

of the vocal cords by the current of expired air impinging upon them. Contrary to earlier beliefs the vibration of the cords is now known from stroboscopic studies to be mostly horizontal (maximum displacement 4 mm) and only slightly vertical (0·2–0·5 mm). Consequently each point on the cord describes an ellipse with the long axis horizontal and the short axis vertical (Fig. XV.2). The amplitude of the movement has been found by some workers to increase as the pressure of expired air increases when the voice is loud but there is not complete agreement on this point.

During part of each vibration, the inner edges of the cords will be in contact, thus closing the air space altogether, then the cords are blown apart, but their elasticity forces them together again, and so the cycle continues. The expired air will escape as a series of rapid puffs, the number of puffs being the same as the number of vibrations of the vocal cords (the 'myoelastic theory'). Such changes of pressure in the expired air represent a sound. This view has been questioned in two ways. First, it has been suggested that the closing of the cords is produced by the suction which occurs during the passage of air through a narrow tube (the 'aerodynamic' theory). A second and more important challenge to the earlier view was made by Husson (1952) who stated that the frequency of vibration of the cords is the same as the frequency of the nerve impulses in the recurrent laryngeal nerve (the 'clonic theory'). On this view, the vibration is an active, not a passive, phenomenon. This view is clearly wrong because muscles go into tetanus with a high frequency of stimulus. For a critical discussion see Portmann (1957).

The first essential for phonation is that the cords must be sufficiently close together to touch during part of their vibration. This action is thought to be brought about by rotating the arytenoid cartilages medially by means of contraction of the transverse arytenoid and lateral cricothyroid muscles. The reverse effect of separating the cords and widening the space between them is carried out by contraction of the posterior cricoarytenoids which rotate the arytenoid cartilages laterally.

Changes in the pitch of the voice, which are, of course, related to the frequency of vibration of the cords, are brought about in several ways. First, contraction of the muscles within the cords (part of the thyroarytenoid muscle) increases their tension because their attachments are prevented from moving inwards by the action of the other muscles of the larynx. Contraction of the posterior cricoarytenoids holds the arytenoid cartilages, the posterior attachment of the cords, as an almost fixed point and the infrahyoid group perform a similar function for the anterior attachment (Fig. XV.3).

Secondly, the cords are also changed in shape so that the thickness of the parts of the cord in contact is varied; sometimes the edges are thin and sharp pointed, at other times thick and well rounded. It is probable that changes in tension in the cords produced by these two mechanisms are adequate for producing normal speech.

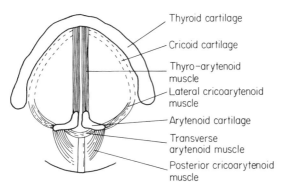

Fig. XV.3. The muscles of the larynx.

Lateral radiographs and slow motion pictures of the larynx show that the cords *lengthen* as the pitch of singing rises, an effect contrary to what might have been expected, but the increase in tension is such that it more than offsets their lengthening. The lengthening of the cords is achieved either by tilting the front of the cricoid cartilage up and the back of it down so that the posterior and anterior insertions of the cords are put farther apart, or, a similar effect but in the reverse direction is produced by a tilt of the thyroid cartilage (Fig. XV.3).

Thirdly, it has been stated that during singing of pitches higher than a frequency of 650 Hz, further increases in tension are brought about by increasing the strength of contraction of the external laryngeal muscles, so that they do not merely hold the attachments of the cords but actually pull on them outwards. Little relative movement is possible, so the energy of these muscles is used not for making the cords longer but for increasing their tension and this also increases their rate of vibration. There may, however, be an upward movement of the larynx as a whole, and the laryngoscope shows that other structures besides the vocal cords (for example, the false vocal cords and epiglottis) move in relation to each other during phonation.

The proportion of each vibratory cycle in which the edges of the cord are in contact seems to vary with the pitch and loudness of the voice. In the lower pitches, the period of closure is greater or equal to the period of opening and laryngoscopic examination may give the impression of a closed glottis. When the closed period becomes smaller, as in high pitches, the glottis may appear to be permanently open. The shape of the glottis also varies with the pitch. At low pitches (about 100 Hz) it is a rounded aperture but as the pitch rises to about 330 Hz (i.e. about two octaves, the normal range of the human voice) it becomes a narrow slit.

The fourth factor in altering the pitch of the voice is the air pressure. If the air pressure is raised by more forcible expiration, not only is the loudness of the voice increased, but a small rise in pitch occurs unless the tension of the cords is reduced as a compensation. There does not appear to be any evidence as to whether this mechanism is normally used to change pitch, but unless this point is appreciated, singers find that on a sustained note in which the volume is increased, the pitch may go sharp.

In extremely high pitches (the highest or 'whistle register' of the soprano) part of the cords are found to be in permanent contact and not vibrating at all, leaving only about one-third of their length to vibrate at, of course, a very high frequency. Under these conditions, the glottis is seen as an elliptical opening usually in the middle or anterior third of the cords. It is also thought that the false vocal cords may touch and press on the upper surface of the true vocal cords thus restricting the width of the vibrating portion which will again result in an increased frequency.

As mentioned above, the chief factor which increases the loudness of speech is the pressure of the expired air. In addition, for low intensities of the voice, the time taken for abduction (outward excursion) of the cords is shorter than for adduction (the return to the mid-point) but when the voice is loud, the reverse is true (Timcke *et al.* 1958). With low intensities, the glottis is not closed as firmly or for so long a time as with high intensities. This change in the behaviour of the cords has the effect of altering the amplitude of the sound waves in the air.

The length of the vocal cords in men averages about 15 mm and in women about 11 mm, a difference which explains the deeper pitch of the male voice. At puberty, the vocal cords of the male grow to about double their previous length over a short period of time which causes the rather rapid breaking of the voice during which the lower limit falls by about an octave. The corresponding growth in females is only about one-third of the pre-pubertal size which is insufficient to cause a fall in pitch of more than about a third of an octave.

Movements of the cords require such precision that feedback control is clearly important. A singer capable of producing 2000 grades of pitch must change the length of his cords by $1-1 \cdot 5 \, \mu m$ for each pitch change. The afferent side of the reflex feed-back arises partly from mucosal mechanoreceptors, which probably make a minor contribution, and mostly from corpuscular nerve endings in the joints of the larynx. The latter are rapidly adapting mechanoreceptors responding to changes of stress in the joint capsule. Their reflex role is demonstrated by measuring the electrical changes in the muscles of the larynx when the laryngeal joints are passively manipulated. The laryngeal muscles also contain a small number of rather primitive muscle spindles and a larger number of spiral nerve endings presumably controlling, by stretch reflexes, the tone of the muscles (Wyke 1967).

The main function of the false cords (or 'ventricular bands') is thought to be that of lubricating the true vocal cords, since they contain many mucous glands. Cinematographic study of the larynx during speech has shown that drops of mucous secretion may fall from the glands in the false cord on to the true cords, an action which clearly improves the efficiency of their rapid change in shape and tension. It is also quite probable that the false vocal cords take part in controlling the vibration of the true vocal cords during the production of very high-pitched notes, as described above.

Action Potentials in the Laryngeal Muscles

The electrical changes in the laryngeal muscles have been studied by Faaborg-Andersen (1957). With electrodes in the cricothyroid, arytenoid and thyro-arytenoid muscles, a resting discharge was observed in the absence of phonation, which increased during inspiration but continued at a low level even when the breath was held. These results are consistent with what the laryngoscope shows, that the larynx plays a part in raising the resistance of the respiratory tract during expiration by narrowing the gap between the cords. The electrical discharge occurring while the breath was held shows also that, like other voluntary muscles, those of the larynx show a resting tone. During phonation, there was a marked increase in the discharge from the adductor muscles, beginning about 0·5 s before the voice was heard, and an inhibition of the resting discharge in the posterior crico-arytenoid (abductor). When in-dividual muscle units were studied, by means of electrodes within the fibres, the resting frequency was found to be about 12 Hz rising to 25–30 Hz (occasionally up to 50 but never higher) before the onset of the audible tone, steadying off to about between 15 and 20 while the phonation lasted. This find-ing is of importance because it disproves claims made by Husson (1952) that much higher frequencies, even up to 500 Hz, can be recorded and that the frequency of discharge is related to the pitch of the sound and to the frequency of the nerve impulses received by the muscles. Electrical stimulation of the recurrent laryngeal nerve in dogs and human subjects by other workers has also been stated to show that the frequency of vibration of the cords is related to that of the stimuli. This implies that the vibration of the cord is an active muscular contraction which is very different from the view which has been held in the past, that although the tension in the cords is controlled by muscu-lar contraction, their vibration is a passive physical process. Faaborg-Andersen does not accept this view and thinks that Husson's results arose from the asynchronous discharge of many muscle fibres.

When the loudness of phonation increased there was no change in the electrical pattern, a finding which confirms the belief that loudness depends on expiratory pressure and not on changes in the larynx. When the pitch of the voice was raised, the amplitude of the discharge increased because more muscle units are brought into action to increase the tension in the cords. Even in silent speech (thinking of various sounds without uttering them) the electrical activity corresponding with the uttered sound took place.

Articulation

Vowel sounds

The differences between vowel sounds are essentially differences in pitch and pressure. This can easily be demonstrated by putting the mouth in the positions for pronouncing different vowels and flicking the cheek with the finger. The note produced by the mouth resonators differs in pitch with each vowel ('oo' and 'ee' show the greatest contrast).

Nevertheless, the laryngoscope shows that the vocal cords do alter during the production of different vowels, even when pitch and loudness are unchanged. Also, different vowels may be produced with the oral resonators in almost the same position, for example, 'e' as in 'men' can be changed into 'i' as in 'it' with little obvious change in the oral resonators. It would seem therefore that the laryngeal note is modified for at least some vowels and the full differentiation is accomplished by resonance effects on these various laryngeal notes.

THE DOUBLE RESONANCE THEORY

It has been found by several methods that vowels consist of sounds having a fundamental note (the 'formant'), which varies from vowel to vowel and also depends on the quality of each particular voice, and two main harmonics which may be of unequal loudness with up to forty or so faint harmonics (the 'double resonance' theory). The frequencies for each of the vowels are given in Table XV.1. Earlier theories were in error in supposing that some vowels had only a single resonance; it is now known that the second resonance is always present but is so faint in these vowels that it had not been detected by the earlier investigators. The evidence for the double resonance theory has been obtained in three ways: (1) subjective analysis of voice sounds—Sir Richard Paget (1930) had an exceptionally sensitive musical ear which enabled him to detect that some vowel sounds were compounded of two pitches and his conclusions were confirmed by later methods; (2) the wave forms of recorded speech have been analysed; and (3) Paget constructed, out of plasticine and cardboard, a series of resonating chambers covering a wide range of pitches. He found that when certain pairs of them were connected in series, and attached to a reed device which produced a fundamantal note, recognizable vowel sounds were emitted, although this method has failed to produce really lifelike imitations of human speech sounds.

TABLE XV.1

Characteristic frequencies of the speech sounds

Speech sound		Vowels Low frequency	High frequency
ū	pool	400	800
u	put	475	1000
ō	tone	500	850
a	talk	600	950
o	ton	700	1150
a	father	825	1200
a	tap	750	1800
e	ten	550	1900
er	pert	500	1500
ā	tape	550	2100
i	tip	450	2200
ē	team	375	2400

Sound	*Some Consonants* Throat resonance	Nasal resonance	Mouth resonance
r	500–700	1000–1600	1800–2400
l	250–400	600	2000–3000
n	200–250	600	1400–2000
ng	200–250	600	2300–2600
m	250–300	600	900–1700

THE ORAL RESONATORS

The following spaces are present in the vocal apparatus, any or all of which might be available as variable resonating chambers:

(1) The vestibule between the true and false vocal cords.

(2) Between the larynx and the root of the tongue, possibly involving the epiglottis.

(3) Between the pharyngeal wall and the soft palate and uvula.

(4) Between the dorsum of the tongue and the posterior surface of the hard palate.

(5) Between the dorsum of the tongue and the anterior surface of the hard palate.

(6) Between the tip of the tongue and the teeth.

(7) Between the teeth and the lips.

(8) The nasal passages.

It is likely that in vowel sounds the lower of the two pitches is produced by resonance in the pharynx and the upper by mouth resonance.

THE POSITIONS OF THE ORAL RESONATORS

In vowel sounds, the air passages remain uninterrupted but the relative sizes and shapes of the resonating chambers vary by movements of the tongue, lips and pharyngeal structures. The position of the oral structures has been the subject of much debate among singers and elocutionists and only relatively recently have precise methods, such as X-ray photographs, been used to investigate the question. These methods have shown that for some sounds there is no uniformity of position even in the same subject.

Speech sounds follow each other so rapidly that the organs of speech can hardly be said to occupy any fixed position at all. Oscillograph records of speech show that the typical wave pattern for each sound is not produced instantaneously, but about one-quarter of the total duration of the sound is spent on atypical intermediate sounds, partly at the beginning as the speech organs take up the correct position, and partly at the end as the organs change to take up the position for the next sound.

In producing the 'ah' sound the positions of the oral structures seem unimportant. The characteristic feature is the narrowing of the space between the epiglottis and the pharyngeal wall. The wide opening of the mouth which may accompany this sound tends to accentuate all the overtones rather than to be highly selective.

In the vowel sounds in 'see', 'set' and 'sit', the pharynx is widened and the tongue is arched in the middle and closely follows the shape of the hard palate. The 'u' of 'muff' is associated either with a flat tongue or with a slight arching at the back. The throat cavities are constricted in 'aw' and 'oo' sounds and the lips obviously play a part in differentiating these vowels. There is evidence that constriction of the throat cavities or of the lips may be interchangeable as methods of producing these sounds.

The dipthongs are produced by combinations of two vowels pronounced in rapid succession. The method of producing the individual vowel is the same as when they are pronounced separately but some of the characteristics of the diphthongs may depend, like those of some of the consonants, on the actual movement of the oral structures from the position of one vowel to the next.

The relative importance of phonation and articulation in forming the speech sounds is still uncertain. It has been stated that whispering consists of articulation only—the vocal cords playing no part—and since whispering in English has almost as high an intelligibility as full speech this implies that phonation is inessential for intelligibility, but merely acts as a means of amplification and of giving inflexion and emotional quality to speech, if this view of whispering be accepted. In some languages, for example some African dialects and Chinese, inflexion is essential for intelligibility and such languages cannot be whispered. However, experiments on the action potentials from the laryngeal muscles show that they change during whispering and the laryngoscope shows alterations in the shape of the glottis. These observations are not compatible with the view that in whispering, the vocal cords play no part. Also, consonants like t and d, which are thought to differ only that one is, and the other is not, accompanied by phonation should be indistinguishable in whispering if phonation is absent from the latter. In fact, these sounds can be distinguished in whispering. It is reasonable to conclude that the vocal cords do play some, very minor, part in whispering but their role is so small that the argument that phonation is unimportant for intelligible speech remains valid.

Consonants

Consonants are produced by an interruption of the passage of air through the pharynx or mouth, by the tongue, teeth or lips. Experiments in which Paget's vowel-sounding models are partially or completely obstructed for a short time have succeeded in producing some of the consonants. For example, if a model tuned to say 'ah' is closed with the palm of the hand and suddenly opened by removing the hand the 'ah' sound becomes 'pah' or 'bah'.

Consonants, like vowels, are produced by the resonance of different shaped chambers and their sounds also can be analysed usually into two main pitches. The nasal sounds 'm', 'n' and 'ng' have been found to be compounded of three main pitches and it is probable that the third pitch is produced while the mouth is obstructed and the sound is diverted to the nasal cavities (Table XV.1). Some consonants ('p', 'b', 't' and 'd') differ from vowels also in the fact that the oral structures have to move while they are being uttered, and not only pitch, but degree and rate of change of pitch help to differentiate these consonants. There is also evidence that the resonances for the consonants may vary with the vowel associated with it. The probable reason for this variation is that the tongue will take up, not a constant position every time the same consonant is uttered, but that position most easily reached after the preceding vowel has been produced, which still gives a sound which the ear can identify correctly.

The position of the tongue in relation to the hard palate during articulation of consonants has been studied by palatograms. These are made by painting the palate with some highly-coloured marker such as a mixture of powdered chocolate and charcoal. The sound is then pronounced and the distribution of the marker is noted, either by direct observations or, more conveniently, by a device designed by Anthony (1954) which photographs the illuminated palate by placing in the mouth one end of a series of mirrors attached to a camera. Artificial palates have also been used on which the pattern of contact of the

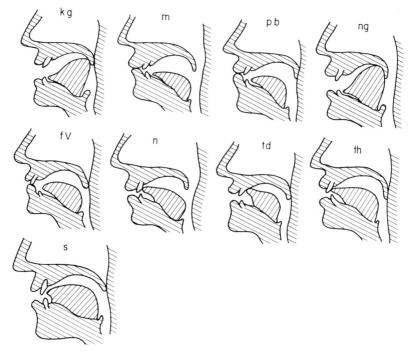

Fɪɢ. XV.4. The positions of the oral structures during the production of certain consonants.

tongue can be observed after the palate has been removed from the mouth. Palatograms may be used for tracing changes in tongue–palate relationships after dentures are fitted (Wictorin & Agnello 1970).

The pressures exerted by the tongue during speech have been measured by means of a rubber membrane mounted on an acrylic appliance made to fit on to the subject's palate; a tube connected to a recording device led into the water-filled space between the membrane and the acrylic appliance. Most of the pressures were found to vary between 35 and 160 g cm^{-2} during speech and between 140 and 320 g cm^{-2} during swallowing in approximate agreement with the results obtained by the electrical method described on p. 534.

Consonants vary from each other depending upon whether they are accompanied by phonation (voiced) or not (unvoiced). Thus the chief differences between s and z, p and b, f and v, is that the vocal cords are silent for s, p and f, but emitting a note for z, b, and v. This cannot be the only difference, however, since laryngoscopic studies show that the false vocal cords come together during the whispering of the so-called 'voiced' consonants and thus a resonating chamber is formed below the false cords, which will modify the resonating behaviour of the vocal mechanism. Although one gets the impression that the lip action is different during the whispering of b and p, this seems unlikely because these consonants are still distinguishable when a pair of artificial plasticine lips (which are, of course, incapable of delicate control) are placed over the mouth.

The consonants may be classified in several ways, one being according to the structures which cause the interruption of the current of expired air, as follows:

bi-labials	b, p and m
labio-dentals	f and v
linguo-dentals	d and t
linguo-palatals	g and k

Another classification is:

plosives or stop consonants	p, b, t, d, g and k	which require a complete stoppage of air,
fricatives	f, v and th	which require only a partial stoppage,
affricatives	ch and j	which, although involving only a partial stoppage of the air, do require a rapid release of this air,
nasals	m and n	which require obstruction of the mouth with the nasal passages open,
lateral	l	air forced to leave side of mouth
rolled	r	

The labials are produced by closing the lips and then reopening them suddenly. With the labio-dentals the lower lip meets the upper incisor teeth and is quickly withdrawn. The linguo-dentals are produced by the removal of the tip of the tongue from the incisor teeth or the hard palate just posterior to the incisors.

To produce the 'th' sounds the tip of the tongue is placed on the posterior surface of the upper incisors and quickly withdrawn, with or without phonation, depending upon the type of sound required. (Compare the sounds of 'th' in 'the' (phonation) and in 'thick (no phonation).)

The sibilants, s, sh and z, depend upon the passage of the expired air through a very narrow space between the tip of the tongue and the anterior part of the hard palate with or without phonation in z and s respectively.

'Ch' and 'j' require the greater part of the tongue surface to be in contact or just out of contact with the hard palate, but allowing a wider space than with s and z, and requiring a rapid removal of the tongue from the palate.

The sounds 'nk' and 'ng' are produced by the posterior surface of the tongue coming into contact with the soft palate and being removed quickly.

The aspirate is simply a short gust of expired air released from the larynx by a brief opening of the vocal cords.

The rolled 'r' is due to the rapid vibration of the tip of the tongue.

'L' is produced by diversion of the expired air from the centre of the mouth to both sides. 'M' and 'n' are labial and dental sounds respectively but as the naso-pharynx is open there is a prominent nasal resonance during their production.

The positions of the oral structures during the production of some of these sounds are shown diagrammatically in Fig. XV.4.

The sounds 'w' and 'y' are also described as semi-vowels since they are special ways of starting other vowel sounds. The 'w' sound is produced by an 'oo' sound uttered rapidly in front of the succeeding vowel; similarly 'y' is an 'ee' placed in front of another vowel. The rapid succession of these pairs of vowels introduces virtually a new consonant sound.

THE ROLE OF THE SOFT PALATE

During the production of most of the speech sounds (except m, n and ng) the soft palate closes off the naso-pharynx from the oro-pharynx. The details of the closure and the relative contributions of the soft palate and the posterior walls of the pharynx have been the subject of much discussion. X-ray studies have suggested that the upward and backward movements of the soft palate are the most important factors and that there is a small but measurable forward movement of the pharynx to meet the ascending soft palate.

The soft palate rises least for the 'ah' sound and touches the pharyngeal wall lightly or not at all. The soft palate rises progressively and therefore touches with increasing force as the vowels 'oh', 'a' (as in late), 'ee' and 'oo' are pronounced.

REFLEX CONTROL

Speech movements are partly monitored by feed-back from the tongue receptors and partly from hearing. Their relative importance has been tested by comparing articulation before and after (1) anaesthesia of the surface of the tongue, (2) nerve block (to anaesthetize the muscle spindles), and (3) masking hearing by applying noise to both ears. The results tend to suggest that tongue receptors are more important than hearing although it is difficult, in these experiments, to measure the quality of articulation.

The anterior part of the tongue, the region responsible for the complex articulations of 's' and 'sh' is much more richly supplied with tactile receptors, muscle spindles and tendon organs than the posterior part which carries out relatively coarse movements. In English, it is these sounds involving the anterior part in which slips and errors are most likely to occur (many tongue-twisters include frequent s and sh sounds). Also, these sounds are among the last to be mastered by children when learning to talk.

Effect of Dental Defects on Speech

Although malocclusion is an obvious possible cause of speech defects, for example it has been stated that 80% of people with a lisp also have a malocclusion, some cases have normal speech because, consciously or unconsciously, they have taught themselves how to compensate for their abnormality. The nature of these compensatory movements has been analysed by Benediktsson (1957).

Open-bite is one dental defect which, if severe, is liable to interfere with speech. F and v will be defective if the upper teeth cannot touch the lower lip and p, b and m are impossible to pronounce correctly if the lips cannot be brought into contact. Difficulty may also be experienced with pronouncing s and z in subjects with open-bite because the amount of air escaping between the hard palate and the tip of the tongue will be larger than usual.

A second dental defect which may influence speech is a recessive mandible, again affecting p, b, m, s and z and th—all sounds depending on the correct position of lips, incisors and tongue.

Prognathism (projection of the jaw) may have a similar influence and f and v are likely to be defective because the upper incisors cannot readily touch the lower lips.

Extraction of the upper incisors will affect f and v. If the upper incisors protrude and normally rest on the lower lip, the lips may be made to meet only with difficulty which will affect the pronunciation of the labials p, b and m.

Lisping (sigmatism), the substitution of s and z by th, may result from any of the above defects, particularly a recessive mandible in which the tongue is too far forward and protrudes between the upper and lower incisors instead of being behind them in attempting to pronounce s or z. Another cause is failure of the sides of the tongue to meet the molar teeth which allows some of the sound to escape laterally giving an impure 'l' sound. Lisping may be caused in denture wearers if the denture is too thick in the rugae area, thus preventing the normal placing of the tongue to make a small air space. Subjects with large tongues, or narrow arches may experience similar difficulty.

The cause, and methods of preventing, 'whistle and swish' sounds in denture patients are discussed by Silverman (1967).

The abnormal position of even a single tooth may interfere with the position of the tongue and cause abnormal speech sounds. For example, a backward displacement of one incisor may cause whistles or hissing sounds when closed sounds, such as d and t, are intended.

After the fitting of dentures, it is sometimes difficult to revise speech habits which have been formed in accordance with the position of the natural teeth, but by a gradual process of retraining the tongue positions, good compensation can usually be achieved.

Speech and its relation to dental defects have been fully reviewed by Bond & Lawson (1969).

Snoring

Snoring, although a potentially serious problem leading, for example, to much insomnia and irritation among married couples, is a neglected subject and there have been few studies on its causes and prevention. The few references which exist were well reviewed by Robin (1968) who also described his own analysis of 200 cases.

MECHANISM

Snoring is an involuntary action which ceases immediately upon waking. The pharyngoscope shows it to be caused by the vibration, usually during inspiration, of the thin edge (or velum) of the soft palate and posterior pillars of the fauces. Snoring may be accompanied by other sounds produced by vibration of the lips or nostrils. The reasons why one person snores and another does not are usually obscure. Some obstruction of the nasal passages was found by Robin in the majority of people who snore. He suggested that the obstruction introduced a resistance to respiration leading to slight reduction in pulmonary ventilation and the consequent anoxia and rise in CO_2 increased the tone of breathing and caused the soft palate to vibrate. Among the factors causing this obstruction are the following: enlarged adenoids and tonsils, allergy giving rise to a vasomotor rhinitis, often seasonal; a deflected nasal septum or collapsed alae nasi. Treatment of these conditions frequently cured the snoring and innumerable gadgets have been tried but Robin expressed the opinion that only about half his patients could be cured. Snoring is said to occur only in the orthodox sleep (the phase with slow EEG waves and the maintenance of muscle tone) and not in paradoxical sleep (fast EEG waves of reduced amplitude, rapid eye movements and muscle atony). This is not easy to understand because snoring cannot occur if the muscles of the soft palate have no tone—perhaps the tone of the muscles in the soft palate differ in sleep from that of the muscles as a whole.

Mouth-breathing and sleeping on the back are popularly believed to be essential for snoring; these factors may favour snoring but are certainly not essential for it.

References

ABBERTON *et al.* (1972) Laryngographic analysis and intonation. *Brit. J. Disorders Communic.* **7,** 1

ANTHONY J. (1954) *Soc. Technol. Ass. Bull.* Oct.-Nov. 2. Cited by HOPKIN G.B. and McEWIN J. D. (1955)

BENEDIKTSSON E. (1957) Variations in tongue and jaw positions in 'S' sound production in relation to front teeth occlusion. *Acta odont. Scand.* **15,** 275

BOND E.K. & LAWSON W.A. (1969) Speech and its relation to dentistry. *Dental Pract.* **19,** 75, 113, 150

CURRY R. (1940) *The Mechanism of the Human Voice.* Churchill, London

FAABORG-ANDERSEN K. (1957) Electromyographic investigation of intrinsic laryngeal muscles in humans. *Acta physiol. Scand.* **41,** Supp. 140

FLETCHER H. (1948) *Speech and Hearing.* Van Nostrand, New York

FRANK B. (1955) A rationale for closer cooperation between the orthodontist and the speech and hearing therapist. *Amer. J. Orthodont.* **41,** 571

GARDNER A.F. (1949) Dental, oral and general causes of speech pathology. *Oral Surg., Med., Path.* **2,** 272

HARDCASTLE W.J. (1976) *Physiology of Speech Production.* Academic Press, London

HOPKIN G.B. & McEWEN J.D. (1955) Speech defects and malocclusion: a palatographic investigation. *Dent. Prac.* **6,** 127; (1966) **7,** 313

HUSSON R. (1952) Sur la physiologie vocale. *Ann. d'Oto. laryng.* **69,** 124 (see also: Exposés annuelles d'oto-rhinolaryngologie. MADOURO R. (1955). p. 187)

KAPLAN H.M. (1971) *Anatomy and Physiology of Human Speech,* 2nd edn. McGraw-Hill, London

KESSLER H.E. (1954) The relationship of dentistry to speech. *J. Amer. dent. Ass.* **48,** 44

LEWTY K.A. (1942-4) The influence of dentures upon voice production. *Dent. Gaz.* **9,** 71

PAGET R. (1930) Reissued 1963 *Human Speech.* Kegan Paul, London

PORTMAN S. (1957) The physiology of phonation. *J. Laryngol. Otol.* **71,** 1

PRESSMAN J.J. & KELEMAN G. (1955) Physiology of the larynx. *Physiol. Rev.* **35,** 506

ROBIN I.G. (1968) Snoring. *Proc. Roy. Soc. Med.* **61,** 575

SILVERMAN M.M. (1967) The whistle and swish sound in denture patients. *J. pros. Dent.* **17,** 144

TIMCKE R. *et al.* (1958) Laryngeal vibrations: measurements of the glottic wave. *Arch. Otolaryngol.* **68,** 1

WICTORIN L. & AGNELLO J. (1970) Speech pattern changes during edentulous and denture conditions. *Acta odont. Scand.* **28,** 729

WRAY E. (1952) Speech therapy in relation to malocclusion. *Dent. J. Aust.* **24,** 103

WYKE B. (1967) Recent advances in the neurology of phonation: reflex mechanisms in the larynx. *Brit. J. Disorders Communic.* **2,** 1

INDEX